0 Preface

0.1 Introductory remarks

This book originally developed from a set of lecture notes accompanying a course on data communication protocols given to final year Computer Science undergraduates at Manchester University, and is mainly intended as an undergraduate or postgraduate text, although it should also be useful reading for practitioners in the protocol design and implementation areas. The book is concerned with the rationale behind information exchange between computers using computer communication networks, concentrating on protocols, and in particular the progress of standardisation culminating in the Open Systems Interconnection (OSI) reference model and the many protocols which have been spawned from OSI.

This book differs in many respects from comparable books in the field. Whereas many books present a purely factual, and sometimes rather dry, account of the protocols covered, this author does not feel that this is the most appropriate approach for the uninitiated. Therefore although this book seeks to be reasonably rigorous, it sometimes gives an informal, and at other times a somewhat personal, interpretation of the various protocol standards, with liberal comments on their effectiveness and suitability. The principal aim has been to provide a thorough coverage of basic concepts, and this has sometimes meant that fine details of specific protocols have had to be omitted. In this way, the book seeks to provide a good coverage of protocol developments without becoming unduly long and expensive. Although the book is intended as a stand-alone text, references for further reading are also provided in some cases; see the introduction to the third edition for further details.

The book is logically divided into five parts. The details of what is covered in each part will be found in chapter one; the following is a brief summary:

- **Part one** examines basic concepts. The reader is taken through the early decisions made by protocol designers, based on the early message switching technique in networks, in the process finding out about the pitfalls of protocol design just as the pioneers did.

- One outcome of early developments was a total lack of standardisation. **Part two** begins by discussing why standards are necessary, and introduces the two principal standards organisations, the International Standards Organisation (ISO) and the International

Telegraph and Telephone Consultative Committee (CCITT). It then examines early attempts by ISO and CCITT at standardising protocols in networks.

- It was soon realised that providing network protocols was in itself insufficient. Far more support was required to allow interworking between user applications. **Part three** starts by looking at UK academic attempts to provide support for such things as file and job transfer over the newly standardised networks. This is used as an introduction to the ISO Reference Model for Open Systems Intercommunication (OSI/RM), which is perhaps the biggest single standardisation project ever attempted. Part three concludes by examining how OSI/RM is applied to local area networks (LANs) and wide area networks (WANs).

- **Part four** looks at the upper layers of OSI/RM, and examines what is needed above network protocols to support applications such as file transfer. The transport layer is first to be discussed, in the context of various types of underlying LAN and WAN. Discussion then moves up to the session and presentation layers. Finally, the structure of the application layer is explained, together with the various common services provided by this layer.

- **Part five** completes the study of OSI by examining various applications which have been developed by ISO and CCITT. While most applications which are either currently standardised or under development are mentioned, most emphasis is placed on file transfer (FTAM), job transfer (JTM), virtual terminals (VT) and message handling systems (MHS). A discussion is also included on emerging standards for the Directory and OSI management.

A sound knowledge of basic computing principles and networking concepts is assumed, and non-technical readers may find it useful first to read a more general introduction to computer networks such as the one by Halsall[1], or for LANs the one by Gee[2], before proceeding further with this book. A list of OSI and related acronyms may be found in appendix A at the end of this book.

Even in a book of this length, it has been necessary to be selective. The emphasis throughout is on international protocol standards and related issues. Thus the reader searching this book for details of communications hardware, software design, proprietary network architectures and protocols (such as SNA, DECNET, TCP/IP, and so on), implementation notes, or detailed case studies of individual networks, will do so in vain; there simply is not enough room, and in any case there is a variety of other books to choose from in these areas. The author makes no apology for these omissions.

0.2 Acknowledgements

The text and tables of this book were prepared using Microsoft Word for Windows, and the pictures using Microsoft Windows Paintbrush. Camera ready copy was produced on a postscript laser printer. Thanks are particularly due to the Department of Computer Science, University of Manchester for making printing facilities available, and to Steve Price of the National Computing Centre, Manchester, for permission to consult the NCC standards library; without this access it would not have been possible to revise the book. Thanks are also due to Dave Morgan of Salford Software Services, Jack Houldsworth of ICL and Peter Furness of ULCC for valuable information on the current status of IEEE 802 LLC, CCR and TP. The author also acknowledges contributions from the Information Technology Standards Unit (ITSU) of the UK Department of Trade and Industry, in particular from a number of useful technical guides they have provided, notably on current developments in relation to OSI. (ITSU no longer provide this service to the extent that they did a few years ago, although they have recently published a Products Guide[3], which also contains useful background material for implementors.)

Finally, I would like to thank my wife Hania for her patient support and encouragement during the production of this book. I must also thank young Thomas for not drawing all over the drafts, and even younger Elizabeth for not tearing them up!

0.3 Preface to third edition

This is the third edition of this book. Developments since the second edition was published in 1986 have been rapid, particularly in the OSI area. A watershed was reached when CCITT published their Blue books, based on the 1988 Plenary Session. There were many changes from the 1984 versions of the CCITT specifications, notably major changes to Message Handling Systems (MHS, alias electronic mail). In addition new areas such as the Directory were covered. There was also major progress towards 'convergence' with ISO in many OSI areas. As a result, the second edition of the book (written in the second half of 1985) had become out of date, and a revision was urgently required. In order to expedite the required revision, the author purchased a 386SX laptop PC. This enabled the book to be typed and printed in various different locations, thereby greatly speeding its production.

There are many changes from the second edition. In particular, a more up to date and complete discussion of OSI is provided, taking into account the most recent developments. The approach is now to discuss each layer in turn, starting at the lowest layer. Major additions include new material on the application layer structure and application support standards such as ACSE, CCR, RTSE and ROSE, and the OSI Directory, as well as chapters devoted to Message Handling Systems, FTAM, JTM and VT. The treatment of the LAN project IEEE 802 is also brought up to date, including details of the new acknowledged connectionless LLC service, and the material on LANs has been moved to a more logical position in the book. In general the emphasis is on OSI as seen by the user, and therefore the discussion concentrates on visible services rather than internal protocols.

Unfortunately this has meant that some material has had to be removed in the interests of keeping the book at a manageable length. The author still strongly feels that a historical approach is the best introduction to OSI. The best way to understand current developments is to be aware of the earlier mistakes which were made, and the decisions which needed to be made at the time. For this reason, the introductory material on protocol concepts and the BSC protocol is retained, albeit in heavily revised and reduced form. However detailed discussion of the early ARPANET protocols has been removed, and whereas four chapters were previously devoted to the UK academic interim ('coloured book') protocols, coverage has now been reduced to a single chapter, as they are rapidly becoming obsolescent, and are now worthy of discussion only in the historical context. For similar reasons, discussion of the Cambridge Ring higher layer protocols has been removed, as these were provided for compatibility with the coloured books, and indeed did nothing to improve the efficiency of usage of such networks. The discussion of the origins and characteristics of LANs has also been removed, as has detailed discussion of LAN topologies and protocols other than those supported by IEEE or ISO standards.

A fundamental problem confronts any author seeking to provide an introduction to OSI. A discussion of OSI and related protocols is difficult because there has been a gradual convergence of various existing protocols with OSI over a period of several years. The evolution of X.25 presents the most obvious example. Work on the first issue of X.25 (in 1976) took place before work on OSI had even commenced, and therefore there was no reason why X.25(1976) should bear any direct relationship at all to OSI. On the other hand, the 1988 revision took place in a now largely stable OSI environment, and was heavily influenced by the need for compatibility with OSI; it differs from the original version in many ways. Therefore it is necessary in any historical treatment to discuss X.25 first, and OSI later. Therefore in this book X.25 is discussed twice.

- The first discussion (in chapter seven) seeks to explain its basic features. and forms part of the steady build-up to the introduction of OSI concepts. Although this discussion is based on the 1988 revision, little attempt is made at this stage to relate X.25 to OSI/RM. Hence this first discussion of X.25 is of necessity incomplete.

- The second discussion (in chapter fourteen) follows the introduction to OSI itself, and is associated with the discussion of the OSI network layer. It seeks to introduce those additional features of X.25 which are related to OSI, as well as discussing X.25's facilities in the context of the OSI network layer.

The X.25 situation is still rather unstable at the time of writing, with a minority of practitioners still working with X.25(1980), whereas others have 'already' converted to X.25(1984). Soon there will be implementations of X.25(1988) as well. The coexistence of these various versions of X.25 poses many problems for OSI compatibility and interworking, some of which will be touched on in this book. Many approaches may exist to the problem of introducing this complex and messy subject area. Unfortunately merely listing the features of X.25(1988), although the least time consuming approach from an author's point of view, is not one of the better ones as far as an uninitiated reader is concerned. Herein is one author's attempt to find a solution to this problem. One can only hope that when X.25(1992) is published, it will be technically close to the 1988 version, and there will no longer be the need to worry about earlier versions.

It is also important to realise that politics has played a significant role in the evolution of OSI. Unfortunately (or perhaps mercifully would be a better term) there is not the space here to do more than scratch the surface of the *reasoning* behind some of the decisions which have been reached in the OSI area, some of which are the result of rather messy compromises between opposing schools of thought. However in chapter five the reader is given a feeling for the standardisation process, as well as some of the problems which have been encountered on the long road to OSI. In addition, where there is a clear (and non-political) reason for the inclusion of some feature in a standard, this will be mentioned, though not elaborated on, as the main object of the book is to explain the concepts involved, not further to cloud an already opaque subject. It is for this reason that X.25(1980) has not been discussed in any detail. Similarly, the 1984 Message Handling Systems (MHS) recommendations are only mentioned in the context of convergence between ISO and CCITT work, the 1988 versions being the only ones discussed in detail.

As with earlier editions of the book, this one includes appendices. They provide a comprehensive list of OSI and related acronyms, a comprehensive list of ISO OSI-related standards, and a selected list of CCITT recommendations.

References to other works in this book fall into three categories:

- References to other books and papers are normally by superscripted number, viz.[1]. These references are listed at the end of the chapters concerned. However where possible it is intended that the book should be reasonably self-contained.

- References to ISO standards are by the standard number enclosed in curly brackets, e.g. {1234}. Refer to appendix B for the name of the standard. Normally the higher the number, the more recent the standard, but there are a number of exceptions to this general rule, where a standard has either been revised with the same number, or was withdrawn and then reissued with a new (higher) number. Unfortunately the ISO numbering scheme lacks any sort of structure.

- References to CCITT recommendations are the recommendation number, sometimes followed by the year in brackets, e.g. X.75 or X.25(1984). Refer to appendix C for the name of the recommendation. Recommendation numbers tend to be far more logical than their ISO counterparts.

Data communications in general, and protocol development in particular, is an area where there are often differences of opinion between experts. There are also inconsistencies in terminology which can be confusing, and not just to the beginner. In this book, the author sometimes takes the opportunity to make personal observations which are at times controversial. The reason for their inclusion is either to elaborate on a point which the author has himself found confusing at some time, or to offer a personal interpretation of some aspect. This technique is also sometimes used to add informative comments which are either not crucial to the current discussion, or rely on material later in the book for a complete understanding. So that it is clear which paragraphs (or parts thereof) fall into this category, a smaller typeface is used for these 'asides', as shown below. The book can be read skipping these asides with minimal loss of information content or continuity.

This is an aside. It contains additional information not essential to continuity, comments relating the material being discussed to material not yet covered, or a personal observation.

Finally, it is the author's hope that this book will prove interesting and stimulating, rather than dry and technical. After all, any reader wishing to read a formal description of a protocol or other standard can consult the appropriate standard document. The problem is that many of these documents are written in opaque (to the uninitiated) 'internationalese', with little or no concession to those not actively working in the field. Indeed there is usually a tacit assumption that the reader is already an expert on the subject. A major aim of this book is to break down some of the mystique surrounding international standard documents, which has posed problems for the author on many an occasion. You the reader must judge whether the objective has been achieved.

Should you wish to comment on this book, in particular if you feel that it can be improved in some way, do not hesitate to email the author. His email address (on the JANET network) at the time of publication is 'marsden@uk.ac.man.cs'.

Dr. Brian. W. Marsden,
9 December, 1990.

0.4   Background reading

The author has found the first two books below useful for background material on networking in general. This list is hardly exhaustive however; there are many good books on general networking on the market. (The third reference is aimed at implementors, but is included for its up to date material.)

1   Fred Halsall, 'Data Communications, Communication Networks and OSI', Second Edition, Addison Wesley (1988).

2   K. C. E. Gee, 'Introduction to Local Area Computer Networks', also published by MacMillan. This is a useful book on local area networks, which concentrates on the physical and architectural issues, and also discusses some types of LAN which are not dealt with in this book.

3   'OSI Products', volume 1, Department of Trade and Industry / HM Treasury / Blenheim Online Publications, 1990. (ISBN 0-86353-225-X). This is mainly a products guide for implementors, but contains some useful reference material on OSI.

Finally a word of warning. There are many books which touch on OSI concepts to a greater or lesser degree. The problem is that this has been (and indeed still is) an area of rapid change. The CCITT blue books were not published until 1989, so that even books published as late as this will probably have missed significant recent developments, notably the 1988 revision of the Message Handling System recommendations, and related changes to ASN.1, RTSE and ROSE. Indeed the second edition of this book, published in 1986, suffered a similar fate, and much of the material herein has had to be completely rewritten. Recent changes have also been made to LAN LLC and CCR, changes which are not widely known outside the standardisation community. New material for this third edition was researched in the second half of 1990, and it has therefore been possible to incorporate the recent material referred to above. The areas of OSI which this book concentrates on have now largely stabilised, and although further developments are still taking place, these are mainly in application areas which are beyond the scope of an introductory text, or address implementation issues. Most areas which were not yet stable at the time of writing are covered in the final chapter, and it is hoped that only this chapter will become out of date quickly. It is further hoped that it will be several years before a fourth edition of this book becomes necessary!

To Hania, Thomas and Elizabeth

0.5 Table of contents

Part one

Fundamental concepts and historical development

We begin by summarising some fundamental networking concepts, a limited number of topics being chosen to assist the subsequent discussion of protocols. We then examine the basic requirements of communication network protocols, as well as giving a brief history of their development. Most time is spent in a critical examination of the old BSC protocol and the technique of message switching, with a view to highlighting the many problems inherent in these early techniques. This is done not by presenting a rigorous definition of BSC (which would by itself be a waste of time), but rather by dissecting it, and critically considering the extent to which it satisfies the basic requirements of a good protocol. This leads naturally to an introduction to the basic principles of packet switching as a means of overcoming some of the deficiencies of message switching and the BSC protocol, and also to a discussion of general aspects of network management and protocol structuring, which are clearly absent from message switching.

1 Setting the scene

1.1 Introduction

This book is concerned with data communication protocols, i.e. the mechanics of using networks to transport information between co-operating user computers. More specifically, we examine protocols used for computer-computer communication over *wide area networks* (*WANs*) and *local area networks* (*LANs*). Throughout the book, the emphasis is placed on the rationale behind the protocols, rather than merely stating definitions. The design and implementation of computer networks is now much better understood than it was even a few years ago, but the scene has changed rapidly in recent years, and although there are signs that the protocol field is beginning to mature and stabilise, there is still much work to be done, and it will be many years (if ever) before a book such as this one can survive unaltered for more than a few years.

There are many pitfalls for the unwary network designer. This book seeks in part to draw on the author's experience of a variety of different types of network, and to pass on some of the lessons learned in the process. Perhaps the best way to understand the problems is to present the subject with a rather historical bias, in effect tackling the problems in roughly the same order as they were tackled in the field. By using this approach, it becomes easier to see why some of the older protocols were devised in the first place, and also why many of them became inadequate and outdated as technology and user perceptions matured. First however it is necessary to define the term. A *protocol* is an agreed set of rules and procedures which, if followed by all participants, will allow the orderly and controlled transfer of *information* between and among these participants.

The reason for referring to information rather than data is that, as will become clear, much of what gets transmitted over a network has nothing directly to do with the data generated by the end user, and is there either for internal network purposes (sometimes referred to as a main network addition), or to clarify the nature of the communication. Referring simply to 'data' would be an oversimplification; referring to information suggests that there is more involved than merely transmitting a stream of data down a line.

The term 'participant' here may be taken to be any 'point of intelligence' inside or directly interfaced to a network, the usual definition of a node; see §1.2. This includes not only the (computer) end-users of the network, but also any intermediate computers whose combined function is to facilitate communication between the end-users, but not to originate any usage themselves. A protocol (or more usually, a set of protocols) must be adhered to by all participants in the communication if it is to achieve its objective, and a well designed protocol must be 'robust', in the sense that it can handle unusual or unexpected events, as well as function efficiently and reliably under normal working conditions. The acid test of a protocol is not that it performs well when all is going according to plan, but how it behaves when things go wrong with the communication. A good protocol will avoid two problems in particular, the lockup and the deadly embrace:

- A *lockup* can occur if one participant runs out of resources, e.g. space to store the received information, and is unable to proceed further, a condition which should not have been allowed to develop in the first place had the protocol concerned been properly designed.

- A *deadly embrace* occurs when both participants in an exchange believe that it is the turn of the other participant to take the next action. Both then wait indefinitely for a response which will never come, with obvious consequences.

Lockups and deadly embraces are almost always the result of inadequate consideration of all possible situations at the design stage, although the problems often do not manifest themselves until the network is in full service, under real conditions.

The technique of simulation can be used, at some cost in time, money and resources, to test whether a protocol will work, without actually having to implement anything, and the author has developed a PC-based simulation package known as ESPRIT, based on an earlier package described elsewhere[3], which has been used 'in anger' to simulate a data link protocol known as the Radio Link Protocol (RLP)[4,5]. The main problems with simulation are twofold. First, life is usually too short to be able to spare the time to do the job completely and rigorously. If the job is done badly or incompletely, it is worse than useless as the results, if incorrect, could lead to bad decisions. Secondly, simulation is very expensive on time and resources and, sadly, a rather more common technique is to define a protocol, implement it, and then revise the specification when flaws are found during its operation.

The design of good protocols is not easy, and is influenced by the intended scope of application, as well as by adherence to sound design principles. Nowadays, formal protocol specification is a science, and established techniques and tools are available to assist the protocol designer, but this has not always been the case. In this book, we trace the development of computer-computer network protocols, from the early days through to the most recent developments. A full appreciation of the significance of developments in this field is only possible if the problems with earlier protocols are understood. Therefore, we start by discussing the earliest message switching protocols, explaining how they work, but in particular showing why they are unsuited to modern day communications. This leads naturally to an examination of alternative techniques, and the ultimate development of international standards. There is insufficient space in this book for a discussion of protocol design techniques. However when OSI is discussed, we will mention some standards which have been developed to assist in the formal description of protocols.

The book is divided logically into five parts. The majority of the book is concerned with wide area networks, where geographically separated computers are linked using long-haul communication lines. This is where most work was concentrated until the last few years. However local area networks are also given appropriate coverage. The content of each part of the book is now summarised; this should be viewed in the same way as an 'outline syllabus', in that no attempt is made here to explain topics mentioned in this summary.

- **Part one** starts with a brief historical summary which sets the scene for the remainder of the book, and also introduces some fundamental concepts which are essential to a discussion of networks and protocols. Basic requirements and characteristics of simple protocols are then introduced. Initially these are related to the old protocols introduced in the 1960s, which were first used between remote job entry stations and mainframes, and later as the basis of the emerging message switching technique on WANs. This technique has long been superseded (in networks at least) by more modern approaches, so it might be asked, why bother to discuss message switching, if nobody uses it any more? The reason is simple. There is clearly no point in wasting valuable space on a detailed specification of a dinosaur, but it might be useful to learn why the dinosaur became extinct. One has to understand why message switching failed, to understand why, and how, it was replaced by more modern, better protocols. In other words an understanding of message switching, in particular its weaknesses, is valuable if current developments are to be fully appreciated.

- One of the major problems with message switching, apart from its obvious technical flaws, was the total lack of standardisation. In fact international standards did exist in this area, but the basic techniques proved to be so flawed that almost every organisation implementing a network felt the need to make 'improvements' to the basic procedures. The problem was that there were now so many variations on the original theme that interworking between different networks was impossible, a problem which became increasingly frustrating for network users. Hence there was increasing pressure for effective standardisation. **Part two** looks at the background to, and issues involved in, standardisation. It may surprise the uninitiated to learn that there are two important standards bodies in this field, The International Organization for Standardization (aka International Standards

Organisation, ISO) and the International Telegraph and Telephone Consultative Committee (CCITT). We examine the roles of these two bodies, and various other agencies involved to a greater or lesser part in standards work, and then examine the earliest network protocols devised by ISO and CCITT, namely ISO HDLC, and CCITT X.25 and the 'triple X' terminal protocols. These led to the provision of a number of national public data networks (PDNs), of which British Telecom's Packet Switchstream (PSS) network, inaugurated in 1980, is typical.

• **Part three** extends the standardisation discussion by introducing OSI/RM. The protocols covered in part two provide a means of getting data across a network, but largely leave unanswered the important question of <u>why</u> the communication is taking place. It clearly makes a difference whether it is a terminal user involved in an interactive user session or a computer transferring a file to another one. So additional procedures were urgently required. But the development of such standards was going to be a long process, and the UK academic community had an urgent requirement to transfer files, job decks and electronic mail between university computers. As an introduction, and to illustrate what was necessary in the absence of universal standards, the interim standards developed for this purpose are discussed briefly. These provide a useful introduction to the basic issues of standardisation and high level protocols.

Interworking plus the ability to define the required *application* (file transfer or whatever) required something more than ad hoc protocol definitions such as HDLC and X.25. What was required was a *reference model*, and it fell to ISO to devise such a model, known as the *Open Systems Interconnection Reference Model* or *OSI/RM* for short. Coverage starts with a discussion of the OSI wide area network reference model, the need to provide a layered structure, and the functions and requirements for each of the seven layers proposed in the model. Service conventions are also covered, as well as such areas as quality of service and addressing. Details of service definitions for the lowest three layers are then provided. Where appropriate these are also discussed in the context of standards such as HDLC and X.25 which already existed at the time.

Part three includes a discussion of the four local area network (LAN) topologies which have been the subject of standards work (CSMA/CD bus, token bus, token ring, slotted ring), in the context of IEEE project 802, which was an US initiative to extend OSI into the area of LANs. Emphasis is placed on the differences between OSI and IEEE 802 in the lower layers, and the IEEE 802 service definitions and protocol specifications.

• **Part four** looks at the upper layers of the OSI reference model. The transport layer is first discussed, in the context of various underlying LANs and WANs. Discussion then moves up to the session and presentation layers. Finally, the structure of the application layer is explained, together with the various common services provided by this layer.

• **Part five** completes the study of OSI by examining the various applications which have been developed by ISO and CCITT. While most applications which are either currently standardised or under development are discussed, most emphasis is placed on file transfer (FTAM), job transfer (JTM), virtual terminals (VT) and message handling systems (MHS). Other emerging standards, including those for the Directory and for OSI management are also discussed, though in less detail.

That, then, is the scope of the book. The approach is, however, rather different from that of many books in this field. The emphasis throughout is on a clear understanding of the reasons for adopting a given approach, rather than simply defining a succession of protocols. Indeed in some cases, certain aspects of standards and protocols are glossed over in the interests of not confusing the reader too much. This book is of necessity theoretical in approach, and it has been the intention to include as much useful information as possible in the available space. The reader will have to look elsewhere for case studies or implementation notes.

1.2   Some basic networking terminology

This section concentrates on some basic network terminology which is used throughout this book. Throughout the book, *italic*, **bold** and ***bold italic*** emphasis are used to highlight particularly important concepts and definitions.

A glossary of terms is no longer provided in this book, although a list of acronyms is now included in appendix A. The problem with a glossary is that if it is to be comprehensive, it needs a lot of space which can be more usefully filled. Appendix E of the book by Halsall has a glossary of OSI and other networking terms. For OSI terms used in this book, consult the index to see where they are defined.

Data communication is concerned with the transfer of information between terminals and computers, or between two computers. A *host* is a user computer which is a source and/or sink of information, and which runs application programs on behalf of users, who will normally be connected to their host using a terminal or workstation. Certain application programs are designed to provide services to other hosts on the network, and these are referred to as *servers* (or daemons). For example, a printer server may allow other hosts to send documents for printing on that host; documents will be directed to the printer server in a suitable format.

One definition of a *terminal* (e.g. as used by CCITT) is any device connected to a network. Except where we are forced to use this wider meaning, we will use the term in its more normal context, i.e. a source or sink of information which, by contrast to a host, is not capable of interposing any intelligence between the user and the network, other than possibly to format the information suitably for transmission, and to obey any protocol required by the network. Thus printers, Teletypes and VDUs qualify as terminals under this more restricted definition, but host computers do not.

The simplest way to connect two hosts so that they can exchange information is to connect them directly by means of a communication *line*. The physical means of connection can vary from a pair of wires to a satellite link, and we are not normally concerned with these physical details, except when local area networks are discussed. The term *link* is usually used in a logical rather than a physical sense, i.e. when the use made of the line, rather than its physical characteristics, is of concern. Normally a line connects two computers, one computer and one dumb terminal, or one computer and several intelligent terminals. A line connecting several VDUs to a central computer is known as a multipoint or *multidrop* line. A line connecting just two devices is known as a *point-point* line. All wide area networks discussed in this book use point-point lines.

Where large numbers of hosts are to be connected, so that any host may exchange information with any other, intermediate computers are usually used, which are referred to as network *nodes*. (Depending on the protocol in use, they can also be referred to as *message switches* or *packet switches*.) A node may be defined as a point of intelligence where the information is transformed in some way. This transformation typically includes storing received information, forwarding the information on another link, and reformatting information in accordance with the protocols in use.

Thus any computer in a network will be a node, but certain devices which may be used in networks are not. For example, a time or frequency division multiplexer may divide one incoming physical line into several outgoing lines (and vice versa), but no transformation takes place at the multiplexer, since the routing decision has already been made by the previous node placing the information in the appropriate time position or frequency band, or on the appropriate line.

Most confusion in terminology arises when naming the units of information which are transferred using networks, which is one reason for being rather vague so far. However the term information unit is too vague, and we must look for alternatives. The first, and simplest definition is the information unit which the host regards as the smallest indivisible unit. This is the *message*. Most experts agree on that at least. A message could for example comprise a single line of a program, a single record of a file, or an entire program or file. One general characteristic of a message is that it is user-related rather than network-related; in particular the maximum size of a message is not generally fixed, and can vary from one application to another. However, in transmitting messages through a network, is not normally satisfactory to transmit the information as entire messages, and some possibly smaller, more consistent unit has to be devised. Thus, a long message will be broken into a number of *transmission units* of fixed maximum length, each of which will normally have some error checking information attached. A transmission unit is the minimum unit of data which has a distinct identity when being transmitted from one node to the next. It is however when examining this area that things start to become confused. For the time being, it is sufficient to say that a transmission unit can be referred to variously as a *block*, a *packet*, a *frame*, or even a message, depending on the type of network or protocol. Although each of these terms has a definite generally recognised meaning, which we will see as the book develops, the names are often confusingly used interchangeably.

When each transmission unit has error checking information, it is possible for the receiver to advise the sender whether an error was detected; this is referred to as an *acknowledgement*, which may be positive (no error detected) or negative (error encountered).

1.3   A brief history of wide area networks

Data communications is still a relatively new and fast changing branch of computer science, virtually all significant developments having taken place over the last twenty five years or so, with the position still altering significantly each year. Therefore this book, although starting with a discussion of the 'traditional' side of data communications, must of necessity concentrate on more recent developments. Protocols which were the mainstay of communications only fifteen years ago are now largely obsolete, although some are still used. These 'traditional' protocols are discussed in the first part of the book. They are generally rather simple-minded and restrictive in their approach to information interchange, and the discussion in part one centres on their deficiencies, and what can be done to overcome them. Early communications were primarily concerned with three areas:

- Protocols were needed to allow communication between remote batch stations and central computers, to transfer card decks, lineprinter listings etc. The IBM HASP protocol is a classic example of this type of application. A simple protocol known by IBM as **Binary Synchronous Communication** (or *Bi-Sync*, or just *BSC*), and by ISO as *basic mode*, was devised, which allowed the card deck (or whatever) to be sent to the central computer in several small blocks, each block usually representing a single card image and being followed by an error check. Blocks would then be acknowledged (positively or negatively) on receipt; if the acknowledgement was negative, retransmission of the block would be required. We will discuss BSC in more detail in chapter three.

- There was a need to allow 'online' terminals to communicate with a mainframe. Generally, such terminals had limited, if any, intelligence, which is why they became known as **dumb terminals**. The classic dumb terminal is the once familiar Teletype. (This is an example of a term being used **generically**, like 'hoovers' for vacuum cleaners. We will encounter the concept of generic addressing later in the book.) Nowadays these have been superseded by 'Teletype compatible' VDUs, or 'glass Teletypes'. With such a terminal, everything typed is sent down the line immediately, and any characters received are printed (or displayed) as soon as they arrive. Therefore a protocol such as BSC which requires decisions to be made and responses to be issued automatically cannot be used, although there can be a rudimentary form of handshaking in the sense that once the terminal user has started typing, the computer may delay its reply until the user has typed a carriage return or some other agreed terminating character.

- Soon, as VDUs began to be used for data entry and other commercial applications, a more sophisticated type was developed. This had an internal buffer which could hold the entire contents of the screen, which could then be transferred to and from the VDU using a technique known as *poll-select*, and a protocol closely related to BSC. The central computer (or front end processor, FEP) would *select* the VDU to send it a message, and would *poll* it to solicit a message from it, a message being sent if a special 'send' (or transmit) key had been pressed by the VDU operator. By including a unique address in each VDU, it was possible to have several on the same line (i.e. a multidrop line), thus saving considerably on line costs. The central computer would interrogate each VDU in turn (polling first, then selecting it if necessary) in some predetermined roll call sequence.

We are mainly interested in computer-computer communication in this book, and details of poll-select procedures are not discussed. We will however be discussing terminal issues three times more, firstly when we mention the poll-select variant of HDLC in chapter six, then when we discuss the interfacing of dumb terminals to X.25 packet switching networks in chapter eight, and finally in the context of ISO virtual terminal (VT) standards in chapter twenty one.

Most of the rest of this chapter is concerned with the historical development of protocols. If the first area of 'primaeval' communications was terminal handling, the second was what came to be known as 'message switching'. Message switching was in fact the first significant application of communication protocols to networks of computers (as opposed to networks of terminals). There were many such networks in the late 1960s and early 1970s, of which the SITA airline network, linking major airports in Europe and elsewhere, is one of the best documented[1]. The philosophy of message switching owes much to Telex, where you dial a number on a Telex terminal, type your message (or feed paper tape through), then hang up. This message is routed through a network much like the telephone network, and is printed on the called terminal. What you send after dialling is known as a message, and this term has remained in general use ever since. Any reply from the called party is a later, separate operation, and Telex knows nothing about two-way dialogue. This type of communication is suited to remote batch terminals, where the card deck or lineprinter listing corresponds roughly to a Telex message, and an immediate reply is not expected in either case. A card deck may contain a job deck, and the output listing may return five minutes or five days later (or not at all!). In this context, a protocol association between the card deck and the returning listing would not be sensible, and since this type of application was dominant at the time, there was no reason why 'experts' at that time should have considered this lack of association to be a problem. The problems came later.

It is useful to be able to define a message as some collection of text which is meaningful in its own right to the user, but the text by itself would have limited usefulness. Firstly, we need to know who sent the message, i.e. the originator's address (or in the Telex case, some identifying logo). In the case of the remote batch terminal (RBT) or multidrop VDU, the central computer needs to know which RBT or VDU sent the message, so that the resulting output can be returned to the correct place. We may also need to know who is to receive the message (again in Telex, some further logo), although in the RBT case there is only one destination on the line, so it may not be necessary to include a destination address in this case. Some additional sequences (ZCZC and NNNN in Telex) are needed to show where the message starts and finishes, although in the Telex case they are merely conventions and are not strictly needed. Finally, when using Telex, the sequence 'E E E...' is conventionally used as a rudimentary form of error correction, and means that the preceding text should be ignored by the reader, and a 'better' attempt will follow, the context of the error presumably being obvious to the reader of the message (typically a spelling mistake). This type of information can be referred to as a *header* or *control information*, i.e. extra information which has to be sent so that the message can reach its intended destination and also be understood in the correct context by the receiver. But basically everything contained within a Telex message is intended to be printed and read.

When the Telex principle was applied to computer-computer communications, it became more sophisticated and formalised, but the basic approach remained. The purpose of the network was the delivery of messages from X to Y, which in the early days were always directly connected, as far as possible without errors. Soon the technique was extended to the case where X and Y were not directly connected, but connected via a *communication subnetwork*. This technique became known as *message switching*. Now other considerations began to matter as well. For example, it was desirable for the message not to become lost and to be delivered within a reasonable time, and Y would not want more than one copy. But, at least in the early days, it was never part of the design goal to worry about <u>why</u> the messages were being exchanged, or to consider that there might be some logical relationship between one message and another. The fact that the technique was fundamentally flawed was not immediately obvious, since there was no previous experience of networking, and initial attempts at using networks were less than ambitious or sophisticated. Messages in these early networks were treated like paper files in an office. These can be passed around various offices, the addresses corresponding to the 'To:' and 'From:' labels on the cover. Paper files cannot vanish into thin air, although of course they can be stolen or mislaid (or even burned!). It never occurred to the very early network designers that electronic files (network messages) <u>could</u> vanish into thin air....

A convention is used in this book that hosts are referred to as X, Y and so on, and nodes inside a network as A, B, C and so on. This differs from the convention used by some other workers, but is used consistently throughout.

The first significant development came in the 1960s with BSC. This defined procedures for the transmission of messages along a single communication link, message formatting (so that the header could be distinguished from the text), and error protection to permit the acknowledgement of receipt without detected errors. It also included facilities for fragmenting messages into smaller units for transmission purposes, since both the probability of a transmission error occurring in a message, and the 'overhead' of retransmitting a message, are proportional to its length. Other suppliers, government departments and so on quickly adopted similar protocols. One problem was that no two implementations were ever quite the same. As a result, a chaotic situation arose where no two BSC implementations could guarantee to interwork, and a variety of extra 'features' were grafted on to individual implementations in an ad hoc and haphazard manner. Today, there is far more emphasis on standardisation than there was in the early days, to the extent that it is now possible for different organisations to communicate using standard protocols over international networks.

It soon became clear that lack of standardisation was not the only thing wrong with message switching, BSC and the like. The protocols were inefficient and full of inconsistencies. Furthermore there were many aspects of communication that were never even thought of when they were devised, and which various enhancements came nowhere near handling effectively. Most notably, BSC was never originally intended for use across networks. What was needed was a new approach. The most significant early breakthrough came with the US Advanced Research Projects Agency network (ARPANET)[2], started in the late 1960s, and designed to link ARPA-sponsored institutions. This initially connected a few University sites in California, but the network grew steadily to the point where it linked over a hundred sites in north America, and well as sites in several other countries. In its heyday, ARPANET also had links to several other networks as well, and the collection of interconnected networks was known as the DARPA Catenet (or internet).

ARPANET reached its peak around 1980. Since then its usage, and the number of nodes, steadily declined. It was finally 'pensioned off' in the summer of 1990.

Basically, ARPANET was intended as a testbed for research into 'resource sharing'. For the first time, people started to address the problems of communicating between hosts in an efficient and (reasonably) foolproof manner, and problems such as flow control, congestion control and the avoidance of deadlocks began to be tackled in a systematic way. This led to what is now the standard approach to wide area network communication, *packet switching*. This is superior to message switching in many ways, as will be discussed in later chapters. Basically, in message switching an entire message is switched through the network; each node (intermediate computer) must receive and store the entire message before it can forward it, a technique known as *store and forward*. Especially where long messages are involved, there are obvious problems in the long time it can take to get messages from X to Y via A, B, C etc., and even more severe problems if something goes wrong. We will examine these problems in more detail in due course. With packet switching, messages are broken into small, more manageable sub-units known as packets, which can be stored and forwarded individually and independently. We shall see how this leads to greater efficiency, reliability and throughput - and also how some additional problems appeared which required solution.

Another, and equally important, breakthrough of the ARPANET designers was to ask, for the first time, why X and Y were communicating with each other. This led to the development of function orientated application protocols. Examples of such protocols which were developed include file transfer, remote job entry and electronic mail. We will examine some protocols of these types in parts three and five.

Also worthy of mention are the early experimental packet switching networks in France (CIGALE/CYCLADES[6]) and the UK (EPSS[7] and NPL[8]), which were also packet switching testbeds, although we will not be discussing them in this book.

This takes us up to about 1974. This is when standards organisations first began to have a major impact on protocol development. There are two very important bodies which have played a major role in this area (and many others which have also made a significant contribution). The two main standards bodies (both United Nations agencies) are:

- **ISO**, the **International Organization for Standardization** based in Geneva. (It is also known colloquially as the **International Standards Organisation**.) As its name suggests, ISO is concerned with *international standards* of all types, and has a computer technical committee (TC97), with subcommittees working in the communications area. ISO is the 'umbrella' organisation for various national bodies such as BSI (UK), DIN (Germany) and ANSI (USA).

- **CCITT**, the **International Telegraph and Telephone Consultative Committee**, also based in Geneva. This is part of the International Telecommunications Union (ITU), and is the umbrella body for the national common carriers (i.e. the national agencies authorised to provide telecommunication services). The formal UK representative is the Department of Trade and Industry (not British Telecom, as discussed in chapter five). CCITT is responsible for co-ordinating the policies of its bodies, and produces *recommendations*, the X-series recommendations being the most important in the protocol area. The X.25 recommendation is probably the best known, and is of particular significance for packet switching.

Major standards bodies are discussed in more detail in chapter five. As will be seen there, there are various reasons why progress towards agreement on standards tends to be slow. This slowness, coupled with an urgent requirement for application protocols such as file transfer and job submission between UK University and Research Council sites, led the academic community there to develop a number of specialised protocols in much needed areas, which have become known as the *coloured books*. (They were earlier known as the rainbow books.) These were intended as interim standards, pending international agreement on comparable protocols. We will discuss the main coloured book protocols in chapter nine.

In 1984, ISO completed work begun around 1977, and formalised the specification of protocols by defining a hierarchy of protocol layers in its **Open Systems Interconnection Reference Model**, or **OSI/RM** {7498}. This seeks to define the scope of protocols and the interfaces between them, but stops short of specifying the protocols themselves. Naturally many established protocols did not fit the model very well, and this led to some difficulty in the case of X.25. OSI/RM is discussed in parts three to five of this book, together with current work by ISO on defining standards consistent with the reference model.

1.4　　Wide and Local Area Networks

1.4.1　　WAN characteristics

So far we have traced the development of protocols for **wide area networks** (**WAN**s). These connect hosts in geographically 'separated' locations. WANs have a number of general characteristics which influence the protocols used with them. For example, hosts are geographically separated. The distance can vary from a mile or two to half way round the world (e.g. Hawaii and London, in the case of the ARPANET). Related to this, hosts must therefore be linked by long distance communication lines, usually provided by the national service provider, which is normally either British Telecom or Mercury in the UK. Such lines are inherently expensive to use, and it would be impracticable on a cost basis (and also inflexible) to link all co-operating hosts in a large network directly to each other. Therefore a *subnetwork* of *network nodes* is provided, through one or more of which information can be staged on its way to the destination host. This can mean a substantial saving in line costs, which in a large network may well more than offset the extra cost of providing the subnetwork nodes.

Furthermore, it provides the flexibility to add or remove hosts without having to provide or remove lines at every other host.

However, having a subnetwork of this type introduces a number of problems:

- Protocols are bound to be more complex than if the hosts are directly connected, because of the intermediate control which is now required.

- Electrical and other constraints place a rather low practical upper limit on long-haul line speeds (of the order of 50 kbps, ignoring recent ISDN developments). This, coupled with inevitable delays due to storage and processing at intermediate switching nodes, implies that network transit times will be significant, and average transit times will also increase if the network becomes heavily loaded. Therefore protocols have to be designed on the assumption that variable delays will occur. This can lead to timing problems, and other complexities will arise as a result of having to react to unexpected events, such as an expected response being unduly delayed, and possibly being received out of context.

- Another problem is the inherent unreliability of long-haul communication lines, and the ever-present possibility of failure of lines and/or intermediate network nodes. To allow effective communication in such an environment, protocols need to be robust and sophisticated.

- A final problem with WANs relates to the fact that a third party will normally own and operate the subnetwork (again, often the national common carrier). In this case, users of the network will be required to conform to a given set of operating requirements (including protocols) as determined by the operating agency, and they will not normally be able to influence these significantly. As a result, the service provided by a WAN may not be ideally suited to the user's particular application. There will also be the usual bureaucracy involved in dealing with large organisations, as well as the cost incurred in using the network.

1.4.2   LAN characteristics

It is quite obvious that there is, and always will be, a need for WANs, and WAN protocols have now reached a high level of sophistication and standardisation (less so at the application level, moreso at the network level). In recent years, an alternative approach has been developed which is suitable where hosts are geographically close. This is the *Local Area*

Network (*LAN*), and various examples are examined in part three of this book. LANs are still in the process of active development; fifteen years ago they were virtually unknown.

The first prototype LANs were designed to link several machines in the same organisation. Two are of particular significance in the historical context.

- The *Cambridge Ring* was designed and built by the Computer Laboratory, University of Cambridge (UK). Several hosts and other devices (such as terminal multiplexers) in the laboratory were connected using a high bandwidth ring. Each host was provided with a ring interface station, and these ring stations were connected together using high speed technology. The main requirement was for something which worked reliably, and so no great research into the most effective topology was done; it merely seemed that a ring was a reasonable approach, and indeed the technique proved very successful.

- The other significant pioneering work was done by *Xerox* Corporation at their Palo Alto Research Center (PARC) in the USA. They chose to connect their hosts in a completely different way. Instead of using a ring, they provided each host with a transceiver which 'plugged into' a coaxial cable bus. This resulted in a linear bus topology. They called their LAN the *Ethernet*, partly because the coaxial bus had some resemblance to the 'ether' made famous by the Michelson-Morley measurements of the speed of light towards the end of the last century, but also because the concept owed much to the Aloha packet radio network in Hawaii[9]. The term Ethernet is now loosely applied to many different variants of the original network; the standard name is *carrier sense multiple access with collision detection* (or, mercifully, just *CSMA/CD*).

Both of these early experimental LANs were built to satisfy a particular in-house need, and at least at first, neither appeared to have great commercial potential. The fact that Ethernet at least is now at the forefront of a rapidly expanding market for LANs is a result of catalysts such as the microcomputer and diskless workstation.

LANs provide a number of advantages over conventional network techniques, particularly if the LAN is entirely in the same building, i.e. geographically 'close' (one definition of a LAN). The main general advantages are as follows:

- With the relatively short distances involved in LANs, the problems of noise and attenuation (which can be severe on long distance communication lines) are considerably reduced, so that much high data rates can be achieved (up to 50 mbps or even higher) with a very low probability of transmission errors, and simpler protocols can thus often be used.

- In the UK, networks entirely within a building, i.e. not 'crossing the public highway', may be designed and implemented without any third party involvement, which can significantly reduce bureaucracy and implementation delays (as well as the cost).

- When designing protocols for LANs, in theory at least it is not necessary to conform to any particular standard. In principle any technique can be used which is appropriate to satisfy individual needs. However in practice, adopting an international standard network is the only sensible choice if interworking is to be possible (including access to hosts via WANs such as PSS). Thanks to the efforts of the IEEE computer society in the USA, standards for supported LANs have reached a high degree of maturity and sophistication.

The international standard LAN topologies and protocols are examined in part three.

The original Cambridge (slotted) Ring technology had a number of problems, and many critics. Advances in technology have allowed substantial improvements in the performance of the Cambridge Ring. However, mainly because it has never had many adherents in the USA, it has yet to be adopted as an IEEE standard, although the access technique has been adopted by ISO.

A discussion of other LAN technologies such as cable-based broadband LANs and 'cheapie' products such as Clearway and Omninet, is beyond the scope of this book. A useful discussion may be found for example in Gee (preface, reference 2).

1.5   References

1   G. J. Chretien et Al, 'The SITA Network, Summary Description', Computer-Communication Network Conference, University of Sussex, Brighton, UK (September, 1973).

2   Several papers on the ARPA network may be found in proc. AFIPS SJCC, 1970.

3   B. W. Marsden, 'Discrete Event Simulation using Standard Pascal', Software Practice and Experience (July, 1984).

4   CEPT/CCH/GSM recommendation 04.22, 'Radio Link Protocol for Data and Telematic Services on the MS/BSS Interface' (November, 1988).

5   B. W. Marsden and H. Madadi, 'A Performance Assessment of the GSM Radio Link Protocol (RLP)', University of Manchester, Department of Computer Science, internal report. (Plans were in hand to publish this at the time of going to press.)

6   See for example L. Pouzin, 'Datagrams - Technical and Political Problems', Proc. AFIPS NCC, pp 483-494, 1976a.

7   R. C. Belton and M. A. Smith, 'An Introduction to EPSS', Post Office Electrical Engineers Journal (POEEJ), vol 66, p 216 (January, 1974). This is the first of a series of papers on EPSS in this journal.

8   P. A. Scantelbury, 'A Model for the Local Area of a Data Communication Network - Objectives and Hardware Organisation', proc. ACM symp., Pine Mountain, Ga. (October, 1969).

9   N. Abramson, 'The ALOHA system - Another Alternative for Computer Communications', Proc. AFIPS SJCC (1970).

2 Basic networking concepts

2.1 Introduction

Chapter three examines various protocol features and requirements, taking examples from protocols and specifications of historical interest. These will be tackled from a comparative rather than a historical standpoint. However before delving into fine details of protocols, it is worth spending some time on background concepts. These form the basis of this chapter. You are asked to refer to the glossary of terms in appendix A for definitions where appropriate.

2.2 Network topologies and terminology

Topology is a term used to describe the logical layout of a network, i.e. the relationship of nodes and the communication links between them. There are two major classes of topology, centralised and distributed. There are also innumerable hybrid networks which do not fall neatly into either category. Here we concentrate on the two main classes.

2.2.1 Star network topology

Typical of a centralised topology is the so-called *star network*. It is referred to as a star because there is a *central* node (host) which is 'more important' than the others, and the network can be visualised as a star with this central node in the middle. In the pure star topology, only connections in the direction of the central site are provided, and the central node is either the source or the destination of all messages. Often a *front end processor* (FEP) is added to the central configuration to relieve the central mainframe of responsibility for mundane but timeconsuming network chores. See figure 2.1.

Star networks are not particularly exciting from a communication viewpoint. Some of the more interesting features are given below.

• The network is hierarchical. This implies an addressing hierarchy for 'outstations' of the type 'AABBCCTT' (see figure 2.1). For example, the front end processor would use the 'AA' part of the address to route to the appropriate AA node, which would use the 'BB' part of the address, and so on in an outward direction.

• All messages destined for the central node ('central') must contain the full originating address, which will be used by central as the destination address for any reply messages, but will essentially be ignored by the network (i.e. not be used for routing purposes). However no destination address is required for incoming messages since central is the only possible destination. (A process identifier may be required if there are several central tasks which can be accessed from the network.)

• All messages originating from central must contain the full destination address, which is used for routing of messages as described above.

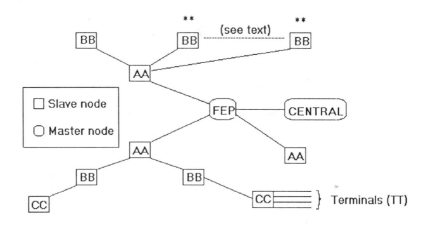

Figure 2.1 - star network

• Since there is only one path from any node to central, routing decisions are not required in the inward direction, and simply require a table lookup in the outward direction. No alternative routes are possible.

• As a consequence, parts of the network may become completely isolated from central in the event of a line failure. It is therefore usual to provide some form of backup to cover this eventuality. Typically leased (dedicated) lines will be used, with public switched telephone network (PSTN) backup.

Pure star networks are generally associated with a completely centralised service, such as a timesharing bureau, where the sole purpose of the network is to allow this central service to be accessed. In cases where outstations wish to communicate with each other, there are two options. The first is to provide direct links between outstations (e.g. between ** and ** in figure 2.1). In the absence of such connections, an outstation would have to send messages to the FEP with the other outstation as destination. The FEP would then have to make routing decisions based on the destination address (possibly assuming central as a destination if the address was absent). This is known as *tandem switching*. Clearly the software in the FEP would need to be more sophisticated in this case.

Nodes such as AA and BB would usually be concentrators, although those with terminals directly attached could also do some local preprocessing, and could have a local disk filestore. Note that multiplexers are simply cost saving conveniences, incapable of such intelligence as routing decisions, and therefore would not appear on the logical map above, since they are not nodes in the accepted sense of the term. However multiplexers are commonly found in star networks.

2.2.2   Mesh network topology

The second major class of topology is far more interesting; most of the book centres around networks of this type. This is the ***mesh network***. Mesh networks became common once a need was seen for communication between sites, as opposed to between outstations and a single central site. The term is used to cover a set of nodes which are multiply connected, so that there are generally at least two ways of getting from one node to another. Typically, nodes will be spread geographically, with hosts being connected to the nearest node. In fully connected mesh networks, there is a direct link from every node to every other one. However this is expensive and not often found in practice. A 'typical' mesh network is shown in figure 2.2; hosts can generally be connected to any network node. Three hosts (X, Y and Z) are shown in the figure, and these will be referred to in later discussions. In this type of network, there is no 'central' host, all hosts being logical equals. Therefore this type of network is commonly used for linking together various host computers with 'equal status'. The ARPANET is of this type, as is the more recent PSS packet switching network in the UK. In this type of network, routing becomes an important consideration, as we will now discuss.

2.3   Mesh network routing algorithms

One important aspect of mesh networks is a consequence of the multiple paths between any two hosts. This is the requirement for routing decisions to be made. Consider for example how to get from node A (host X) to node K (host Y). There are several possibilities, which include:

- Links 4, 6, 9, 11 (4 hops).
- Links 1, 2, 3, 10, 11 (5 hops).
- Links 4, 5, 8, 12, 13 (5 hops).
- Links 4, 6, 7, 12, 13 (5 hops).

Other more tortuous routes can be seen as well, but these are the 'obvious' ones. Note that normally the network is laid out 'logically', so that it looks reasonably neat on paper. The layout does not necessarily give any indication of the geographical locations of the nodes, or the lengths of the links. In practice these factors may influence routing decisions, but we

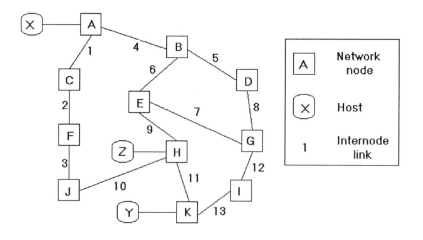

Figure 2.2 - partially connected mesh network

will ignore this. The first question we must ask is how a route from X (A) to Y (K) is arrived at?

A routing decision is made at each node (i.e. some **routing algorithm** is applied), to *select an outgoing link* which will take the message (or whatever) in the 'general direction' of the destination. Such a decision must be made at each node. How should this decision be taken? In principle it could be done manually, but this would clearly be neither cost effective nor efficient. Therefore it must somehow be done by software. However programs cannot 'look at a diagram' and make the 'obvious' choice, so the nodes must be given some help. Before we examine the various options, it is worth mentioning some pitfalls. If each node takes routing decisions based on the best path to the destination, and one or more nodes get it wrong, one of the following could happen:

- *Path loops.* For example, a message from A to K going along links 4, 5, 8, 7, 6, 5, 8, 7, 6 ... Assuming that each node (B, D, G, E) makes the same routing decision each time, this could go on for ever! Even worse, this would mean that every message for Y would in turn become stuck, the traffic would build up out of control, and the network would rapidly 'die' of suffocation. This might sound absurd, but without care in the selection of routes, it can happen.

- *Oscillation.* For example the message going along links 4, 5, 5, 5, 5 (backwards and forwards). This could happen with bad design if link 8 failed, and D routed the message back to B, which then returned it to D, etc.

- All messages converge on a given node (E say), which as a result becomes so *congested* that it can no longer handle the traffic. Note that it is possible to get from any node to any other via node E (or any other node for that matter), although in some cases the route might seem a little strange.

- If nodes and/or links fail, it may become *impossible to reach the destination* at all. A similar result will occur if the destination itself fails. If a network persists in trying to deliver messages to destinations which cannot be reached, trouble will inevitably arise.

What is required is a means of imposing some control, which can be provided by a routing algorithm[1] which will, ideally:

- Select the 'shortest' or 'cheapest' route (outgoing link) from each node;

- avoid routing traffic to areas which are congested, and additionally select routes on the basis of known or projected traffic to minimise congestion;

- prevent messages from circulating endlessly;

- not return messages on the same link on which they have just been received;

- not forward messages if it is known that they cannot be delivered.

It is possible that a destination has not failed, but is simply not connected to the network at the moment. This can be a particular problem in countries with different time zones. For example, if all hosts of an organisation in the USA are connected from 8 am to 6 pm local time, there will be periods in the early morning and late afternoon when not all hosts are connected to the network. There have been cases of networks where account was taken of this by storing messages in the network until they could be delivered. However several problems can be encountered if this approach is used. These relate to storage requirements, delivery of messages in sequence, and message accountability. The network is also likely to be very costly and inefficient. Without spending too much time on justification, we will assume that messages which it is known cannot be delivered, should not be forwarded.

We will now discuss several different routing strategies in turn.

2.3.1   Fixed (deterministic) routing

In this scheme, each node (A, B, C and so on) maintains a routing table which contains one entry (or more; see below) for each destination (based on the network node to which the destination host is connected, not the host itself). Whenever a message arrives for a given host, the outgoing route is selected from the routing table, and the message is placed in the queue for the appropriate outgoing link. Figure 2.3 shows a possible routing table for node E in figure 2.2.

This table serves to highlight several interesting points. Firstly, a special entry in the routing table tells the node in effect what its own address is. When a node with a * entry is reached, a different routing algorithm is applied to select the local host.

Another point is that there appear to be two routes of 'equal length' from E to D, using links 6 then 5, or 7 then 8. Why has link 7 been selected rather than link 6? Before a routing table of this type is decided on, traffic calculations will be performed, based on projected usage of the network. Usually the shortest route between two nodes will be the aim, since this will tend to minimise traffic on links (and also maximise throughput). In store and forward message switching networks, it is better for storage and throughput if the number of nodes involved in switching the message can be kept to a minimum. Where there is no obvious shortest route, likely traffic on each alternative is examined before a decision is made. Therefore link 7 would have 'won' because, taking possible routes into account, overall traffic is likely to be more even than if route 6 had been chosen.

There is clearly some difficulty if the actual traffic turns out to be significantly different in practice from what the calculations (or guesses) suggested. Also, traffic patterns in any network will change with time. Therefore it is usual for the routing table to be updated at regular intervals (typically of the order of weeks to months), or whenever new nodes or hosts are added to (or removed from) the network, and generally when some obvious problem with the existing routes becomes apparent.

DESTINATION NODE	OUTGOING LINK
A	6
B	6
C	6
D	7
E	*
F	9
G	7
H	9
I	7
J	9
K	9

NOTE:

*   No entry if the current node is the destination

Figure 2.3 - possible routing table for node E in figure 2.2

There is another difficulty. The routing table in figure 2.3 takes no account of possible link failures. If link 7 fails, there will be no route from E to D, G or I, whereas it is obvious that messages could still get there via link 6. It is therefore possible to provide a *secondary* or *alternative route* to each destination, for use if the *primary route* (either the link or the node at the other end) becomes unusable.

The British Telecom PSS network uses deterministic routing, but no secondary route is provided. If the primary route fails, the network informs both hosts that the association has failed. The network makes minimal attempts to recover on behalf of the hosts. Modern thinking favours minimising attempts to recover <u>inside</u> networks, thereby making them simpler and cheaper. Of course this passes the problem to the hosts. This point should become clearer after reading chapter four.

It was also possible in some message switching networks for manual operator intervention on an individual message basis, but this was usually only used as an emergency measure, in view of the administrative overhead involved. (It usually involved operators inspecting message queues, and issuing routing commands, on a control console at the node concerned.)

Deterministic routing is the oldest of the routing techniques available. In the days of message switching networks it was used almost universally. Even now it is one of the commonest routing algorithms. Its main drawback is that it can result in inflexibility in networks where traffic patterns can change significantly over a short period of time. It has however the advantage of being simple, and is in fact used in current X.25 packet switching networks. There are several alternatives to deterministic routing which are potentially worth consideration, and some of the main contenders will now be briefly discussed.

2.3.2   Least cost routing

Normally such mundane if crucial issues as network usage charges are not of great interest in this book, although they may influence the choice of a network by the user if alternatives are available. Any user will wish to minimise costs whilst maximising throughput. Some networks, notably in the USA, provide a variety of types and speeds of internode line (e.g. 1200-50000 bps, with optical fibre, four wire, microwave or satellite links) at differing costs, or can provide access at extra cost to third party facilities. (This is an example of the *value added* technique.)

A related concept is the value added network, where some special enhancement is provided (at extra cost) over and above the basic network function (of getting information from X to Y). An attempt by British Telecom and IBM to offer IBM's Systems Network Architecture (SNA) over BT networks failed, largely for political reasons. This would have been a typical example.

Least cost routing involves the source host's network node providing the host with details (and cost) of the various possible routes to a particular destination. The sending host may then select the most cost effective route through the network, in effect causing the network to customise a routing table at each node for this particular sending host. What is most cost effective will depend in some way on the total cost, maximum possible throughput on the links involved, and transit time across the network (long if satellite links are involved). Having decided on a route, it will then be used for subsequent messages to the given destination, i.e. it is deterministic. Transit time, error rates and throughput could also be taken into consideration in determining the 'grade of service' offered by the various options.

In chapter four we will discuss the technique of virtual circuits (or virtual calls), where (at least you may assume this for the moment) several messages are associated with the call. In this case, a variant of this technique is used where the route is decided at the start of the call, and will be the same for all messages sent during the call. However a different route may be selected on a per call basis, depending on network conditions rather than user requirements.

This type of routing is only useful if the network usage charge is in some way dependent on the path through the network, and if the network user is in a position to make such decisions (is aware of the alternatives available, and can make a sensible choice). Most networks which charge for usage impose a charging structure which takes no account of the route taken through the network. In the case of British Telecom's PSS network, the actual route through the network is unknown to the user, and the cost is not dependent on how far apart the hosts are.

2.3.3   Random (stochastic) routing

In this technique, each node selects one of the 'sensible' outgoing links on a random or pseudo-random basis, i.e. it cannot be predicted in advance which link will be taken. This requires less involvement in the design of tables and traffic calculations. However there can be no certainty that traffic will always be routed in the most sensible direction, and there is a probability that a minority of messages will take unacceptably long routes across the network. Furthermore, the algorithm is still insensitive to traffic fluctuations, and there is no way in which the routing tables can be changed, since they do not exist. This technique is of limited usefulness, and will not be discussed further.

A variant of this technique is what is sometimes referred to as *flooding*. Here, the transmission unit is sent on all appropriate links, and this guarantees that, provided a route to the destination exists, the transmission unit will get there, and all valid routes will be tried, including the 'shortest' route. Safeguards are clearly required to ensure that the transmission unit is not sent more than once on any particular link. The main problem is that the traffic in the network can grow to an unacceptable extent, and for this reason it can hardly be considered to be a viable algorithm in most networks.

2.3.4   Adaptive routing

With adaptive routing, network traffic is continually assessed, and decisions are made on a per transmission unit basis at each node. As with stochastic routing, the route to be taken cannot be determined in advance, but the difference here is that traffic in the network is taken into account when deciding on the route to be taken. There are two basic approaches to adaptive routing, centralised and distributed.

Adaptive routing with centralised control

This technique relies on the existence of a *network control centre* which can make traffic decisions on behalf of the network nodes. The idea is that each node will periodically send status reports to the network control centre. These will be analysed on a network-wide basis, and each host will be provided with regularly updated routing information by the control centre. This appears to have two desirable effects.

• Continuous statistics on network performance are continually being gathered, which can be of great value to the network administration.

• The routes taken by messages in the network will somehow reflect the traffic presented to the network. Again in an ideal world, all congestion and bottlenecks can be ironed out before they become a problem.

Sadly, the second supposed benefit is an illusion. Using a network control centre in this way also has a number of undesirable effects:

• Extra traffic is generated between nodes and the control centre. Traffic information and routing instructions must be sent as messages, which compete for network resources. Therefore the attempt to minimise congestion is in fact likely to contribute to it.

• The control centre is most needed when the network is heavily congested. But this is precisely when delays in getting messages to and from it will be at their longest. Therefore the reaction of the network to traffic changes will be slowest precisely when an immediate response is needed.

• Traffic fluctuations tend to be short term in nature. The delays involved in communicating with the control centre could be such that the changes to routing tables are out of date, and hence no longer appropriate, before they are even received; if the suggested changes were applied, they could make the situation worse.

Again, this seems not to be a very good technique. A network of any size cannot be effectively controlled from a central point. However the statistics so obtained can be valuable in other ways. It is useful to have details of network traffic and performance, and statistics can be obtained by nodes, then forwarded to a measurement centre, if desired, at times of low network loading. A technique like this was used in the ARPANET for measuring network performance.

Distributed adaptive routing

Here again, nodes make routing decisions on the basis of current traffic patterns, but they do it themselves, rather than being instructed what to do by a central location. As an example, the original ARPANET routing algorithm will be briefly described[2].

Routing decisions require knowledge of the current state of the network. In ARPANET, this was done by each node (known as an Interface Message Processor or IMP) measuring the delay to each destination by various routes. Each IMP passes this information to its neighbouring IMPs. An IMP can thus calculate the delay to a given destination by adding its own estimate of the delay to its neighbour, to its neighbour's information. The routing algorithm selects the 'fastest' outgoing link to the destination for each transmission unit. IMPs are not informed of routes via themselves; this provides protection against the 'shuttlecock syndrome' described earlier. If a destination cannot be reached, all routes to the destination will indicate an infinite time. Transmission units will not be forwarded if no path to the destination can be found which gives a finite delay. Instead, an indication of 'net trouble' is returned to the sender, and any information currently in transit will be discarded.

Information is exchanged between neighbouring IMPs about twice a second, more frequently if there is no traffic on the line. This does not add significantly to network traffic, since each routing packet is short, and only travels a single hop.

Although this technique has undoubted flexibility, it can be rather messy to implement in X.25 networks (see chapter seven), and tends not to be used with this kind of network. Even in the ARPANET, the use of this type of routing algorithm resulted in some implementation problems, notably reassembly lockup[4].

2.4   Message formats

2.4.1   Why a message needs formatting

We have discussed routing, and seen that messages require addresses which allow them to be routed through the network to their intended destination(s). Other information is also present which is not part of the user text, but is required for protocol reasons. This may include sequencing information, acknowledgements, possibly a text length field and error check information. This is *control information*, and is also sometimes referred to as a *main network addition*.

Control information implies an overhead, in that additional information is present which is of little or no concern to the user, but which adds to the information in the network, and hence to network loading and transit time. A further overhead is involved, since extra characters need to be included to allow the user text to be distinguished from the control information. In the case of user text, unless encryption or other techniques are used, it may generally be classified as either readable text (usually ASCII) or binary. Whatever protocol is used, the text part at least will be reasonably the same. There are however two basic ways of encoding control information. The technique used in traditional message switching will now be discussed. A better alternative will be developed in chapter four.

2.4.2   Basic ASCII-based message format

The first message switching protocols were entirely based on the ASCII code set. As an extension of Telex, it was considered that the user text would be just that, a stream of human readable characters together with 'format effectors' such as CR (carriage return) and LF (linefeed). Other ASCII characters known as *transmission control* (TC) characters were used for communication protocol functions. See figure 2.4.

CHARACTER	CODE	USAGE IN MESSAGE PROTOCOLS
SOH	^A	start of message header
STX	^B	start of message text
ETX	^C	end of message text
ETB	^W	end of intermediate transmission block
EOT	^D	end of transmission
SYN	^V	synchronous idle (and time fill)
DLE	^P	data link escape
DLE X		extra TC 'characters' e.g. ACK0 WACK RVI
ACK	^F	positive acknowledgement
NAK	^U	negative acknowledgement
ENQ	^E	enquiry: bid for control, repeat last response, block abort, temporary text delay (after STX)
ITB	---	EBCDIC not ASCII; like ETB

NOTE:
ACK0, WACK and RVI are discussed in §3.4.

Figure 2.4 - ASCII transmission control (TC) characters

A basic message consists of header and text. TC characters are used to indicate the start of the message header, and the start and end of the user text (as well as for acknowledgements etc.). A single error check (**BCC** or **Block Check Character**) is appended to the message. On synchronous lines, a few SYN characters will precede the message to allow the receiver to synchronise to the character stream; these are not shown. The basic ASCII message format is shown in figure 2.5.

Figure 2.5 - basic ASCII message format

Before we discuss what the header looks like, it is clear that there will be at least one problem. The character STX cannot appear in the header, nor can ETX appear in the text part. In fact more rigid restrictions are usually imposed, which say that no TC character can appear in either the header or the text.

One attempt to ease this restriction used DLE STX, DLE ETX and so on rather than STX and ETX, to format blocks. In this case it is possible to have STX inside the text part, and a DLE in the text part must be duplicated. This variant is known, rather optimistically, as <u>transparent mode</u>.

In either case, it is a messy job trying to send binary 'text'. One way to do it is to force bit 7 to be 1, so that control characters cannot be simulated (see figure 2.6). In addition the parity bit is not available; ASCII requires this to be set depending on the line type (odd parity for synchronous lines, even for asynchronous). This is one of many reasons why ASCII-based message formats are now archaic. Other reasons are more subtle. We will see what they are in due course.

BITS	USAGE
8	parity bit (most significant bit)
7-6	used to distinguish numbers and letters (both zero for control characters)
5-1	may take any value (allows 32 control characters)

Figure 2.6 - use of bits in ASCII characters

2.4.3 Subdivision into transmission blocks

The probability of a transmission error is proportional to the length of the unit being transmitted. The overhead in retransmission if an error is detected is also proportional to the length. Since communication lines are not error free, it is wise to restrict the length of a transmission unit (i.e. what is protected by an error check), otherwise when the line error rate exceeds some value, it will prove impossible to transmit a message without an error somewhere, which is clearly an undesirable state of affairs. A subsidiary problem is that no error checking algorithm can detect every error. Some of the more primitive types (e.g. the BCC) fail to detect a significant proportion of errors. It is therefore desirable to keep the error checked unit reasonably small.

It is possible to calculate the optimum 'block' length using queuing theory, although the details are not pertinent to this discussion[3]. At very long block lengths, the overhead of retransmitting even a single block becomes unacceptable, and in the extreme it becomes impossible to transmit successfully at all on unreliable lines. If on the other hand the block length is very short, the extra overheads of additional formatting characters and acknowledgements, together with the delays introduced by turnaround of the communication line (related to the electrical requirements of some terminals and Modems) become unacceptable for an error free line. Therefore for a communication line with some given error characteristics, there will be an optimum block length which minimises the overheads whilst keeping the throughput acceptable. Unfortunately this varies with the line error rate. Protocols must agree on some fixed value however, and it turns out that a maximum block length of 240 characters is about right for 'typical' communication lines as existed at the time (the 1960s). Therefore this length has been adopted as a de facto standard for ASCII based message switching protocols.

It is worth mentioning that a variant of BSC exists for use with multidrop lines, where many intelligent VDUs share the same physical line and are polled and selected by having a unique address. In most variants of BSC for this type of application, it is unusual to subdivide messages into transmission blocks, so that message lengths can be up to the maximum screen size (typically about 2 kbytes). The point here is that using transmission blocks complicates the protocol used in the VDUs, and the lines are likely to be fairly localised, and have above average reliability.

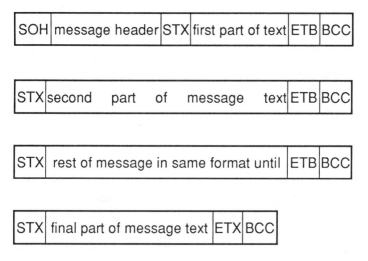

Figure 2.7 - ASCII message subdivided into transmission blocks

Subdivision of a message into blocks requires extra TC characters to delineate the blocks. The commonest scheme is as shown in figure 2.7 for a 4-block message. (As always with this type of protocol, there are numerous variants).

It should be noted that all blocks except the last one end with ETB not ETX, and all blocks except the first one will start with STX. The first block always starts with SOH (there is a header in the first block only), and the last block always ends with ETX. The last block will normally be less than 240 characters long; all others will be the full length. Each block is individually protected by a BCC, computed from all characters in the block.

There is a limitation on the header length, which cannot exceed the maximum length of a block (240 characters). This is because a header longer than this could not be carried into the second block, as this must start with STX, which would end the header. In practice the header will seldom be longer than about 50 characters. It typically contains such information as the source and destination addresses, the message sequence number, the priority, and possibly security codes, text format and so on. Header fields are usually separated by ASCII SPACE or CR LF, and are all human readable, e.g.

SOH ABCDEF GHIJKL *CR LF* (addresses) 1234 HIGH *CR LF* (sequence number, priority) *STX*

2.5 References

1 A useful discussion of topology and routing issues, including quantitative aspects, may be found in the following book: V. Ahuja, 'Design and Analysis of Computer Communication Networks', McGraw Hill (1985).

2 J. M. McQuillan and D. C. Walden, 'The ARPA Network Design Decisions', Computer Networks, vol. 1, p. 243 (1977). See also Frank H. et al., 'Topological Considerations in the Design of the ARPA Computer Network', Proc. AFIPS SJCC, vol. 36, p. 581 (May 1970). The routing algorithm on ARPANET was subsequently altered, but the distributed adaptive philosophy remained similar.

3 The classic, but now dated, book by James Martin, 'Systems Analysis for Data Transmission', published by Prentice Hall, deals with quantitative aspects such as queueing theory in great detail.

4 Kahn R. E. and Crowther W. R., 'Flow Control in a Resource Sharing Network', Commun. ACM, vol. 15, p. 221 (April 1972).

3 Fundamentals of protocols

3.1 Introduction

The first two chapters covered general networking principles. In this chapter we examine some basic requirements of the protocols which are used in wide area mesh networks. This discussion will largely be based on the traditional message switching technique and the BSC protocol. This will give us a chance to look at some of the problems which were encountered in early networks which used this technique. It is important to gain a good insight into what is fundamentally wrong with the BSC protocol, and this will become increasingly clear as the chapter progresses. It will also become clear that there are serious deficiencies with the message switching technique itself.

What constitutes a message is for the originating host to decide; transmission blocks are used merely to break down the message into units of manageable size for transmission purposes. Once all blocks of a message have been accepted by the receiver, it can take responsibility for the message. Thus the message will (one hopes) pass along various links in the mesh network and ultimately reach the destination host. BSC's job therefore is to forward blocks across links between adjacent nodes. This is why BSC is referred to as a *link protocol*.

We start by outlining some features general to all protocols. We will examine the need for each feature, and various ways of satisfying each requirement. Where alternative approaches exist, they are briefly compared. We will examine the problems in the context of BSC later in the chapter.

3.2 Detection of transmission errors

In an ideal, error free network, we could guarantee that any text which we send would reach its destination, and would be exactly as it was when we sent it, i.e. the destination host could rely absolutely on the integrity of the received data. However no network is error-free; although some LANs come quite close, WANs hardly ever do. The data may become corrupted for a variety of reasons. For example electrical signals are subject to attenuation and distortion, water can enter cables causing electrical shorts, clicks in telephone exchanges caused by switching can corrupt data, and lightning strikes near underground cables can have a serious effect. Even if only a single bit is changed from 0 to 1 or vice versa, the information content of the data must be regarded as corrupted. In a human readable message in natural language, the occasional corrupted letter can probably be tolerated in most cases, since the information content of the message will not be degraded (e.g. 'c@mputer' can readily be recognised as a corruption of 'computer'). Where numeric data is concerned, the situation is quite different. A bank could not tolerate a network which was liable to fail to detect errors such as the corruption of a transaction from £1000 to £9000. Corruption of the address could result in a message being delivered to the wrong destination, which could be embarrassing if the information was sensitive.

Therefore the first essential element of a protocol must be the ability to handle transmission errors. This requires the addition of some redundant information to the transmission unit, to which the receiver can apply some algorithm which, one hopes, reliably indicates whether a transmission error has occurred. If it has, it can be handled in one of two basic ways:

• If sufficient redundant information is attached, it may be possible for the receiver not only to detect the error but also to correct it as well. This is known as *forward error correction*. Hamming codes are examples of this technique. Unfortunately this involves a considerable amount of additional information, which is uneconomic on communication lines where, at worst, a relatively small fraction of transmission units will be corrupted. Equally importantly, there is no mechanism for the receiver to indicate problems to the sender in the event that the error could not be corrected, or some other problem arises, and normally we require an interaction between sender and recipient. Therefore this technique is not used in network protocols.

• The second technique is known as *backward error detection*, where the receiver simply notes that an error exists somewhere in the transmission unit, and discards it. The destination makes no attempt to correct the error itself. Some means will normally be provided (by a protocol) for a second copy to be sent to the receiver.

Three backward error detection techniques of widely varying effectiveness are briefly outlined:

• *Vertical parity*. This is only available if transmission is based on some code, such as ASCII, which has a separate parity bit. This can then be set so that the number of 1-bits in the character is either even (asynchronous lines) or odd (synchronous lines, as in networks). Clearly a transmission error has occurred if a character with incorrect parity has been received. But this is inadequate unless supported by additional procedures.

- **Block Check Character** (*BCC*). This is similar in concept to vertical parity, but is applied to the entire transmission unit. Each character is XORed with the next, until the end of the transmission unit is reached. The result is appended as the BCC. For this reason it is also referred to as *longitudinal parity*. This technique is used in BSC in conjunction with vertical parity. The BCC can take any value, and in the context of an ASCII-based code a BCC is expected as the 8-bit 'character' immediately following ETX or ETB. (This can of course lead to difficulties if the ETX or ETB is corrupted, as the end of the transmission unit will not be detected.) Again the BCC technique is not considered good enough, and tends only to be used with traditional protocols such as BSC.

- Modern protocols rely on protection of transmission units using a **cyclic redundancy check** (*CRC*). This is a 16 (or possibly 24 or 32) bit field added to the end of packets, and is generally used in non-ASCII-based packet switching protocols. There are a number of variants, the most commonly used being the CCITT approved variant. Hardware 'sums' the packet as it is transmitted, and a 'remainder' is computed using a generator polynomial and appended to the packet. The standard CCITT polynomial is

$$x^{16} + x^{12} + x^5 + 1$$

although there are others in use. Chips can be purchased off the shelf which perform CRC generation and detection automatically. The CRC technique provides a high degree of immunity from undetected transmission errors, and is used in current standard WAN and LAN link protocols. The CCITT error check guarantees that all errors less than 16 bits long will be detected, and most longer than this as well.

3.3   Acknowledgement

Merely detecting transmission errors and discarding transmission units which are corrupted is not normally of much use by itself. Usually we will want to know that it has been discarded, so that a further copy can be sent. This requires some means of finding out whether the receiver accepted a transmission unit or not. *Acknowledgement* is a means of providing confirmation (or otherwise) of this, so that remedial action can be taken if required. Anything which has been transmitted but has not yet been acknowledged is said to be *outstanding*.

3.3.1 Acknowledgement schemes

There are four basic acknowledgement techniques which could be considered. We examine each in turn to see whether it is feasible.

- The technique which seemed most logical to the early protocol designers was based (as was much else at that time) on what happened in a telephone conversation. It is obvious that both parties cannot talk at once, and it is equally clear that each party must send 'cues' meaning either 'yes I understood that' or 'sorry I didn't understand - please say it again', so that each knows whether the other party has understood correctly what has been said. The 'got that' cue is in effect a *positive acknowledgement*, meaning that the 'transmission unit' (e.g. sentence) was received and understood. In practice this may be implicit, since one often assumes that the other person understands what one is saying unless he indicates otherwise. Similarly 'please say it again' implies a *negative acknowledgement*, and what was just said will need to be repeated.

Translating these informal requirements into an *acknowledgement scheme* for a protocol, the same approach was adopted, but the protocol had to be formalised, so that the action in a given situation was consistent. Therefore it was made a requirement that every transmission unit must be acknowledged, either positively or negatively. Furthermore if the acknowledgement is negative, the transmission unit must be sent again, until such time as a positive acknowledgement is received. Only then can the next one can be sent. The other principal feature of a telephone conversation was retained, that only one party could speak at once. In BSC terms, one station on the link could transmit blocks, and the other would acknowledge each one in turn, returning NAK if a transmission error was detected, and ACK if all appeared to be correct.

In fact this basic scheme needs further refinement and formalisation if it is to work, and we will return to this in §3.4.1.

- An alternative which seems logical is to say nothing if all is well, but to issue NAK if a transmission error is detected. This works in phone conversations, but if used on computer communication links it has a fatal flaw, which is that if the NAK itself is corrupted, the sender will assume that all is well, which it clearly isn't, as two wrongs don't make a right. The result of this is that the sender fondly assumes that the corrupted transmission unit was correctly received. We had better forget this approach!

- A third alternative is for the receiver to issue ACK if no error was detected, and discard corrupted transmission units without comment, i.e. *positive only acknowledgement*. This would clearly not work in a telephone conversation, but is a valid approach on a communication link provided that there is a mechanism which allows the sender to retransmit information units which were not acknowledged. There is, but we will not be able to discuss these mechanisms adequately until the next chapter. In any case this scheme requires transmission blocks to be distinguishable, which they are not in BSC.

- Finally the ultimate acknowledgement scheme is to acknowledge nothing at all! This may sound absurd, but in fact there are some applications where it matters little if the occasional transmission unit is lost, in which case the overheads or acknowledging transmission units seem unnecessary. There may well also be procedures beyond the scope of the link protocol which can detect and recover lost transmission units.

What should already be becoming apparent is that procedures which will work for telephone conversations are not necessarily sensible for computer communication protocols, a point which the early protocol designers completely missed; we shall see how wrong some of their decisions were as the chapter progresses.

Mention should be made at this point of what the author regards as unhelpful terminology which surrounds acknowledgement schemes. This is the term automatic retransmission (or repeat) request or ARQ for short. The technique used in BSC where everything is acknowledged is then referred to as Idle ARQ, which means that the sender must wait (be idle, unable to transmit further blocks) after sending a block, until either the acknowledgement has been received or recovery is initiated. The term continuous ARQ is used if the sender need not wait for an acknowledgement. The author finds the ARQ terminology unhelpful, indeed confusing, and therefore references to ARQ herein are as asides. The main problem is that a number of very different techniques are classified under the same heading, which is an abuse of the generic concept.

3.3.2   Acknowledgement in BSC

A few words of elaboration on the acknowledgement scheme used by BSC will allow a number of other concepts to be introduced. Basically a message is broken down into transmission blocks (transmission units), which are sent in turn. Each must be acknowledged, either positively (ACK) or negatively (NAK) before the next can be sent.

Why was this acknowledgement scheme chosen? Is it the 'best' scheme, given that there are alternatives? When BSC was developed, there was no experience whatsoever of communication networks. The techniques applied, including the acknowledgement scheme used, were adapted from existing conventions for voice communication. As we will see, it turns out to be a poor choice for a number of reasons. To understand the problems, we must first examine some further features of BSC and message switching.

3.4   An overview of the BSC protocol

In this section we progressively introduce various additional features of BSC in order to explain some fundamental protocol concepts. At first we will relate these purely to BSC, but we will then go on to discuss critically the extent to which BSC satisfies the requirements placed on it, that is to implement store and forward message switching over a mesh network.

3.4.1   Timeouts and retries

The first thing we must do is to examine the acknowledgement scheme in a little more detail. Figure 3.1 shows part of a typical BSC dialogue. The station (node) on the left is transmitting blocks, and the station on the right is returning acknowledgements. Unfortunately things are going wrong. As you can see, there is now far more involved than simply returning ACK and NAK as appropriate.

- Since the sender must receive a reply, either ACK or NAK, the situation where for some reason no reply is received must be catered for. In other words *recovery procedures* are required, otherwise there would be a deadly embrace, with neither station able to proceed. It may be that the block was mangled and thus unrecognisable at the receiver, or that the reply (ACK or NAK) was lost. It could also result from a failure of either the receiver or the link itself; we will consider these cases as well.

- The solution to this problem is to implement a *timeout* at the sender. A *timer* is started immediately the block has been completely sent. A timeout occurs if this timer reaches some predetermined limit without a valid reply (in this case ACK or NAK) having been received. (If a valid reply is received, the timer is cancelled.) If a timeout occurs, the recovery procedure used in this case is to send the ENQ character, which asks the receiver to repeat its last reply. The ENQ is similarly 'guarded by timeout'.

- The first difficulty is that it is immediately obvious that there are two distinct situations which could have resulted in no reply being received, and ENQ being issued. The most recent block could have been garbled beyond recognition, so that the receiver was unaware of its receipt and offered no reply. Alternatively the block might have been successfully received, but the ACK returned was garbled. The two cases will result in ACK being returned for different blocks. Therefore if a simple ACK is used, there is a risk of blocks being lost (or duplicated), as the sender will not know which block is being acknowledged. Therefore the procedures were modified to use two *numbered acknowledgements* ACK0 and ACK1 (encoded as DLE 0 and DLE 1; see figure 2.4).

SENDER	INFO	RECEIVER	COMMENTS
----->	BLOCK 1		
	ACK 1	<-----	
----->	BLOCK 2		
	ACK 0	<-----	
----->	BZOCK 3		corrupted
	NAK	<-----	resend please
----->	BLOCK 3		again
	ACK 1	<-----	
----->	BLOCK 4		
	ACK 0	<-----	
----->	block 5		unrecognisable
			sender timeout
----->	ENQ		repeat last reply
	ACK 0	<-----	to block 4
----->	BLOCK 5		retransmitted
	ACK 1	<-----	ok this time
----->	BLOCK 6		
	ack 0		reply lost
			sender timeout
----->	ENQ		repeat last reply
	ACK 0	<-----	to block 6
----->	BLOCK 7		
	ACK 1	<-----	and so on

Figure 3.1 - BSC block acknowledgement procedure

- The possibility also exists that something more serious may have gone wrong. As well as the two cases above, it is possible that the line or the receiving node may have failed totally, in which case however many times ENQ is sent, no response will be forthcoming. To prevent a lockup where ENQ is endlessly repeated, it may only be *retried* up to n (say 8; implementation dependent) times. If after n attempts a valid reply has still not been received, recovery procedures will be invoked. (In fact this involves shutting down the link; more on this in due course).

To summarise, either an ACK or a NAK must be returned. In the absence of either response, ENQ is sent to solicit a repeat of the receiver's last response. Numbered ACKs are used in an attempt to make this response unambiguous, although this does not remove the problem completely. (ACK 0 could conceivably become corrupted to ACK 1, for example.) It is worth noting that all blocks in a message (apart from the very first and last) start with STX and end with ETB. Therefore they cannot be distinguished by BSC. This is why a block must be acknowledged before the next is sent, and also why it is so easy to lose or duplicate blocks if something goes wrong. In due course we will see that these are both undesirable characteristics.

However first we will look at management aspects of BSC.

3.4.2   Gaining control of the link

Figure 3.1 shows blocks being transferred from left to right, with ACK/NAK being returned in the other direction. This leaves a number of questions unanswered:

- Why are blocks being transferred in this direction?

- Can blocks be transferred in the other direction at the same time?

- If not, how does the other node get its turn to transmit?

Initially the link is said to be in the *idle* state. In this state, no block transfer is possible. The answer to the first question is that in order to transmit blocks, either station may *bid for control* of the link. If this bid succeeds, this station may now send blocks. It is possible that both stations may simultaneously bid for control. Since only one may acquire control at a given time, a situation known as a *collision* has occurred. In BSC, there is no mechanism for negotiating which station will 'win', so this is built into the software at each end; one station gains control and the other gives way.

In fact this also answers the second question. The station (node) permitted to transfer blocks is known as the *master*, and the receiver as the *slave*. This type of protocol is said to be *unbalanced* since only the master station may transmit blocks; the slave station may not do so unless and until it gains master status. (The 'imbalance' is that the two stations do not have the same repertoire of operations simultaneously.) It may also be referred to as a *half duplex protocol*, since information (i.e. block) transfer can proceed in either direction, but only in one direction at a time.

The answer to the third question is that, at any time when the slave could have returned ACK0 or ACK1, the slave may instead issue a *reverse interrupt* or RVI. This serves as an acknowledgement, and also instructs the master station to relinquish control of the line, which then reverts to the idle state. The former slave station is then given a certain period of time (sometimes referred to as a 'time window') during which it may bid for control without challenge. The former master station must accept this bid, and now becomes the slave. Thus the direction of transmission is reversed.

The astute reader may have noticed that RVI serves as either ACK 0 or ACK 1. If this is sent in response to a received ENQ, consider whether this could lead to loss or duplication of a block. [Hint: the BSC protocol designers did not perceive it to be a problem.]

One important point to note is that this can happen at any time when ACK can be issued by the slave, i.e. after the successful reception of any block, and can therefore happen in the middle of messages. The implications of this are serious, and are discussed in chapter four.

3.4.3   Sequence control

Suppose that I wished my local host to send two messages to a remote host operating my bank account. The first is an instruction to deposit £1000 in my account, and the second is an instruction to pay a bill of £1200. The initial balance was £500. If the messages arrive in the correct order, there will be no problem. If they arrive out of order, the bill payment may fail as my account would become overdrawn. Things would get worse if one of the messages vanished altogether, and although I would be happy for the deposit to be duplicated, I might be less happy if the bill was paid twice!

This example highlights a standard problem with protocols operating over networks. Referring first to entire messages transmitted between end hosts, there are normally two basic requirements:

- The messages must arrive in the same order in which they were transmitted.

- Messages must not be lost or duplicated inside the network.

Leaving aside for now the question of whether these aims can be achieved in a message switching network, it is clear that some means needs to be provided whereby messages can be identified in a way which both indicates their ordering, and guarantees that loss or duplication will be noticed. One way to achieve this is to provide a **sequence number**. This could start at 1 say, and be incremented for every successive message sent from one host to a given destination host. Then, if messages arrive at the destination host out of sequence (as is quite possible with deterministic routing if backup links are used for some messages), the destination host will be able to reorder the messages, discard duplicates, and identify gaps in the message sequence.

The next logical extension is to provide sequence numbers on the link. Unfortunately in BSC this is not possible, since a transmission block is merely a 'chunk' of text encapsulated by STX and ETB/ETX, and therefore *link sequence numbers* cannot be utilised without redesigning the protocol.

Note that we have discussed no procedures which can allow the destination host to <u>do</u> anything if messages fail to arrive. As we discuss in the next chapter, this is one of the crucial problems with the message switching technique. The absence of link sequence numbers poses further severe problems, which are also discussed in the next chapter.

3.4.4   Flow control

Flow control is a familiar concept to any driver. There are two basic forms of flow control which are explained here in motoring terms. A formal definition of flow control algorithms will come much later.

- Traffic lights impose a form of *stop-go* flow control. Ether the light is green, with no restriction imposed, or it is red, and nothing may pass. This can be likened to allowing block transmission without restriction, or banning it until further notice.

  At the risk of carrying the traffic analogy too far, the half duplex nature of BSC imposes a form of stop-go flow control which acts like a roadworks traffic light, allowing traffic in only one direction at once. But this 'feature' of BSC is not really flow control as such. It is a deficiency of the protocol which forces unwanted flow control on the link. Genuine flow control has been designed for a purpose, and can be operated as and when needed.

- Another way of imposing flow control is by *restricting* the flow rather than stopping it completely. This is the type of flow control commonly used in multi-storey car parks. When the car park is full, no more vehicles may enter until one has left. In networks this is typically done by allowing up to n messages (or whatever) to be in the network (or outstanding) at once. When the limit has been reached, no more can be transmitted until some have been removed (typically by being acknowledged). This discussion is deliberately vague because the concepts necessary for a full understanding of the technique have not yet been presented. This technique is more sophisticated than stop-go flow control, but plays no part in BSC networks or protocols; for a further discussion refer to chapter four.

Examples of this type of flow control are the <u>sliding window</u> flow control imposed on links in HDLC, and across networks in X.25 packet mode. These protocols are discussed in detail in chapters six and seven. Chapter four lays some of the necessary groundwork.

The reason for requiring flow control is equally clear. In networks there are two main problems which can arise, both of which can be alleviated, if not solved, by imposing some form of flow control.

• Traffic presented to a node on incoming links may exceed either the processing or storage capacity of that node. If the former, the node would be unable to respond in a timely way to stations at the other ends of the incoming links, which would lead to protocol violations, timeouts, retry attempts, and all manner of other side-effects, the servicing of which is the last thing the overloaded node needs at present. If storage capacity runs out, the receiving node would have to start discarding information it received correctly.

This situation is known as node *congestion*. The appropriate flow control mechanism is stop-go. Silencing some or all of the sending nodes allows the node a chance to recover, either by reducing the amount of stored information, or reducing the load on the processor.

This type of congestion can arise even in a well designed network if links fail, forcing additional traffic on to other links and overloading the receiving node, or if a node finds that one or more of its outgoing links have failed.

• Another type of congestion can arise when information is entering a <u>network</u> at a faster rate than it can be delivered to the destination host (i.e. removed from the network). Eventually if nothing is done, the network will seize up as all of the internal nodes become congested; the effect will propagate backwards from the delivery point bottleneck. This cries out for a form of flow control applied on a *network end to end* basis. For example the number of messages in a network issued by host X for delivery to host Y could be limited to n say.

The main problem with BSC is that the only form of flow control provided is for the receiver to *delay* the reception of blocks on a link by means of a special WACK (wait before acknowledge) response. This in effect means that the receiver is acknowledging the block, but requires extra time to process it before the next block is sent. This is only a temporary measure, after which the receiver must either resume accepting blocks or issue a reverse interrupt (RVI). BSC has nothing to offer on an end-end basis, as mechanisms for regulating message transfer in this way are entirely absent. The implications of this lack of effective flow control in BSC are discussed in the next chapter.

3.4.5   Recovery procedures

This is a very complex subject. We have already mentioned the recovery procedures used by BSC when no reply is received from the slave. (The master sends ENQ up to n times; if a reply is still not forthvcoming, the master shuts down the link, i.e. sends EOT.) However there are other aspects of recovery which will now be discussed.

For the present we will restrict the discussion to link protocols in a mesh network. Refer back to figure 2.2, and consider traffic on link 6. There are several reasons why recovery might be necessary:

• The error rate on the link may have become unacceptably high. Nodes B and E might monitor the proportion of transmission errors, and take some action if this proportion exceeds some predetermined value.

• A given number of attempts (ENQ) to obtain an acknowledgement from the receiver could have failed. This is the case we discussed in §3.4.1. It is generally the result of a link failure, or the failure (i.e. crash) of the receiving node. The standard procedure in BSC is to shut down the link (by sending the EOT character). Unfortunately if the link has failed, the EOT will not reach the receiver, and if the receiver has failed, it is again a waste of time.

• The retry limit for retransmission of a transmission unit may have been reached. This will usually be because of a high line error rate, rather than as in the previous case. Again EOT will be sent and the link shut down; again it is not clear that the EOT will reach the receiver.

• The arrival rate of transmission units may exceed the node's capacity to forward them. This could be due to a poor routing algorithm resulting in a bottleneck. It could also be the result of a noisy outgoing line, where error retransmissions are reducing the effective outgoing line capacity. The only assistance BSC offers here is for the receiver to return WACK as often as permitted for every block received, which it doesn't need much imagination to see will merely push the problem back to the sender. As a last resort, the receiver may force a turnaround of the link by sending RVI, but that doesn't assist the sender either.

• Arriving transmission units must be queued somewhere within the node until they can be forwarded. With message switching networks it is usual to have disk storage, so that it may be possible to buffer a large number of incoming messages on disk before the problem becomes critical. This has some obvious implications which could be unacceptable if low network transit times are desirable (although, as we shall see, low transit times cannot be achieved in message switching networks, and were not generally considered important in any case in networks of this type).

• Some combination of failures may mean that it is no longer possible to find a path to the destination host. In the context of deterministic routing, this could mean that both the primary and secondary links from some network node on the route are unserviceable. The case where the destination host (or its link) fails is similar.

The destination host need not have failed. In networks spanning several time zones, as in the USA for example, it is possible for an East Coast host to be up and running before one in California has come on stream in the morning. In this case we are not just talking about failures.

Recovery is again clearly necessary. But what can be done? Messages could be held at this node until one of the outgoing links (or the destination host) becomes available. This is unacceptable, as we cannot expect a network node to store an indefinite number of messages for an indefinite period. But the only alternative is to discard the messages. Should the originating host be informed? How can this be achieved? One solution would be to return a message to the sending host, informing it that the message has been discarded. There are (at least) two problems with this approach. One is that in store and forward message switching the network is supposed to guarantee delivery, so that there is no reason why the source host should still have a copy of the message. Another problem is that there is no assurance that the informative message will reach the source host; it could suffer the same fate as the discarded message!

Clearly there is something fundamentally wrong with recovery procedures in this type of network. We have already seen that because individual blocks of messages are not addressable, they can be lost or duplicated unknown to the BSC protocol. Two additional problems arise because of this.

• If transmission of a message on a link has to be abandoned due to link (or receiving node) problems, the entire message must be retransmitted via another link, not just that part which has not yet been sent. The reason is that part of a message is useless to a node, as it can only be stored and forwarded in its entirety, individual blocks having nothing to identify their position within the message.

• There is a special problem if there is a failure after the last block of a message has been transmitted, but before the sender has received the acknowledgement. This is because the ACK merely indicates that the last block was successfully transmitted, not that the message as a whole was safe stored by the receiver. If the receiver fails after sending the ACK, the message could vanish. If the link fails while the ACK is in transit, the sender will be uncertain as to the message's fate, and must assume the worst and reroute the entire message, which could then become duplicated, as the receiver has no means of knowing that the ACK it sent was lost.

One solution which was attempted was to add additional procedures above BSC, including a special 'message ACK' message which would be returned to confirm safe storage. This requires the link to be turned round so that it can be sent, and can at best be described as messy. It is also not clear how long the sending node should wait for this message ACK, or what action it should take if it is never received.

3.5 Review of message switching problems

To recapitulate, messages originate at some host X, and are forwarded to its network node as a sequence of transmission blocks, using the BSC link protocol. When the entire message has been received, it is 'safe stored'. At this point, this node accepts 'responsibility' for the message, and the host can delete its own copy. This process is repeated for each 'hop' across the network, until the message reaches its destination, or something goes wrong. We have seen some of the things which can go wrong. Rather than deal with each problem in turn, in the remainder of this chapter we will review some of the major problem areas, with some examples of specific problems in each area.

3.5.1 Problems with BSC procedures

Although we have not discussed all of the elements of the BSC protocol, it should be clear that as a link protocol it leaves much to be desired. The following are some of the worst deficiencies:

• The protocol is based entirely on the ASCII code. All block formatting and control is done using ASCII transmission control characters. This places severe restrictions on what can be transmitted inside the text part of blocks, which is particularly frustrating when attempting to transmit binary data.

Because of these problems, a transparent mode was devised, as outlined in an aside in §2.4.2. The idea was that transmission control characters could now be sent inside blocks. But we still cannot transmit pure binary because of the requirement that all characters have odd parity. So this is not a great improvement.

Another difficulty with relying on the ASCII code is that bit significant header fields cannot be used. If there are 256 destination host addresses, each could be assigned a binary value in the range 0 to 255, and any address could be encoded in an 8-bit bit significant field. This would also be a convenient format for software to use. But encoding the address in ASCII requires it to be sent as the three characters '123' say. Not only does this require 24 bits, but effort is required by software to translate this into a useful internal form (e.g. for routing table lookup).

• Some of the procedures used in BSC are fragile to say the least. The ENQ character is used in three different ways according to context. (As well as a request for the slave to repeat its last reply, it is also used on an idle line to bid for master status, and can be inserted anywhere in a block to abort transmission of that block.) When problems arise, it is too easy for a node to interpret ENQ in the wrong context, which can cause chaos.

In addition, sequences such as ENQ, ACK 0 and NAK are protected only by the parity bits in individual characters. There is a real risk not only of the sequences being corrupted and hence unrecognisable, but also of ACK 0 being corrupted to ACK 1 say. If this happens (and there is considerable anecdotal evidence that such problems did occur), BSC will cause undetectable corruption to blocks and messages, which no amount of investigation by systems programmers will solve, as the protocol itself is flawed.

• BSC is by nature a master-slave protocol. A further difficulty is that while the master can initiate recovery in the event of some problem, no mechanism is provided for the slave (receiver) to enquire of the status of the master. In addition, when the link is shut down, this is done merely by the master station sending EOT. As there is no handshaking, it is quite possible for the two stations on the link to disagree as to its current status.

• A further, less obvious, flaw is that, by its nature, BSC is not amenable to implementation in firmware (i.e. on a serial port chip). More modern link protocols are designed from the start with this in mind.

BSC is a 'bad' protocol. For this reason almost as many enhancements were proposed as there were implementations, few of which were compatible with the ISO so-called standards {1745, 2111, 2628, 2629}.

3.5.2   Problems with a half duplex protocol

The half duplex nature of the BSC protocol was a natural consequence of basing link procedures on established techniques for voice communications. After all telephone conversations where both parties talk at the same time do not tend to be useful, and it seemed entirely natural to apply the same rules to data communication as well. With the benefit of hindsight this was an absurd decision, and it introduced several problems:

• Over 50% of the link capacity is wasted, as no information at all can pass in one direction, and information flow in the other is repeatedly interrupted while acknowledgements are awaited. If a transmission error occurs, everything effectively grinds to a halt until the current block is positively acknowledged.

• While node A is sending blocks to node B, in general node B will become increasingly burdened with messages waiting to be sent to A, which will eventually require B to reverse interrupt, assuming that A does not relinquish the line first. But this merely passes the problem to A; it does not solve it. Clearly the half duplex nature of the protocol is an open invitation for congestion.

3.5.3   Problems with the message format

Again it seemed natural to base all transmission on a human readable code. In fact the only parts of a block which are not human readable are the control characters. The division of a message into blocks by, in effect, chopping it up into identical (as far as BSC is concerned) pieces introduces several further problems:

• The blocks are indistinguishable (except the first and last). So loss or duplication of blocks will go completely undetected.

• The receiver is unable to forward a message until it has received the last block. Therefore valuable buffer space is tied up, making network nodes complex and cumbersome. The implications for network transit time (time to get from X to Y) are clear.

• There is nothing in the BSC protocol which provides any information on how many blocks there are in the message. To deduce this, the receiver will have to look at the message header, which in some implementations includes a message length field. But there is no requirement to include this information, and BSC offers no procedures which could make use of it.

A generally implemented option was to allow short 'urgent' messages, of maximum length one block; these could be inserted into longer messages. But the fact that the block starts with SOH and ends with ETX does not in itself mean that it is urgent; again the header must be perused. The receiver seems to have a lot of work to do when it receives the first block, and may need to delay returning ACK for the first block of the message until it has processed the header. The difficulty is that the timeout period at the sender must take into account the maximum time it takes to return an ACK. It would not be acceptable for the sender to time out prematurely. But since the timeout value must be the same for all blocks, this will lead to yet more inefficiency, since if an error occurs, the sender will often wait longer than necessary in the hope of a reply.

We will see in chapter six that there is a similar problem with HDLC timer T2, which must take into account the maximum time needed for a station to respond. Depending on what is happening, the actual response time required coulld vary quite markedly.

• As the receiver must receive all blocks of the message before it can forward it, all blocks received so far must be discarded if the link fails before the message has been completely received. If the sender cannot deliver the entire message, all of the message must be retransmitted via a different link. This is not only inefficient, but is increasing network traffic at precisely the moment we would wish to minimise it.

3.5.4   Message accountability issues

The basic message switching approach is to treat messages like paper files. If you put a file in the out tray, it is collected, taken to the sorting office, and eventually arrives in someone else's in tray. By definition the current possesser of the file has responsibility for it. So the same technique was applied to messages in networks. Again refer back to figure 2.2. A message from X to Y is considered to be successively 'owned' by X, A, B, E, H, K and finally Y. When a node 'safe stores' a message, it is taken to have accepted responsibility for it, and the sending node may delete its copy. There are in fact two issues here.

- The fundamental flaw is to assume that messages in a network have a concrete existence. They do not. Node or link failures can wipe out messages beyond trace, as we have seen. Therefore host X would be wise to retain a copy of the message until it can be certain that it has reached Y.

- The problem is that no procedures exist within BSC to confirm message delivery, other than by returning ACK for the last block, a procedure which is not of assistance to the originating host, and is in any case flawed.

3.5.5   Network management issues

By network management we mean an effective framework for monitoring and controlling activity within a network. All that we have so far is the BSC protocol with all its flaws, together with some half formed ideas for add-on 'features' such as message acknowledgements.

What can be done to improve the situation? It was soon clear to the early protocol designers that message switching could not possibly work unless an additional 'layer' of control was provided above BSC. The difficulty was that, at the time, there was no previous experience to draw on, and there was no consistency between enhancements in different implementations. Various implementations included message ACKs, notification of delivery to the originating host, notification to the originating host if the destination failed or could not be reached, procedures for marking messages as 'diverted' or 'possible duplicate', and so on.

We have not looked in detail at the BSC protocol[1], but it is clear that it has major flaws, as well as being inefficient. It was 'enhanced' in an ad hoc manner. As an introduction to the next chapter, here are some of the things which are not possible with the type of message switching network discussed in this chapter:

- Message delivery cannot be guaranteed. When problems arise, no effective recovery is possible, nor can the originating host normally be informed.

- No means is provided for associating messages so that a group of messages can be identified as belonging to the same 'conversation'.

- No means is provided for identifying <u>why</u> a message is being sent. Is it part of a file? Or perhaps a database enquiry? Nothing so far discussed is of any assistance here.

- The technique exists simply to get a message from X to Y (with luck, eventually). This is rather like a glorified Telex network. No mechanism is provided for establishing a <u>dialogue</u> between a pair of hosts, or for setting up any association between a pair of hosts, so that they can co-operate on some task (such as transferring a file from X to Y).

- No effective flow control is provided. The WACK mechanism provided in BSC is inadequate and counterproductive, and no attempt is made to control the flow of information <u>into</u> the network.

We have described the situation which prevailed during the early 1970s. There were many problems to be solved. In a book like this, it would be easy to gloss over the difficulties which were encountered in those days, and merely present the situation as it is now. But this would be to lose considerable insight into the fundamental issues involved. An equally fundamental problem was the weakness of standards organisations in the data communications area. Most practitioners will have heard of BSC (IBM's name), but fewer will have heard of Basic Mode (ISO's name).

Thus there were in fact two distinct issues, sound protocol design and standardisation. Tremendous advances have been made in the last 15 years or so. The development of sound protocols came first. The idea that interworking should be possible between hosts regardless of supplier, operating system, supporting underlying network and owning organisation came later. After all in any field one has to learn to walk first and run later, and networking was no exception.

- In the next chapter we look in more detail at some of the protocol design issues, and introduce the concepts of packet switching, virtual circuits, datagrams and protocol reference models.

- In part two we start by discussing the roles of some of the main standards organisations, and then examine some of the earliest 'modern' protocols.

3.6   Reference

1   This book does not seek to cover more than the basics of BSC. The second edition, especially chapter 3, had more detail on BSC procedures, including TTD, WACK, RVI and link setup. Indeed there is no shortage of books which discuss the procedures involved. Beware however; not all books describe the same variants of BSC.

4   Towards better protocols

4.1   Introduction

So far we have discussed the early attempts at providing communication across wide area networks. As well as seeing how existing Telex techniques and telephone conversations were used as a basis for protocol design, you have also been introduced to a number of concepts which are fundamental to an understanding of protocol design.

The discussion revealed much that was wrong with these early techniques. A detailed exposition along the lines of that provided in the second edition of this book would take up too much space, given the amount of additional material which has had to be accommodated. Therefore in this chapter the aim is to bring the reader's understanding of protocols up to the state of the art around the mid 1970s, when the first generation of new protocols were starting to be introduced. Although the first attempts at standard protocols developed at this time, such as ISO High Level Data Link Control (HDLC) and CCITT recommendation X.25(1976), differ in many ways from the current versions, the basic principles underlying these protocols have not changed to the present day.

In order to build this understanding, we will take various problem areas from the previous chapter, and examine ways in which the situation can be improved.

4.2   How to produce a better link protocol

As the crumbling edifice of message switching was built on the 'foundations of sand' known as the BSC link protocol, that is a sensible place to start to seek improvements. The aim is not to build an 'ideal' link protocol from scratch, but rather to examine the techniques which can be applied so that a better link protocol can be designed.

4.2.1   Why use the ASCII code?

The ASCII (American Standard Code for Information Interchange) code, otherwise known as CCITT International Alphabet number 5 (IA5), was designed in the context of Teletypes and other hardcopy terminals and printers. Various transmission control (TC) characters were defined to support the BSC protocol, as well as various format effectors (FE) to support simple print head movements. Fortunately the ASCII code designers had the foresight to include two additional codes, DLE (data link escape) and ESC (escape) to extend the repertoire of TC and FE characters respectively; both characters proved to be much needed.

But we have seen that basing block formats on the ASCII code is restrictive in that it has a number of drawbacks:

• It leads to inefficiently encoded and 'machine hostile' header fields. The original idea of human readable fields was so that they could be displayed or printed; if the odd header needs to be displayed however, it can easily be converted from some machine friendly format. It seems wasteful to encode every header inefficiently just in case one needs to be printed every so often.

• It makes it difficult to encode binary data in the text fields. In the days when only text messages were every transmitted, that did not matter. Nowadays, information in any format, including pure binary, needs to be exchanged between hosts. It should not be necessary to indicate in a header field what the format of the text field is, so that it can be suitably decoded. The content of the text part is of no concern to the link protocol, whose job is to get it to the next node intact, not to worry about its format or meaning.

The obvious answer is to remove the dependency on the ASCII code, and to use a more flexible technique.

4.2.2   Better block formatting

So we can use bit significant fields for addresses, block priority, sequence numbers and so on. This has the additional advantage that these fields can then be made of fixed length. The receiver can then locate the required field purely by its position in the bit stream, rather than having to grind through several preceding fields of variable length (e.g. ASCII encoded addresses).

A further possibility is to include a field which indicates the length of the text field. In BSC this was fixed (usually) at 240 bytes, but there is no a priori reason for this restriction. If this technique is used, the receiver knows precisely where the block ends, and can automatically process the error check field without it having to be preceded by ETB or ETX.

The fact that either ETX or ETB can precede the BCC makes it necessary to search for either, which is inefficient. This is not an ideal technique if it is intended to build the basic protocol functions into a port chip. An alternative technique is used in HDLC. This involves looking for a defined ending bit pattern rather than providing a field length count. As this technique is more complex we will defer a discussion until chapter six.

So we can easily improve on the BSC block format. Another obvious improvement is to abandon the BCC in favour of a better error checking algorithm such as a 16-bit CRC. We will take this for granted. But we are still only scratching the surface of the problem.

4.2.3   Addressable blocks: packets

We have seen that many of BSC's problems stem from the lack of addressability of blocks. If we add *block sequence numbers* to blocks, we now have what are known (generically) as *packets*.

Several problems arose from having no sequence numbers in BSC blocks. Here is a brief summary of what they were:

• Individual blocks were indistinguishable. Therefore if a block was lost, this would be undetected (except possibly by the destination host - but by then it would be too late).

• If a link failed before the entire message had been acknowledged, the entire message would have to be rerouted, not just the part which had not yet been sent.

• Each node had to receive the entire message before it could be forwarded. As well as a drastic increase in transit time for long messages, disk storage was required at network nodes because of the large volume of data which has to be buffered.

Provision of sequence numbers appears to be the major breakthrough we have been looking for. Unfortunately it does not need much thought to realise that, in itself, making blocks into packets does not improve matters very much. We can drastically reduce the risk of blocks being lost due to their indistinguishability, which is a bonus. But it is not yet clear how we can route parts of messages independently through a mesh network without defining additional procedures. Nor is it immediately clear whether a receiving node can start to forward packets before the entire message has been received, nor what it should do if part of the message is never received.

Certainly there is potential for improvement here, but we have not yet identified the additional procedures which will be required to take full advantage. But we shall now abandon the use of the term block, and refer to packets instead.

This follows practice at the time. Unfortunately as we shall see in chapter six, this is not the name which finally became associated with link protocol transmission units. This name is the frame. Indeed there has always been terminological confusion in this field.

We will defer any further discussion of what procedures are needed until §4.3.

4.2.4   Full duplex operation

Another crucial failing of BSC is that blocks can only be sent in one direction at a time. Even in that one direction link utilisation is poor, since everything has to stop until ACK is received. So clearly any procedure which allows full duplex operation will be a great improvement.

We will therefore relax the procedures to allow packets to be transferred in both directions simultaneously, i.e. a *full duplex protocol*. But in order to be able to do this, it is necessary to devise a better acknowledgement scheme.

4.2.5   Improving acknowledgements

Assume that we are sending a sequence of packets in each direction. Each has a *link sequence number*. (This has nothing to do with any message sequence number which may be present in the first packet of a message.) In theory at least, we should be able to send acknowledgements for received packets in the other direction. This sounds obvious, but first a number of problems have to be solved.

• When can we send acknowledgements? We must clearly wait until we have finished sending the current packet. This could take some time if the current packet is long, and we have only just started transmitting it.

• What timeout value should we set while waiting for an acknowledgement?

• Assuming that this acknowledgement takes some time to be returned, can we send further packets before it is received? If so, how many? After all it seems reasonable to be able to do this as packets have unique sequence numbers.

• Unfortunately there is no such thing as a unique link sequence number. It has to fit in a field of defined length. So if this field is 3 bits long, permitted sequence numbers would be in the range 0 to 7. This is a modulo 8 numbering scheme.

• In this case, we could have at most 7 packets outstanding before we would have to transmit one with the same sequence number as one which is already outstanding. This cannot be allowed, as there would then be ambiguity regarding what was being acknowledged.

The simplest scheme seems to be to return an acknowledgement (positive) as each packet is correctly received. We will immediately dismiss the idea of sending negative acknowledgements, and only acknowledge packets which have been correctly received. We must also make sure that acknowledgements are adequately protected by a CRC, so that in effect they become very short packets with a header containing the link sequence number being acknowledged, and no text field.

We are now in a position to attempt to define a simple positive-only packet acknowledgement scheme. We will start with a basic attempt, them enhance it as difficulties are encountered.

- Packets may be transmitted provided that the window *limit* has not been reached. This is the maximum number of packets which can be outstanding at any time. In the example above this cannot exceed 7, but a lower limit may be agreed, perhaps even one packet only.

- If an acknowledgement is not received for a given packet within some agreed time, that packet is retransmitted automatically. The receiver will discard any packet received twice or more, but will always acknowledge its receipt.

- Efficiency of the protocol can be improved by allowing acknowledgements to be *piggybacked* on packets in the reverse direction. In other words there will be a header field in each packet transmitted, which can be used to acknowledge packets received.

- For modulo 8 numbering, one simple and obvious way to do this would be to have an 8-bit field. Each bit could be set to 1 to indicate acknowledgement of a particular packet (bit 0 for packet sequence number (PSN) 0, bit 1 for PSN 1, and so on (assuming bits numbered from 0 to 7). If all bits were zero, this packet would not be acknowledging any (additional) packets. A scheme similar to this was used in the original ARPANET link protocol, and it has a certain attraction. In fact many acknowledgement techniques were tried during the early experimental days. Most, including this one, differ from the technique used in HDLC, which has become the standard one, as we shall see in chapter six.

One of the more unusual acknowledgement techniques was used by the early British Telecom (then known as Post Office Telecommunications) Experimental Packet Switching System (EPSS) network, developed in the early 1970s. When a packet was correctly received, an acknowledgement was returned at a precisely determined time. The sender knew precisely when to look, and would attempt to interpret bits received at this time as an acknowledgement. Acknowledgement bits could therefore be inserted in the middle of packets being sent in the reverse direction. This scheme worked, but clearly both the line transit time and the response delay must be accurately known, and the resulting delay will be different for every communication line, since the propagation delay, although small, depends on the length of the line. In addition, forcing an immediate acknowledgement prevents the receiver from exercising any discretion in when to issue acknowledgements. EPSS was experimental in nature, and this was not one of the techniques which was pursued in its successor, the PSS network.

• In addition the case has to be considered where there are no packets travelling in the reverse direction on to which acknowledgements could be piggybacked. To avoid a lockup, it is therefore necessary to define a special short 'acknowledgement only' packet, which contains just the acknowledgement field (plus another field identifying the packet type, of course).

There are flaws in the above definition. For example no mention has been made of recovery procedures. There are a number of additional questions to be asked.

• How many times may a packet be transmitted without being acknowledged before error recovery procedures are invoked?

• If the retry limit is reached, what should the receiver do with 'later' packets which have already been acknowledged? It is quite possible that packet 2 has not been acknowledged, but packets 3 and 4 have. Should they be discarded? If not, what additional procedures are required to obtain a copy of packet 2?

• Is it necessary for the sender and the receiver to have a consistent view of what has been acknowledged? This was not an issue in BSC since the next block may not be sent until an ACK has been received for it. In the above example, it may be that the receiver acknowledged packet 2 but this acknowledgement was lost. It would clearly facilitate recovery if the sender could be certain precisely which packets had been accepted. This appears to suggest that additional procedures over and above simple acknowledgement are needed. A related problem is that it is inefficient to keep retransmitting a packet if it has actually been correctly received, and it is the acknowledgements which are being lost.

It is not the intention to answer these questions at present. In chapter six we will explain how HDLC approaches the problems. HDLC was the culmination of much experiment and research into how link protocols should operate. It should at least be clear from the above discussion that there are a number of complexities to be tackled, and that it is not simply a matter of adding sequence numbers to packets and returning acknowledgements.

4.2.6   Flow control on the link

We suggested in the previous chapter that the 'delaying tactic' offered by the BSC WACK procedure was not what was required. This was in part because the remainder of the message must still wait until the delayed block has finally been acknowledged. Furthermore the WACK does not instruct the sender to stop altogether; BSC has no mechanism for this other than RVI, which hardly qualifies as good flow control.

However both of the other flow control techniques can be applied. (See §3.4.4 for the basic definitions.)

• Stop-go flow control requires the definition of further packet types, 'stop sending' and 'resume sending'. One presumes that these can also include acknowledgement fields.

• Restrictive flow control could be implemented by the receiver delaying acknowledgements to packets correctly received, so that the sender would reach the window limit for unacknowledged packets. This seems possible, but there are some pitfalls for the unwary. Without a means for the sender to force the receiver to acknowledge everything correctly received, there is a risk of either lockups or unnecessary recovery procedures being invoked.

HDLC offers both forms of flow control. We shall see in chapter six how flow control is handled in HDLC.

4.2.7   Link recovery procedures

We saw in the previous chapter that BSC offers no link recovery of any value. BSC's ultimate solution is for the sender (master station) to transmit the EOT character, and shut down the link. Whether this causes the receiver any problems, or even whether the receiver actually receives the EOT, are of no concern to BSC. This results in unnecessary link shutdowns, wastage of link capacity, and further problems resulting when the two stations on the link do not agree on its current state. A station receiving ENQ may interpret it incorrectly, with chaotic results.

What is required is a systematic attempt at defining useful recovery procedures. A good link protocol should provide the following types of recovery:

• Sufficient attempts should be made to get a packet acknowledged so that 'negative' recovery procedures are not invoked unnecessarily.

• It will never be possible for the peer (i.e. equal partner) stations on the link always to agree on its current status, e.g. which packets are currently outstanding. However it should be possible for procedures to be devised which allow a *handshake* (i.e. an exchange of control information), the result of which is that the status of the link is now unambiguously known by both parties.

• If a link shutdown becomes necessary, e.g. because of repeated transmission errors, each station should make best attempts to ensure that the other is aware of this. If this proves impossible, e.g. because of a total link failure, timeout mechanisms in both stations should cause the link to be declared 'dead' by both stations in a consistent way.

• If a link has to be shut down for some reason, there should be defined rules on when, and how, an attempt should be made to reopen the link.

4.3   Message accountability

So far we have been tinkering with the link protocol, and have conveniently ignored the fact that although we have given packets link sequence numbers, they are still part of longer messages which have to be delivered intact by the network. The next question to ask is whether this was a reasonable approach in the first place.

One area where message switching came unstuck was in trying to use a link protocol, BSC, which only understood transmission units (blocks), to transmit messages. Not only did BSC have no procedures for handling entire messages, but in §1.2 we defined the message as the shortest unit of information regarded as indivisible by <u>the host</u>. This holds the key to a crucial breakthrough, although it took many years for the significance of this to be fully appreciated; more on this in a moment.

The crucial point is this. **Since the message is a concept of interest only to the host, why should nodes inside networks be expected to understand what a message is?** Once this question is asked, it soon becomes clear why message switching ran into so many problems. A little more analysis soon leads to the entire message switching edifice collapsing like a pack of cards.

- Since only hosts 'understand' messages, only hosts should have to accept responsibility for them.

- In this case, network nodes do not need to know that packets form part of longer messages. This leaves the network nodes free to store and forward on a per packet basis.

- All attempts must be made by network nodes to get packets to their destinations, possibly by different routes. However if individual packets fail to reach their destinations, this is a matter for the destinations (or originators) concerned to worry about, not nodes inside the network.

Another way to express this is to say that **only hosts should be accountable for messages**. In other words X retains responsibility for the message until Y confirms that it has been received. This is indeed a major breakthrough, but we are still a long way from a solution to the problem. For one thing we do not yet have any procedures which can be used between the ends of the network. This aspect will be discussed in §4.5.

4.3.1   Review of message switching

To summarise message switching, each node (starting with the source host) must ensure that the entire message reaches the next node. This node then 'safe stores' the message, accepts responsibility for it, and forwards it to the next node, and so on until the destination host is reached. We have seen that this led to many problems, of which these are the most serious:

- If problems arise inside the network, entire messages can either vanish or become duplicated.

- Since the technique relies on networks being trustworthy, no procedures are provided for recovery if messages become lost. Indeed it is not clear that such loss will always be detected in any case.

- No procedures are provided which can be used to notify either host if problems arise inside the network.

- No procedures are provided which allow the destination host to confirm that it has received a message. Even if such procedures were provided, it is not clear how the destination can be sure that a message has actually been lost, given that transit times across such networks are slow and unpredictable.

- No procedures exist which can control the flow of messages into the network. As a result it is possible for the entire network to seize up if X submits messages faster than Y can remove them at the other end. This could happen if the line from X to the network had a greater capacity than that from the network to Y, and for many other reasons as well.

In short, the technique of message switching is basically flawed.

4.3.2   Message fragmentation and reassembly

We have already suggested that a possible solution is to switch packets inside the network, leaving the hosts to worry about how individual packets relate to a message. This implies additional procedures at (or near) X and Y.

- At or near X, the message has to be broken down into smaller packets, which are routed independently through the network. Whether the routes differ for individual packets depends on several factors, including the routing algorithm used, whether link failures occur, and the recovery procedures invoked if link failures do occur.

As part of this process, link sequence numbers must be added to the packets so that they can be transferred successfully using the link protocol, as discussed in §4.2.5. These are in addition to the message sequence numbers, which we shall assume for the moment are also contained in the packet header.

- Different, and more complex, procedures are required at (or near) the destination host Y. Packets belonging to particular messages may arrive out of sequence, depending on the routing algorithm in use, or if link failures occur, as different packets may follow different paths through the network. Therefore *message reassembly* may be required. This implies that 'somewhere near' Y there will be a node with *reassembly buffers*, which are used to gather together the fragments of a particular message. Once all of the message has been received, it can be forwarded to the host. This reassembly could be done either in the host itself or in the network node adjacent to the host.

There are some obvious problems, of which the following only gives a first impression. How long must the reassembly node wait in case a missing packet arrives by another route? If it gives up just before a missing packet arrives, there could be problems if this missing packet is taken as the first of a new message. Alternatively the destination may attempt to get a second copy of the missing packet from the source. The initial ARPANET design used the following approach:

- The source host sent a complete message to its adjacent IMP (Interface Message Processor, i.e. network node). The maximum length permitted was such that it would require breaking into at most 8 packets. These were transmitted using distributed adaptive routing (see §2.3.4.2), so that they could follow a variety of paths through the network, and arrive at the destination IMP (the one to which Y is connected) in any sequence.

- The destination IMP would then reassemble the packets into messages, forwarding the complete messages to Y.

A number of problems were encountered. The main one was *reassembly lockup*[1]. A fixed number of *reassembly buffers* would be provided at each IMP. (Every IMP is potentially a destination for packets.) The problem arises if these buffers become filled with partially reassembled messages. There is now no room left to complete any message, and until a message is completed, no buffers can be released!

The solution adopted by the ARPANET designers was to devise an additional protocol, the *source-destination IMP protocol*. The idea was for the source IMP to reserve buffers in advance, thus avoiding reassembly lockup at the expense of additional complexity (and inefficiency).

4.3.3 The modern view

There are a number of objections to the early ARPANET approach[2]. The principal one is that network nodes (IMPs) are <u>still</u> required to know about messages. This means that <u>every</u> IMP in the network is concerned with message breakdown and reassembly, which complicates both the IMP design and the protocols used over the network. Additional protocols are needed (which have not been mentioned) to cater for the situation where the source IMP, having accepted a message, cannot deliver it.

A further problem is that the definition of a message had to be compromised, in that an artificial upper length had to be imposed in the interests of keeping IMP buffer sizes at a manageable level.

The modern approach is to remove the responsibility for messages entirely from the network, leaving network nodes with the much simpler task of switching packets only. We are not yet ready to define in detail how this may be achieved, but it should immediately be apparent that network nodes will not have to be as complex, although it is also clear that this approach leaves hosts with more work to do. But it is entirely logical to require hosts to handle messages, as only the host understands the context of a message, and the function of the network should be to forward transmission units to their destination, not to 'worry' about how packets relate to messages.

We are now in a position to examine the problem of how hosts communicate with each other.

4.4   Host-host dialogues

In the early days, it was considered an achievement to be able to get messages from X to Y at all. But as more networks became available, users began to realise their potential, and began to seek ways in which to use networks to their advantage. Initially there were so many operational difficulties that most effort was concentrated on finding a reliable way of communicating across a network, which is what we have been discussing so far. However it soon became apparent that there were various different *applications* which could be used across a network. Some of the first applications to be identified were as follows:

• **File transfer**. A means of getting a file from X to Y, and saving it in Y's filestore.

• **Interactive terminals**. A means of connecting an interactive terminal to a remote host via a network.

• **Job transfer**. A means of composing a job at X, and transferring it to Y for processing.

• **Electronic mail**. A means of exchanging information and ideas between practitioners at different sites.

ARPANET was the first major network to offer applications of this type. But before we can start to define applications, it is necessary to find a means whereby hosts X and Y can set up an *association*, for without such an association, there will be no way in which to implement the application.

There are in fact many ways in which X and Y can communicate.

4.4.1   Circuit switching

With circuit switching, there is a single, dedicated path between X and Y. This is what happens in the telephone or Telex network. A physical circuit (or possibly a channel on a multiplexed circuit) is constantly available. By definition everything follows the same route, and will therefore arrive at Y in the same order as it was transmitted. Unfortunately this technique is of little use in WANs, as the circuit will remain idle if not used, so that sufficient capacity would have to be provided to allow every host to communicate with every other, even though few may want to at the present time.

For this reason it is normal to share links inside networks between several different host-host 'conversations'. For this to work, the transmission has to be organised, typically into a sequence of packets, each of which has sufficient routing information to identify the destination host. There is no predetermined ordering of packets, and the link may therefore be shared in any desired manner among traffic between several pairs of hosts. This is clearly superior to circuit switching for most applications.

There are basically two types of association which are important. Both assume an underlying packet switching technique.

4.4.2   Virtual circuits

The first one is the most obvious choice, and is closely comparable with how a telephone call works, except that there is no dedicated path between X and Y. In the *virtual circuit* (*VC*) or *virtual call* method of operation, host X indicates its wish to communicate with host Y by sending a *call request* packet (the names differ from one protocol to another, but the concept is always the same). This has the following effects:

• Certain resources are reserved in the network. One is a *virtual circuit number*, which can subsequently be used by X (and Y) as a 'shorthand' way of addressing the destination, rather than having to include the full destination address in every subsequent packet. Another effect, particularly in networks which charge for usage, is to create a record of the resources used for the virtual call, such as the amount of data transmitted and the duration of the call.

• In certain types of network which use deterministic routing, a path through the network is established at this stage, in which case the virtual circuit number is provided to all intermediate nodes, so that they can allocate resources for this call.

• More significantly, successive packets on a given virtual circuit can now be numbered in sequence, permitting the application of flow control within and across the network on a per virtual circuit basis. Additionally, the number of simultaneous virtual circuits which X may set up can be restricted, or used as a basis for charging X's administration.

• It is common to apply not only flow control on individual links, but also *end-end flow control*, so that the number of packets inside the network can be restricted for each virtual call. This also implies *end-end acknowledgement*. Clearly this cannot be part of the link protocol; we discuss different scopes of protocol in §4.5.

Normally, host X must explicitly set up a virtual circuit before it can communicate with Y, which clearly imposes an overhead (see below). However, there is sometimes the option of defining a *permanent virtual circuit* (*PVC*) which is available between a defined pair of hosts at any time, and on which VC setup is not required. However this ties up resources at X and Y (and in the network) on a permanent basis, and is mainly used for 'permanent' connections to a given destination.

Once X has requested a VC, Y has the option of accepting or refusing the incoming call. The network may also refuse it, in the same way as some telephone calls can fail due to a 'trunk bar', or because Y is unavailable, or because of equipment busy conditions. Assuming that the call setup succeeds, X will get confirmation of this by means of a *call connected* packet or similar. Data may then be exchanged on the VC until either X or Y indicates that it has finished, or something serious goes wrong, in which case it will be *cleared down*, whereupon it ceases to exist (unless it is a PVC, in which case it cannot be cleared down of course). The main advantages of VCs are evident when X and Y have a large amount of data to exchange, and the increase in efficiency gained by being able to refer to a VC number rather than a (longer) destination address can be marked. VCs are also more amenable to charging and flow control.

On a virtual circuit it is normally a requirement that every packet transmitted by X be received at Y, and in the same order as it was transmitted. Therefore virtual circuits are suitable for bulk data transfer where the integrity of the transfer must be assured, and loss, mis-sequencing or duplication of packets is unacceptable. It follows that the protocols necessary for use with virtual circuits will be complex, with a heavy emphasis on sequencing, acknowledgement and recovery. A typical application for which virtual circuits are suitable is file transfer.

4.4.3   Datagrams

However not all applications are best suited to the virtual circuit approach. If X wishes to access Y in an intermittent way, for example to access transaction based software such as an enquiry-response system, a different set of criteria apply. Now, the requirement to set up a virtual circuit becomes cumbersome, particularly if only a single packet is to be sent. Also, the overhead in the network of setting up entries in virtual circuit tables seems pointless if they are to be deleted again almost immediately, or will be unreferenced for extended periods. Clearly, this type of transaction could better be catered for by an alternative approach.

The opposite approach is where individual packets are simply routed to the destination, and a 'best attempt' is made to deliver them to their intended recipients. Flow control will not normally be provided, nor will acknowledgements. If available at all, these will be additional features. In this, the pure *datagram* approach, it is assumed (by the network) that there is no relationship between individual packets sent from one host to another. This approach has a number of implications:

• As there is no relationship between packets, the full destination address must be provided in each and every packet. No virtual call is set up.

• The network need not be concerned with the sequencing of packets. In theory at least, it can deliver them in whatever order it chooses to the destination host.

• End-end flow control is not provided. As there is no logical connection between packets, they cannot be assumed to be in any defined sequence, so that it would be difficult to impose flow control usefully. In an enquiry-response application, there will only be one packet at a time in any case.

• Successive packets have no time relationship; the next packet could follow immediately, or there could be no more forthcoming.

• It is not even necessary to return any sort of end-end acknowledgement over the network, since nowhere in the network is the packet retained in case of possible retransmission. However, some form of 'delivery confirmation' is often an option. In an enquiry-response system, the enquiry can be repeated if no response is obtained within a given time (either because the enquiry was not delivered, or because the response became lost).

• It is inevitable that a proportion of packets will be lost. It is assumed either that this does not matter provided the proportion is not too great, or that there will be procedures outside the network which can recover lost packets.

So datagrams lead to much simpler protocols inside the network, and seem suitable for one-shot applications. They are also suited to digitised voice, where voice samples are 'packetised' for transmission across the network. Provided only a small percentage of packets is lost, duplicated or arrives out of sequence, the reconstituted voice signal at the end will be corrupted, but still intelligible. If it is still intelligible, the protocol is adequate for its purpose.

Does it matter if no delivery confirmation is provided? By implication from the above, the answer is 'no'. In our enquiry example, the absence of a reply may be assumed to mean either that the enquiry never reached Y, or that the response from Y never reached X. It could also mean that host Y is not connected to the network. In this case, there may be no point in trying again, and it would seem sensible to let X know that (at least for the time being) there is no point in a retry. This approach was adopted in the original ARPANET protocols (which did not offer a datagram service) by using two special supervisory packets, 'host dead' and 'net trouble'.

There is however another issue. In a datagram network with no delivery confirmation, how long should X wait for an expected reply? The answer is not clear, but the problem is not severe in an enquiry system since repeating the enquiry does not have any unpleasant side effects. In the case of an update however, we want to be sure that the update is not applied twice, as it could be if X resent the packet because the response had been lost. In this case delivery confirmation would be required.

We can approach this dilemma in two ways. The first is to provide sequence numbers for all of the packets from X to Y. However these would have to be host-host sequence numbers of no interest to the network, and would therefore have to be generated by some protocol outside the network. The second possibility is to allow either Y or its adjacent network node to return a delivery confirmation packet independent of the application at Y, which then might itself generate a further response to the actual transaction. However a delivery confirmation is not particularly useful in an error-prone network environment unless we can assure the delivery of the confirmation, and a delivery confirmation generated by the network is no guarantee that the host actually processed the packet. For example, it could have 'crashed' immediately after accepting the packet. In any case, a network in which some packets are guaranteed delivery while others are not, is becoming rather complex.

It is becoming clear just how complex recovery issues are in WANs, and why we are still less than 20% of the way through this book!

4.5 Protocol scopes

It is already clear that there must be some form of protocol hierarchy inside a network, and between hosts. We have seen that there is a link protocol, operating over a single link within a network. Below that there must be procedures for interfacing with the underlying hardware (such as the choice of modulation or encoding technique). We have also touched on issues which clearly operate between the endpoints of the network, such as end-end acknowledgement and flow control. It is clear that above this there are 'scopes' which operate between the hosts, such as those which control the particular application (file transfer or whatever).

In the remainder of this chapter we will make a first attempt at formalising protocol scopes. In effect we will be attempting to define a protocol *reference model*. This will still be a long way away from OSI/RM, but will at least give us a framework into which to fit the protocols (HDLC, X.25 and so on) discussed in part two.

4.5.1　The physical scope

As implied above, the 'physical scope' is concerned with the physical hardware concerned with communication, such as the types of line, modulation and encoding of data, and any physical interfaces, such as a host-modem interface. We do not generally discuss physical aspects in this book.

4.5.2　The link scope

This covers any protocol required to communicate between adjacent nodes in the network. This includes the host-node link as well as internode links.

This protocol is responsible for the delivery of transmission units (e.g. packets) to the next node in the network. Its responsibilities include error control, so that it is reasonably certain that transmission errors have been detected. (We can never be 100% certain of course.) The link protocol therefore handles acknowledgements and any necessary retransmissions. Transmission units on a link usually (but not always) need to be sequenced so that missing transmission units can be re-requested (or implicitly retransmitted), and duplicates discarded.

Flow control is also required on the link, for example in case the receiving node is congested, so that the sending node can be instructed to suspend sending until the receiving node can cope again. One suitable approach is a stop-start mechanism, rather than the BSC approach of deferring acknowledgement. We will return to this area in later chapters.

4.5.3　The network end-end scope

This can be defined as control between the ends of a network. For the time being we will gloss over the problem of whether the 'end' is the host or the node to which the host is connected, and simply assume the latter.

The network protocol is responsible for ensuring that transmission units are sent in the correct host sequence. (This has nothing to do with the link sequence). The destination network protocol may also be required to ensure that transmission units are delivered in order to the host, and without duplicates or gaps.

The network protocol is also responsible for end-end flow control. This could contain two elements. Firstly, we could turn the end-end flow on and off (like a tap), but this could be difficult since there could be many transmission units already in transit. However we can also restrict end-end flow by deferring end-end acknowledgements to the originating node. (We can also apply the same philosophy to the link protocol.)

The network protocol also has responsibility for routing, since any routing decision amounts to which ongoing link is to be used, i.e. which particular instance of a link protocol will be involved. We discussed routing in some detail in chapter two.

To summarise, the network protocol is responsible for getting information from one end to the other in an orderly manner, and as far as possible without loss, duplication or corruption of information. In practice there are many reasons why this may not be possible (e.g. part of the network fails). We might therefore also require the network protocol to inform the host of any failure in communication.

4.5.4 The host-host scope

At present, we will take this to include anything which is not directly concerned with transmission inside the network. Again there are some grey areas. For example, is the host or the network responsible for virtual circuit management? However it is clear that the host should be responsible for acting on the information content of transmission units, and relating successive transmission units into host-meaningful messages (contrast the early ARPANET approach). Other activities relating to the host protocol include any translation between host formats (e.g. ASCII to EBCDIC code), and decisions related to the application (e.g. interactive, file transfer, job submission, mail).

It should be clear from the above list that there is actually more than one scope here; in OSI/RM there are four layers related to the host.

4.5.5 Network independence

A further ideal requirement is that hosts should be able to communicate via any underlying network, regardless of the protocols used in the link and network scopes. In other words, the same set of procedures should be capable of accessing any underlying network. If this is to be possible, we will need a further 'interface' scope between host protocols and network protocols. This adds an additional level of complexity, so that procedures above this level can be simplified. (That is what layering is all about.)

4.5.6 Application protocols

These are the protocols at the top of the hierarchy. These are the ones which govern why the hosts are communicating. Although we have identified applications such as file and job transfer, we are as yet a long way from being able to discuss any of these in detail. We are in fact in a similar position to the protocol designers of the early 1970s, with plenty of good ideas, and numerous experimental packet switching networks, all incompatible with each other, but no internationally recognised standards on which to base the new *public data networks* (*PDNs*) which were increasingly being demanded by the user community.

In part two, we will examine the protocols which were designed for use on PDNs such as British Telecom's PSS network. To set the scene, the next chapter looks at some standards issues and organisations.

4.6 References

1   Reference 4, chapter two.

2   An excellent discussion of the original ARPANET protocols may be found in the book 'Communication Networks for Computers', by D. W. Davies and D. L. A. Barber, published by Wiley. This book is now very dated, and was superseded by 'Communication Networks and their Protocols', by Davies, Barber, Price and Solomonides. While this is also an excellent reference text which concentrates on more recent issues, it is now also dated.

Part Two

Early ISO and CCITT Network Standards

In the second part of the book we will examine the development of standard packet switching protocols for WANs. Most important of these are ISO's HDLC link protocol, and CCITT's X.25 packet switching public data network (PDN) access protocol. Therefore most emphasis will be placed on these. In addition, CCITT recommendations for terminal access to PDNs will be examined. These were the first international standard protocols of any significance to be developed, so first of all we will discuss the need for international standards, review the various organisations involved in standardisation, and examine the process of standardisation.

5 Standards bodies and issues

5.1 Why are standards necessary?

A few years ago, The UK Department of Trade and Industry released a cassette tape entitled 'OSI - The Debate'. It began with a familiar scenario. Mr. X, who lives in Brighton, is returning by plane form the USA to Gatwick airport, where he is to catch a train to Brighton. Due to fog at Gatwick, his plane has been diverted to Birmingham. Therefore he phones his wife to tell her that he has been delayed, and will have to catch a train from Birmingham instead, and will arrive home a few hours late.

This hardly appears to be world-shattering, until we examine the standards issues involved. What follows is based on the discussion on the tape.

• If the rail network had not been standardised, Mr. X would probably have had to change trains at each county boundary, due to incompatibilities in track gauge.

This may seem ridiculous. However this is precisely what happened in Australia in the 19th century. Each State (NSW, Victoria, Queensland, and so on), wishing to assert its independence from the others, decided on a different rail gauge. Hence passengers had to change trains at State boundaries. The chaotic results of these absurd early decisions are still felt. We are fortunate that the competition between the early railway companies in the UK did not have a similar outcome.

• The scenario also assumes compatibility of the telephone network. If each county had installed its own telephone system, not adhering to any standard, a phone call from Birmingham to Brighton would have been impossible.

So what has all of this to do with computers, one might ask? The answer is that interconnecting any two host computers running different operating systems, via various intervening networks, is still largely a dream for the future. Interworking is even now largely impossible, except in specific areas. Interworking is what OSI is all about.

We take it for granted that we can phone anywhere in the world. This is however only possible because CCITT has for many years imposed tight standardisation on its members. This is something which did not happen in computer networks until too late. Had standards been enforced in the early days, there would have been one version of BSC and the like, however deficient, which would have made the task of converting to a new standard such as HDLC much easier. The other problem with leaving standardisation too late is that the standards are always trying to catch up with current practice, rather than dictating it. This has caused many headaches for the OSI designers. With the benefit of hindsight (always useful, or course), the early failure to impose standards in data communications seems as absurd as decisions to have different rail gauges in each county or State; the effect on effective communications is similar.

CCITT's early vision is much appreciated, but unfortunately for many years the USA regarded CCITT as 'European' (despite the fact that it is a United Nations agency), and tended to use its own ('Bell') standards for such things as Modems and line signalling. There are still some significant incompatibilities in this area which can cause problems when using leased lines between Europe and the USA.

We saw with BSC what tends to happen to a protocol if there is no widely accepted standard. There are more than 50 variants on the original Bi-sync protocol invented by IBM. Why are there so many variants?

First, there were obvious deficiencies in BSC, which came to light as BSC was used for applications for which it was never originally intended. For example, BSC was never intended to be used as a link protocol in a multinode network. In the absence of a strong standards organisation, each manufacturer or organisation felt free to make ad hoc 'enhancements' to the original protocol, as it saw fit for its own purposes. This might be satisfactory as far as that organisation was concerned, as it could run the same version of BSC throughout its own network. However it would be difficult for it to add 'foreign' machines, which would probably be supplied with software and hardware to support a different, and almost certainly incompatible, version of the protocol. The protocol handler would have to be patched or rewritten to allow the new equipment to be used in the existing network.

There is a related problem, which has political overtones. It can sometimes be in the manufacturer's interest to make its implementation deliberately incompatible with others, to discourage the addition of 'foreign' equipment to its networks. This may suit the manufacturer, but it is restrictive for the user.

As time progressed, there was an increasing requirement for networking between organisations, partly triggered by the success of ARPANET, and the realisation of what could be achieved by co-operative networking. However this was difficult if not impossible with so many incompatible protocols in existence.

However, as we have seen, it is not enough merely to agree on a standard set of protocols. They must also have a defined structure, so that the responsibilities of different levels of protocol (e.g. node-node, network end-end or host-host) can be clearly defined, and overlap of function avoided where possible. The early ARPANET protocols showed what could be achieved, but further study revealed that they had inconsistencies (e.g. the handling of flow control) and there was also overlap of function (e.g. in the use of messages and packets). Suitable international standards should seek to be well structured, and this requires substantial design effort.

5.2   The main standards organisations

One is reminded of the old music hall joke. 'What a lot of standards. Which one shall I choose?' It may come as a surprise that there are around 10 bodies which make contributions to standards in this area. This is largely for historical reasons and, sadly, in the early days, these bodies did not always pull in the same direction, and one result was that large equipment suppliers such as IBM could in effect impose de facto standards on the user community simply because of their huge size and 'muscle'.

Nowadays not only do the important standards organisations co-operate closely, but the influence of giants such as IBM on standards development is waning.

Any reader doubting this need look no further than IBM's recent progress with the OS-2 operating system and the MCA bus for its new range of PCs.

In this section we examine the roles of some of the more important standards organisations. Most emphasis is placed on ISO and CCITT, but others are mentioned which have had a major role to play in specific areas[1]. A further list of 'less important' standards organisations may be found in §5.5.

5.2.1   ISO

The **International Organization for Standardization (ISO)**. This is a United Nations Agency based in Geneva, and is the 'umbrella' organisation for the various national standards bodies, such as ANSI in the USA, DIN in Germany and BSI in the UK. The official name is somewhat cumbersome, so that ISO is often referred to as the **International Standards Organisation**, which also matches the acronym.

ISO is concerned with international standards of all kinds, and tends to do pioneering work. ISO is based on a large number of *Technical Committees* (*TCs*), one of which (TC97) is responsible for all types of computer standards, including those in the data communication field. There are a number of *Sub-Committees* (*SCs*) working in the data communications area, each comprising various *Working Groups* (*WGs*), so that, for example, TC97/SC6/WG1 is responsible for data link protocols. The following are among the sub-committees of particular interest in this field:

- SC1: Interconnection of equipment.

- SC2: Information retrieval, transfer and OSI management.

- SC6: Telecoms & information exchange between systems.

- SC18: Text and Office Systems.

- SC21: Most other applications.

5.2.2   CCITT

The **International Telegraph and Telephone Consultative Committee (CCITT)** is part of another United Nations agency, the International Telecommunication Union (ITU), and is also based in Geneva. CCITT is the umbrella organisation of the national 'common carriers' or PTTs (Public Telegraph and Telephone agencies). CCITT draws its membership from interested countries, and in fact has three tiers of membership for any given country.

- The first tier is the so-called national *common carrier*. Only one representative of this category is allowed per member state. Initially, the UK had only one agency authorised to provide telecommunication services. This was Post Office Telecommunications, a government agency. This was therefore the common carrier in the UK.

- When Post Office Telecommunications was renamed British Telecom (BT) and privatised, it was now in competition as a private service provider, and the Department of Trade and Industry (DTI) became the official common carrier as far as CCITT was concerned, even though it does not directly operate telecommunication services. BT became a member of a second tier of membership known as *Registered Private Operating Agencies (RPOAs)*. There can be more than one RPOA per member country. In theory RPOAs are 'second class' members of CCITT, but this theory is not put into practice for obvious reasons.

- A third category of membership is for 'other interested concerns', such as commercial and industrial organisations.

All communication networks run by common carriers or RPOAs are expected to conform to CCITT recommendations, as are all users of such networks. In the UK, BT (then Post Office Telecommunications) introduced a packet switching network as early as 1974, the Experimental Packet Switching Service (EPSS), but this network used specially designed protocols, and served mainly as a testbed to gain experience and to gauge user reaction[2]. The first packet switching network in Europe to conform to CCITT recommendations was a research network called EURONET, which linked a few selected sites in a number of countries. National networks were soon to follow, however. Examples of national PTT public data networks (PDNs) include BT's packet switching service (PSS, currently known as Packet Switchstream), TELENET in the USA, TRANSPAC in France and DATAPAC in Canada. Internetworking is now becoming possible between the national PDNs as well (e.g. IPSS), and access to ARPANET is also possible from many PDNs.

STUDY GROUP	AREA OF RESPONSIBILITY
SG I	Non-Voice Services/Operations
SG II	Telephone network
SG IV	Maintenance issues
SG VII	Data Communication Networks
SG VIII	Telematic Terminals
SG XI	Signalling Systems
SG XVII	Data over Phone Networks

Figure 5.1 - Some CCITT Study Groups

As far as standards are concerned, CCITT has a more specialised role than ISO, and provides recommendations as dictated by the needs of its own member organisations. Where appropriate, it will adopt international standards, possibly adapting them to suit its own requirements. However CCITT recommendations tend to be adopted more widely than just by the PTTs, since any users of networks which conform to CCITT recommendations must also conform, and other networks therefore use them in order to be able to communicate with these networks.

As far as nomenclature in CCITT is concerned, *data communication network recommendations* are numbered in the *X series* (e.g. X.25). A *Study Group (SG)* is responsible for each set of recommendations; figure 5.1 shows the responsibilities of some of the main ones of relevance.

As can be seen from the table, SG VII is responsible for 'data communication networks', and itself comprises various *Working Parties (WPs)*, so that, for example SG VII/WP 2 is responsible for network access interfaces.

Recommendations relating to hardware are generally numbered in the series V.nn. Examples of particular relevance are V.21 for low speed modem signalling (as used for terminal access to PADs; see chapter eight), and V.24, which corresponds to US (EIA) standard RS-232C for line interfaces (as specified as an option for use with X.25; see chapter seven).

While ISO and CCITT are and will remain separate bodies, they have worked in close collaboration for several years on protocol standards, and many new OSI standards, originally developed by either ISO or CCITT, are now produced jointly as ISO standards and CCITT recommendations, the only significant differences being in the introductory wording at the start, and the use of some different naming and layout conventions. (Many experts are on both ISO and CCITT committees, which clearly helps.)

5.2.3 CEPT and CEN/CENELEC

As well as national members of CCITT, there is a European arm known as the *Conference of European Post and Telecommunication Administrations*, or *CEPT*. CEPT does not normally produce its own standards, but there are some exceptions to this rule, usually related to European Community (EC) harmonisation. In chapter six we will examine the CEPT-originated Radio Link Protocol, which is an adaptation of the HDLC link protocol, proposed for use on mobile radio links (such as those provided in the UK by Cellnet and Vodaphone). Some standardisation activities of CEPT have recently been transferred to a new body, the *European Telecommunication Standards Institute (ETSI)*, which has the responsibility for generating European Telecommunications Standards (ETS or NET, the latter again the French acronym). It is the intention that by 1992, all equipment supplied for use on PDNs within the EC shall conform to the appropriate ETS, and that multiple applications for approval for different EC PDNs will become unnecessary.

The European arm of ISO is known as *CEN* (the French acronym for the European Standardisation Centre). A related body, *CENELEC*, is the European wing of IEC, which is more concerned with electronics aspects.

In general we will not be concerned with these European standards bodies, which are mostly mentioned only for completeness.

5.2.4 ANSI and BSI

The *American National Standards Institute (ANSI)* is the US member of ISO. Similarly, the *British Standards Institute (BSI)* is the UK affiliated body. While strictly it is unfair to single out one member of ISO in isolation, ANSI in particular has pioneered much work in the communications field, and continues to play a far more active part in ISO standards activity than most other constituent members. ANSI committee X3 is responsible for US standards in information processing systems, with subcommittees X3S3, X3T5 and X3T9 being particularly involved in the data communication area.

In order to maintain as international flavour as possible, we will deal with ISO rather than ANSI or BSI standards, but it should be remembered that there are ANSI and BSI equivalents of these standards in most cases. ISO international standards are available from BSI. They are technically identical, but have a separate BSI numbering, which is in the BS nnnn series for approved standards, and the DD nnnn series in the case of 'drafts for development'. We do not refer to BSI standards in this book.

5.2.5   IEEE

This is the US *Institute of Electrical and Electronic Engineers* (not to be confused with the UK IEE). Their main contribution to the standardisation progress has been in the LAN area, where *project 802* is concerned with the definition of a reference model for LANs, and the specification of associated protocols and access methods for three LAN technologies strongly supported in the USA. These included CSMA/CD bus (Ethernet, supported by Boeing), token bus (supported by General Motors) and token ring (supported by IBM). These standards have all been adopted by ISO. [It will come as no surprise that IEEE did not include the slotted ring technique, as implemented in the Cambridge Ring - supported by many UK Universities.]

Boeing and General Motors incorporate their preferred LAN architectures in reference models known respectively as TOP (Technical Office Protocol) and MAP (Manufacturing Automation Protocol). As these are OSI related, we will discuss them briefly in chapter twenty three. Token ring has other adherents as well as IBM, although the support of IBM guarantees it a hearing, of course.

5.3   Advantages of standardisation

The advantages of standardisation are plain. If a clear, unambiguous standard can be adopted universally, then all communication software written to conform to the standard should be able to interwork. Additional equipment which conforms to the standard should be able to be 'plugged in' without the need for modification or enhancement. Standards bodies such as ISO can also devote time and energy to research and development into standards of the future, an exercise which few other organisations unaided would be able to do, or even be interested in. Standards organisations are also likely to be more impartial than more local organisations with national or commercial self-interest to consider. However that is not the whole story.

5.4 Some problems with standardisation

There are many problems and pitfalls which accompany any attempt at standardisation. Two examples which illustrate these problems are as follows:

• Can the proposed standard satisfy all needs? Usually the answer is 'no'. For example, a networking standard which is ideally suited to bulk file transfer will almost certainly be quite unsuitable for interactive terminal access to a remote filestore.

• Can all parties agree on what the standard should provide? Complete agreement on what a standard should contain is rare.

Thus, as we shall see in the following sections, standardisation is a long and complex process.

5.4.1 The ISO standardisation procedure

The following scenario illustrates some of the processes involved in the development of ISO standards, processes which, as you can see, can be slow and cumbersome.

There have recently been some changes in terminology resulting from the merger of ISO and IEC information technology interests. This discussion uses the old terminology; a summary of the changes appears at the end of this section.

Most (but not all; see below) ISO standards begin life as a **new work item**, which is assigned to a working group (or experts' group) of the appropriate sub-committee. After due consultations, various *discussion documents* are produced for comment. These typically have numbers such as TC97/SC6 N1234. and are circulated to interested parties, to provoke further discussion and comments. Feedback is considered by the working group in consultation with the interested parties, which will normally include other standards bodies such as CCITT. After much discussion, and usually some disagreement, progress reaches the stage where the working group feels able to issue a **draft proposal** (**DP**). This is then offered for **ballot** to member organisations, who will seek comments from national organisations. This may take some months. Votes may be 'yes' (for acceptance as a DP), 'yes with comments', or 'no with comments'. The result of the ballot is passed to the ISO secretariat, which decides whether the document should be accepted as a DP. The decision takes into account not only the number of yes and no votes, but also the attached comments, some of which may be of a fundamental nature, others relating to more minor matters such as wording. A 'rapporteur' is appointed for each emerging standard by each national body (e.g. BSI, ANSI) to collate comments following ballots. There can be many comments in the case of a complex standard; the latest ballot on TP (transaction processing, discussed in chapter twenty three) attracted no fewer than 930 pages of comments!

By a process of iteration, modification, feedback and compromise, the proposal will be the subject of one or more further ballots before, with luck, it reaches the next stage, a *draft international standard* (*DIS*). More than one ballot may be required before this is achieved. In the event of a negative result, the DP will be referred back to the working group for further study. Once the document has reached the DIS stage, it may well be sufficiently stable for implementations based on it to be attempted (with care).

During the development of OSI, the Information Technology Standards Unit (ITSU) of the UK DTI prepared a number of *intercept recommendations* based on OSI DISs, in cases where ITSU felt that the emerging standard was sufficiently stable to warrant adoption as an interim standard. Technical guides were also provided to accompany these intercept recommendations, in which the evolution of the draft standard, suggested interpretation of various aspects of the document, and some 'grey areas' were discussed. The second edition of this book relied heavily on these documents, many of which are no longer available. In most cases, the final standard differed very little from the intercept recommendations. There are further comments about ITSU in §5.5.

The final step is a ballot for acceptance as an *international standard* (*IS*). This may take several years from the raising of the new work item. It is almost certain that the standard will differ substantially from the original draft proposal.

Unfortunately this is not the end of the matter. Many of the early International Standards (in particular that for HDLC) were incomplete, and in some cases ambiguities became apparent. There are a number of difficulties which may arise:

- It is often the case that there are two diametrically opposed schools of thought, or two existing approaches which are mutually incompatible, and which cannot coexist within a single standard. In this case the disagreement will be apparent from the comments returned with the ballot replies. This difficulty is often 'resolved' by specifying optional modes of operation, possibly to be selected when the system is first brought into use, or by negotiation.

A notorious example is the numbering of bits within a byte. Are they numbered from 0 to 7, or from 1 to 8? Is bit 0 (or 1) the least significant or most significant bit? Unfortunately there is no single answer which is compatible with all computers or programming languages, so that any 'standard' in this case can only allow a selection between the various possibilities. This problem is sometimes referred to as the 'big-enders versus little-enders syndrome'!

• Various options may be permitted to take one of a defined set of values at the discretion of the implementor. This may reflect the inability of ISO members to reach a concensus. Having options allows the opposing schools of thought to be satisfied within a single standard, and individual countries (or organisations) may select which actual values they wish to use. One example of this occurs with the ASCII codes to represent symbols of 'national significance' such as #, £ and $, which can cause difficulties for terminal users, including the author whilst typing this sentence! Another example is the way in which a date is represented. 010590 is January 5th to an American, but May 1st to an Englishman. The alternative 900501 for May 1st appears unambiguous, but will not be after the turn of the century.

• Sometimes provision is made for optional features which need not be present in all implementations. Clearly however, organisations which desire to interwork have to use compatible implementations of the standard, and may well be advised not to use additional 'optional facilities'. Their usage can sometimes be negotiated, but reliance on some facility which may not exist is clearly not to be recommended.

• Another common problem is the need to progress the document to IS status before all matters have been resolved. It may be that some areas are too difficult to resolve in the time available, or that additional features have been identified but not agreed, which can be added later without compromising the existing standard. In this case it is common for certain areas to be 'reserved for future study'.

One problem with the original version of HDLC (High-level Data Link Control) was that certain unused values in fields in HDLC frames (packets) were left undefined rather than 'reserved for future study', because they were in effect surplus to current requirements. This resulted in IBM and others using some of the unused fields for their own purposes, and announcing proprietary versions of the HDLC 'standard'. Thus we had, among others, IBM's SDLC (S for Synchronous) Burroughs' BDLC (B for Burroughs), Univac's UDLC (U for Universal), and ICL's IDLC (I for International). All were in effect supersets of HDLC, but it was not the intention that the additional features should be compatible between versions. This should be regarded as a mistake by ISO. Reserving unused fields prevents this sort of ad hoc extension. ISO learned from this. In fact it turned out that some of these fields were needed in later extensions of HDLC, leading to possible incompatibility between HDLC and (say) SDLC. Fortunately most 'SDLC chips' on the market are in effect HDLC chips but, thanks to IBM's dominance at the time, the term SDLC has stuck, and is perhaps even better known than HDLC itself. (Echoes of BSC and Basic Mode?)

• No standard can be regarded as fixed for all time. Standards eventually need revising and extending. One way to do this is to revert the standard to DIS status, with the same number. This has happened twice to one of the HDLC standards {4335}. If the changes are of a fundamental rather than an evolutionary nature, an existing standard may be deleted and replaced with a DIS with a new number. Thus another HDLC standard {7809} replaced two earlier ones {6159, 6256; not in the appendix}. This then follows the normal progression to IS status.

• If the changes are relatively minor, and can be regarded simply as extensions, it is normal to issue an **addendum** to the standard. Some standards end up with several addenda.

• Sometimes mistakes are found in an IS. In this case a **technical corrigendum** may be issued.

We have seen that the progress from a new work item to a full IS can be slow, and may take several years (seven years for OSI/RM). This is necessary for a new technique or protocol, but in some cases there are established, non-ISO standards, which some parties consider worthy of adoption as International Standards, in which case the full procedure described above would clearly be pointless. What is needed is a quick decision on whether the existing standard qualifies.

This situation is catered for by what is known as a **fast track ballot**. Here, the existing standard is immediately proposed as a DIS. If the ballot result is favourable, progress to IS status will normally be rapid, although some changes may be necessary for political or other reasons. On the other hand political (or other) objections may be so strong that the ballot fails, in which case a new work item will have to be raised.

• The IEEE LAN standards for CSMA/CD, token ring and token bus took the fast track route, as did the Cambridge Ring slotted ring technique.

• On the other hand there was a recent attempt to 'fast track' a proprietary Remote Procedure Call protocol used on client-server LANs. This was in relation to OSI applications, but failed for a variety of reasons, some of them political. So the fast track approach is not guaranteed to succeed.

Also worthy of mention is a further class of document produced by ISO, the **technical report** (**TR**). This format is used to provide background material relating to standards, although the document itself does not qualify as a standard. These have a similar path to ISs, starting life as a *proposed draft technical report (PDTR)*, then a *draft technical report (DTR)*.

There are two days in each month when ISO reviews the progress of DP and DIS ballots. Therefore, in principle, there are 24 dates in each year when a new IS may be approved.

ISO recently merged its IT standardisation work with that of the *International Electrotechnical Commission (IEC)*. As a result there have been some changes in nomenclature. ISO TC97 is now known as ISO/IEC JTC1 (Joint Technical Committee one). Draft proposals are now known as *committee drafts (CDs)*. Addenda are now known as *amendments (AMs)*. Abbreviations for draft amendments are now DAM and CDAM (Committee DAM), rather than DAD and PDAD. A PDTR is similarly now a CDTR (Committee Draft Technical Report). However all this is of purely semantic interest as far as the standards themselves are concerned, and in this book we will use the tradidional names.

5.4.2   The CCITT standardisation procedure

We have seen that the ISO standardisation procedure is complex. That of CCITT is simpler. CCITT working parties consider recommendations on a continuous basis, but only (re)issue recommendations following Plenary sessions at the end of each four year *study period*, the most recent of which was in 1988. (The impact of the 1988 recommendations is still being assessed at the time of writing.)

Each plenary session agrees on a set of **questions**, which are in effect areas of study for the next four year study period. Since this would be bureaucratic and restrictive if applied too literally, there is provision for questions to be carried over from one study period to the next, and new questions to be raised in between plenary sessions.

The main advantage of the CCITT approach is that, every four years, a complete set of the current recommendations is issued, with a different colour for each year (yellow for 1980, red for 1984, blue for 1988). This allows a recommendation to supersede an earlier version with the same number, by appearing in a different form in the next issue of 'coloured books', a much simpler process for the layman to understand than that of ISO. It also means that implementors can work with a recommendation which is guaranteed to be stable for four years. Unfortunately CCITT have not adopted the DP/DIS/IS approach, so that it is not always clear how stable a recommendation is.

One slight eccentricity with CCITT recommendations is that, in a few cases, alternatives exist. Thus there are two recommendations for the physical interface to X.25 networks, X.21 and X.21 bis. Very occasionally there is a third, referred to as ter. These are French terms, reflecting a generally French bias in CCITT naming conventions. (CCITT itself is an acronym of its French name.)

5.4.3　　　Comments on the standardisation process

These processes may seem unnecessarily cumbersome. You may feel that it would be better if ISO and CCITT could simply define the standard and then insist that it be adhered to by all members. This is in theory possible in the case of CCITT, since its members are network operators, and users would have no option but to use the implemented recommendations. Indeed in the past, CCITT tended to define recommendations on a 'need to know' basis, telling users how to access or use their facilities, rather than how they worked internally. This proved to be a problem with the first release of X.25, as we shall see. But it makes more sense for CCITT to work on a concensus basis, as indeed they do nowadays.

In the case of ISO, it would be impossible to attempt to impose solutions. One problem is that ISO is only an advisory body. Member organisations such as BSI are only national representatives, and there is no statutory requirement on individual organisations in the UK or anywhere else to adhere to ISO/BSI standards merely because they exist. Furthermore, there are many conflicting national requirements and interests, not to mention 'special cases'. Unless a new standard satisfies the majority of potential users, it will either be largely ignored, or will be subjected to the sort of ad hoc modification from which BSC suffered. Obviously the existence of a standard is only useful if the great majority of organisations undertake to adhere to its requirements, and do not feel the need to 'improve' or otherwise alter it.

However one thing is clear. Once a standard has been agreed upon, all concerned must adhere to it. If it has significant weaknesses, they will become only too clear as it is put to the test of implementation and usage, and agreed changes can be made. However, it is important to evaluate all standards critically, and not simply assume that because some feature is in the standard, it is necessarily the most academically respectable approach; most compromises, however necessary, fall short of the ideal. Always examine a standard, protocol or whatever critically, starting with HDLC and the related RLP protocol in the next chapter.

5.5　　　Some other standards bodies

As well as the main standards bodies mentioned in §5.2, there are many others with some interest in standardisation.

- Historically, *IBM* has often been a de facto standards authority, simply because of its huge size in relation to other computer manufacturers. Where IBM led, others tended to follow.

To a certain extent this is still true; that it is less so is in part due to the influence of ISO and CCITT, and also to the fact that IBM's sheer size sometimes makes it hard to react to rapid changes, such as those currently taking place in the OSI area. IBM were largely responsible for the original BSC protocol, which other manufacturers proceeded to copy, each in their own incompatible way; a similar scenario is most unlikely today.

• More recently, various US manufacturers, including IBM, defined proprietary network architectures based on layering. These include IBM's Systems Network Architecture (SNA), DEC's Digital Network Architecture (DNA or DECNET) and Burroughs' BNA. The DARPA Catenet (formerly ARPANET) now has a network architecture as well, which includes such network protocols as TCP (transmission control protocol), UDP (unconfirmed datagram protocol) and IP (internet protocol), as well as application protocols such as Telnet (terminal handling), FTP (file transfer) and electronic mail. However these are all proprietary products, primarily intended for use in networks of the manufacturers' or organisations' own computers, and although all propose layered models superficially similar to OSI/RM, these architectures differ from each other and from ISO/RM, and can only be made to interwork with difficulty, if at all. We exclude a discussion of such proprietary network architectures from this book.

• In the LAN field, DEC, Intel and *Xerox* formed a consortium (known as DIX) to promulgate and market a LAN based on the Xerox Ethernet 'standard'. Again this was proprietary, but it proved so popular that a modified version became adopted as an international standard (via the fast track route).

• Partly as a defence mechanism against the dominance of IBM (and other US manufacturers), the European manufacturers (ICL, Siemens, Bull, Olivetti etc.) set up their own body, known as *ECMA* (the European Computer Manufacturers' Association). This body also engages in standardisation work of its own, and although we will not be discussing ECMA standards as such in this book some ECMA work was used as OSI input by ISO (for example in the development of the session service).

The UK's contribution to EC standardisation took a body blow when ICL, by far the largest UK computer company, was sold by its parent STC to Fujitsu of Japan in 1990. As a result, there is currently debate about whether ICL should still be regarded as a European computer company. This is a particularly sensitive issue where EC initiatives are concerned. (1990 was a bad year for the UK computer and telecommunication industry. STC itself merged with Northern Telecom of Canada in late 1990, effectively leaving GEC as the only major UK supplier of telecommunications equipment. GEC and Siemens had earlier taken over Plessey, then the third major UK telecommunications force.)

- In the USA, there is a proliferation of standards bodies of all types. There is room here only to list the main ones without comment. As well as ANSI and IEEE, there are the National Bureau of Standards (NBS), the Electronic Industries Association (EIA), the Federal Telecommunications Standards Committee (FTSC), and the Defense Communications Agency (DCA). Most of these have specific interests which can be inferred from their titles.

- In addition to international bodies and supplier groups, various independent organisations and government establishments have developed private 'interim standards' to satisfy their own urgent needs, pending (or in the absence of) the development of suitable international standards. In the USA, a variety of protocols (virtual terminal, file transfer, electronic mail and so on) have been developed specifically for use on *ARPANET*, which again we will not be discussing in this book[3].

- In the UK, a protocol standards group has been formed which provides standards for the academic community. It is 'masterminded' by the *Joint Network Team* (*JNT*) of the Computer Board and Research Councils. The National Physical Laboratory (NPL) and several universities are also actively involved in this work. Their main concern has been to provide urgently needed standard protocols for file transfer, job transfer and terminal handling, for use in networking between University and Research Council sites, together with a protocol intended to provide a standard interface between these application protocols and different types of network. We will briefly review UK academic community interim standards in chapter nine.

- The UK Information Technology Standards Unit of the Department of Trade and Industry (DTI *ITSU*) has prepared a set of intercept recommendations[4]. These cover the use of standards from CCITT, ISO, IEEE, JNT and certain other bodies, where these are considered to be 'sufficiently stable and widely supported' to be worthy of wider dissemination. ITSU does not however originate standards, rather it makes information on selected standards available to interested parties in the UK, together with advice on their usage (in supporting technical guides).

- In the USA, *NIST* (the National Institute of Standards and Technology) is developing OSI profiles suitable for use by various types of industrial and commercial organisation. We mention some of these briefly in chapters twenty one and twenty three.

• *EWOS* (the European Workshop for Open Systems) performs a similar role in Europe. We briefly mention EWOS VT profiles in chapter twenty one.

5.6 A brief history of standardisation progress

The first significant truly international standard protocol was produced by ISO. This was the High Level Data Link Control protocol (HDLC). Despite its somewhat grandiose title, it is purely a data link protocol for use between adjacent nodes, and was designed to replace both point-point and multidrop variants of BSC with a single, and consistently defined, packet switching protocol. It was specifically designed to handle not only information exchange on point-point lines in a communication subnet, but also protocols between VDUs and central computers on multidrop lines.

The protocol first became an international standard in the mid 1970s (after several years of discussion). After some initial teething troubles, and numerous revisions and enhancements, it is now widely used and well standardised. However its built-in limitation of being only a link protocol led quickly to the specification of a more powerful protocol (X25; see below).

HDLC was designed to solve the many problems posed by BSC, but only defined communication between adjacent nodes in a network, or between directly connected hosts. There was a clear need for a network-wide protocol of this type, and CCITT incorporated HDLC in a protocol with wider scope. This is known as recommendation X.25. It was originally issued in 1976, and has since been reissued three times, in 1980, 1984 and 1988. Since CCITT reissues recommendations as 'coloured books' every four years, the next reissue of X.25 will be in 1992.

In its original form, X.25 consisted of three 'levels'. Level 1 is a definition of the physical hardware environment. Level 2 is a subset of HDLC (the point-point part), and level 3 is a 'packet level', intended to have some end-end significance. For the first time, some layering of protocols is becoming evident. Many problems, deficiencies and inconsistencies were encountered in the first issue, many of which were clarified in the 1980 revision. The current (1988) version of the standard is discussed in chapter seven, together with its application to a typical common carrier network.

Both the terminology of X.25 and the facilities offered have undergone change. The 'levels' of X.25 disappeared with the 1980 revision, to be replaced with 'physical procedures', 'link access procedures (LAP)' and 'packet mode procedures'. A datagram service was introduced as an option in 1980, but disappeared again in the 1984 revision. This particular omission will not concern any implementors, as although it was included mainly at the request of ANSI, it has never been used in any common carrier network. However, datagrams apart, one problem with revising X.25 or any other standard is that organisations generally do become committed to the facilities provided by the old version. Therefore, like the various versions of FORTRAN, the new standard has to be downward compatible to the old version. The implications of the new X.25 recommendation are still being assessed.

While X.25 is in some sense a layered protocol, it is intended to cover only the network side of a communication. As far as the wider context of host communication is concerned, there was much discussion concerning how many layers there should be, and what functions should be provided in each layer. ISO have defined an Open System Interconnection Reference Model (OSI/RM) with 7 layers. The lowest layer provides an interface to the hardware itself, and the highest layer interfaces to the user application. In between come the network and host layers. The issues here are complex, and the model seeks to define the requirements of each layer, together with their interfaces, rather than to specify any particular service or protocol at a given layer.

X.25 now fits into this model reasonably well, but earlier versions did not, as would be expected since X.25 predated the OSI/RM. The 1988 release of X.25 now comes close to meeting OSI/RM requirements. We discuss the relationship of X.25 to OSI in part three.

Since OSI/RM merely defines the areas and scope of each protocol layer, it follows that there could be a variety of implementations which satisfy the requirements of a layer. It has even been argued that a definition of a network architecture such as RM/OSI should not even be called a standard[5], but we will not become involved in that particular discussion here.

While ISO were developing OSI/RM, and before any services or protocols conforming with OSI/RM had been finalised, CCITT were busily developing application protocols of their own. These were required to allow the provision of services over PDNs in two principal areas:

> • *Telematic services.* These include facsimile (fax) and *teletex*, which to all intents and purposes is a sort of 'super Telex', capable of transmitting at up to 9600 bps rather than the inadequate speed of the conventional Telex network, and also designed to use a

much richer character set than the 5-bit, capitals only, one used by conventional Telex. Teletex recommendations first appeared in 1980, in the S-series. They were subsequently re-issued in 1984 in the T-series. *Facsimile* and *videotex* are other telematic services which received study. We will not be dealing with telematic services in detail in this book.

- In order to facilitate the provision of electronic mail services such as Telecom Gold over X.25 networks such as PSS, CCITT commenced work on what they refer to as *message handling systems* (*MHS*) in the 1981-1984 study period. This work culminated in the X.400(84) series of recommendations.

Strictly speaking, MHS is a telematic service as well. We distinguish it from facsimile, videotex and teletex since these are primarily concerned with the encoding of information, whereas MHS offers support for full blown applications.

The main problem at that time was that OSI was not sufficiently advanced at the time for this work to be entirely compatible, as only the basic framework was in place. Only the middle OSI layers (network, transport and session) were even approaching stability. As a result, CCITT had to make its own decisions, rather as the UK academic community had to do before it. Some aspects of MHS in particular contained features which subsequently appeared rather eccentric in the OSI context, and indeed the design of the upper OSI layers (transport, session, presentation and application services), was strongly influenced by existing CCITT standards for Teletex and MHS. ISO could not simply disregard CCITT's work, as they had done with most of the UK academic community interim protocols, and so a convergence exercise was undertaken, with parts of MHS migrating into generalised OSI standard documents.

To add to the difficulties, the 1984 versions of some CCITT recommendations were to varying degrees at odds with corresponding OSI services and protocols. In particular, the application layer was not yet either stable or well understood. Much effort was thus devoted during the 1985-1988 CCITT study period towards reaching a state where the application layer was sufficiently well defined and stable to support MHS and other applications. One consequence of this was that CCITT recommendations and ISO standards were increasingly technically identical, and this required changes to both ISO standards and the MHS recommendations, which were completely revamped in the 1988 'blue book'. CCITT now has a set of OSI recommendations in the X.200(1988) series which are technically identical to the equivalent OSI standards (and incidentally have a comprehensible numbering scheme as well).

Work on the lower layers of OSI/RM is now largely complete. ISO (in many cases in conjunction with CCITT) is currently well advanced in the specification of application services and supporting protocols. This task is made easier since many experts are members of both ISO and CCITT study groups. Now when a new ISO OSI standard appears, it often corresponds to a technically identical CCITT recommendation (although there are some OSI areas which are not of interest to CCITT, and some CCITT recommendations which have not been adopted by ISO). The definition of 'application support' services is now fairly stable, and many applications themselves have either already become ISs (e.g. file transfer), or are at DIS stage at the time of writing (e.g. MHS). Although it will be many years before OSI can be said to have fully matured, interworking between applications on different open systems is becoming increasingly feasible.

Meanwhile, of course, there is the problem that some implementations of earlier protocols, such as X.25(1980) and the UK interim protocols discussed in chapter nine, which are not consistent with OSI, are still in use, and there are not inconsiderable problems in converting to OSI standards for such organisations. There is the further problem that OSI has yet to take off in many areas. The situation however looks particularly encouraging in the public sector, and many governments now require new hardware and software products to be 'OSI compliant'. (Government OSI profiles are discussed in chapter twenty three.) OSI is also strongly supported by such companies as General Motors and Boeing in the USA. There are however still many areas where OSI does not appear to have aroused much interest as yet.

This then is the current state of the art. 'Low level' protocols such as X.25 packet mode and HDLC (X.25 LAPB or LAN LLC) are now stable and well established, as are the bottom six layers of OSI/RM (apart from the physical layer at the bottom). Currently most attention is being devoted to application protocols and issues of general OSI management, notably an OSI directory and OSI registration procedures. The major problems to be faced in the next few years will not only be connected with conversion from earlier interim (or unstable) standards, but more importantly with providing mechanisms (such as the directory and registration procedures) which will enable the theory of OSI to be turned into practice. After all, to give a simple analogy, having a telephone is of little use unless you know the numbers of some people to phone up. OSI currently lacks both a universal way of naming and identifying applications, and a global means of obtaining the addresses of other hosts, which explains the urgency of providing OSI registration and directory services.

One major impetus for OSI is that there is increasing pressure from governments and other organisations on suppliers to provide OSI-compatible products. Many governments now have what are termed *OSI*

Profiles (e.g. GOSIP in the UK), setting out those aspects of OSI with which products must conform if they are to be considered for purchase. We have come a long way since IBM's attempt to offer its proprietary Systems Network Architecture over the PSS network. But although that attempt might have failed (for political reasons), the battle against proprietary network architectures is by no means won yet. We will trace the development of OSI[6] in the rest of the book. If you reach the conclusion that networking has reached a major turning point, you will have judged correctly.

5.7   References

1   A list of standards bodies, with many details of relevant committees, may be found at the end of an article on standardisation by A. Lyman Chapin, in ACM Computer Communication Review (January, 1983).

2   R. Feldmann and D. Mildenhall, 'The British Post Office and Packet Switching', Computer Communications (Butterworths), vol. 1, no. 2, p. 91 (1978). This paper examines the lessons learned from the EPSS experiment.

3   See for example the recent book by Tanenbaum, 'Computer networks' (second edition), Prentice Hall (1988), and the rather more dated one by Davies, Barber, Price and Solominides, 'Computer Networks and their Protocols', Wiley (1979).

4   ITSU will provide information on to interested parties in the UK, on written application to IT Standards Unit, Department of Trade and Industry, Kingsgate House, 66-74 Victoria Street, London SW1E 6SW.

5   ANSI hold this view; see reference 1.

6   Reference 1 is the first of a set of progress reports by the same author on standardisation, published in Computer Communication Review from time to time. They make interesting reading, not least for their insight into the workings of standards bodies.

6   ISO High Level Data Link Control (HDLC)

6.1   The purpose of HDLC

This protocol was first developed by ISO in the early 1970s, and has since been the subject of many revisions and extensions. HDLC defines procedures for information exchange on communication links between adjacent nodes in a network. It does not perform any other function than link management. Therefore nothing in HDLC has any significance other than on a particular link, and it is left to other protocols to deal, for example, with end-end or host-related issues.

While HDLC started life as a single standard, it proved necessary to re-issue the basic standard and provide supplementary standards which sought to bring together the various diverging strands into a common framework. Thus as well as the standard documents themselves {3309, 4335, 7776}, further documents {4335 ADDs, 7809, 8885} amplify or 'consolidate' various aspects of the protocol. In this chapter we are mainly concerned with the WAN variant which forms the basis of the X.25 link access procedures {7776}. An extension for use with LANs, part of IEEE 802.2 Logical Link Control (LLC) was originally developed by IEEE, and has now also been adopted by ISO {8802-2}. We will examine this in chapter thirteen. Also discussed briefly in §6.13 is a recent CEPT derivative known as the *Radio Link Protocol* (*RLP*), designed to offer HDLC-like procedures over unreliable radio links with long propagation delays.

HDLC was specifically designed to provide similar procedures for all of the common types of communication in wide area networks. It was also designed so that as many of its functions as possible could be easily implemented by standard hardware. By including an HDLC chip in the line interface, the computer can be relieved of many of the routine tasks of communication such as error checking, generation of acknowledgements and sequencing of transmission units, which can be time-consuming if performed by software. HDLC provides a number of operational modes. These include the following scenarios for wide area networks:

- Communication between adjacent nodes on full duplex lines in a point-point communication network. In this respect it serves as a direct replacement for that part of BSC which functions as a data link protocol, without containing any of its 'enhancements'. It is assumed that other, higher level protocols will provide these extra services, using HDLC as an underlying link protocol. One protocol to do so is CCITT recommendation X.25, where HDLC is referred to as 'balanced link access procedures' or LAPB, as discussed in the next chapter. Two modes of operation are provided, which also form part of the X.25 recommendation. The principal one, which is 'preferred' for use in X.25, is known as *asynchronous balanced mode* (*ABM*). The term 'balanced' refers to the fact that the two ends of the link are in effect 'equal partners' in the communication. Both can initiate and terminate a connection, and send data on an established connection (subject to the rules) without waiting to be asked (once the link is set up, and subject of course to flow control etc.). Once the link is set up, it is available for use in both directions. The term 'asynchronous' refers to the fact that there is no direct interaction ('synchronisation') between the two directions of flow; contrast BSC, where one station must obtain master status in order to be able to transmit information. The term asynchronous, when used in this context, is thus a logical rather than a physical concept, and in fact the protocol would normally be used on communication lines which, physically, operate in a synchronous manner.

• Communication between VDUs on a multidrop line and a central controlling computer. This is an application which has typically been handled by BSC-like poll-select protocols. An HDLC mode of operation is provided which allows a master station to poll and select up to 255 secondary stations. This is referred to as *normal response mode* (*NRM*) or unbalanced mode. The term 'unbalanced' implies that one station (the master or primary station) has complete control over the line, and it alone determines how and when the other stations (the secondaries or slaves) will respond to its commands. We will not be discussing this variant in any detail.

There has been reluctance on the part of some manufacturers to adopt HDLC for use with multidrop VDUs. This is partly because the existing BSC-like protocols worked much better for VDUs than in mesh networks, so that the incentive for change was not as great. Also, converting to HDLC would require additional software, since hundreds of thousands of BSC-based VDUs were (and indeed still are) in use, and still have to be supported, and it does not make economic sense to modify or replace VDUs which function satisfactorily, and which have extensive software support. However there are other reasons why HDLC has been rather slow to penetrate the multidrop VDU market. Some are of a political nature, and include a natural reluctance to adopt a standard VDU protocol which can then easily be 'cloned', as happened with the IBM PC. The issue of VDU protocols is however irrelevant in the context of networking between hosts; multidrop VDUs only have to communicate with a single host. Thus, although the situation is gradually changing in favour of HDLC, multidrop VDU issues have had little or no impact on wider networking issues, except in the sense that attempts have been made to define an 'abstract multidrop VDU' in connection with OSI applications. [In the case of dumb terminals, the situation is quite different, as we shall see in chapter eight.]

• A third mode of operation, *asynchronous response mode* (*ARM*), has been provided in HDLC. This provides for half duplex working on point-point lines, and is conceptually closer to BSC than asynchronous balanced mode. One station, the primary, sends commands and information. The other, the secondary, returns responses. Conceptually at least, both nodes implement two logically distinct stations, primary and secondary, and there are two logically distinct sets of commands and responses (one in each direction). This also means that it is possible to set up one direction of transmission while the other remains inactive. (In the case of ABM, there is a logically combined primary/secondary at each end.) This was the mode of operation specified in the original (1976) X.25 recommendation, but many networks subsequently elected to use ABM instead, which was not originally envisaged by CCITT. Since 1980, new implementations are advised to use ABM, which is now 'preferred', although the continued use of ARM is not excluded for 'existing implementations'.

In this book we will be mainly concerned with ABM as it is applied to computer-computer point-point links, particularly in the context of X.25. However NRM will also be mentioned from time to time in the discussion of the various fields. ARM is now obsolescent, and is no longer recommended for use in X.25 networks. It is essentially similar to, but less flexible than, ABM.

NOTE: various options are allowed in the HDLC specification, including extended formats. We will cover only the standard format in this book, except in chapter thirteen, where a LAN application of HDLC using the extended format is discussed.

There are some terminological features of HDLC which seem quaint today, but which were entirely logical when the protocol was first developed. The term 'high level' now seems utterly inappropriate for what is basically a low level link protocol. At the time, it was the highest level of protocol which had been standardised. When we discuss OSI/RM, we will see that the data link layer is layer 2 out of 7, which is hardly high level! Another oddity is that the poll-select variant is referred to as 'normal mode'. This may have been the case 20 years ago, but nowadays the commonly known variant is ABM, not NRM. It only goes to show how much the context of HDLC has changed over the years. However the terminology, however quaint it may seem at times, is here to stay. The advice is simply not to take some of it too literally.

6.2   The HDLC frame

In HDLC, all exchange of information, control and acknowledgements is formatted into transmission units of strictly defined format. These are known as *frames*. ISO use the term frame, rather than block or packet, partly to avoid the possibility of confusion of terminology, and also to provide an entirely new name for a transmission unit, free from possible preconceptions associated with words such as block or packet..

6.2.1   Frame format

Figure 6.1 shows the general format of a frame. Frames have the following characteristics:

FLAG	ADDRESS	CONTROL	INFORMATION (not all frame types)	FCS	FLAG

Figure 6.1 - HDLC frame layout

- Frames are subdivided into (up to) four sections. These are referred to as the address part, the control part, the information field, and the frame check sequence (FCS, a 16 bit polynomial error check). With the exception of the information field, they are of fixed length.

- There are three different types of frame. Not all frames contain an information field, but the other three sections are always present.

- The information field normally contains user data, together with anything else which is not used for HDLC control. Such information is *transparent* to HDLC, i.e. the protocol has no interest in the contents, merely in preserving its integrity. In one or two cases the information field contains diagnostic information for use by HDLC itself.

- Frames are separated by flags. A *flag* is a defined bit sequence (01111110) which cannot appear inside a frame. Therefore a flag precedes every frame, and the end of the frame is marked by another flag.

- When there are no frames to be sent on the link, the flag sequence is repeated indefinitely. This sequence will be generated automatically by the HDLC chip in the absence of other instructions from the computer.

- The address part of the frame is used to identify the sending or receiving station on the link. It is important to note that this address has no significance beyond this link; in particular it is <u>not</u> used for routing purposes in the WAN ABM variant discussed in this chapter). The standard length of the address field is 1 *octet*, i.e. 8 bits, and we will henceforth refer to it as the ***address octet***. (Again, this term was chosen in preference to byte in order to avoid any possible ambiguity or confusion concerning the length of a 'byte'.) In asynchronous modes, the address is that of one of the two stations on the link. In normal mode, it is used to identify the secondary station which is being addressed by the primary station, or from which a frame is being received by the primary station. Typically this corresponds to the address of a multidrop VDU.

- The control part is also one octet long. This octet is bit significant, and is further subdivided into fields as will be explained later. It is generally referred to as the ***control octet***.

- The ***information field*** is not present in all frames. Where it is present it may, in theory at least, be of any length up to an agreed maximum value. In practice, most implementations insist on its being an exact number of octets long. The information field length is not stated in the frame. Instead, the frame is structured in such a way that it is easy for hardware in the receiving computer's line interface to detect the final flag of the frame, and thus determine the length of the information field.

This aside concerns the implementation of certain HDLC functions in a chip. Typically, the frame will be passed through a 16-bit shift register at the receiver. When the final flag is detected, the shift register will be left containing the FCS, and as it is clear that the FCS immediately follows the information field (or the control field, if there is no information field), this uniquely defines the end of the useful part of the frame. The entire frame contents will already have 'passed through' to some receive buffer in the receiving station. (Of course they must be discarded if the FCS turns out to be incorrect.) This is all done automatically. It would be messy to do this in software, but it is amenable to hardware decoding since, unlike BSC, all transmission units are terminated in the same way. There are many HDLC chips on the market (although they are often marketed as SDLC chips).

Since everything is formatted into frames, no unformatted character sequences such as ACK and ENQ are sent on links. Acknowledgements are built into the control sections of frames. Again this results in simpler procedures, and the acknowledgements can also be generated automatically by hardware.

6.2.2 The address field: commands and responses

On a multidrop line there is a clear requirement for an address field. There may be many VDUs on the line, and the address octet allows up to 256 distinct addresses (e.g. 255 VDUs plus an address meaning all VDUs).

But what about a point-point link? With only two devices on the link, it is obvious which device is to receive an incoming frame, so why bother with the address, one might ask? The answer is that some features of HDLC operate as a dialogue. One station issues a *command*, and the other replies in a *response* frame. The address in an incoming frame identifies whether the frame is a command or a response, as follows:

- A frame is a command if the address field contains the receiver's address.

- A frame is a response if it contains the sender's address.

This is entirely consistent with polling a VDU by specifying its address; the VDU responds with its own address.

On a point-point link with only two stations, it seems a waste to reserve 8 bits, and indeed some variants (such as RLP mentioned at the end of the chapter) use a single *command/response bit* instead, which seems far more sensible. One problem is that the various parts of HDLC frames are designed to be an integral number of octets long, and using a single bit for the address would of course mess that up!

Another question you may ask is why commands and responses cannot be distinguished by the command type say. The reason, as will become clear in due course, is that the same frame can be either a command or response according to context; there would be ambiguity without the additional information on whether the frame is a command or response.

6.3 Code transparency and bit stuffing

A basic design philosophy of HDLC is that any combination of bits can be sent within a frame. This is desirable for several reasons. Firstly, it allows optimum use to be made of the control octet, so that it can be coded using the minimum number of bits. This results in improved utilisation of the line, by reducing the overhead of transmitting control information. Secondly, it is necessary in order to send a binary FCS, which can take any 16-bit value, depending on the contents of the frame. Thirdly, it allows binary information to be transmitted without the necessity for special reformatting, as was necessary in BSC.

Whereas BSC relies on ASCII TC characters to perform specific functions such as delimiting fields and terminating blocks, the significance of fields in an HDLC frame is determined solely from their position in the frame. Thus code transparency goes hand in hand with a freedom from the artificial constraints inherent in BSC.

6.3.1   Bit stuffing

There is however one obvious problem which must first be solved. If we can send any possible sequence of bits in a frame, then clearly we can send a sequence of bits which looks like a flag. How is the receiver to know that this is not a genuine flag, and not incorrectly detect the end of a frame? Clearly if it did, information would be lost. Worse than this, the receiver would then proceed to determine an incorrect FCS, which would appear to be in error. However many times the frame was transmitted, it could never be received correctly.

The solution to this problem lies in the use of *bit stuffing*. This works as follows. A flag is defined to be the bit sequence 01111110, i.e. exactly six successive one bits. In order not to allow a flag sequence inside the frame, the sender is required to insert a 0 after five successive 1 bits have been sent. The receiver similarly removes any 0 following exactly five successive 1s. This is done regardless of what the next bit after the 11111 sequence may be. This is clearly necessary so that the receiver can always remove a 0 after a 11111 sequence. Again, this is easy to implement in hardware (an HDLC chip), but it would be messy (and time-consuming) to attempt to implement this feature in software. Figure 6.2 shows an example of the use of bit stuffing.

FRAME CONTENTS	1001011010111110100110101111101
AS SENT ON LINK	**01111110**10010110101111*0*10100110 1011111*00*10**1111110**

NOTEs:
1   **Bold** digits are flags inserted by the sending chip, and used by the receiving chip to detect frame boundaries.
2   *Italicised* digits are inserted by the sending chip, and removed by the receiving chip.
3   This bit sequence is not intended to represent a valid frame.

Figure 6.2 - illustrating HDLC bit stuffing and flag insertion

When there are no frames to be transmitted on the line, the flag sequence is sent continuously. Optionally, one of the two 0s between the 111111 sequences can be omitted, as shown in figure 6.3.

Either	111111001111110011111001111110..
or	11111101111110111111101111110.......

Figure 6.3 - HDLC interframe time fill

6.3.2   Frame abort sequence

Sometimes it may be necessary for a sender to abandon the transmission of a frame before it has been completely sent. BSC does this by prematurely terminating a block with ENQ. In the case of HDLC, a similar approach is used, but in the spirit of code transparency. Rather than terminating the frame with a flag, the frame is prematurely terminated by a special abort sequence which looks like an extended flag. This consists of at least 7 successive 1 bits (one more than a flag) and not more than 14, as shown in figure 6.4. A command to the chip will result in this sequence being generated automatically. Bit stuffing would obviously not be applied to this sequence.

1010110001010101111111110111111011...
frame   aborted   revert to flags

Figure 6.4 - HDLC frame abort sequence

6.3.3   Emergency link disconnect

There is a specific frame which can be sent to request 'graceful' shutdown of the link (DISC; see §6.8.1). However this will not be possible if one of the computers 'goes down'. A sequence of 15 or more 1s causes the receiving chip to notify its computer that the link has been shut down. See figure 6.5. The computer will then execute some recovery procedure. For example, it could divert queued information on to an alternative link. Again, this sequence is not bit stuffed.

00101001000111111111111111111...
frame   disconnect

Figure 6.5 - HDLC emergency link disconnect sequence

HDLC chips can be designed to transmit this sequence automatically if they 'lose contact' with their controlling computer (in which case 1-bits would normally be sent indefinitely, as will also be the case if a power failure occurs). This can save time at the other end (timeouts, retransmissions etc.) but is only intended as an emergency measure, if the normal link disconnect frame cannot be sent (i.e. graceful shutdown is not possible).

6.4   Functions performed by HDLC

As already indicated, HDLC is a data link protocol. Considering mainly ABM, the following basic functions are provided for:

• The setting up of a data link by means of a command selecting e.g. ARM or ABM, or possibly extended formats (ARME or ABME). In the case of ARM, the two directions of transmission are set up independently. With ABM one link setup command enables both directions of transmission.

• The closing down of a data link at the end of its use by means of a disconnect command.

• While the link is active, the exchange of information frames in full duplex mode. Frames sent in one direction may contain acknowledgements for frames received in the reverse direction, and frames can be sent in both directions simultaneously (in asynchronous modes).

• Provision of link flow control by sequencing of frames, and by restrictions on the number of frames which can be outstanding (unacknowledged) at any time.

• Provision of link flow control by means of commands which instruct the sender to cease sending information frames, and subsequently permit the sender to resume.

• Error detection on frames by means of the FCS. Frames with an invalid FCS will be ignored completely by the receiver and will require retransmission.

• Recovery procedures in the event of individual frames being lost or mangled.

6.5   Types of frame

In order to provide these functions, three distinct types of frame are provided, as follows:

6.5.1   Information frames

These frames are used to send the actual 'user data'. This comprises anything not directly used as control by HDLC. Where HDLC forms part of X.25, this includes all higher level X.25 control, as we will discuss in the next chapter. This is the principal type of frame, and is the only one in which user data can be transported in the information field. (This only applies to the WAN ABM variant; a UI frame is defined which also conveys information, and discussed in §6.8.3.) These frames are referred to as *I-frames*. The frame type is determined by the first bit of the control octet. The control octet contains N(S), the link sequence number of the frame itself, a poll/final (P/F) bit, and a second sequence number N(R), which is used for acknowledging the receipt of I-frames travelling in the opposite direction on the link. The format of an I-frame is shown in figure 6.6; the fields in the control octet are discussed in more detail in §6.6.1.

FLAG	ADDRESS	0-CONTROL	INFORMATION	FCS	FLAG

CONTROL	N(S)	P/F	N(R)
bits	3	1	3

Figure 6.6 - HDLC I-frame format

6.5.2   Supervisory frames

The format of an *S-frame* is shown in figure 6.7. These frames do not contain user data, so that the information field is absent. The frame type is determined by the first two bits of the control octet. These frames contain sequence numbers which represent acknowledgements for received frames, but are not themselves sequenced. The frames are used for sending four *supervisory commands* as described in §6.7; the absence of the N(S) field allows a 2-bit SS field for this purpose.

FLAG	ADDRESS	10-CONTROL	FCS	FLAG

CONTROL	SS	P/F	N(R)
bits	2	1	3

Figure 6.7 - HDLC S-frame format

6.5.3   Un-numbered frames

FLAG	ADDRESS	11-CONTROL	[REASON]	FCS	FLAG

CONTROL	UU	P/F	UUU
bits	2	1	3

Figure 6.8 - HDLC U-frame format

The third class of frame is used for miscellaneous control functions. The format of a *U-frame* is shown in figure 6.8. As can be seen, only the

P/F bit remains from the I-frame control field. U-frames contain no sequence numbers. This leaves space for a 5-bit *U-command field,* giving up to 32 **un-numbered commands/responses**, some of which are discussed in §6.8. Not all possible un-numbered commands and responses are defined, and the repertoire varies between different classes of procedure. This is the area where IBM and others used some of the (at the time) spare ones for their own use. Only standard U-frame commands and responses will be discussed in this book.

The 'reason' is present where the information field would appear in some responses, and in this case provides additional information (e.g. why a command was rejected for a 'frame reject' frame).

IEEE-initiated enhancements to HDLC for local area network use include the provision of datagram services using 'un-numbered information' frames, which contain an information field, but which bypass normal acknowledgement and flow control procedures. However, these are not part of normal HDLC as specified for use in wide area networks. Further details on this aspect may be found in chapter thirteen.

6.6   Information frames

I-frames are the most important type of frame, and many salient features of HDLC can be explained in the context of the control octet of I-frames.

6.6.1   I-frame control field

The basic functions of sequencing, acknowledgement and flow control are largely governed by the contents of the control octet of an I-frame. Figure 6.6 above shows the detailed format of the control octet. The fields are used as follows.

- *Poll/final bit P/F*. This bit is used for various 'handshaking' functions between the stations on the link. Sending a frame with the poll bit set results in a reply frame being received with the final bit set. Whether the bit is to be interpreted as the poll or final bit depends on whether the frame is a command or a response, which is usually determined from the address octet; see §6.2.2. The usage of this bit is discussed in more detail in §6.9.

- *Send sequence count N(S)*. This is the sequence number of the frame, which is modulo 8 for the standard (short) frame format. This means that successive I-frames will be numbered 0 1 2 3 4 5 6

7 0 etc. (Modulo 128 is used in the extended format, which is used for example in the LAN variant of the protocol.)

- **Receive sequence count N(R)**. This is the sequence number of the last received I-frame acknowledged plus one (modulo 8). In other words, it is the sequence number of the *next in-sequence I-frame expected*. It is important to remember this; it is not the sequence number of the last I-frame received.

6.6.2   Sequencing, acknowledgement and windowing

Each node maintains two *state variables* for the link.

- Each station transmitting I-frames maintains a **send state variable V(S)**, which is the N(S) of the next in-sequence I-frame to be transmitted. Each successive new (i.e. not retransmitted) I-frame is given a value N(S)=V(S), and V(S) is then incremented. Thus I-frames are numbered in sequence (subject to modulo 8 arithmetic). V(S) is initialised to 0, so that the first I-frame after link setup is given N(S)=0.

- Each station also maintains a **receive state variable V(R)**, which is one more than the last N(R) acknowledgement issued, normally the N(S) of the next expected in-sequence I-frame. Similarly, when an I-frame is received (in sequence), the V(R) of the receiver is set to its N(S) plus 1 (modulo 8). When the receiver transmits a frame containing an N(R) field (an I-frame or S-frame), it places the current value of V(R) in the N(R) field. (This does not apply to SREJ S-frames; see §6.7.4.)

Note however that V(R) is not necessarily one greater than the highest N(S) received so far. There are two reasons why this may not be the case:

- The main possibility is that one or more I-frames has been corrupted due to transmission errors, and has thus been ignored by the receiving chip. I-frames received later which were not corrupted will therefore appear to be out-of-sequence. V(R) will never be increased beyond one plus the last in sequence I-frame received; later out-of-sequence I-frames will be discarded, and will have to be retransmitted. (This does not apply if SREJ is being used; see §6.7.4.)

- A second possibility is that the receiver wishes to delay acknowledgement of some I-frames for the moment. In other words it chooses to return an N(R) value which is less than the current value of V(R). The reason for this decision may be shortage of buffer space or temporary congestion at the receiver, which does not wish to acknowledge received I-frames which it may subsequently be forced to discard. HDLC procedures do not generally require I-frames to be acknowledged as soon as possible, although it is not sensible for a station to delay acknowledgements unnecessarily, as this will degrade link performance. Should the sender not receive an acknowledgement within a 'reasonable time', it may use checkpointing to force the receiver to acknowledge, as explained in §6.9.3.

When the service is first set up, the 'network administration' determines the size of the acknowledgement window, which is then built into the hardware and software. (It can also be negotiated; see §6.8.3.) The *window limit* (referred to as k in the standard documents) is the maximum number of consecutive I-frames which can be outstanding at any time (i.e. not yet acknowledged). Clearly this cannot exceed 7 with a modulo 8 numbering scheme, or ambiguity would arise over sequence numbers. A value of k=2 is often used in WANs.

The sender may continue to send I-frames with incremental N(S) values provided

$$V(S) < N(R) + k \qquad \text{(taking modulo 8 numbering into account)}$$

where N(R) is the last received sequence count (acknowledgement) and k is the window width. The receiver may elect to acknowledge frames in groups, i.e. not to increment N(R) until a further k frames have been received, or it may acknowledge them individually. This is a matter for the implementor. The N(R) value may thus remain the same in a number of received frames, either because no further frames require acknowledgement, or because the station for whatever reason does not wish to acknowledge any more received frames at present. However, when k frames become outstanding, it will be necessary for the receiver to acknowledge at least one outstanding frame, otherwise the sender will be unable to transmit any more I-frames, and may need to checkpoint; see §6.9.3.

6.7   Supervisory frames

S-frames are used to send supervisory commands, and the N(R) field may be used to acknowledge received I-frames in cases where there is no I-frame awaiting transmission at present. S-frames do not however contain N(S) or information fields, and therefore cannot be used to transmit information.

STATION A V(S) BEFORE TX	FRAMES SENT		STATION B V(R) AFTER RX
3	<----I----<	N(R)=3	3
3	N(S)=3	>----I---->	4
4	N(S)=4	>----I---->	5
5	N(S)=5	>----I---->	6
6	N(S)=6	>----I---->	7
window limit reached			
7	<----I----<	N(R)=7	7
7	N(S)=7	>----I---->	7

NOTEs:
1 The V(S) before TX is that before sending the next I-frame.
2 The V(R) after RX is that after receiving the last I-frame.
3 A window width k=4 is assumed.

Figure 6.9 - use of the acknowledgement window in HDLC

Figure 6.9 shows how the window flow control mechanism works in practice for a window width of 4. All frames in the figure are assumed to be I-frames, although the frames travelling from B to A could be S-frames. Note also that there is a corresponding dialogue in the reverse direction (which are not shown). In this example, the receiver has for some reason elected not to acknowledge any I-frames until the window limit has been reached. It would be more usual to acknowledge I-frames as soon as practicable (i.e. within some maximum time after their receipt); the figure aims to show the basic mechanism without becoming too complex.

The 2-bit S field in the control octet allows the definition of four *supervisory commands*. These are used for start-stop flow control and for error recovery. The commands are described in turn. In each case, SREJ excepted, the N(R) field serves as an acknowledgement of received I-frames, in exactly the same way as it does in an I-frame.

6.7.1   Receive ready (RR)

This is used for two purposes. Firstly, the N(R) contained in the control octet may be used as an acknowledgement of I-frames, in the case where the receiving node does not currently have any I-frames to send, but wishes to (or is required to) acknowledge the receipt of I-frames.

As its name implies, the command also indicates a willingness on the part of the sender of the command to receive, or continue to receive, I-frames. It is therefore also used to cancel the effects of a RNR, discussed next.

6.7.2   Receive not ready (RNR)

This is used by a station to instruct the other one not to send any more I-frames until further notice. This could be as a result of congestion at the receiver. It is assumed that this inability to receive I-frames is of a temporary nature, but will last sufficiently long that merely deferring acknowledgements to I-frames will not suffice. RNR is normally cancelled by RR (but the busy condition may also be cancelled in several other ways; see §6.8 and §6.9.3).

When taken together, RR and RNR provide a stop-go flow control mechanism which functions in addition to, and independently of, the window flow control described above. Note that the receipt of an RNR does not prevent the receiver from acknowledging or receiving I-frames; acknowledgements can still be sent in RR or RNR frames as appropriate. It is important always to remember that balanced HDLC is two-way; there is a matching, and independent, set of frames and commands in the reverse direction.

RNR is only intended to handle short-term congestion. In the case of an irrecoverable busy condition, it would be more sensible to issue a DISC which disconnects the link; see §6.8.

6.7.3   Reject (REJ)

This command is used for error recovery. It informs the sender (of I-frames) that one or more I-frames it previously transmitted have not been correctly received, normally because of transmission errors. In other words an out-of-sequence I-frame has been received by the other station, and the station receiving the REJ is now required to retransmit all I-frames with sequence numbers starting with N(S) equal to the N(R) contained in the received REJ. Up to k I-frames may have to be retransmitted as a result. In a typical implementation, REJ will be sent as soon as possible after a station has detected a gap in the N(S) sequence numbers of received I-frames. A *REJ condition* comes into effect at the receiver when it issues a REJ; this is cancelled by the receipt of an I-frame with the same value of N(S) as that requested by the N(R) of the REJ. Note that this also means that a station sending I-frames must retain copies of them until their correct receipt (in sequence) at the other station been acknowledged. In addition, the following points should also be noted:

- Once a REJ has been issued, further out-of-sequence I-frames may be received before the one whose retransmission was requested with the REJ. This will not result in the issue of further REJ commands specifying the same N(R). This is not to say that REJ cannot be repeated after timeout, but this is a separate error recovery issue which is discussed in §6.10.

- If an I-frame is received with an unexpected (out-of-sequence) N(S), the information field will normally be discarded, and the station may send a REJ as a result. However regardless of whether the information content is to be accepted or not, fields in the control octet will be acted on in the usual way.

- It is not mandatory to provide support for REJ in a minimal HDLC implementation (see §6.11). An alternative approach is for the receiver to remain silent, and wait for the sender to notice that missing I-frames have not been acknowledged, and initiate recovery itself; see §6.9.3. There are however clear advantages in using REJ where possible, as will be seen in due course.

- It will become clear after reading §6.7.4 that REJ cannot be used at the same time as SREJ in the same direction of transmission. The information content of an out-of-sequence I-frame may be accepted if SREJ is to be returned for the (earlier) missing I-frame(s), as discussed in §6.7.4. However REJ can be used if no SREJ is currently outstanding, and vice versa.

6.7.4   Selective Reject (SREJ)

Where it is provided, this can be used as an alternative to REJ, to request the retransmission of a single I-frame with sequence number N(S) equal to the N(R) of the SREJ frame. When the command is issued, a *SREJ condition* is set in the node issuing the command; the condition remains in force until it is cleared by the receipt of the missing I-frame, or until timeout occurs with no I-frame with matching N(S) having been received. The normal sequence of I-frames is not affected, and these can still be accepted.

It was intended that SREJ would be used when a single frame had been lost, and was provided so that the overhead of possibly having to retransmit up to k frames could be avoided, an overhead which could be excessive with a high value of k, or if the error rate on the link was very high. However this implies that several I-frames have been transmitted before the SREJ is issued, which is unlikely unless there is a long propagation delay on the link or a high transmission error rate.

The use of SREJ markedly increases the complexity of the HDLC station. A major factor is the requirement to retain out-of-sequence I-frame information fields in the hope that an earlier one can be recovered using SREJ. In addition several SREJ conditions may be active at the same time, for different N(R) values, leading to implementation complexities. Other difficulties include decisions such as how many consecutive SREJ requests should be raised if several consecutive I-frames are lost. In general these complexities are not considered worth the marginal increase in throughput which might result. Provided that REJ is issued as soon as a gap in the sequence numbers is detected, it is unlikely that many I-frames will have to be retransmitted on a terrestrial link with minimal propagation delay. In addition, any I-frame in the process of transmission when a REJ is received which makes its continued transmission pointless can be aborted (see §6.3.2). Therefore, strictly speaking, SREJ is not really necessary in most conditions, and has hardly ever been implemented. In particular, SREJ is not available in the X.25 adaptation of HDLC {7776}, even on satellite links with long propagation delays.

A recent addendum to the HDLC standard {4335 DAD4} proposes procedures for *Multi-Selective Reject*. The idea here is that if, say, three consecutive I-frames had been lost, it would be possible to issue a single 'multiple SREJ' specifying the first and last I-frames to be retransmitted, rather than having to issue three separate SREJ frames, one for each frame. This requires the definition of (yet) another U-frame. Given that there are few applications where SREJ is considered worthwhile, it seems unlikely that this extension will be reflected in very many implementations.

6.8   Un-numbered frames

The final frame type, the *U-frame*, does not include any sequence fields, although the poll/final bit is still present. The two parts of the U field count as a single 5-bit field, allowing up to 32 *un-numbered commands/responses* to be specified. However some are not (yet) defined by ISO, and the use of many is optional.

Whenever a U-command is issued by a station, a matching U-response is expected in return. Some U-responses have an information field of fixed length. Where it is present, it is used to convey additional information (e.g. for the 'frame reject' response described below, it gives the reason for the rejection). This is not of great interest, and details of these information field formats will not be provided.

6.8.1   U-commands

The repertoire of U-commands (and responses) available depends on the HDLC variant being used. In the WAN variant {7776} the following are defined among others; the LAN variant {8802-2} includes several more. See also §6.11.

Set xxx mode (Sxxx)

where xxx represents the acronym for the desired operational mode, giving **SARM, SABM, SNRM**. These are used on an idle link to select the desired mode of operation, as discussed in §6.1. A similar set of commands is available for selecting Extended formats: **SARME, SABME, SNRME**.

It should be noted that the availability of extended formats is by mutual agreement, and it will not necessarily be possible to select both normal and extended format on the same link. Furthermore, not all modes of operation will necessarily be available in a given implementation; for example, it would be an unusual link which could support either asynchronous or normal operational modes.

The response normally expected to a 'mode select' command is UA; see below. These commands cannot be issued if the emergency disconnect signal is present on the line, but they can be issued if line usage was terminated gracefully as follows:

Disconnect (DISC)

This is used to terminate a previously selected mode (e.g. ABM), on completion of use of the link for information transfer, or when best attempts at error recovery (§6.10) have failed. The sender is indicating that it is suspending operations. The link is now said to be in the idle state, where I-frames and S-frames may not be transmitted. A response (UA) is expected as confirmation. Note that if the link is disconnected in this way, any I-frames which have not been acknowledged will not be, and it is for protocol layers above HDLC to perform any necessary recovery of lost information. (The link disconnect bit sequence described earlier has a more drastic effect, in that no response at all is possible while the condition persists on the link.)

6.8.2   U- responses

Each U-command must be acknowledged by an appropriate response, which may be one of the following:

Un-numbered acknowledge (UA)

This is returned in response to un-numbered commands such as SABM and DISC, if the command was received and accepted.

Frame reject (FRMR)

This is returned if the format of a received frame, or the value of some field, is incorrect. For example an I-frame will be rejected if the information field is absent or its size exceeds some agreed maximum value, and may be rejected if it is not an integral number of octets long (required in X.25, and usually by implementors as well). Any frame will be rejected if it is too short (less than four octets long, including the FCS). An S-frame will be rejected if it contains an information field, and a U-frame may be rejected if the U-command is unknown or not implemented. (Of course if the FCS is wrong, no FRMR response will result, as in this case the frame will have been discarded by the receiving hardware, and the receiving station will never 'see' it.)

Early versions of HDLC included an additional 'command reject' (CMDR) U-response. This was merged with FRMR, as their usage was very similar.

Disconnected mode (DM)

This has the effect of disconnecting the link. Whereas DISC is used for normal disconnection, DM is used as a form of error recovery procedure, e.g. after a temporary failure of a link station, to indicate to the other station that it is now working, but that a mode select command (e.g. SABM) is expected. In this usage, the DM response is not necessarily a reply to an un-numbered command.

Another use of DM is to resolve 'collision' of un-numbered commands. As an example, on links where both ARM and ABM are permitted, it would be possible for one station to issue SABM, and at the same time the other station to issue SARM. Since only one mode of operation is possible at a time, both ends will respond DM, and mode selection will have to be attempted again.

DM is also the required response if, for example, an I-frame is received when the link is disconnected. (This would be a protocol violation by the station sending it.)

6.8.3   Other U-commands and responses

A number of other U-commands and responses have not been mentioned so far. These include the following, although this is by no means a complete list; further details may be found in the relevant standard document {3225}:

• *SIM* and *RIM* for setting and requesting initialisation mode. This is a non-operational mode which is entered in cases where station software appears to be faulty and needs regeneration, or if station parameters need changing.

• *RSET* for resetting a link. This is a relatively recent addition, introduced to support OSI reset procedures which will be discussed in part three. In effect resetting the link is equivalent to a disconnection followed by an immediate reselection of the same operational mode. In other words it re-initialises the link with possible loss of information. Having said that, it is not used in any of the standard HDLC versions. In particular neither LAPB nor LLC make use of it.

• *UI* is *un-numbered information*. The original idea was that this could be used to transport a *datagram*, so that this is a special case of a U-frame with an I-field. As there is no N(S) field in a U-frame, acknowledgement in the normal way (via N(R)) would not be possible. This is an important feature of the LAN HDLC variant discussed in chapter thirteen. At the time of writing, a draft addendum {8802.2 DAD2} is reaching stability which further modifies UA so that an acknowledgement can be provided if possible. This in effect provides a *confirmed datagram* service, which will be discussed in more detail in chapter thirteen.

• *TEST* is a frame which results in a matching response from the other station. It can be used to determine whether the other station is available and, to quote the standard document, 'performs a basic test of the data link control'. It can possibly also be used to measure the round-trip delay on the link, although the standard document makes no mention of this.

• *XID*, or *exchange identification*, is used to exchange station identification and details, and thus allows a limited amount of negotiation between the stations.

6.9   Use of the poll/final bit

This bit has three uses, which depend on whether balanced or response mode is in use. The bit is referred to as the Poll or *P bit* when sent in a command, and is referred to as the Final or *F bit* in a response. This bit is always used in a handshake. If for some reason one station sends a frame with the P bit set, the other station must reply as soon as possible with a frame in which the F bit is set. There are three principal cases where this type of handshake is used, and these are discussed in the following sections. Although the basic principles are not difficult to grasp, the precise rules are complex in some cases, and as a result some detail has had to be omitted from the discussions.

It is worth reiterating at this point that a single P/F bit serves both purposes, and can occur in any type of frame. Whether it is to be interpreted as the P bit or the F bit depends on the address of the frame (or the command/response bit where this is used in lieu of an address). In a command frame it is the P bit; in a response frame it is the F bit.

6.9.1   Use of P/F in normal response mode

In normal response (poll-select) mode, the primary (central) station will send the P bit to solicit I-frames from a secondary station (e.g. VDU). The VDU will use the F bit to indicate the end of its response. This allows it to send more than one frame in response to a command, with the F bit set in the last frame. In other words, the P bit when set in a command must be matched by an equivalent F bit set in a later response. For example the VDU may need several I-frames to transmit the entire screen contents. It uses the F bit to signal that it has finished. (In this sense, it is analogous to the EOT character in comparable BSC procedures.)

6.9.2   Use of P/F in U-command handshaking

In asynchronous mode, the bit is used for U-command handshaking. If a U-command is sent with the P bit set, the matching response must have the F bit set in return. For example, a UA response must have the F bit set if the P bit was set in the SABM. This can be used to resolve ambiguities when there are two outstanding U-commands which both result in the same U-response, by setting the P bit in one of them but not the other. When a mode is not selected (i.e. the link is in the disconnected state), any command in which the P-bit is set (other than a mode select) results in a DM response with the F-bit set.

6.9.3   Use of the P/F bit in checkpointing

The third use of the P/F bit is in many ways the most important. It is use of the P bit to force acknowledgement of outstanding I-frames by the receiver, a technique known as *checkpointing*.

If an I-frame or S-frame is transmitted with the P bit set, it must of course be matched by a received I-frame or S-frame with the F bit set. The important point is that the P bit is received in an I-frame or S-frame, this puts the receiver on the spot. . It must return a matching I-frame or S-frame with the F bit set. The important point is that the N(R) placed in this frame *must acknowledge all correctly received in-sequence I-frames*. If for some reason the station does not wish to do this, it must discard any I-frames which it does not now acknowledge. (The latter course of action may be appropriate for any I-frames received after RNR has been sent.)

When a reply to a checkpointing request is received (i.e. an I-frame or S-frame with the F bit set), the N(R) field is examined. If it does not acknowledge all I-frames which were outstanding at the time the P bit was issued, the station initiates a *rollback*. This means that this station's V(S) is set equal to the N(R) just received, and all unacknowledged I-frames must be retransmitted. In fact the rules for checkpointing are rather complex, particularly if REJ is being used as well. The full details can be found in the standard document; the aim is to avoid unnecessary rollbacks.

I-frames transmitted after the P bit was sent clearly cannot be acknowledged by the F bit frame, as they could not possibly have been received at the time the F bit frame was generated. Therefore these frames are not taken into consideration. A further point to note is that the F bit frame may both acknowledge some (earlier) outstanding I-frames, and cause rollback to retransmit other (later) I-frames.

Checkpointing is essential for error recovery, as discussed in §6.10. At this point it is worth mentioning a few eccentricities associated with checkpointing.

- If the other station has one or more SREJ conditions as yet unsatisfied, it will repeat the oldest unsatisfied SREJ N(R) with the F bit set. In this case I-frames may be acknowledged by the N(R), but rollback does not apply for any later I-frames.

- If a station has received RNR, it must regularly checkpoint to ensure that the RNR condition still applies. (If so, the reply will be RNR with the F bit set.) This is because a previous RNR can be cancelled by a single RR frame, which could of course be lost due to a transmission error. In the absence of checkpointing, a lockup would result in this case.

• Finally, any received I-frame or S-frame with the F bit set implies RR, with the obvious exception of SREJ and RNR frame itself. Thus a station may cancel an earlier RNR it sent by transmitting an I-frame with the F bit set.

6.10 Error recovery in HDLC

Error recovery is required in any protocol, and HDLC is no exception. Transmission errors will occur, leading to sequence gaps in received I-frame streams, failure to receive the F bit in reply to the P bit, and many other error situations. The difference between HDLC and BSC is that HDLC has rigorously defined error recovery procedures (which in some cases required very careful wording in the standard documents to avoid ambiguity), whereas BSC has almost none.

Error recovery, while complex in detail, basically involves three steps:

• Transmit something (e.g. REJ or the P bit), and await the desired response (e.g. the matching I-frame or the F bit).

• If the required response is not received within some time limit, repeat the attempt. (In the case of no acknowledgement being received for one or more I-frames, initiate checkpointing by sending the P bit.)

• If some predetermined number of attempts fail, shut down the link (or reset it to some known initial condition).

6.10.1 Timers and counters

One crucial aspect of recovery is how long to wait for the required response. Premature timeout cannot be accepted, as a delayed response would then be unexpected and could cause chaos. But an unduly long timeout period wastes time, leading to inefficiency.

HDLC defines two timers, T1 and T2.

• *Timer T1* is the maximum time a station is prepared to wait for a response. On timeout, the action will be retried up to n (system dependent) times; if the required response has still not been received, the link will be reinitialised (with possible loss of information).

• *Timer T2* is the amount of time a station receiving a command (or the P bit) is allowed in which to generate a response (or the F bit). This value must be chosen with care. It is quite possible for a station to receive a P bit just after it has started transmitting a long I-frame. Unless the frame being transmitted is aborted, the F bit will have to wait. Another problem is that while a long frame is being transmitted, several frames may be received which require responses. Possibly the worst case is where SREJ is being used (see the next section). If a station detects that 4 consecutive I-frames have been lost, it may elect to issue 4 SREJ commands, one for each frame. This requires 4 I-frames to be sent, one for each SREJ. All of these SREJ requests could reach the peer station while it was transmitting a single I-frame; it could take some time to respond with all four retransmitted I-frames.

Clearly T2 has to be chosen with great care, and it is not possible for the standard document to suggest values, which are left for implementors to determine. But once T2 has been decided, T1 must be at least T2 plus the *round trip delay*, i.e. T2 plus twice the link *transmission delay*, which may have five components:

• The time it takes a station to determine the required action and generate the frame contents. Given modern technology, this is likely to be insignificant.

• The time the station has to wait (if any) for transmission of the current frame to complete.

• The time it takes to transmit the frame, which is a function of the frame length and line speed.

• The propagation delay, i.e. the delay from starting to send a frame from one station to starting to receive it at the other station on the link. This has components relating to how long it takes an electron (or photon) to travel the distance concerned on a terrestrial (or satellite) link, which is distance dependent. On terrestrial links this is typically of the order of a millisecond, i.e. negligible. On satellite links it is two orders of magnitude longer.

• Any delays introduced by modulation or demodulation equipment. Normally these are also negligible, but they can be significant when using cellular radio (see RLP, §6.13), where complex interleaving procedures also have to be taken into account.

What all of this means is that for maximum efficiency, T1 and T2 have to be determined based on maximum frame length, line speed, modulation technique and a number of other factors. In §6.13, we discuss this matter again in relation to the Radio Link Protocol.

6.10.2   Recovery of lost and missing I-frames

Checkpoint recovery

We have already discussed the mechanisms for checkpointing. It is typically used when, having transmitted an I-frame, no acknowledgement has been received by the time timer T1 has expired (i.e. received $N(R)$ values have not included this I-frame). Of course it may be that this applies to more than one I-frame at any given time, and it may be necessary to send the P bit again as soon as the F bit is received.

A count is also kept of the number of times a particular I-frame has been transmitted. It may be retransmitted after rollback, or because REJ or SREJ was received. If n (system dependent) transmissions of a particular I-frame have still not resulted in an acknowledgement within T1, it is normal to shut down or reinitialise the link.

REJ recovery

Checkpointing is error recovery initiated by the sender. REJ, on the other hand, is initiated by the receiver. Unless SREJ is being used, it is invalid to accept the information field of an out-of-sequence I-frame, so the receiver will discard any such I-frames (having first processed the control octet), and will return REJ within T2 of detecting the sequencing error, specifying as $N(R)$ its current $V(R)$, which is the next in-sequence frame expected. The sender will then roll back. Further out-of-sequence I-frames will simply be discarded while the REJ remains unsatisfied, or until it times out. If the REJ is not satisfied within T1 (i.e. an I-frame with the requested $N(S)$ is not received), it may normally be repeated up to n times in the usual way, before a link disconnect is required.

It is more timely for the receiver to initiate error recovery, particularly if the transit time on the link is significant, and rollback can usually be achieved more quickly than if checkpointing alone is used. However it is worth noting that checkpointing is still required with REJ error recovery, as REJ can only be issued once the receiving station has detected a $N(S)$ gap, which will not be possible if the last I-frame in a sequence is lost. In the absence of checkpointing, a lockup would occur in this case. There are further rules which aim to prevent a station from rolling back twice in cases where a REJ is closely followed by the final bit, or vice versa, and these specify the same $N(R)$.

SREJ recovery

As previously discussed, it is unlikely that SREJ will be used in WANs, as it is very complex and messy to implement. There are also some design issues which have to be addressed, of which the following list is only a sample:

> • For how many consecutive missing I-frames should SREJ commands be issued? For example if $N(S)$ values of 1 and 7 are received, it would be feasible to issue five SREJ commands in succession (one each for 2, 3, 4, 5 and 6). However this appears to be messy, and we may wish to set some lower limit on the maximum gap size.

> • This raises the related question of what to do if the sequence gap (5 in this case) is higher than this maximum. Setting an upper limit implies that some out-of-sequence I-frames will be accepted (subject to SREJ), whereas others will not. There is then the related problem of whether to use REJ when all SREJ conditions have been satisfied but it is known that some later I-frames have already been discarded.

If all of this sounds complex and messy, it is indeed. This author has simulated RLP (§6.13). Even though RLP is considerably simpler than HDLC, 95% of the simulation effort was devoted to implementing and debugging the SREJ procedures. It is not surprising that SREJ has few adherents!

Adherents of the ARQ terminology may wish at this point to learn that sliding window acknowledgement is continuous, REJ is go-back-n, and SREJ is selective ARQ.

6.11   HDLC classes of procedure

The HDLC standard {7809} defines three fundamental classes of procedure, and was produced in order to rationalise the (at the time) somewhat chaotic set of options available in various versions of the standard. The classes defined are *Unbalanced Normal, Unbalanced Asynchronous* and *Balanced Asynchronous*; these include respectively the commonest classes NRM, ARM and ABM, together with various extended format classes such as ABME.

The basic repertoire of frame types is the same for each class, viz. I-frame, RR, RNR, mode select (as appropriate) and DISC commands, and I-frame, RR, RNR, UA, DM and FRMR responses. Note that both REJ and SREJ are excluded from these basic repertoires.

The wide range of possible deviations from these basic sets are catered for by defining 14 optional functions. These include (among others) the ability to send un-numbered I-frames (UI), XID, RSET, REJ and SREJ commands and responses. A further option is the ability to define a 4-octet FCS, for use in cases where the standard error checking field is deemed inadequate. Further details of these optional functions may be found in the standard document.

6.12   HDLC compared with BSC

Before introducing X.25 in the next chapter, it is instructive to compare HDLC with the BSC protocol discussed in part one. Since HDLC was designed as a replacement for BSC, and we did a pretty comprehensive 'character assassination' of the BSC protocol, we can presume that HDLC is the better protocol! But it is worth examining to what extent this is so. We will compare the two protocols under various headings.

Message switching or packet switching?

BSC switches blocks between adjacent nodes, but these are still logically part of a message. BSC takes account of this by its use of SOH, STX, ETX and ETB. The problems if a link fails midway through sending a message are clear, and have already been discussed.

HDLC knows nothing about messages, only frames. I-frames are the nearest equivalent to BSC blocks. HDLC does not care about the contents of the information field of I-frames, and it is left to higher level protocols to worry about this. HDLC makes no attempt to associate I-frames. This seems to be the better approach, and it is also more in keeping with current ideas on protocol structuring.

Independence of transmission units

One major weakness of BSC lies in the fact that the transmission blocks are not stand-alone, since they are formed by 'chopping up' a longer message into 'fragments' which can be transmitted more efficiently on error-prone lines. This leads to problems in case of errors, since only the first block of a message contains any identification or sequencing. We have already discussed these problems in some detail.

HDLC sequences each frame. This makes it easy to acknowledge frames in a simple, unambiguous way. Moreover, up to 7 frames can be acknowledged at once, so that the sender does not necessarily have to wait for an acknowledgement after each frame has been sent, although if the window width was 1, this would still be the case.

Code transparency

BSC has no transparency, as discussed earlier. While binary data can be sent, it is messy and involves padding of characters (or the use of DLE) to avoid control characters being sent in the data.

On the other hand HDLC offers complete data transparency by means of bit stuffing and bit significant fields.

Acknowledgement schemes

BSC must use a positive and negative scheme because of the non-addressability of blocks. This is inefficient and requires ENQ to be used if the ACK is not returned, making it messy as well.

HDLC uses a positive only scheme. An acknowledgement must be returned when k (window width) I-frames have not been acknowledged, so that several frames can possibly be sent before the sender must have an acknowledgement. However it is either up to the receiver to send REJ (or possibly SREJ) if it detects a missing frame, and/or the sender to use checkpointing, to recover from lost frames; there is no automatic retransmission of I-frames on timeout. The flexibility of the acknowledgement scheme, plus the rich repertoire of error recovery techniques available, means that HDLC is much the better protocol in this respect.

Flow control

BSC flow control, such as it is, is achieved by deferring the ACK, or by deferring the block. This is bad for several reasons. Firstly, since the protocol is half duplex, it effectively ties up both ends, whereas only one end might need to slow down. A possible effect of this type of flow control is that both ends could end up being congested. Also, there is a limit to the delay which can be achieved by this means, after which recovery procedures will come into play. A further problem is that stop-go flow control cannot be provided within the framework of the BSC protocol, and if required, has to be implemented by special 'service messages' which are logically at a different protocol level. This also assumes that the service message can be sent, which will not be possible if WACK is being received. In short, BSC is not very good at flow control.

HDLC provides facilities for flow control by delaying acknowledgements (subject to checkpointing). This does not affect traffic in the reverse direction, since HDLC is full duplex. RR and RNR in HDLC allow a stop-go type of flow control independent of the window flow control.

Error protection

BSC error protection of blocks is inadequate, and supervisory sequences such as ACK are only protected by the parity bit.

HDLC uses a 16 (or 32) bit error checking polynomial, providing protection which is far superior to what BSC offers. This covers acknowledgement and other sequences as well, which again is more satisfactory.

Error recovery

BSC's only error recovery is for the master station to give up and transmit EOT to the slave if all goes wrong. Whether the slave receives the EOT is of no concern, nor is what happened to the message transmitted so far. There is a risk that the two stations will then disagree on the link's current state; this can cause chaos given the several meanings of the ENQ character.

In HDLC, all error recovery is by means of handshaking, and there are defined procedures which cover almost any eventuality. Although we have only scratched the surface of a complex topic, it should be clear that HDLC is far more robust than BSC.

Summary

HDLC is clearly a far better protocol than BSC. It appears to be a 'good' link protocol, but is has no pretensions to any higher form of control. Further protocols are clearly needed, both within the network and between hosts. In particular, HDLC offers no mechanisms which allow a route to be determined through the network as a whole, and indeed knows nothing about the ultimate destination of information in I-frames (nor should it). The development of such protocols is the subject of the rest of this book.

6.13   An HDLC derivative: the Radio Link Protocol

HDLC was designed for use on terrestrial links in WANs. Although it is also used on satellite links and in LANs, neither application required any fundamental rethink of the protocol itself. However HDLC was recently considered for use on cellular radio networks, such as those operated in the UK by Cellnet and Vodaphone. Two problems in particular presented themselves:

• The error rate depends on such factors as whether there are buildings between the mobile station (e.g. car) and base station, so that the error rate not only fluctuates wildly, but there can be periods of severe fading, with several frames in succession corrupted as a result. Therefore it is necessary to define a small maximum frame length, so that there is some realistic hope of transmitting frames without corruption.

• The second problem is that there is a long transit time, approaching 200 msec in each direction of transmission. This is mainly caused by delays introduced by the modulation and demodulation hardware, and interleaving and other complexities introduced by the cellular technique.

The upshot was that it was decided to retain the basic philosophy of HDLC, but it proved necessary to make a number of major changes, the most significant of which are as follows:

• A fixed length (30 octets) is defined for all frames. Frames are transmitted contiguously, with no intervening flags or gaps. In the absence of any information to send, RR (or RNR) is repeated indefinitely (assuming that the link is set up for information transfer, of course).

• A number of formatting changes have also been made. The address octet is replaced by a single command/response bit, and I-frames also contain a supervisory command (so that they are known as IS-frames). Figure 6.10 shows the format of an RLP IS-frame; a maximum of 24 octets are available for user information, as the first octet indicates the number of octets of information actually present, and other octets may be used to convey signalling information, the details of which are not pertinent here. A 3-octet FCS is used for additional error protection. This is a compromise between the 2-octet and 4-octet lengths available in HDLC.

• A link speed of 12000 bps is available for each RLP link. This means that it takes 20 msec to transmit a frame. Since the transit time is approaching 200 msec, this means that around 10 frames will be in transit at any time, and about 20 frames will have been transmitted before a response to the first can possibly be received.

• Not surprisingly further changes are required. Modulo 8 arithmetic becomes unacceptable, as the window limit would be reached long before an acknowledgement could possibly be received. Modulo 32 arithmetic was used instead. (Space inside the frame was at a premium, so a higher modulus was not considered.)

• Given the number of frames in transit, SREJ is the only error recovery policy which has any chance of success, since the delays introduced by using REJ would be unacceptable, leading to large numbers of retransmitted frames every time a sequence gap was detected. Even using SREJ, loss of a single I-frame means that the window limit will be reached before the missing I-frame can be recovered and acknowledged.

FIELD	E	C/R	T	SS	N(S)	P/F	N(R)	INFORMATION	FCS
LENGTH (BITS)	1	1	1	2	5	1	5	25*8	3*8

NOTEs:
1   E   extension bit (reserved for future expansion).
2   T   frame type bit (IS, S or U).
3   The first octet of the I-field contains a byte count. As the total length is fixed, the I-field may be partly unused.

Figure 6.10 -format of RLP IS-frame

So we have a variant of HDLC which allows information and supervisory commands to be transmitted in the same frame, a very short and fixed frame length, and a reliance on SREJ error recovery. This protocol is still in the process of development[1], and the author's simulation study[2] has revealed some unusual performance characteristics which, at the time of writing, suggest that some further changes to the protocol specification would be advantageous. Indeed there is concern among some experts regarding the use of SREJ, in view of its extreme complexity. The prevailing school of thought at present feels that SREJ should not be retried on timeout, which suggests that the receiver should then 'roll back' and either issue a REJ or await a checkpointing request. Unfortunately this would severely limit the effectiveness of the protocol, as only very low throughputs would then be achievable in the event of significant error rates. At the time of writing, RLP is still the subject of active debate.

Finally, let us briefly examine the multi-SREJ extension outlined in §6.7.4 in the context of RLP. This allows the retransmission of several I-frames to be requested with a single 'SREJ'. Since SREJ is crucial to the operation of RLP, it might seem that it would be a useful addition. Unfortunately in the context of RLP, multi-SREJ is not going to provide any advantage. Since every frame is of the same length, it will take the same length of time to respond to a single multi-SREJ as it would to several separate ones. Furthermore, since the SREJ commands may be 'piggybacked' on I-frames, there is no throughput penalty for the sender in sending several SREJ frames.

6.14   References

1   CEPT/CCH/GSM recommendation 04.22, 'Radio Link Protocol for Data and Telematic Services on the MS/BSS Interface' (November 1988).

2   B. W. Marsden and H. Madadi, 'A Performance Assessment of the GSM Radio Link Protocol (RLP)', University of Manchester, Department of Computer Science, internal report. (Plans were in hand to publish this at the time of going to press.)

7   CCITT recommendation X.25

7.1   Introduction

As discussed in chapter five, CCITT provides recommendations for its constituent bodies. These are published as a series of coloured books. The full set of recommendations is revised and reissued every four years by CCITT, and copies of drafts and implementation guides for X.25 are readily available[1]. In this chapter and the next, we will examine in some detail the principal recommendations pertaining to packet switching networks. By far the most significant recommendation is X.25, which defines the means by which user 'packet terminals' (hosts) connect (i.e. interface) to packet switched data networks. We will cover recommendation X.25 in this chapter, devoting more attention to it than to the other recommendations. In chapter eight, we will examine three other recommendations, relating to the connection of character ('dumb') terminals to X.25 networks, as well as examining general issues concerning terminal interfacing. The main relevant CCITT recommendations are as follows; a more complete list may be found in appendix C:

- X.3, functional specification of the X.25 packet assembly-disassembly unit (PAD).

- X.21, physical level X.25 procedures, defining synchronous access to PDNs; this will not be discussed in detail in this book. X.21 bis defines 'interim' procedures based on V.24 (RS-232C) which are acceptable 'for the time being'.

- X.25, packet mode interface to public data networks (PDNs), including link access procedures (HDLC compatible). First issued in 1976, this recommendation has been revised in 1980, 1984 and 1988.

- X.28, definition of the terminal dialogue with X.25 PADs, for the connection of character terminals to PDNs.

- X.29, control procedures between an X.25 PAD and a remote DTE.

- X.75, procedures for communicating between X.25 networks (internetworking); again this will not be discussed in detail in this book.

Together, X.3, X.28 and X.29 are often referred to as XXX or *triple X*, and are discussed in the next chapter. X.21 forms the lowest level of X.25, i.e. the physical interface.

7.2   The scope of X.25

Before discussing the recommendation in detail, it is important to understand the scope of applicability of the protocol. X.25 is intended to provide the definition of **access procedures** to common carrier networks. These are run by the PTTs on behalf of the users, but it is not the intention of CCITT in X.25 to specify the internal mechanisms of these networks, as these are not considered to be of direct interest to the user. Instead, what CCITT seek to provide with X.25 is a specification of the interface between the user's equipment and the network. In theory, this leaves the PTTs free to use any protocol they wish inside a PDN, provided the X.25 interface to the host is preserved. In practice, however, we can be fairly certain that the X.25 link access procedures will apply between nodes inside the PDN as well.

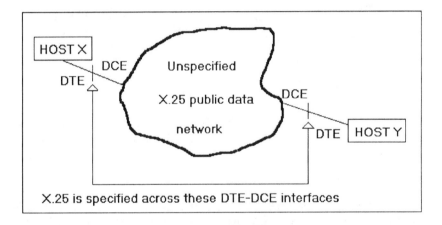

Figure 7.1 - scope of X.25 recommendation

Two terms are used in the recommendation, the significance of which must be grasped if X.25 itself is to be understood. These are:

    • **DTE** (**data terminal equipment**). This is the user's equipment which is connected to the network. See figure 7.1. Typically this is a host computer, together with any modems and line interfaces on the user's premises. It is not a terminal in the commonly used sense of the word. In the context of X.25 (and in common carrier jargon in general), a 'terminal' is any device connected to the network but not part of it, a source and sink of information which the network is required to pass to another terminal in a reliable and controlled manner.

- **DCE** (*data circuit terminating equipment*). This is the other end of a 'logical wire' from the DTE towards 'the network'. As far as X.25 is concerned, the network is a 'black box', and the user only sees the DCE in terms of the physical connection to it, and the packets and frames exchanged over the link to it.

  You should be warned that some authors refer to the DCE as 'Data Communication Equipment'. This is not the CCITT approved terminology.

There is a DTE-DCE connection at each end of the network, to which consistent procedures apply. It is important to note that if X.25 is applied to direct host-host connections, problems will arise, since in this case each host will have to function as both a DCE and DTE according to context. However we will not discuss the ramifications of this in this book.

The original (1976) X.25 recommendation was divided logically into three levels. For reference, the *1976 terminology* was as follows:

- *Level 1*: Physical level: DTE/DCE interface characteristics. This may either use recommendation X.21, which specifies a 15-pin connector, or (more familiarly) the supposedly 'interim' alternative X.21 bis, which is in effect the familiar 25-pin V.24 (RS-232C) host-modem interface. We are not concerned with the physical level in this book.

- *Level 2*: Link level. This broadly corresponded, at that time, to a subset of the HDLC ARM (asynchronous response mode) procedures.

- *Level 3*: Packet level DTE/DCE interface.

The terms level 1 to level 3 were discontinued in the 1980 revision, to avoid possible confusion with OSI/RM, which uses the similar term 'layer', but in a rather different context. Beginning with the 1980 revision, X.25 no longer contains references to levels. Instead, the *1980 onwards terminology* is as follows:

- Level 1 was renamed *physical procedures*.

- Level 2 was renamed *link access procedures* or *LAP*. This implied HDLC ARM in X.25(1976). However when ABM became the recommended mode of operation, this mode was referred to as *balanced link access procedures* or *LAPB*, so that either LAP or LAPB was available from 1980. To add further confusion, now that virtually all implementations use ABM, the term LAP is sometimes taken to mean ABM, the B being implied. We will always refer to LAPB.

  Additional procedures exist which allow packets to be transferred on multiple DTE-DCE links, which can improve efficiency. These are known as *multilink procedures* (*MLP*), as opposed to the single link procedure (SLP). Multilink procedures will not be discussed.

- Level 3 was renamed *packet mode procedures*.

We will use the more recent terminology in this book, but you may find the older nomenclature in the literature as well, so you should be aware of it.

7.3   Main functions of X.25

X.25 implements a link access procedure similar to HDLC ABM over a defined physical medium. HDLC (and hence LAPB) has already been discussed.

At the packet level, X.25 provides three basic types of service, as follows:

- **Virtual circuit** (**VC**). These allow *virtual calls* to be set up between DTEs, and involve call setup, data transfer and final call cleardown. *Logical channels* (*LCs*) are defined for use by virtual calls, and sequencing and flow control are provided on a per LC basis. Certain additional facilities can be provided such as reverse charging, closed user groups and call statistics on cleardown. A VC is set up to a specific destination, and successive calls may select a variety of destinations.

- **Permanent virtual circuit** (**PVC**). These are used in the same way as VCs, except that the call is considered to be permanently set up, and all packets will be sent to the same prearranged destination. Thus it is less flexible, but more efficient if it is only desired to communicate with a single destination.

- **Fast select** (CCITT terminology) or *minicall* (PSS terminology). The overheads of setting up and clearing down a virtual call are relatively high, as will be seen. If only a small amount of data is to be transferred, the overhead can be unacceptable. Fast select provides a mechanism for reducing the overhead of setting up a virtual circuit, and was originally devised for calls which would have little data to transmit. It is discussed in §7.7.4. This became part of X.25 in 1980 (but some PTTs were already providing, or planning to provide, this facility). Like all post-1976 additions, it has to be declared 'optional', since existing networks may not provide the facility.

It should be noted that the term fast select is also used in multidrop VDU protocols, to describe a technique where the VDU is sent a message without first seeking its permission. (If permission must first be obtained, it is referred to as slow select.) This bears no relationship whatsoever to X.25 fast select.

   • The 1980 issue of X.25 also saw the provision of a further optional facility, *datagrams*. This service was provided in an attempt to cater for applications which are not suitable for virtual circuits. A submission on this subject was made by ANSI to ISO[2] as early as 1977. However despite its inclusion as an option in 1980, the datagram service has never been offered in any commercial X.25 network, and the service was subsequently removed from the 1984 reissue of the recommendation.

At this point it is also worth mentioning that X.25 packet mode is full duplex, in the sense that both DTE-DCE and DCE-DTE communication is possible at all times. One problem with HDLC ARM as used in X.25(1976) was that each direction of transmission was set up independently, whereas with ABM, both are set up at the same time. Therefore with ARM, there is (in theory) the possibility of attempting to operate full duplex packet mode procedures over an underlying HDLC link which has only been set up in one direction, which would clearly be absurd.

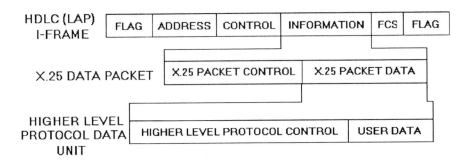

Figure 7.2 - relationship between fields in the X.25 protocol hierarchy

7.4   X.25 packet mode procedures

The packet mode procedures define how X.25 packets are exchanged across the DTE-DCE interface, and the formatting and significance of each packet. We will consider only the most important features here. Note that an X.25 packet does not necessarily correspond exactly to a LAPB frame. The X.25 packet is the transmission unit at the packet mode level of X.25, and as such may be contained within the information fields of one or more LAPB I-frames; the address and control octets of the LAPB frames form part of the link access procedures of X.25, but are of no interest at the packet level.

An X.25 packet consists of X.25 packet level control and 'data'. In this context, the data is everything except X.25 control, and is transparent to X.25. However the data may contain control information for higher level protocols, in exactly the same way as packet mode control information is treated as data by LAPB. See figure 7.2. The original issue of X.25 did not explicitly state that information fields should be an exact number of octets long, but this is generally a requirement. Where necessary, X.25 packets are required to be padded out so that they are an exact multiple of 8 bits long.

7.4.1   Logical channels

A DTE (host) may be permitted to have more than one virtual call in progress at once; see §7.8. This allows a host to set up more than one simultaneous 'conversation' with other hosts. (Normally the user will be charged extra for this facility.) In order to distinguish between virtual calls, each is assigned a unique logical channel (LC) identifier. In fact this comprises a *logical channel number* (*LCN*) and a *logical channel group number* (*LCGN*), but for most practical purposes the two fields may be regarded as a single entity. For simplicity, we will refer to the composite identifier as a **logical channel number** or **LCN**. An LCN normally takes a value in the range 1 to 255, but may optionally be in the range 0 to 4095.

These LCNs are assigned during the call setup phase. By convention, the DCE uses available LCNs starting at the lowest value, and the DTE starts at the highest value, to minimise the chance of the same LCN being used simultaneously by both DTE and DCE (see call collision below). There are further rules concerning the allocation of LCNs to PVCs and incoming-only or outgoing-only LCs, but we will not discuss them here. The LCN remains assigned to the virtual call and is included in all packets during the data transfer phase. The LCN is released at call cleardown. One or more LCNs may be reserved for PVCs, and packets containing this LCN will automatically be routed to the predefined destination DTE, without the need for explicit call setup.

7.5   Packet types and structure

Each X.25 packet transferred across the DTE/DCE interface (in either direction) will be at least 3 octets long. This is the minimum length of the X.25 packet header. Most packets require a header longer than this. A maximum of 128 octets in an X.25 packet (i.e. LAPB information field) is usually considered to be a minimum service requirement. Individual PTTs may elect to use a different limit from a specified set of values. See below under data packets.

Figure 7.3 shows the packet types used in X.25, for the two main cases of virtual calls (VC) and permanent virtual circuits (PVC). We will discuss the features of X.25 under the same general headings as in figure 7.3.

PACKET TYPE		SERVICE	
From DCE to DTE	From DTE to DCE	VC	PVC
CALL SETUP AND CLEARDOWN			
Incoming call	Call request	Yes	No
Call connected	Call accepted	Yes	No
Clear indication	Clear request	Yes	No
DCE clear confirmation	DTE clear confirmation	Yes	No
DATA AND INTERRUPT			
DCE interrupt	DTE interrupt	Yes	Yes
DCE interrupt confirmation	DTE interrupt confirmation	Yes	Yes
FLOW CONTROL AND RESET			
DCE RNR	DTE RNR	Yes	Yes
Reset indication	Reset request	Yes	Yes
DCE reset confirmation	DTE reset confirmation	Yes	Yes
	DTE REJ (note 1)	Yes	Yes
RESTART			
Restart indication	Restart request	Yes	Yes
DCE restart confirmation	DTE restart confirmation	Yes	Yes
DIAGNOSTIC			
Diagnostic (note 1)		Yes	Yes
REGISTRATION (notes 1 and 2)			
Registration confirmation	Registration request	Yes	Yes

NOTEs:
1   These packet types are optional and are not always available.
2   These are used for online facility registration.

Figure 7.3 - X.25 packet types and usage modes

The description of X.25 will be followed by a discussion of some special facilities available. A brief discussion of some of the problems which were encountered with the original (1976) version is included at various points; more details on this aspect may be found elsewhere[3].

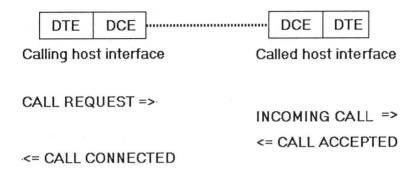

Figure 7.4 - sequence of X.25 packets for setting up a virtual call

7.5.1   Call setup and cleardown

The procedure to set up a virtual call is triggered by a DTE sending a call request packet to its adjacent DCE, initiating the *call setup phase*. This is passed through the network (assuming that all goes well; see below), and it becomes an incoming call packet from the destination DCE to its DTE. Assuming that the DTE wishes to accept the call, it returns a call accepted packet to the DCE, which is relayed back to the calling DTE as a call connected packet from its DCE. See figure 7.4. X.25 only specifies what is exchanged between DTEs and DCEs. Precisely what happens inside the network is for the network designer to decide, but typically each node would identify the next link to the intended destination, using deterministic routing (without a secondary link being specified). As each node is reached, tables are updated giving details of the LCN being set up. This allows subsequent packets to refer th the LCN rather than including the full address of the destination host.

The routing algorithm just described guarantees the same path for all packets. Therefore they are guaranteed to reach the destination DCE in the correct sequence. One problem with the original version of X.25 was that it was vague about this matter, so that it was not entirely clear what should be done if packets arrived out of sequence.

Once exchange of these packets is completed, the call enters the *data transfer phase*, where data and interrupt packets can be exchanged, as will be discussed later.

There is also the possibility that the call cannot be connected. There are several reasons why this might occur. A list of reasons is given later when discussing call clearing.

Figure 7.5 shows the sequence for a failed call for two cases, firstly where the call was refused by the destination DTE, and secondly where the call was refused by the (network or) local DCE. Variants of a clearing packet are exchanged.

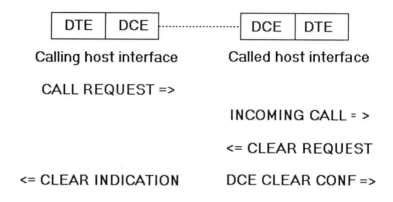

CALL REQUEST =>

INCOMING CALL = >

<= CLEAR REQUEST

<= CLEAR INDICATION   DCE CLEAR CONF =>

Destination DTE refuses incoming call

CALL REQUEST =>

<= CLEAR INDICATION

DTE CLEAR CONFIRMATION ->

Network (DCE) refuses call

Figure 7.5 - sequence of X.25 packets for failed call

7.5.2   Call collision

This occurs if, at about the same time, the DTE sends a call request packet, and the DCE sends an incoming call packet, specifying the same LCN. These will cross, and neither the DTE nor the DCE can 'retract' the packet it has already sent. Since each call must have a unique LCN, it is not possible for both calls to proceed. This problem is resolved by the DCE abandoning the incoming call by following the incoming call packet with a 'clear indication' packet; the remote caller is informed that the destination

DTE was unable to accept the call. This situation is analogous to ENQ collision on an idle link in the BSC protocol. A situation of this type is sometimes referred to as a *race condition*.

It should be noted that the allocation of LCNs identifies calls across the local DTE/DCE interface only. The LCN is not an end-end concept. Being an interface recommendation, X.25 does not define how LCNs are mapped from one end of the network to the other; the LCN will not necessarily be the same as that used over the remote DCE/DTE interface.

7.5.3   Clearing sequence

Either DTE may request that the call be cleared down. In the case of some irrecoverable errors, the DCE may also clear the call. In the case where the DTE clears the call, clearing packets are exchanged in much the same way as call setup packets were used to establish the call. See figure 7.6.

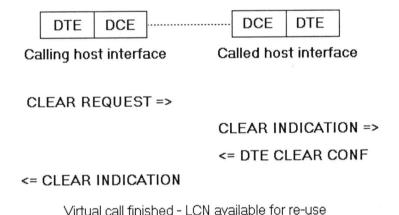

Figure 7.6 - sequence of X.25 packets for clearing call (by a DTE)

The procedures for DCE clearing are similar. A DTE clearing packet is returned by the DTE in response to the DCE clear indication, and the call is cleared. Where the network (DCE) clears a call in the data transfer stage, the clear indication will be sent to both DTEs. The clearing cause (figure 7.9) gives the reason for issuing the clear indication.

7.5.4 Call request and incoming call packet format

Figure 7.7 shows the layout of X.25 call request and incoming call packets. A description of the fields is provided below. Note that they are in effect the same packet; the name refers to whether the packet is being sent by or to a DTE. The only significant differences between the two cases are:

- where a single address is provided, in which case it will (of course) be the called DTE for a call request packet, and the calling DTE for an incoming call packet;

- if the GFI is altered during negotiation; see §7.6.1.

The detailed coding of many of these fields is mainly of interest to implementors, and will not be given.

- The *general format identifier* (*GFI*) identifies the packet format in use. Figure 7.7 shows the GFI for standard modulo 8 sequencing. There is also an optional modulo 128 sequencing which has a GFI AX10. The leftmost bit (marked A in the figure) is known (in this type of packet) as the *address bit*, and is used to distinguish between the standard BCD address format (A=0) and a new format which allows more efficient use of the address space, and is currently under study. (Interested readers may consult X.121 and X.301 for further details.) The bit marked X is used to negotiate the use or otherwise of *delivery confirmation*; see §7.6.1. This format of the GFI is used for call request, incoming call, call accepted and call connected packets.

More generally, the GFI takes a value ??01 for packets with modulo 8 sequencing, and ??10 for modulo 128 sequencing, where the precise values of ?? depend on the type of packet. (For all packet types below, we will assume modulo 8 sequencing.) The leftmost bit has a special significance in data packets as discussed in §7.6.3.

- The *packet type* identifier identifies, in this case, a call request packet. This applies to most types of packet. There will be a different code for each packet type, although precise details are not of interest here.

- The *address*(es) provided are preceded by their lengths in half-octets. The called DTE address must be provided by the caller; this will be followed by the calling DTE address, where this is provided as well. Where only one address is provided, it is either the called or calling DTE according to context (see above). The address field must end on an octet boundary; this may mean that padding of 0000 has to be included at the end. This specification of addresses allows for flexibility in address assignment by an administration, subject to the constraint that addresses must be numbers encoded as BCD digits. (For example 9 is encoded as 1001.) The situation is analogous to the telephone numbering system, where telephone numbers may be of different lengths for different exchanges (in the UK, at least). With effect from the 1984 revision, the address fields were extended, for OSI/RM network layer compatibility (see chapter fourteen).

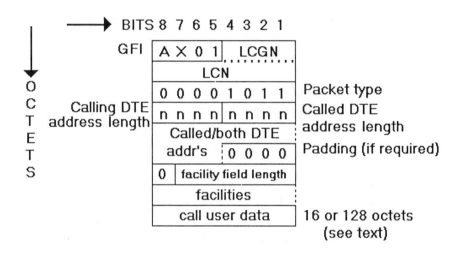

NOTEs:
    A   address bit
    X   delivery confirmation negotiation
    Up to 128 octets allowed in the call user data field if fast select used.

Figure 7.7 - format of X.25 call request and incoming call packets

The facilities field is preceded by its length in octets; details of facilities are provided later.

Up to 16 octets of call user data (or 128 octets in the case of fast select) may be appended to the call request packet; there must be an integral number of octets. Typically this 'user data' is in fact control for some protocol at a higher level. For example we will see in chapter nine that the 'yellow book' transport service uses the whole of this field (and usually the first data packet as well) for its 'connect' command, in the case where it is mapped on to X.25.

The first four octets of the call user data field may be used to include high level protocol identification, in the case where the connection is not between packet mode DTEs (e.g. for X.29 over X.25; see the next chapter).

138

Further details may be found in the recommendations concerned (e.g. X.29).

7.5.5 Call accepted and call connected packet format

This packet has a very similar format to the call connected packet. See figure 7.8. There are two formats, normal and extended. The extended format is used for fast select. This is requested in the facilities field of the call request packet.

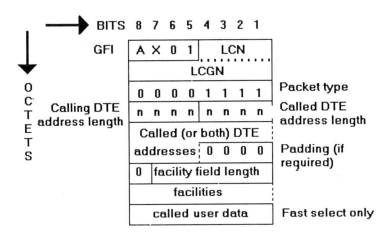

NOTEs:
1   Address and facilities fields are optional in call accepted and call connected packets. (Length fields are mandatory.) There is no called user data in the standard format, but 128 octets are allowed for fast select.
2   The X bit indicates whether delivery confirmation will be used in this call (i.e. its use has been successfully negotiated).

Figure 7.8 - format of X.25 call accepted and call connected packets

The address and facilities fields are not normally used, but may be present for special uses. For example, where the calling DTE requests some optional facility, the reply facilities field can be used for confirmation (or otherwise) of the requested facility. It should be noted that the address and facility length fields must be present, although they will be set to zero if no addresses and/or facilities are provided.

The GFI is the same as for a call request packet, except that the X bit now indicates whether the D-bit must be set in <u>all</u> data packets for this call;

see §7.6.1. Up to 128 octets of called user data may be appended to the call accepted packet if the extended format is used (fast select).

7.5.6   Clearing packet format

The format of clear request and clear indication packets is shown in figure 7.9.

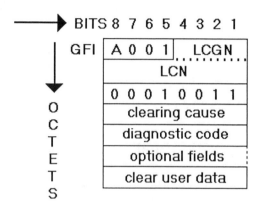

Figure 7.9 - format of X.25 clear request and indication packets

• The *clearing cause* is the reason for clearing the call. The originator (DCE or remote DTE) is also indicated. The following is a list of the main reasons, which also apply if the clear was in response to a call setup attempt:

- number busy (call failed)
- out of order (call failed or terminated)
- remote procedure error
- no reverse charging (call failed; see later)
- incompatible destination (facilities)
- fast select not allowed
- ship absent (for mobile maritime service)
- invalid facility request
- access barred (e.g. to closed user group; see later)
- local procedure error
- network congestion (call abandoned/setup failed)
- RPOA (network) out of order (see §7.8)
- number not obtainable (unknown destination)

- The *diagnostic code* may be used to provide additional information, for example on a facility which was not allowed by the remote DTE or the local DCE.

In addition to the fields shown in figure 7.9, a number of additional fields may be appended if an extended format is used; this is not necessary for most calls. These fields are as follows:

- Address lengths and address(es), for use only if the Called Line Address Modified Notification (CLAMN) facility is present (see §7.8).

- Facility length and facilities, used where indication of some optional facility is required in the clearing packet.

- Clear user data, for use only with a fast select call (which has not been converted to a normal call, as discussed in §7.7.4).

7.5.7   Data packet format

When call request and call connected packets have successfully been exchanged, data packets may be exchanged between the DTEs. The format of a data packet is as shown in figure 7.10. The Q-, D- and M- bits, and also the P(R) and P(S) fields, are discussed later under end-end flow control and acknowledgement.

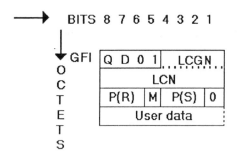

NOTEs:

Q	data qualifier bit (Q-bit)
D	delivery confirmation bit (D-bit)
M	more data bit (M-bit)

Figure 7.10 - format of X.25 data packets

Note that the P(R) and P(S) fields are in the reverse order to the N(S) and N(R) fields in the LAPB control octet; there seems to be no logical reason for this apparent inconsistency, apart from the fact that the two standards originated in different standards organisations. A further point to note is that the bit after P(S) is zero in this position only in data packets. (Check this for yourself by examining the other packet formats shown.) Therefore there is no need for an explicit packet type octet in this case.

The maximum length of the data field is an administrative matter, but 128 octets is common. (PSS uses this value.) PTT networks generally support at least this length. Other maximum lengths may be agreed for use in particular networks; typical values are 16, 32, 64, 256, 512, 1024, 2048 and 4096 octets. It is normal for data fields to be an integral number of octets long.

7.5.8   Clear confirmation packets

These comprise the first 3 octets of the clearing packet as described above, with a packet type identifier of 00010111. Optional address and facilities fields may also be present if the DTE has requested the charging information facility, in which case coded details of the cost of the virtual call are provided.

7.6   End-end flow control and acknowledgement

Acknowledgement of data packets is provided by means of the *packet send and receive sequence counts P(S)* and *P(R)*. The parallel with LAPB (HDLC) N(S) and N(R) is clear, and the same window concept applies. However these were originally not used as end-end packet sequence numbers, being of significance, and acknowledged, only across the DTE-DCE interface. Starting with the 1980 revision, they are of end-end significance if the D-bit is set; see below.

This lack of end-end significance was one of the main areas which caused concern to implementors after the initial issue of X.25 in 1976. The main question which arose was to what extent the acknowledgement of X.25 packets up to a certain value of P(R) [minus one] by the local DCE could be taken as an indication that these packets had actually reached the destination DTE. After all, this would seem to be a reasonable interpretation as far as a user was concerned. Unfortunately, the nature of the original issue of X.25 as purely an interface specification implied that no such assumption could be made. A consequence of this was that it could not be truly end-end, since nothing in the original specification referred directly to the destination DTE. This meant that it was entirely at the discretion of the local DCE to use the window mechanism for flow control as it saw fit, in the context of what was happening inside the network. Unfortunately, X.25 can tell us nothing at all about what happens there.

These problems were a consequence of CCITT's early 'need to know basis' approach, in that as far as they were concerned, all the user needed to know was how to interface to the network; what happened inside was none of the user's business. Partly for this reason, end-end issues were overlooked in the first version of X.25. It was soon realised that a DTE at least needed to know what was happening at the other DTE, not just across the local DTE-DCE interface.

7.6.1   Use of the D (delivery confirmation) bit

It was generally felt that the 1976 position was inadequate, and the 1980 revision saw a significant concession to those users who wished the P(R) acknowledgement to have end-end significance. The main change was the provision of an optional *delivery confirmation bit* in the GFI, the *D-bit*. This corresponds to the X-bit in the call request packet GFI. There are two cases to be considered:

• **D=0** in a data packet. When a data packet with P(S)=p is sent, the corresponding P(R) [p+1] returned by the local DCE is of *local* (DCE) significance only. In other words the packet concerned has been correctly received (in sequence) by the local DCE. This allows the local DCE to control throughput purely on the basis of network conditions, and independently of the end-end network propagation delay. As a consequence there could be far more than k (the window width) packets in transit at the same time in a large network. This is in the spirit of the original recommendation. Unfortunately the sending DTE has no way (within the X.25 procedures) of knowing if data packets have reached the destination DTE, which would, to say the least, be useful information.

• **D=1** in a data packet. In this case, the return by the DCE of P(R)=p implies that all packets with P(S)<p have correctly reached the *destination* DTE in sequence. (This of course implies some additional communication between the DCEs, the details of which are not stated in the recommendation, but can easily be guessed at.) Setting the D-bit will usually result in a significantly lower throughput, especially on a large network, since the sender's DCE must wait for delivery confirmation from the remote DCE before acknowledging packets to the sender. However if something goes wrong (e.g. a reset; see §7.7.1), far less data is likely to be lost as a result.

To summarise, a DTE can set the D-bit in data packets if it wishes the returned P(R) values in received data packets to have end-end significance, in which case the DTE can be 'certain' that the data packets thus acknowledged have reached the destination. If the D-bit is not set, the local DCE alone decides on the P(R) values to return.

It is worth remembering that the fact that data packets have reached the destination DTE intact does not necessarily mean that it has done anything useful with them. For example it may have crashed immediately after acknowledging their receipt. Therefore while such *receipt confirmation* is useful, it is no guarantee of further processing. This is one of many reasons for needing host-host protocols.

Unfortunately this is not the end of the story. In the 1980 revision, CCITT omitted to specify rules regarding when the D-bit could be set. In particular it was not possible to agree in advance whether it should be used or not. Conforming implementation could thus quite legally set the D-bit in some data packets and not in others. As there was no way in which X.25 could sensibly police this bit, the protocol would not work properly if the D-bit was not used consistently in a given direction of transmission. Clearly for the D-bit to have any real usefulness, it should either be set in all data packets or not be used at all.

The 1984 revision required the use (or otherwise) of the D-bit (by DTEs) to be *negotiated* at call set up time, and the result would be binding on both DTEs. The X-bit in the GFI of call setup packets is used for this purpose; see figures 7.7 and 7.8. If its use was agreed, it would always be set, otherwise it would never be set. The negotiation will be discussed in detail in chapter fourteen, where X.25 is related to the OSI network service.

It is also worth noting that a receive state variable is not defined for X.25. This is because the window does not necessarily have end-end significance, so that the called DTE does not necessarily know what packets the calling DTE has sent (and vice versa). It is possible for a DTE to send packets faster than the other DTE can accept them, and this will be dealt with by the remote DCE imposing backward flow control (e.g. via DCE RNR packets). It is also assumed that the remote DCE delivers packets to its DTE in sequence, and again the original specification was not entirely clear on whether the DCE or DTE was responsible for recovering lost packets.

NOTE: P(R) and P(S) apply to the X.25 packet mode, and have no relation whatsoever to N(R) and N(S) in LAPB frames. Indeed if multilink procedures are used, different physical links could be used for different packets. A packet may (at least in theory) comprise more than one frame, although a frame may not contain more than one packet. There will of course be comparable N(S) and N(R) fields at the LAPB level as well, over the same interface, but these are at a different level of protocol. Only data packets have both P(R) and P(S) sequence numbers.

7.6.2 Use of the M (more data) bit

The *more data bit* or *M-bit* may be set in data packets to indicate to the receiving DTE that the logical unit of data (broadly speaking, a message or high level protocol data unit) is longer than can be fitted into a single X.25 data packet. Thus, in a three-packet message, the more data bit would be set in the first and second packets. While the value of the M-bit is preserved through the X.25 network, it is not used by X.25 in any way. However in some cases, the network may elect to concatenate two or more short packets with the M-bit set, for reasons of operational efficiency. In cases where more than one X.25 network is involved and these have different maximum packet lengths, similar effects may also occur.

Unfortunately, as will be seen in due course, it is against the spirit of OSI to use this bit, as it implies that X.25 somehow knows about the meaning of the data it is transmitting, when this should be of no concern at this level of protocol. OSI makes no use of this bit, although the UK interim academic transport protocol (YBTS; see chapter nine) does use the M-bit.

7.6.3 Use of the Q (data qualifier) bit

Use of the *data qualifier bit* or *Q-bit* allows two 'flavours' of data to be sent in X.25 data packets. For example, when a higher level protocol is being used over X.25, the Q-bit can be used to distinguish between commands and data at this higher protocol level. Again, this bit is preserved but not used by X.25. It is assumed that the Q-bit will be set to the same value in all packets of a multi-packet sequence (i.e. where the M-bit is used).

Again the use of this bit is not in the spirit of OSI, although the bit is again used by YBTS (chapter nine), as well as by the X.29 character terminal handling protocol (chapter eight).

7.6.4 RR, RNR and REJ packets

These are similar in basic function to the equivalent LAPB packets, except that they operate on packets instead of frames. It should be noted that they operate between the DTE and the local DCE, not at the end-end level. RR and RNR packets contain P(R) values, and govern the flow of data packets across the DTE-DCE interface. An RNR condition is cancelled by the receipt of an RR packet in the same direction (or by a reset; see §7.7.1). Either the DTE or DCE may issue RR or RNR packets.

There are two eccentricities associated with the packet mode REJ which do not apply to the LAPB equivalent. One is that no provision is made for a DCE to issue REJ at all. The other is that permission for a DTE to issue a REJ is an optional facility. Therefore REJ can only ever be available in one direction of transmission, and may not be available at all. If the DTE is permitted to use REJ, this will probably cost the host organisation extra money, as use of this optional facility will give the DCE more work to do, as it will now have to retain transmitted packets in case rollback is required. The reason for these somewhat curious restrictions is an attempt to keep error recovery procedures as simple as possible. The DTE or DCE can always use reset (§7.7.1) as a means of restoring the LC to a known state.

7.7   Further features of X.25

The other most significant features of X.25 will be discussed without reference to detailed packet formats. All packets start with a GFI. Except for call setup, clearing and data packets, where the first two bits have special uses, only the last two are significant. Thus the GFI is always 0001 for modulo 8 sequencing, and 0010 for modulo 128 sequencing for other types of packet. The GFI is followed by the logical channel identifier (except for restart, diagnostic and registration packets, where this field is all zeros), and a packet type field. Further details of packet formats may be found in the recommendation.

7.7.1   Reset procedures

A *reset* may be issued by either the DTE or the DCE in the event of some 'minor' error condition which cannot otherwise be dealt with. Reset packets may only be issued in the data transfer phase. One example we hinted at in §7.6.4 was the receipt of an out-of-sequence packet when REJ was unavailable. A more complete list of reset reasons is given later.

Provision of full error recovery inside PDNs can be complex, and such provision would increase their cost and complexity, and hence would result in increased usage charges for the network. Therefore some implementors elect to use reset rather than become involved in messy and timeconsuming recovery.

When a reset is issued or received, the effect is to reinitialise the VC (or PVC), by resetting the next expected P(S) to 0, and discarding any data packets either received and unacknowledged, or awaiting transmission. Thus all data packets in the network are 'flushed' by a reset. (This also implies that nodes inside the network will also flush on reset, which X.25 cannot directly tell us, since it doesn't say anything about what goes on in and between internal network nodes.) Until the confirmation is received, any RR and RNR packets which may be received will be ignored. It follows that if a reset is issued, data will normally be discarded in the network and hence be lost, and it is the responsibility of higher level host protocols to take any appropriate steps to recover the lost data. Reset is thus a simple, albeit rather crude, way of dealing with such matters as packet loss, by reinitialisation of a virtual circuit.

Note that a reset is specific to a single LC or PVC, and has no effect on other LCs for the DTE concerned. It is therefore used for relatively minor error conditions affecting data transfer on a single LC.

A reset may be issued for any of the following reasons. There are some differences between VCs and PVCs as indicated in the following list. Some of the reset reasons for PVCs are provided to notify the DTE that the status of the PVC has changed in some way, and are not necessarily to do with data loss on the PVC. In the case of a reset indication, the DTE is also informed of the originator of the reset (DCE or remote DTE):

- remote DTE out of order (PVC)
- remote procedure error (PVC, VC)
- local procedure error (PVC, VC)
- network congestion (PVC, VC)
- remote DTE operational (PVC)
- network operational (PVC)
- incompatible destination (PVC, VC)
- network out of order (PVC)

When a *reset indication* is issued by the network (i.e. by a DCE), it will in practice be issued to both DTEs, which must each respond with a matching *DTE reset confirmation* packet. The reset procedure is considered to be complete when confirmation packets have been received from both DTEs.

When a *reset request* is issued by a DTE, it is passed to the remote DTE as a reset indication, and the remote DTE is required to respond with a DTE reset confirmation. This is returned to the issuing DTE as a DCE reset confirmation. Thus again a reset and its response can in effect be considered to have traversed the entire network. No data packets may be transmitted until the reset confirmation is received, and any data packets received while waiting for the reset confirmation are discarded. In this way the VC or PVC is completely flushed of data.

In the context of the internal workings of an X.25 network, it may be assumed that where a reset originates from a node inside the network, the reset is considered complete when both responses have returned to that node. Since a reset 'passing through the network' destroys any data it encounters (for this LC), this handshaking ensures that all data in transit will also have been purged by the time the confirmation reaches the issuing node.

When resets have been exchanged, the VC or PVC re-enters the data transfer state as if the call had just been set up. (If confirmation has not been received after a timeout, they may be reissued, or the call may be cleared down.) According to X.25, resets have only local significance over a DTE-DCE interface, but in practice in many PDNs, they have end-end significance. If resets are issued because of a network problem, for example a temporarily severed network connection, both ends will notice this, and will reset independently.

Reset collision occurs where both the DTE and DCE issue resets at about the same time, so that the two resets cross. The DCE will accept the reset request from the DTE in lieu of a DTE reset confirmation packet, and will not send a DCE reset confirmation. Similarly, the DTE assumes that the reset from the DCE is a response to its own (which strictly it is not, of course).

A DTE may respond to a reset indication by clearing the call; this is a perfectly valid response, in which case the reset confirmation will of course not be returned.

7.7.2   Restart procedures

There are in fact four levels of error recovery in X.25. In order of severity they are as follows:

    • The simplest recovery procedure where one or more data packets have been lost is to issue a *REJ* packet, which causes rollback in the same way as in HDLC, except that X.25 packets are involved. Permission for the DTE to issue a REJ packet is an optional facility; see §7.8. Furthermore X.25 provides no DCE REJ packet. (Note that the X.25 packet mode offers no checkpointing procedures.)

    • In case of minor problems involving irrecoverable data loss on a single LC (or where REJ would have been appropriate but cannot be used), that LC will be *reset*. This may well result in packets being lost on that LC, and in general will require recovery at some higher protocol layer. (As we shall see in due course, this is - in theory at least - the OSI transport layer.)

    • Where the situation is more serious, but still only affects one LC, that LC may be *cleared* down by the DCE. As this will be unsolicited, again data loss will occur. In this case the network connection has to be set up again as well. Again recovery is by a higher protocol layer.

• A *restart* is used for conditions more severe still. A restart reinitialises the entire packet level DTE-DCE interface. This affects all virtual calls and all PVCs. A restart causes the *clearing of all VCs*, and the *resetting of all PVCs*. Procedures and packets are similar to those for reset, but may be applied over many remote DTE-DCE interfaces. A possible condition requiring a restart is a temporary problem causing isolation of the entire network.

A *restart request* may be issued for the following reasons, which are encoded in the cause field; as usual, a *restart confirmation* is expected in reply:

- local procedure error
- network congestion (or failure)
- registration/cancellation confirmed
  (online facility registration)
- network operational (after failure)

7.7.3   Interrupt procedures

An *interrupt packet* is similar to a data packet, except that it bypasses normal data packet flow control procedures. This means that an interrupt packet may 'overtake' normal data packets, but may not be overtaken by them. Unlike data packets, these packets do not contain P(R) or P(S) fields. Instead, they are acknowledged by matching DTE *interrupt confirmation packets* (from the remote DTE), which are relayed to the originator as DCE interrupt confirmation packets.

It is most important to note that interrupt packets are not intended for use as a priority data channel. There are two reasons why this is not sensible.

• Although since the 1984 issue of X.25, up to 32 octets of data may be included in an interrupt packet, as opposed to only 1 octet previously, this is still a more expensive way of transmitting information in networks which charge on the basis of the number of packets transmitted, as more data can usually·be fitted into a normal data packet for the same cost. In the decreasing number of networks which still use the 1980 version, the situation would be very much worse of course.

- The other problem is that interrupt data is what is known (in OSI parlance) as a *confirmed synchronous service*, which is a fancy way of saying that only one interrupt packet can be outstanding at any time, and the next one cannot be sent until delivery of the previous one has been confirmed. Therefore the overall throughput would also be abysmal.

X.25(1984) interrupt packets may be used to implement the OSI/RM network service expedited data facility, in conjunction with the expedited data negotiation facility; see chapter fourteen. Concepts such as the one in the previous paragraph are discussed later in the book.

7.7.4   Fast select

When British Telecom implemented PSS in 1980, they included a facility (at the request of the users) which they called a *minicall*. Other PTTs found a demand for a similar facility. Therefore a broadly similar facility was included in X.25(1980). The original reason for providing this option was to provide a means of using a virtual call to send a small quantity of data, without having to enter the data transfer phase. The calling DTE sends a special variant of the call request packet, which contains a user data field. The destination replies with a clear request, which may also contain user data. This will clearly be more efficient than fully setting up the call, exchanging a single data packet, then clearing the down again. This technique, now known as *fast select*, is an optional facility which is specified in the call request packet. As it is optional, the called DCE may of course refuse the call if the called DTE does not cannot receive fast select calls.

This is a sort of 'half way house' between VCs and datagrams. The X.25 datagram service specified in 1980 never saw the light of day, and vanished again in 1984.

A further option allows the fast select call to mature into a normal call with a data transfer phase, if the calling DTE is agreeable. The overheads of call setup are thereby reduced if there is little data to send, and the remote DTE can convert the fast select call into a normal call if the sender permitted this in the call request packet.

It may come as a surprise to learn that the main usage of fast select nowadays is in cases where the call does mature in this way. Why specify fast select when it is known in advance that the call will mature into a normal call? The reason has to do with protocol structuring and high level protocols. Without going into too many details here, there are severe restrictions on the amount (if any) of 'user data' which can be sent in normal call setup and clearing packets. This has unfortunate consequences for higher layer protocols, as a host may be forced to set up an X.25

connection completely, simply to ascertain that the remote host is, for some reason, unwilling to proceed! This is because the higher level protocol parameters must be sent as X.25 user data and, unless fast select is used, effectively only data packets can be used for this purpose. Even if fast select is used, there is no guarantee that all of the required parameters will fit into the user data field of the call request packet, so that sometimes it may still be necessary to enter data transfer mode, and at other times not.

This sounds, and indeed is, rather a mess. Problems of this type do still exist, as there are still restrictions on data field lengths in call setup and clearing packets, whereas there are fewer (or no) corresponding restrictions in OSI layers above X.25, as we shall see in due course. However at least using fast select means that if the higher level protocol connection attempt fails, it may still be possible to clear down the call without entering the data transfer phase, provided that the reason for failure will fit in the clear request user data field.

In fact this implies that sufficient information can be encoded in the call request user data field to allow the receiver to make the decision whether it is worth proceeding. If so, any remaining sender parameters can then appear in the first data packet. If not, there is no point in sending them anyway as the call will have been cleared down. However this discussion risks becoming too tied in with implementation issues, and will be terminated at this point.

7.7.5 Online facility registration

§7.8 discusses the various optional facilities which are defined in X.25. Some may be selected on a per call basis, whereas others are fixed for all calls unless altered. X.25(1984) introduced the idea that some facilities could be altered by sending a special *registration request* packet. This removed one of the original headaches with X.25, which was that any change of facility required form filling and bureaucratic delays, there being no online means of altering facilities such as the number of simultaneous VCs allowed.

A *registration confirmation* packet is returned by the DCE, indicating that (or if) the requested change has been acted on. As with many X.25 packets, the detailed encoding is complex, and of interest mainly to implementors.

7.8 X.25 Facilities

X.25 offers a number of *optional facilities*, for some of which an extra charge may be made by the network administration. There are, in general, three ways of requesting a given facility:

- Some facilities are requested by setting appropriate bit(s) in the facilities field in the call request packet, i.e. they can be selected on a per call basis. The local DCE knows which facilities a given DTE is allowed to use, and may refuse the call if the use of a requested facility is not permitted (or if the facility cannot be handled by the called DTE).

- Some facilities are *negotiated* during call setup, using the GFI. The use of delivery confirmation and extended format fall into this category.

- Other facilities cannot be negotiated in either of these ways, as they are longer term characteristics, such as (see below) membership of a CUG, or the number of simultaneous LCs which can be set up. Some PDNs now support online facility registration as discussed in the previous section.

We have already discussed **fast select**. This is one optional facility (as is **fast select acceptance**), but there are many others as well, some of which are outlined below, and others in chapter fourteen. (The ability to register facilities online is itself a facility.)

Extended sequence numbering (modulo 128). The GFI of the call request packet indicates whether modulo 8 or modulo 128 is required.

Packet retransmission at the request of the DTE. This governs whether a DTE REJ packet may be sent, as discussed earlier. This is not a standard provision, and an extra charge may be made for this facility, as more complex procedures (software) are needed in the network in order to handle this. (If the DTE is not allowed to issue a REJ packet, it must issue a reset instead. Recovery without data loss may of course be possible if REJ can be used.)

Incoming calls barred. If this facility has been requested, the local DCE will return a clearing packet to any calling DTE, with this reason code. The intended called DTE is not informed of this action. This facility is provided for users who wish to access other hosts via the network, but do not wish any other network users to access their own facilities. This applies to all calls until changed.

Outgoing calls barred. The DCE will not accept call request packets. Any attempts to set up a call will result in a clearing response from the local DCE. (In addition, the user may be charged the minimum call setup fee.) This facility could for example be suitable for service bureaux which provide a service to other network users, but wish to prevent local users from making outgoing calls. This also applies to all calls until changed.

One-way logical channels. Any LCN may be restricted to either incoming calls or outgoing calls, independently of other LCNs. This may be useful in order to guarantee that at least one LCN is always available to make outgoing calls. This applies to all calls on that LC until its status is changed. In fact there are numbering rules determining which LCNs can be used in the various operational modes.

Non-standard default packet and window sizes. It may be possible to use a maximum data packet size other than the default, which is often 128 octets. It may also be possible to use a window width other than the default (often 2).

Closed user group (CUG). A CUG may be formed by a group of hosts which wish to access each other via the network, but which also wish to bar access to all other network users, i.e. only members of the CUG may call each other. A DTE may belong to more than one CUG. CUGs are intended to provide a more secure networking environment for groups of DTEs such as banking systems, where additional protection against unauthorised access is required. A caller to a CUG host must specify the CUG identity in the facilities field of the call setup packet; the call will not be allowed to proceed unless both parties are in the CUG requested, and this 'password' is correct.

Although CUGs are intended to give additional access protection for sensitive users such as banks, the banking community has traditionally regarded open access networks such as PSS with deep suspicion. Banks prefer to run their own private networks, as this reduces (does not necessarily eliminate) the risk of unauthorised access. This is not to say that banks do not wish to adopt international standards; it is merely that they cannot tolerate the risk of unauthorised access which is possible on an open network if a malfunction or security breach occurs.

CUGs with outgoing or incoming access. This eases some of the CUG restrictions, so that, for example, CUG members may make calls to non-members. There are also some more esoteric facilities relating to CUG access which are not discussed here.

Reverse charge calls. If reverse charging is specified, the called DTE administration pays for the call; normally the caller will pay. This could be useful for access to service bureaux. If all callers specify reverse charging, the bureau will then receive a single consolidated bill for all incoming calls, and can charge its users as appropriate. As well as simplifying the bureau's accounting procedures, this also gives the bureau a record of network usage, which could be valuable for planning purposes. This facility is requested in the facilities field.

Reverse charging acceptance. Clearly a host administration must reserve the right to refuse to accept reverse charge calls. As well as always having the ability to reject individual calls on this basis (possibly after checking the source host against a list of hosts allowed to reverse charge), a DTE may also elect to refuse any incoming reverse charge call, regardless of the originator. In this case, any attempted incoming reverse charge calls will fail at the DCE, rather than the remote DTE deciding on a per call basis. If this facility is requested, it applies to all subsequent calls until changed.

Local charging prevention. This prevents a DTE from setting up or receiving any calls for which the remote DTE is not paying. Thus a DTE may only make reverse charge calls, and the DCE will ensure that it does not receive reverse charge incoming calls.

Call statistics on cleardown. If requested in the call request packet, full details of packets sent and charge units incurred will be provided for the originating DTE, in the clear confirmation packet. There will normally be an extra charge for this service. The facility is useful for budget-conscious users, or where a user has a fixed budget for network access, which must not be exceeded, and thus needs to know what he is being charged on a running basis. (Most academics in the UK honding research grants would fall into one of these categories!) The information appears in a standard format, and is requested in the facilities field.

Call redirection/deflection and notification. When the remote DTE is not available, incoming calls may be rerouted to an alternative destination at the request of the remote DTE. A similar thing happens if you phone a Doctor's surgery out of hours. The difference between redirection and deflection is that the former is done by the remote DCE, whereas the latter is done by the remote DTE. Call deflection is a recent addition to the recommendation.

Called line address modification notification (CLAMN). This somewhat ugly name describes a facility for notifying the originating DTE that (and why) the call has been redirected (or deflected) to a different destination DTE.

RPOA subscription and selection. This relates to the connection of so-called *Registered Private Operating Agency* X.25 transit networks to 'official' X.25 PDNs. The original idea was that full CCITT members could install X.25 networks, and other members with RPOA status (see chapter five) could register to connect 'subsidiary networks' to them. DTEs could then nominate which RPOA networks they wished to access via the main network. Unfortunately that was before deregulation, and British Telecom now has RPOA status, even though it is the main common carrier in the UK. So the term RPOA can now effectively be taken to mean which other X.25 networks the DTE may have access to.

An example is the UK academic Joint Academic Network (JANET), which has gateways to the PSS network. JANET users must register for access to PSS, which charges for usage. (JANET does not directly charge.)

Hunt groups. This facility is similar to that provided in the telephone network, where a number of lines are available, and the first free one is located by dialling the first of several possible numbers. DTEs can similarly be associated. If the first is busy (i.e. all available LCs are in use) or otherwise unavailable, other DTEs in a given group can be tried in turn in the hope that one will accept the incoming call.

Connections to PSS are normally by datalines, which are specially customised leased lines from the host premises to the nearest Packet Switching Exchange (PSE). A DTE will be allowed to make up to n (default 1) simultaneous virtual calls (or have up to n PVCs) on each dataline. When this limit is reached, that dataline is in effect busy as far as callers are concerned.

Dial-up by packet terminals (hosts). This allows access to the PDN via the public switched telephone network (PSTN). The procedures are detailed in X.32. Prior to X.25(1984), only character terminals could access X.25 networks (via PADs; see the next chapter) in this way. It normally makes no sense to access PSS in this way from a host, as a typical PSTN line will have poor error characteristics, and there are no obvious compensating advantages. The main use will be for host sites remote from a PSE, where it is uneconomic to install a dataline.

That concludes the discussion of the 'traditional' X.25 facilities. One or two relating to OSI/RM are discussed later in the book. It should also be noted that the above description of X.25 facilities has been oversimplified in the interests of brevity and clarity. Complete details of all facilities may of course be found in the recommendation[1].

7.9   Areas not covered

A number of aspects of X.25 have been omitted in the interests of brevity and clarity. The following points in particular should be noted in this regard:

• X.25 is specified in terms of *operational states*, and the recommendation includes state transition diagrams which indicate how the various types of packets cause transitions between the various states, and which packets can and cannot be sent and received in the various states.

• Several counters and timers are defined, together with advice on what action should be taken if the timers expire or the counter limits are exceeded.

- The detailed coding of some fields has not been discussed. In particular, a table in the recommendation indicating how the diagnostic code field in a clearing packet should be coded extends over several pages, and the coding of facilities fields is also complex.

- Provision is made for the selection of higher level protocols such as X.29, using agreed encodings of the first part of the user data field. However this is a complex area, and there are a number of problem areas and potential conflicts, and no further discussion will be provided here.

Implementors of X.25 will of course need to know full details of these aspects, but a complete treatise on X.25, including implementation issues, could easily occupy an entire book on its own.

We will return to this important protocol twice. In the next chapter, we will examine protocols designed to allow access to X.25 networks by users of character terminals. In chapter fourteen, we will examine the current status of X.25 as it relates to the OSI/RM network service, although for reasons of space, interim proposals for using older versions of X.25 in the OSI context are no longer discussed in this book.

7.10   CCITT Recommendation X.75

X.25 defines procedures whereby a host (DTE) may access an X.25 network (DCE). X.75 defines similar procedures whereby X.25 networks may communicate with each other. The following is merely intended to give a feeling for the scope of the recommendation, which will not be discussed in detail.

X.75 defines procedures between what are referred to as *Signal Terminating Equipment* or *STEs*. X.25 is in many ways similar to X.25, in that three levels of procedure are similarly defined, as are the three phases of call setup, data transfer and call cleardown. Additional procedures are of course required to cater for the fact that this protocol is designed to handle virtual calls spanning connected X.25 networks. X.75 serves to correlate similar internal procedures in adjacent X.25 networks by providing a link (and management procedures) between networks. Just as procedures apply within each X.25 network, which are not visible to the DTE, but whose outcomes are reflected in the packets returned to the DTE (e.g. call connected, and P(R) fields in data packets), X.75 is likewise not visible, and is not normally of concern to host implementors.

It is perhaps worth noting here that the original maximum address length in X.25 call setup packets was insufficient to handle connections across multiple networks, and was increased as a result. Part of the reason has to do with OSI, as we shall see in due course.

7.11   References

1   The details of X.25 in this chapter are based on the 1988 revision, which is published by CCITT, Geneva, as part of their 'blue book' series. The packet level protocol {8208} and link access procedures {7776} are also available as ISO standards.

For those interested in earlier versions of X.25, draft versions of the 1976 and 1980 recommendations were reproduced in ACM Computer Communication Review. They are also of course available in the CCITT coloured books as appropriate (e.g. yellow for 1980 and orange for 1984). UK readers may also consult British Telecom Technical User Guide (TUG) no. 17 (covering PSS, and first issued in November, 1980).

2   ISO/TC97/SC6 N1403, 'Generic Requirements for Datagram Service', reproduced in ACM Computer Communication Review (October, 1977).

3   The same journal contains several articles which seek to clarify the original X.25 recommendation, and to point out some of its problems. See in particular the October, 1977 issue.

8   Character terminal handling in X.25 networks

8.1   General considerations

Part two concludes with an examination of the problems involved in interfacing character terminals to packet switching networks. A character terminal is a 'dumb' terminal, one which possesses no intelligence. When a character is typed, it is simply transmitted down the line without modification, usually as a single, asynchronously formatted ASCII character with even parity. When a character is received on the line, it is simply printed or displayed. No special protocol action is taken on what is received, and although there may be a receive buffer in the terminal, it will be used merely to store a few characters if they are being received faster than they can be printed. This definition of a character terminal includes the simplest types of microprocessor controlled terminal emulator, but excludes multidrop terminals operating under some variant of BSC or HDLC NRM. The definition also includes simple hardcopy terminals such as Teletypes. (Although strictly 'Teletype' is the name of a leading US terminal manufacturer, the term is commonly used generically to describe any terminal of this type.) Also included in the definition are Teletype compatible VDUs ('glass Teletypes'), which are in effect Teletypes with screens instead of hard copy. The simplest types of line printer may also be regarded as character terminals, although clearly these will normally be output-only devices.

Character terminals have long been used to access mainframe computers. The rows of terminals in university computing departments' terminal rooms are typical of this type of application. These terminals are normally connected by direct lines to the computer, and can only access a single mainframe. However, terminals soon started to be used to access remote mainframes (such as service bureaux) using dial-up PSTN connections. The user would dial the number of an auto-answer port on the computer using a dataphone and modem (typically using V.21 signalling), and the terminal would be automatically connected to a login server on the computer.

Although this has been the standard way of using terminals to access such facilities for many years, the advent of packet switched networks (PDNs) has led to major developments, where instead of dialling the mainframe direct, the terminal user can dial a special network interface, and be routed to the required mainframe through the network. This method of access has a number of clear advantages:

• Dialling the number of the desired host computer clearly gives flexibility, but as the number of hosts which can be accessed increases, it becomes increasingly tedious having to remember the correct number to dial in each case.

• While hosts connected to packet switching networks must obey the same procedures when communicating with any other remote host through the network, there is no similar requirement for hosts to adopt standard procedures for handling dial-up terminals. The user wishing to access several different sites may need to become familiar with several different access methods.

• The cost of using PDNs is usually related largely to the number of packets of data transmitted. In the case of character terminals, typically operating at 110, 300, 600 or 1200 bps, the data rate is not likely to be large, particularly as they tend to be inactive for a large proportion of the time. Therefore this method of charging is likely to be more cost effective for the user than having to pay time-dependent telephone charges, especially if trunk telephone rates are payable for a direct connection to the host.

• Most major countries now have well established PDNs. The great majority of terminals will be within the local call area of at least one PDN node. In some countries, local calls are either free, or cost a fixed amount independent of call duration (though this is not the case in the UK). It will be cheaper to dial a local call to the nearest PDN node than a trunk or even international call direct to the host.

• Host administrations which have interfaced to a PDN can use a single network connection at the host to access a number of different remote hosts. It is more efficient for them to use the same connection for terminal access as well, rather than having to provide large numbers of separate terminal dial-up ports. Even if a few dial-up ports are provided as well, there will be a probability of the ports all being busy at peak times, so that a direct terminal connection attempt may well fail.

Connecting a character terminal to a packet switching network is however not a trivial task, and poses several major problems:

• A computer host can be programmed to communicate in packet mode with a PDN as an X.25 DTE. There is no possibility of a character terminal doing this, as it is incapable of formatting the data into suitable packets. An interface must be provided between the terminal and the network, which can format the stream of characters from the terminal into packets and vice versa, and can also initiate, maintain and clear down virtual circuit connections on behalf of the terminal user.

• Different terminals have widely varying characteristics, and these individual characteristics need to be taken into account. It is not sufficient simply to provide packet formatting and so on. For example, while it may be quite acceptable to send 50 lines of continuous output to a hardcopy terminal, this would be most inappropriate for a VDU which can only display 24 lines at once; the other 26 lines would vanish from the screen before the user could read them. This implies that some means is required for defining a common network representation of the various terminal characteristics (e.g. page or screen length, and whether the terminal has hard copy), i.e. to define a *network virtual terminal* (*NVT*). This means that a **virtual terminal protocol** is required.

• Where several different hosts can be accessed, there is the problem that several different host operating systems will be involved. For historical reasons, operating systems have been designed in a way which forces terminal users to adopt procedures to suit the type of job control language provided by the operating system. These procedures tend to demand different things from terminals. For example, the UNIX operating system returns every character transmitted back to the terminal (i.e. *echoes* them). It assumes (requires) that the terminal does not echo typed characters, and does it on their behalf (except for passwords). Other operating systems, including those running on most mainframes, assume the opposite, and do not return any typed characters to the terminal. There is the additional complication that a terminal may be unable to switch its local echo off, but may wish to communicate with an operating system which normally echoes.

• Operating systems also differ in when they process terminal input. Whereas UNIX processes input characters as soon as they are received, many older operating systems will merely place them in an input buffer until (usually) carriage return (CR) has been typed, and then process the entire input line at once. If the terminal user wishes to edit his input, e.g. character or line delete, there can be difficulties if it is not clear whether the data to be edited is still in the terminal-network interface awaiting transmission, is inside the network, or has reached the remote host. These are only two of many examples of *terminal attributes* which need to be negotiated consistently between the terminal user, the network interface and the host.

• There are many possibilities, some quite bizarre, if this negotiation goes wrong. If confusion exists regarding whether the terminal or the host is expected to echo typed characters, there are two equally embarrassing possibilities. One is that nothing typed is echoed at all. The other is that everything typed appears twice on the printout (screen). In the second case, the problem is even worse if the copy is being returned by a remote host over a large network, since the second copy of the character echoed could arrive several seconds later, appearing in the wrong place, and the output on the terminal may well be unreadable.

• Terminals directly attached to hosts may also require access to remote hosts via a network. Protocols need to be designed which can allow a remote host to service terminals similarly, whether they be connected directly to the network or indirectly via another host. This has been a particular issue in designing X.25 terminal access protocols, as will be discussed later in the chapter.

Many different terminal handling protocols have been developed. The ARPANET was one of the first networks to provide character terminal support, via special devices canned 'Terminal Interface Message Processors' or TIPs. A useful paper by Magnee et al[1] gives a useful review of the state of terminal handling protocols in 1979. However we will concentrate here on the protocols developed to support X.25 packet switching networks, known as XXX or *triple X*. This is the set of recommendations X.3, X.28 and X.29. As usual we will concentrate on the 1988 versions; in fact there has been far less change to these recommendations than was the case with X.25 itself.

8.2   Terminal handling on X.25 networks

Terminal handling on X.25 networks such as PSS is covered by several CCITT recommendations, as shown in figure 8.1. The recommendations cover the case where a character terminal dials up a special terminal interface known as a *packet assembly/disassembly unit* or *PAD*, which forms part of an X.25 network node.

The main recommendations involved are as follows:

• **X.25**: This is used to communicate the packets between the PAD and the remote host. In X.25 terminology, the PAD can also be referred to as a 'character DTE', or *DTE-C* for short, and X.25 procedures apply between this DTE-C and the local DCE. As with the ARPANET TIP, both the DTE-C and the DCE will be part of a network node, the difference in the X.25 case being that the DTE-C is a special device, obeying an extra set of procedures on top of X.25; in the case of ARPANET, the 'terminal host' in the TIP pretends to be a normal host.

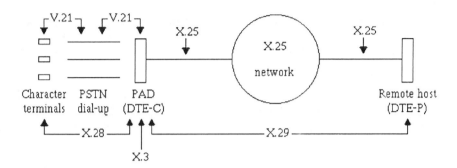

Figure 8.1 - scope of 'triple X' terminal handling recommendations

• **X.3**: This recommendation defines the characteristics of the PAD, in terms of a set of terminal-related *PAD parameters*. In effect, it provides a set of negotiable options which form the basis of a network virtual terminal definition.

• **X.28**: This recommendation defines how the terminal communicates with the PAD. It allows the terminal user to set up and clear down X.25 connections, manipulate PAD parameters, and so on. It also provides for limited editing by the terminal of data held at the PAD. We will see however that the selection of PAD parameters is not a trivial matter.

• **X.29**: This recommendation defines a 'high level' protocol between the DTE-C and the remote *DTE-P* (packet terminal, i.e. host). This protocol is designed to operate above X.25. It provides, among other things, for the remote host to access and manipulate PAD parameters, for the remote host to indicate that it wishes to clear down the X.25 connection, and for the equivalent of break pressed on a terminal to be relayed across the network. To summarise, X.29 is a virtual terminal protocol bearing some resemblance to the ARPA Telnet protocol[2].

8.3 The PAD in more detail

8.3.1 PAD operational modes

Before discussing the main PAD parameters, a few general comments are necessary on the PAD itself. A PAD forms an interface between a terminal and an X.25 network. As well as handling the relevant CCITT recommendations, it provides the terminal user with two main facilities:

- A *terminal buffer*, into which typed characters will be placed pending their forwarding in X.25 data packets. Under certain circumstances, this can be edited by the terminal user before the packet is forwarded.

- A *command mode*, in which the terminal user can communicate with the PAD via a command language rather than have the characters forwarded to the remote host (*transparent mode*). The user can switch between modes by typing an agreed character on the terminal. A terminal user will at times want to communicate with the PAD, and at other times will wish typed characters to be relayed direct to the remote host (data transfer mode).

In command mode, the terminal user communicates directly with the PAD. In the case of a PDN (e.g. PSS) PAD, this will be by means of the X.28 protocol. This allows, among other things, the user to set up, reset and clear down virtual calls, and to set/read various X.3 PAD parameters. (X.28 now allows PAD profiles to be selected as well; see later). Some workers dislike the X.28 user interface, particularly the way in which the host address must be specified. In many *private PADs* (in user premises) or *host PADs* (PAD functions implemented as part of host software), useful additions to X.28 are often provided. These include online help facilities and the ability to refer to frequently used hosts by name (e.g. MCC.CMS for the Manchester Computing Centre CMS service), rather than as a long stream of digits.

The operation of a PAD is essentially defined in terms of the current settings of its X.3 parameters. Some PAD parameters (by no means all) can be modified by the host as well as the terminal. There are two major modes of interaction between a terminal and a host, as follows:

- *Message mode*. This is the mode of access which is suitable for the majority of mainframes. Here, either the PAD or the terminal will echo typed data, which is forwarded to the remote host on typing some end of message character, usually (but not necessarily) carriage return. The input line can be edited in the PAD's terminal buffer before the PAD forwards it to the host.

    • *Native mode.* There are a number of applications which require an alternative which requires minimal PAD involvement. Consider a host running an operating system such as UNIX. The host expects to echo itself, and there are a number of special characters (such as ^C and ^S) which cause special action at the host (in this case, terminate process and stop output respectively). These characters could not be used correctly by the host if the PAD forwarded packets purely on a line by line basis. However, when using PDNs such as PSS which charge on the basis of the number of data packets transmitted, it is important to avoid sending a data packet for every character typed, because of the high cost and reduced efficiency, and so it usual to forward a packet when the user stops typing, e.g. when (say) three seconds has elapsed since the last character was typed. In this mode, all editing of characters must be done at the host, since the terminal user cannot assume that typed characters will still be in the PAD buffer. Native mode is also required for some types of highly interactive application (e.g. using a word processor).

A number of standard terminal-host interaction modes have been identified, to suit common terminal types and operating systems. Each mode implies that a defined combination of PAD parameters will be used. These are known as **PAD profiles**. The intention is to provide the remote host with a shorthand summary of all relevant parameter settings.

The PSS network allows a PAD profile to be defined in the protocol identification field of a call request packet (a specially formatted call data option). The start of the user data field of the X.25 call request packet is also used to identify the fact that X.29 is being used above X.25. The Q-bit in X.25 data packets is used to differentiate between terminal-host and PAD-host (X.29) packets. This sort of usage is not in the spirit of OSI, as we shall see in due course.

8.3.2   PAD (X.3) parameters

Figure 8.2 gives a list of X.3 parameters. Parameters with the highest numbers are the most recently specified, and therefore may not yet be provided by all PADs. Each parameter has various options, which can normally be set by either the terminal user (via X.28) or the remote host (via X.29). In all cases, there will be a default value which applies on initial connection of the terminal, and which will remain in force unless it is explicitly altered.

NUMBER	USAGE DETAILS		PERMITTED VALUES
1	Escape from data transfer mode to command mode possible?	•	nominated character/no
2	PAD will echo typed characters?	•	yes/no
3	Data forwarding characters	•	various combinations
4	Data forwarding timeout	•	none/n*50 msec (to12.8 secs)
5	PAD may use XON/XOFF flow control?		yes/no
6	Suppress PAD service signals?		yes/no
7	Action of PAD on BREAK	•	various (see text)
8	Deliver data to terminal?		yes/discard
9	Padding required after CR (print head delay)?	•	depends on data rate/number of characters
10	Line folding (long lines)	•	no/after n characters
11	terminal speed (cannot alter)		50 bps - 64 kbps
12	Terminal may use XON/XOFF flow control?		yes/no
13	PAD should insert linefeed after carriage return?		yes/no
14	Padding required after linefeed?		no/n characters
15	Terminal editing allowed in data transfer mode?	•	as defined in 16-18/no
16	Character delete character		none/nominated character
17	Line (buffer) delete character		none/nominated character
18	Line (buffer) display character		none/nominated character
19	Terminal type		display/hardcopy/don't care
20	Don't echo these characters		nominated characters (if any)
21	Terminal uses parity?		no/(check and/or send)
22	Page length (number of lines to send to terminal before waiting)		no wait/1-255 lines

NOTE:
  •   Parameter discussed in more detail.

Figure 8.2 - list of X.3 PAD parameters

In the following sections we will examine some further PAD issues in the context of the X.3 parameters available. It should be noted that the whole area of terminal handling is a messy compromise, because of the wide variety of terminal types and host conventions. Readers interested in some of the background on issues in this area could do worse than read references 3-5.

8.3.3   Echoing

When connecting a terminal to a remote host via a PAD, there are in fact three possible options for echoing characters. Under certain circumstances, the remote host may set this parameter. Care must of course be taken to ensure that the PAD, the terminal and the host all agree on where the echoing will actually take place, otherwise anything between zero and three copies of the typed character may appear on the terminal screen. Since echoing via the network may be delayed, the screen could end up looking a complete mess!

- The terminal itself may be set to 'half duplex' mode, so that characters are printed/displayed as they are typed. This is appropriate when the host runs a 'traditional' operating system which expects entire lines from the terminal. Such operating systems are developments from the days when input was via means of punched cards; each terminal line is treated as a 'card image', and it is assumed that the terminal will echo typed characters itself.

- The remote host may expect to echo characters as they are received. In this case the terminal is not expected to echo characters itself, merely to transmit them down the line. This is typical of more modern host operating systems. As characters are received, they are returned automatically to the terminal. (Exceptions exist. In particular, passwords are not echoed, and control characters such as ^C may either not be echoed or be converted to printable form such as that above.)

- Situations can arise where the terminal is incapable of echoing, but the host operating system does not echo. In this case it is possible for the PAD to echo characters. This is clearly necessary otherwise nothing typed would ever be displayed on the terminal.

The PAD may echo characters from the terminal, or echo nothing. In the first case, it is assumed that neither the terminal nor the remote host will echo. Where the PAD does not echo, the terminal may be set to 'simplex' and echo characters itself, or (in native mode) the remote host may be echoing characters typed.

8.3.4   Data forwarding considerations

As characters are typed on the terminal, they arrive at the PAD, which has to format them into X.25 data packets for transmission to the remote host. The problem is when the PAD should do this. There are several possibilities to be considered.

• The PAD could form a data packet for every character received. This will certainly be timely from the user's point of view, but would also be grotesquely inefficient. This was the dominant usage mode on ARPANET; it did not cause major problems there since there was no charge for network usage, and the network seldom became heavily loaded in any case. X.25 network managements such as British Telecom (PSS) 'discourage' this type of profligate usage by making the customer pay 'through the nose'. For example on PSS, it could cost up to 64 times as much as if data packets were filled with 64 characters each.

• Alternatively the user could try to minimise costs by requiring a data packet to be forwarded only when full. It is not hard to see that a lockup can occur in the absence of any other strategy.

• A third possibility is to nominate some character (e.g. carriage return), which will force the PAD to forward buffered characters. Unfortunately some operating systems (such as ICL's George 3) use the ESC character not carriage return, and UNIX is also happy to take either carriage return or linefeed. So in practice various sets of characters can be specified, e.g. carriage return, linefeed and ^C.

• Unfortunately this is of little assistance with 'native mode' operating systems, which respond as each character is received. So there is an additional option, which also avoids the lockup scenario hinted at above. This is to set a *data forwarding timeout*. If the user stops typing for (say) 3 seconds, the buffer is forwarded from the PAD regardless. This applies in addition to any other forwarding criteria. The timeout can be specified in multiples of 50 msec up to the maximum value which can be encoded in a single octet.

Clearly there is no set of options which can optimise both data packet utilisation and remote host response time, so the entire messy business has to be seen as a compromise. At least the options provided give reasonable flexibility.

8.3.5 Other PAD parameters

In this section we look in more detail at a few others of the more interesting PAD parameters. Not all parameters are examined, only those which are particularly interesting.

• **Action of the PAD when the BREAK key is pressed** on the terminal. BREAK generates a special signalling condition on the line, and is not an ASCII character. It is sometimes used as an interrupt on directly connected lines. But since it is not an ASCII character, it cannot be encoded, and thus it cannot be directly placed in a packet. The PAD can however be instructed to take one of several different actions if the user presses BREAK. It can be instructed to do nothing at all, or various things including sending an X.25 reset or interrupt packet (and/or an X.29 indication of break message; see §8.4), and placing the PAD in command mode.

• **Padding and line folding.** Some terminals (e.g. Teletypes) take a finite time to return the carriage to the start of the line, so that padding characters (e.g. NULs) may need to be inserted after the newline character(s) in order to give the print head time to return to column 1. This can be achieved by sending an agreed number of ASCII NUL characters, which simply provides a time delay. Line folding governs the optional forcing of a new line after every n characters. This is to prevent overprinting at the end of overlong lines (>72 or >80 for a typical Teletype, and >132 for a typical printer). (This is not normally required for VDUs which fold lines anyway, but is essential with some Teletypes). Similarly, it may be necessary for the PAD to insert LF after CR, if the host does not do so and the terminal requires one.

• **Local editing** (by the PAD). If this option is enabled, the user may nominate specific characters to be used as character delete, line (buffer) delete and (re)display buffer. Clearly local editing is inconsistent with some data forwarding options. Basically it is not available unless the user can be certain that the buffered data has not yet been forwarded in a data packet. It must also be clear that any editing must always be done by the same device (PAD or remote host). Problems such as long echoing delays over some networks must be tolerated when using native mode operating systems; PAD editing is not a solution.

• **Flow control.** X.3 provides a means of specifying XON/XOFF flow control in each direction, and also a means for the user to ask the PAD to stop sending after every n lines. XON/XOFF flow control acts as follows. When XOFF (^S) is sent by the terminal, the remote host is expected to stop sending, until such time as the terminal sends XON (^Q). Some terminals (such as the Zenith Z29) have a 'no scroll' key which alternately generates XOFF and XON, so that the user can freeze the display during a long listing. XOFF may also be sent by terminal emulation software if buffer space is running short.

Unfortunately, when used over networks, the response to XOFF pressed on the terminal may not be timely. In general XON/XOFF flow control does not work well in this situation. An alternative which is available to the terminal user is the 'stop after n lines' parameter, which works like the UNIX more command. The remote host waits after every screenful (or whatever) of information, until the user explicitly asks it to resume.

At this stage a 'health warning' must be issued to UNIX users. Screen editors such as Emacs and Jove may be user friendly and powerful, but the advice must be not to attempt to use them over networks. Apart from the slow response, if the terminal or PAD has to issue XOFF (^S), this will not silence UNIX, but will instead be taken by the screen editor as a request (^S) to enter search mode. Buffers will then overflow, with garbage displayed on the VDU screen, and Emacs (or Jove) search mode will have been entered, simply as a result of trying to display the first screen of information. This is a classic example of what happens when different parts of the software use the same control character for different purposes.

8.4   CCITT recommendation X.29

The purpose of X.29 is to allow the PAD and remote DTE to maintain control over the terminal-DTE dialogue. The principal aim of X.29 is to allow the remote DTE to enquire of the status of X.3 parameters, and in some cases to alter them. This is necessary so that the DTE (host) knows how to communicate with the particular terminal accessing it (or can customise the PAD by setting parameters which are consistent with the host's requirements).

The PAD informs the remote DTE that this is an X.29 call by using an internationally agreed value in the protocol identification field of the call request packet. X.29 control packets (formatted in accordance with defined procedures) are then relayed in X.25 data packets with the Q-bit set, whereas this bit is not set in packets containing terminal data. The following commands are available. A brief (and in some cases somewhat oversimplified) description is provided below for the principal commands:

• **Set PAD parameters** (host -> PAD). This is used by the host to instruct the PAD to alter the value of one or more of its parameters. Not all parameters can be set by the host. The PAD does not reply to the host, even if the command has been ignored. For this reason, its use is not recommended, as it could result in the host having incorrect information on the current state of PAD parameters.

• **Read PAD parameters** (host -> PAD). This is used by the host to enquire of the current setting of PAD parameter(s). The values will not be altered, but a reply (parameter indication) will be returned. The host needs to read PAD parameters, either so that it can alter them, or so that it can communicate with the terminal in a way which will be consistent with the current settings of the parameters.

• **Set and read parameters** (host -> PAD). Not all of the host's attempts to set parameters will necessarily succeed, as some parameters may not be altered. By asking the PAD to return the new value of the parameter, the host may determine if the change requested has been acted on or ignored by the PAD. The PAD again responds with a

• **Parameter indication** (PAD -> host). This is a response to a read parameter, or set and read parameter, command.

• **Invitation to clear** (host -> PAD). This is issued by the host to the PAD if the host wishes to terminate the call. For example the user service may be about to close down. This X.29 message is sent rather than the host simply issuing an X.25 clearing packet, so that any terminal data buffered at the PAD (or in transit in the network) can be forwarded to the host. A clearing packet would result in the loss of any such data. The PAD is expected to issue a clear request itself when all data has been delivered, and not to accept any further data from the terminal. (Note that the clearing packet will follow, and not overtake, preceding data in the same direction.) The host is entitled to clear the call itself if the PAD fails to do so within a certain time.

• **Indication of break** (PAD -> host). This is used by the PAD as a means of informing the host that the terminal user has pressed the BREAK key. Precisely what the host should do in this case is not specified in X.29, as this an internal host operating system matter. It may simply be ignored by some host operating systems. In theory at least, the host could issue this command to the PAD, but this is not recommended (nor is it at all clear what the PAD would be expected to do in this case).

• **Error** in command (either direction). This is used to notify X.29 command errors.

• **Reselection** (host -> PAD). The host wishes to clear the call and (in effect) divert it to another host. This could be appropriate if the terminal user had accessed a directory server; if the directory server passes particulars of the required destination to the PAD with a request to connect the terminal there instead, the user is thus relieved of the need to make the new call himself.

As can be seen, the X.3 parameter set allows a means of 'customising' terminal-host communications. However this approach falls short of the more generalised virtual terminal protocol provided by the ARPA Telnet[2] protocol. OSI work on virtual terminal handling (VT) will be discussed in chapter twenty one, where it will also be seen that the triple X approach violates OSI conventions, and must ultimately be abandoned for OSI compatibility

8.5   References

1   F. Magnee et al., 'A Survey of Terminal Protocols', Computer Networks, vol. 3, p. 299 (1979).

2   A description of the Telnet protocol may be found in the book by W. Stallings, 'Data and Computer Communications' (second edition), MacMillan (1988). The book also has detailed discussions of various other proprietary protocols and architectures.

3   'Character Terminal Protocols on PSS' (the 'green book'), issued by Study Group 3 of the British Telecom PSS User Forum, SG3/CP(81)/6 (February, 1981).

4   'Recommendations of Enhancements to X.3/X.28/X29', issued by Study Group Three of the PSS User Forum. This was first issued as a draft for discussion in August, 1981.

5   'Design Notes for PAD Implementors', produced by the Character Terminal Implementors' Group of the British Telecom New Networks Technical Forum, CP(84)/03 (March, 1984)

Part three

Introduction to OSI/RM and lower layers

In part three we introduce the OSI Reference Model (OSI/RM). To set the scene, we first discuss briefly some interim high level protocols developed for use in the UK academic community. These protocols were developed to satisfy urgent requirements, particularly for file and job transfer between and among University and Research Council sites, at a time when ISO had only just begun work on OSI/RM, and relevant application protocols were still some way off. We then introduce OSI/RM itself, together with brief descriptions of the functions of each layer. OSI service conventions are also discussed, as are general issues such as addressing and quality of service. To end this part of the book, we examine briefly the physical layer, and in more detail the data link and network layers of the WAN Reference Models, these layers corresponding most closely to HDLC (X.25 LAP) and X.25 packet mode. LAN topologies and the LAN Reference Model developed by IEEE are also covered in detail.

9   The UK academic interim 'coloured book' protocols

9.1   Introduction

The following standards for wide area networks were developed in the late 1970s for use in the UK academic community. Collectively they were known colloquially as the 'rainbow books', and more recently became known as the 'coloured books'. The colour given in brackets is the colour of the cover of the protocol specification, and is included since these protocols are often referred to as e.g. the 'yellow book'.

Beware: Many practitioners, especially outside the UK academic community, also refer to the CCITT recommendations as the coloured books. As usual there is ample scope for terminological confusion!

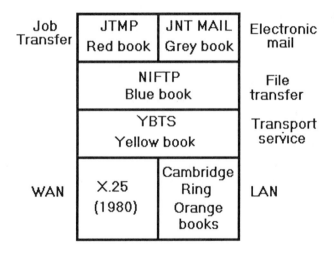

Figure 9.1 - the UK academic interim protocol hierarchy

The coloured book protocols form a hierarchy, intended to be implemented over either X.25(1980) WANs or Cambridge Ring (CR) LANs. Figure 9.1 shows the hierarchy, including the underlying networks. The individual protocols are briefly outlined in the following subsections, then discussed in rather more detail later in the chapter. (Although YBTS is designed to operate over the CR, for simplicity we will generally refer only to its operation over X.25(1980) in future. The CR is discussed briefly at the end of chapter thirteen.) When used above X.25, there is a six layer hierarchy, which as you read on will seem superficially similar to the OSI hierarchy. The layering is as follows:

- JTMP (or JNT MAIL)
- NIFTP
- YBTS
- X.25 packet mode procedures
- X.25 link access procedures
- X.25 physical procedures

As we develop OSI/RM and related protocols, we will at times return to the coloured book protocols, in order to see how well (or in most cases how badly) they fit into the OSI framework.

9.1.1 Yellow Book Transport Service (YBTS)

The *Yellow Book Transport Service (YBTS)*[1] was developed during the late 1970s, at a time when British Telecom were at an advanced stage of design of the PSS network, which was to use X.25(1980), and also at a time when the CR LAN was becoming popular in the UK academic community. The intention was to be able to write application protocols, namely for file transfer, job transfer and electronic mail, which would work equally well over either X.25(1980) or the CR.

The rationale behind YBTS therefore is that these application protocols can communicate with peer processes (i.e. of equal status) in other hosts using a set of *transport service primitives*, to a great extent without becoming concerned with the details of particular underlying network protocol implementations. In theory at least, the same application software can be used over any type of network, as it is not necessary for NIFTP to map to X.25 (or CR) packet types. YBTS is discussed in more detail in §9.2.

9.1.2 Network Independent File Transfer Protocol (blue book NIFTP)

The *Network Independent File Transfer Protocol (NIFTP)*[2], is a protocol which was devised to allow the transfer of entire files (or any other document which can be represented as a file, such as card reader input, lineprinter listings or job decks) between UK University and Research Council sites. A set of file transfer commands is provided by means of which the two hosts involved may co-operate in transferring the file, and these map on to YBTS primitives. NIFTP is discussed in more detail in §9.3.

9.1.3 Job Transfer and Manipulation Protocol (Red Book JTMP)

The *Job Transfer and Manipulation Protocol (JTMP)*[3] allows remote batch jobs to be submitted for processing at other hosts on the same or connected networks, and also provides facilities for specifying, modifying, interrogating and routing jobs. JTMP is based on NIFTP in that job decks, job output and job status information are transferred as if they are files, using NIFTP as an underlying file transfer mechanism. This protocol is discussed in §9.4.

9.1.4 Mail protocol (Grey book JNT mail)

The *JNT Mail Protocol*[4] is an electronic mail protocol based on the original ARPANET protocol[5], one of the earliest application protocols to be implemented over any network. (The exchange of documents and messages between participating users has always been a major use of ARPANET. For example, there is a Network Information Centre which holds an online library of ARPANET documentation.) The JNT mail protocol again uses NIFTP to transfer mail messages as if they were files. This particular protocol will not be discussed further in this book. The more recent, and OSI-compatible, CCITT Message Handling Systems (MHS) and Interpersonal Messaging System (IPMS) will be discussed in chapter twenty two.

9.2 Description of YBTS

Historically, YBTS evolved from a 'bridging protocol'[6] designed for use with the old experimental EPSS network provided by BT from 1974, and phased out from 1980. EPSS was BT's (then known as Post Office Telecommunications) first experiment with packet switching, and the bridging protocol was designed to provide users with a clean, high level interface to EPSS, so that applications could be written using a set of standard primitives which could be mapped automatically on to EPSS packets. Stated more formally, a transport service of this type seeks to achieve a clear division between the mechanisms which provide interprocess communication (the network) and the interpretation of the information so transferred (the application). Details of this bridging protocol (and EPSS) will not be covered in this book. It is however worth noting that this bridging protocol was designed specifically for use over EPSS, and did not claim to be 'network independent'.

Development of YBTS began in the late 1970s. Like its predecessor, it is a host-host protocol, but it was designed with the aim of use over two different underlying networks, which explains its earlier name, the *Network Independent Transport Service (NITS)*. YBTS provides a set of primitives (i.e. commands) for use by the next highest protocol layer in the hierarchy. YBTS claims to (but in fact does not) provide a network-independent interface between NIFTP and underlying networks, thus (in theory) obviating the need for NIFTP or higher level protocols to be specified in terms of a particular underlying network architecture or protocol.

It was originally anticipated that YBTS would be used below a number of different application protocols. However as file transfer was the most pressing requirement, all initial work was devoted to the provision of a file transfer service. Soon it became clear, as ISO work on the definition of OSI progressed, that there was no long term future for YBTS, and the only other protocol in addition to file transfer which was provided for use above the yellow book is TS29.

TS29 was a somewhat ill-fated attempt to run the X.29 PAD-DTE protocol over a YBTS connection, rather than directly over X.25. There was a potential conflict in that both YBTS and X.29 use the X.25 protocol identification field in call setup packets, so that any use by YBTS would be nonstandard. However a more serious problem encountered was that only academic community hosts knew anything about YBTS. In particular, PSS PADs had no knowledge of TS29 and would use the conventional X.29 over X.25 approach to all hosts. In this case a YBTS host connected to PSS was still liable to receive X.29 calls from third parties, even if it used TS29 to communicate with private PADs within the academic community. Thus TS29 could only be used between a host PAD or private PAD using YBTS, and a remote DTE also using YBTS. In practice therefore hosts had to implement both TS29 and X.29 over X.25, which would hardly seem an ideal approach! In fact X.29 itself violates the OSI philosophy, in that it is an application protocol sitting directly above a network service, as will become clear in the next chapter. Substantial progress has already been made on a replacement for triple X, a virtual terminal (VT) application service and protocol; see chapter twenty one.

9.2.1   The transport connection

YBTS provides a transparent connection between two NIFTP processes. We can generalise any service of this type in a layered hierarchy, as being provided by a given layer (the *service provider*) to the layer immediately above it (the *service user*). In this case YBTS is the service provider, and NIFTP is the service user. YBTS itself uses the underlying X.25 network to implement the service, as shown in figure 9.2. The way in which YBTS works internally, or accesses lower layers, to implement its service, is (in theory) of no interest, and indeed unknown, to the service user. In the case of YBTS, the theory is therefore that the designers of NIFTP (and protocols above NIFTP) should not need to be aware that the underlying network is X.25(1980) or the CR. As we shall soon see, this idea that NITS offers network independence to the protocols above it proves to be a myth.

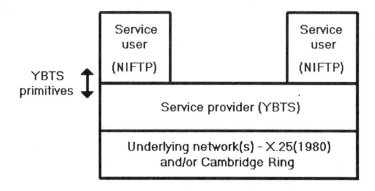

Figure 9.2 - users and providers of YBTS

The basic philosophy of YBTS is to set up a *transport connection* between two hosts. This may be over a single network, or may span several networks, in which case YBTS is also implemented in the *gateways* connecting the intermediate networks, as shown in figure 9.3. As far as the hosts running NIFTP are concerned, YBTS provides the means to transmit an octet stream of amorphous data, together with the ability to define data marks for synchronisation purposes.

9.2.2   YBTS primitives

As already mentioned, YBTS was primarily developed to operate over X.25(1980). As a result, the YBTS primitives provided closely match what can be achieved with an X.25(1980) underlying network. This immediately raises the question of whether YBTS can be regarded as truly network independent. In fact it was never truly network independent, and as X.25 evolved, it became impossible to use YBTS over more recent versions of X.25, and due to its interim nature, there seemed little point in modifying YBTS to fit X.25(1984) in any case.

A functional specification of YBTS appears in the Yellow Book[1]. The specification includes details of how to implement YBTS over X.25(1980), although as this version of X.25 is now obsolete, there is little point in discussing this mapping here. Instead we will briefly discuss the primitives provided; this will serve as a useful introduction to the primitive concept as used in OSI, although YBTS is in no way compatible with the OSI transport layer discussed in chapter fifteen, as we shall see.

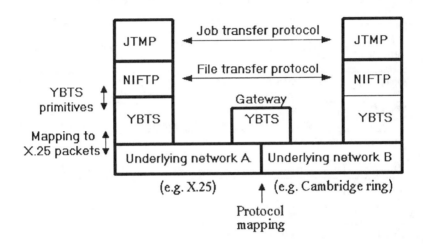

Figure 9.3 - Use of YBTS across two networks

Figure 9.4 summarises the YBTS primitives and their parameters, and also indicates the X.25 packet types on to which the primitives are mapped. A brief discussion of each primitive will suffice to give a basic understanding of YBTS. Although still widely used at University sites at the time of writing, YBTS is rapidly becoming obsolete, and plans are well advanced at most sites for its replacement. At the end of the chapter we will summarise the reasons why YBTS is now obsolete.

It is perhaps worth reiterating that YBTS is given primitives by the layer immediately above it (NIFTP), and relays them to the peer NIFTP. YBTS generates its own primitives only to notify NIFTP of errors which have been encountered on the underlying network connection (notably X.25 resets and disconnects).

Connect

This is used (by NIFTP) to set up a connection to another host, so that a file may be transferred (or whatever is required by the protocol above NIFTP, as appropriate). Therefore both X and Y host addresses are provided. These addresses are nowadays unique host addresses as defined by the Name Registration Service (NRS), based at the Manchester

Computing Centre (MCC). All YBTS stations can use these structured addresses to find a suitable route through the various connected networks. The destination address typically also contains a *generic service name*. In other words it contains, for example, a name which means 'any instance of an NIFTP service at Y'. Thus the receiving NIFTP knows to set up a new association. (For an exception to this rule, see under accept below.)

PRIMITIVE NAME	PARAMETERS	FUNCTION	X.25 EQUIVALENT
CONNECT	host addresses, quality of service, text	request setup of transport connection	call request, incoming call
ACCEPT	recall address, quality of service, text	confirm acceptance of transport connection	call accepted, call connected
DISCONNECT	reason, location, text	close or refuse transport connection	clearing packets
DATA	data	user data	data packets
PUSH	(none)	data mark, force delivery	M-bit not set in data packet
DATA + PUSH	data	data + data mark	as PUSH
EXPEDITED	priority data	'fast' delivery	interrupt packet (note 1)
RESET	reason, location, text	reset transport connection	reset packets

NOTEs:
1   Only one octet of data can be placed in an X.25(1980) interrupt packet. In addition no expedited channel exists over a Cambridge Ring. Therefore this primitive is virtually worthless.
2   An ADDRESS primitive was originally provided in case host addresses needed transforming between networks. A global host naming scheme (Name Registration Service, NRS) made this redundant.

Figure 9.4 - YBTS primitives

The *explanatory text* field is not particularly interesting; it is merely provided for a comment to be displayed on a system console, or stored in a log file. It could, for instance, be a brief description such as 'transfer file F from X to Y'.

The *quality of service(QOS)* field is more interesting. This is a concept which is important in OSI. A protocol layer can require some minimum functionality from the layers below. For example, it could specify a maximum acceptable error rate and transit time, a maximum failure probability and/or a minimum acceptable throughput. If the underlying network(s) cannot provide the required QOS, enhancement is then required somewhere below the requesting layer; this layer is typically an application at the top of the protocol hierarchy.

The idea of QOS is closely related to network independence. Provision of a consistent QOS regardless of the underlying network is crucial to the design of OSI applications. Unfortunately YBTS never had the capability to provide any enhancement, so that in the context of YBTS, the QOS merely remained an interesting theory. The QOS field therefore contains a default value which means 'whatever is available'. The fact that failures in X.25 networks simply get passed on to NIFTP does not help the latter at all. OSI takes QOS much more seriously, and 'best efforts' are normally made to recover from network failures and the like.

Accept

This is returned by Y if it is happy to set up the YBTS connection. The criteria used by Y to decide this are not specified by YBTS, but typically the connection would be accepted if the requested NIFTP (or JTMP, or JNT mail) service was available. For a new association, the *recall address* returned indicates a specific instance of NIFTP (or whatever), and this recall address can be used later to re-establish a transport connection which failed mid way through a file transfer (e.g. because of the failure of an intervening network). In this case the connect used to re-establish the failed connection contains the recall address, not a generic one.

Disconnect

This primitive is used (by NIFTP) either to refuse the transport connection in the first place, or to terminate it when both hosts have finished with it. It is a *confirmed service*, i.e. a matching disconnect is expected in return from the peer NIFTP station.

Unfortunately disconnects can also occur because of failures in an intervening network, in which case they are issued by YBTS, the location parameter indicating (roughly) where the failure occurred (which host or gateway YBTS issued the disconnect). It is not clear how this information can be of use to NIFTP, and it is equally clear that YBTS makes no attempt to recover a failed connection on behalf of NIFTP.

Data

Any amount of data can be sent in data primitives, which are simply mapped to X.25 data packets with the M-bit (more data bit) set. Packets are normally transmitted as and when they can be filled, and all data packets are considered to be associated until a push primitive is issued.

It is perhaps worth mentioning that data is distinguished from other YBTS primitives by setting the Q-bit in X.25 data packets unless they are being used to convey data. The first few octets of data in a data packet indicate the primitive type if the Q-bit is set.

Push

In itself this data forwarding algorithm is inadequate to avoid lockups, for reasons similar to those discussed in §8.3.4 for character terminals. So push is used to force the sending transport station to forward all buffered data, even if it will not completely fill a data packet. In addition the M-bit is not set in this packet, so that the push will be visible at Y. This allows the push to be used as a data mark by protocols above YBTS.

In addition, a push can be implied at the end of a data primitive by using the **data + push** variant.

Expedited

This is, according to YBTS, similar to the data primitive, but specifying the transmission of the data via some 'priority channel' through the underlying network(s). You are already aware that in X.25(1980) only one octet can be placed in an interrupt packet, and that receipt of each interrupt packet must be confirmed (by Y) before X can send another one. So this hardly qualifies as a fast data channel! Given that the CR provides no priority data mechanism at all (other than possible 'queue jumping' within a station), it will come as no surprise to learn that this primitive was not found particularly useful.

As we will see in chapters fourteen and fifteen, the equivalent OSI service is a *negotiable* option, which takes into account the fact that a suitable service may not be available for transporting expedited data across an underlying network. (If it is unavailable, then it may not be used.) Unfortunately YBTS says nothing about the expedited primitive being optional, which is one of the yellow book's many problems. In practice the expedited primitive, though defined, is never used.

Reset

When an X.25 reset is received (or a YBTS reset relayed from a remote gateway in an X.25 data packet), this means that data has probably been lost. A matching reset is returned in confirmation. X.25 resets and YBTS resets behave similarly, in that any data encountered by the reset is destroyed. A well behaved OSI transport station would do something to recover this lost data, as will be explained in chapter fifteen. But YBTS merely passes the reset on to NIFTP, leaving the application protocol to worry about data loss inside the network. We will see that this is not in the spirit of OSI.

The YBTS reset primitive has parameters for a 'coded reason', location (e.g. the host or gateway which generated the reset) and explanatory text. But again there is a problem. This is that if the reset is issued by X.25 itself, it will not contain enough information to allow YBTS to fill in the parameters when it passes the reset on to NIFTP. Also any reason parameter in a YBTS reset will be lost if it collides with an X.25 reset. This is yet another grey area.

9.2.3   Current status of YBTS

YBTS was to some extent a 'panic measure' so that protocols such as NIFTP could be written to operate over either X.25(1980) or the CR. The primitives provided map (in a sometimes rather ugly way which we will not discuss) on to X.25 packet types. They did not map in any sensible way on to existing CR protocols such as the Basic Block[7] and Byte Stream[8] protocols, which necessitated the abandonment of these protocols, and the specification of a rather ugly four-layer protocol stack above the CR, described in the orange books[9].

Since YBTS is in effect little more than a thin shell over X.25(1980), it hardly hides its eccentricities from NIFTP. In particular resets and disconnects resulting from X.25 will merely be passed on, and there is no sensible way in which the YBTS expedited primitive can be implemented on X.25(1980) networks. Furthermore, no attempt is made to define the QOS, although a QOS parameter is provided. So clearly YBTS could have been improved significantly. The problem was that by the time all sites had implemented it, it was rapidly being obsoleted by OSI developments. Therefore the current thrust is towards replacing YBTS (and NIFTP and the rest) as soon as suitable OSI products are available. A suitable replacement for YBTS itself has been available for several years now, and replacements for NIFTP, JTMP and JNT mail are now available as well. The difficulties are mainly in phasing the conversion to minimise disruption, and the provision of conversion between the old and the new protocols, to cater for the situation where hosts which have converted to OSI require to communicate with those which have not yet done so. The price to be paid for being pioneers is the effort required to convert to a later standard which the interim protocols are in no way compatible with.

9.3   Description of NIFTP

9.3.1   Basics of NIFTP

In this section, we examine the 1981 version of NIFTP[2]. The function of this protocol is to allow bodies of information (documents or files) to be transferred between remote computer systems over an unspecified underlying network. Central to the protocol are the ability to define any file in terms of a set of standard characteristics or *file attributes*, and a way of indicating the means by which a file should be transferred and stored (or printed, etc.). NIFTP is designed to support transfers involving hosts varying from the most sophisticated mainframes down to simple devices such as card readers, printer controllers and simple microcomputers.

Although NIFTP was originally intended for use within the UK academic community, it gained the support of some manufacturers, and also a few European organisations. It should however be remembered that NIFTP was always intended as an 'interim' protocol, pending further developments relating to OSI. An OSI file transfer, access and management (FTAM) service and protocol now exists {8571}, and this will be examined in chapter nineteen. NIFTP itself will be further discussed in the context of OSI in the same chapter.

9.3.2   The virtual filestore and attributes

Any conventional filestore can be described abstractly in terms of a single, standard representation. This approach is used in NIFTP. The representation defined in NIFTP, the *virtual filestore*, is used in the protocol to specify the file transfer to be undertaken, with mapping performed by both communicating hosts between the real filestores and this virtual filestore description.

The virtual filestore is a set of attributes which identify or define the file, and how it is to be transferred. Some attributes (e.g. the filename) have values which may be constant throughout the life of the file. These are known as *storage attributes*. Others specify the conditions of the transfer, and may have no significance once the file is transferred; these are known as *transfer attributes*. The way in which a file is mapped on to or from the virtual filestore may differ considerably between hosts. However the information exchange is always conducted in terms of the set of standard attributes. This approach is similar to the way in which a character terminal is defined in CCITT recommendation X.3, as was discussed in chapter eight.

9.3.3   Brief outline of a file transfer

A file transfer using NIFTP proceeds in three distinct phases, as follows:

- **Initiation (negotiation) phase.** The NIFTP process on the host initiating the file transfer, known as the P process, issues a file transfer request, including a set of desired attributes, to its peer Q process on the other FTP host. This is the *start file transfer (SFT)* command. The Q process may accept the attributes (i.e. agree to the file transfer) unconditionally, or it may agree to the transfer conditionally, proposing a modified set of attributes. Either of these is relayed back via a *positive reply (RPOS)* command. Alternatively Q may reject the file transfer request, generally because the attributes are incompatible with the Q process' requirements or facilities. For example a request for Q to send a file which does not exist cannot be accepted. This is done via the *negative reply (RNEG)* command. The P process may also decide not to proceed with the file transfer if the RPOS from the Q process specified attributes which are incompatible with its own requirements, in which case the termination phase is entered. For example P may wish to receive a file from Q, and it turns out that P has insufficient room to store the file. (P will not know this until Q returns the length of the file as an attribute in the RPOS.)

It should already be clear that a file transfer will only be possible between peer processes which can come to some agreement over a set of attributes, and this requires careful specification of the virtual filestore. Thus the outcome of this initial negotiation either results in the data transfer phase being entered to send the file, or the termination phase being entered to give up, as explained below.

The *mode of access attribute* is the most interesting one, and is worthy of some further discussion. It determines both the direction of transfer, and (in general terms) what should happen to the copies of the file at the sender and receiver once the transfer has completed successfully. For example it specifies whether a received file may replace one with the same name, or be appended to it. If either is not permissible (depending on the direction of transfer), P will not allow the file transfer to proceed. A further variant specifies whether the sender should keep or delete its copy after the transfer has successfully completed. It is important to note that the direction of transfer is as viewed by P. This is an asymmetric procedure. Transfers from P to Q are considered to be received (read) files, and vice versa.

Two further eccentricities are worth mentioning. One is that JTMP and JNT mail use agreed mode of access attributes (read and make) the physical results of which have nothing whatsoever to do with reading or writing a conventional file in a filestore. Furthermore, to cater for hosts which did not support JTMP at all but implemented NIFTP, and wished to be able to support job transfers, further values give/take job input/output were also defined. There is a discussion of the eccentricities of this structuring at the end of the chapter.

• **Data transfer phase**. Assuming that the attribute negotiation has been completed successfully, the data transfer phase is entered, in which the file is transferred as a sequence of records of agreed maximum length (an attribute). As the transfer may be either from P to Q, or from Q to P, the NIFTP stations are referred to as S (sender) and R (receiver) during this phase.

The data transfer phase uses various Sender and Receiver commands, which allow for the definition and acknowledgement of data marks, rollback to an earlier data mark, resumption in a later file transfer, the selection of the transfer code, and various commands for terminating or aborting the transfer, and for notifying errors. Note that the sender can be either P or Q. In fact many of the facilities offered are similar to those offered by the OSI session layer, as will be discussed in chapter sixteen.

One important facility which is provided in the data transfer phase allows for the insertion and acknowledgement of *data marks*, so that a file transfer which has ran into difficulty part way through (e.g. due to network trouble) can be *rolled back* to the last acknowledged data mark before the transfer failed. These map on to YBTS push primitives. Rollback will typically occur if an X.25 reset (relayed as a YBTS reset) is received, as data will then have been lost. The use of data marks also allows the possibility of *resumption* in a later file transfer (from the start or any acknowledged data mark). This is an optional facility the possible use of which is negotiated in the initiation phase. It is particularly useful in cases where there has been a serious failure in the underlying network(s), such as loss of the underlying X.25 VC (relayed as an unexpected YBTS disconnect) making it impossible to complete the file transfer at the present time. It can also be used to give up the transfer for the time being because, say, P or Q is about to shut down its service, and not all of the file has been transferred yet. Provision of a resumption facility was a fundamental design aim, as the cost implications of having to retransmit a large file in its entirety, when the great majority of it has been correctly received, are obvious on a network such as PSS which charges on the basis of the amount of data transmitted. In the latter case the recall address is used as was returned in the original YBTS accept primitive; see §9.2.2.

• **Termination phase.** When all of the file has been transferred, or at the request of either process during the data transfer phase if problems arise, or if the initial negotiation fails, the file transfer may be terminated by the exchange of *stop* and *stopack* commands. If a transfer has to be aborted prematurely (as opposed to being abandoned gracefully), the termination phase cannot be used.

9.3.4 Relationship of NIFTP with other protocol layers

NIFTP is implemented over YBTS. For example, the initiation phase requires a connect primitive to be issued, and an accept to be returned, before the communication can proceed. The file itself is transferred using data primitives, and disconnects will be exchanged following normal termination of the file transfer. It should be noted that the termination phase must be completed before a disconnect is issued, otherwise one or both of the signoff messages could be lost, leaving the file transfer in an unknown state, and causing recovery problems.

The parameters of the NIFTP SFT, RPOS and RNEG will not completely fit into X.25 call setup packet user data fields. So even if SFT can fit in the user data field of a YBTS connect, several X.25 data packets will have to be sent after the virtual call is set up. Similarly, the parameters of the STOP and STOPACK will not fit into the user data fields of clearing packets, and must therefore be sent as X.25 data packets before the X.25 call is cleared down.

YBTS reports all communication errors and failures in underlying networks to NIFTP. It is incapable of correcting them itself. For example if an X.25 reset occurs, NIFTP will receive a reset primitive from the transport station, and must then assume that data has been lost. This will typically result in rollback to the last acknowledged data mark. In this context, it should be noted that the fact that data marks and acknowledgements are part and parcel of NIFTP means that no assumption is made that all errors which have occurred in the underlying network have been corrected by YBTS. Indeed, it is common for high level protocols to include recovery facilities of their own. This is in fact a complex issue which we will return to more than once.

Above NIFTP, JTMP and the JNT mail protocol use NIFTP as an underlying mechanism for transferring job decks and messages. JTMP protocol commands map on to NIFTP commands. (Details will not be provided.)

9.4 Description of JTMP

9.4.1 The need for a job transfer protocol

The information provided here relates to the September 1981 release of JTMP. What follows is intended only to give a flavour for the protocol, and a number of significant features are either not discussed, or are glossed over. The full specification for JTMP may be found in the red book[3].

JTMP is a protocol for transferring and handling remote batch jobs. Although mainly intended for use in a wide area network environment, there is no reason why it should not also be used with hosts connected to CR LANs, since the underlying YBTS has been implemented over this network. The protocol uses NIFTP; job descriptions, output, etc. are transferred between sites as 'files' in the context of NIFTP. NIFTP is not concerned with what is in the file; it is merely transparent data as far as NIFTP is concerned.

The environment in which JTMP is designed to operate can best be illustrated by considering a job submitted to a University Regional Computer Centre such as the ones at Manchester, Edinburgh or London. When a user submits a job, he does so by means of a job deck. This is checked for validity and, if it seems to be valid, it is queued depending on the priority, until it can be run on the target machine. The job deck includes a variety of information, of which the following is most pertinent:

- Which machine the job is to be run on, if there is more than one available.

- What actions are to be performed on the job, for example compile and execute, list file, compile and save object file to filestore, execute only, compile with listing and execute.

- What output is to be returned to the user, for example a job log indicating what happened to the job, a listing of the source program, the results of the execution, or a copy of the object file.

- Where output is to be sent, for example to a printer, to the filestore, or back to the originator via the network.

• What other peripheral devices are involved, for example card punches and magnetic tapes.

• Various accounting and control information, such as the time at which the job should be run, how long the job should be allowed to run for, the usercode and password of the user, and the job priority.

Providing suitable job control to achieve this is not too difficult if you are familiar with the job control language (JCL) used by the site. Users quickly learn how to submit the types of jobs they want to run. They might even be able to enquire as to the status of a job or cancel it, although submitting batch jobs to many batch processing services is like putting them into a 'black hole'.

What happens in a wide area network context, where several sites are interconnected, is that a demand arises for job submission between sites. Jobs can potentially be run on a wide variety of machines in University computing services and elsewhere. However in the absence of a job transfer protocol, how are these sites to be accessed, and how is the remote site to be informed of the nature of the job?

JTMP has been designed to overcome some of these problems, so that jobs can be submitted between sites, and their progress monitored, and to a limited extent modified, as required. NIFTP allows files to be exchanged between sites without needing to know too much detail about the fine details of the filestores at the remote sites. Thus, in the same way that NIFTP includes a virtual filestore definition, JTMP in effect includes a definition of a 'virtual job processing resource'. JTMP similarly has no knowledge of the details of the job it is transferring.

It follows from this that JTMP does not the user of the need to know the JCLs at the sites on which he runs jobs. The 'data' part of a job description is transparent to JTMP, and it is this which contains job-specific details such as 'compile file X using FORTRAN' or whatever. Alas, while the idea of having a virtual job control language sounds an excellent idea in theory, the problems involved in defining a universal virtual JCL which is not unbelievably complex (far moreso than any individual JCL) are daunting, and little progress has been made to date by any standards body in this regard. Machines differ far more widely in the way they process jobs than in the way they handle filestores, and some facilities provided defy neat classification.

Therefore JTMP is not, nor should it be expected to be, a substitute for learning how to format job decks, and which JCL commands are required at a given site. Nor does there seem to be any prospect of such a substitute in the foreseeable future. However JTMP provides several valuable services, as will now be outlined.

9.4.2 General outline of JTMP

JTMP provides a variety of facilities which, taken together, enable the following functions to be supported:

- The submission of a job at one site for processing at a different site; this includes the possibility of a job being partly processed at several different sites.

- The definition of job transfer mechanisms in a consistent manner, and independently of the eccentricities of individual host operating systems.

- The specification of how the output from a job should be handled (disposed); this includes the ability to return the output to a third party site.

- The interrogation and/or alteration of the status of a job after it has been submitted (e.g. for the purpose of suspending or abandoning it, or merely to see how it is progressing).

JTMP functions by transferring and processing *tasks*, which are treated as files and sent using NIFTP. JTMP is concerned with the content of the tasks, and the actions required to be performed relating to these tasks. The mechanics of transferring the tasks are basically the concern of NIFTP, although JTMP includes a set of commands that broadly map on to those of NIFTP.

There are a number of different types of task, the type determining the action JTMP will take on its receipt. Tasks are formatted into *descriptors*, which include the task type. The main types of descriptor are as follows:

- **Execution**. This contains something which can be 'executed', most typically what would be commonly understood as a batch job.

- **Document disposition**. This contains information on what to do with the output produced by a job.

- **Status/modify request**. This contains a request to modify job particulars, or to return job status.

- **Status/modify response**. The response to the request, containing status information or confirmation (or otherwise) of the modification.

- **Report disposition**. These are used to report significant changes in job descriptors, such as the creation ('spawning') of a new descriptor, or the migration of a descriptor between host sites.

It is worth noting that a JTMP job may be specified to be partly executed at several different sites, e.g. submitted by W, to be compiled at X, to be executed at Y, and the object code to be stored at Z. JTMP is powerful and complex, too much so for more than a brief description to be possible here. When an execution descriptor is sent to another site, e.g. from W to X, it will be necessary for W to include information on any subsequent activity relating to the same job, such as that in the above example, as well as instructions for the immediate attention of X. In order to do this, it is necessary for W to include some information in the execution descriptor sent to X about future execution and document disposition descriptors which are to be generated later by sites X and Y. This is done by including, at the end of the descriptor, sufficient information to allow X and Y to generate new descriptors. This potential descriptor is known as a descriptor *proforma*. In this case, the proforma would also need to contain information on precisely what processing had to be done, as well as the type of the descriptor.

Each proforma contains the means for the receiving site to generate a new descriptor based on that proforma. For example a job which requires partial processing at sites X, Y and Z will be sent to X as a task, with the inbuilt capability for X to *spawn* a new proforma containing details of the action required at Y, which is then sent from X to Y, Similar actions would take place at Y, for Y to Z. In other words multiple *nesting of proformas* is possible, and in theory at least, any number of sites may be involved.

One difficulty in running JTMP over NIFTP is that a job deck is not really a file, and it is not clear what the instruction 'take this file and store it in your filestore' is supposed to mean, if it is actually a job for execution. For this reason agreed values of this NIFTP 'mode of access' have been agreed, which relate more to the direction of transfer than anything else.

One final point worthy of mention is that each JTMP site maintains a *network status table* or *NEST*, which contains details of those JTMP sites (of interest to this host) which are currently able to offer a JTMP service. The idea is to keep these records accurate, so that sending long job decks to sites which then refuse to process them is avoided as far as possible.

9.5 Why the protocols are now obsolescent

We have at various points in the chapter suggested that the coloured book protocols are on the way out. For completeness, the main reasons for their demise will now be summarised.

- YBTS is based on the obsolete X.25(1980). When PSS and the Joint Academic Network (JANET) upgraded to X.25(1984), YBTS became unable to utilise many of the new features provided. Indeed, as hinted at in the asides above, YBTS is not even fully compatible with X.25(1980).

- Apart from X.25, YBTS is only designed to operate over the CR. But while CR was popular at the time, the LAN world is now dominated by three technologies, CSMA/CD bus (Ethernet), Token Bus and Token Ring. Indeed the number of Ethernets alone in the academic community far outstrips the number of CRs. Not only are these three LAN technologies dominant, but they are the only ones for which there has been significant OSI-related activity. Unfortunately YBTS cannot operate over any of them.

- Perhaps most seriously of all, the coloured book hierarchy is completely incompatible with OSI/RM. We shall see in due course that NIFTP includes features pertinent to no fewer than four different OSI layers. Worse than that, we have one application (JTMP) above another (NIFTP), whereas in OSI they should be equal partners in the same layer.

- Another problem with the YBTS/NIFTP/JTMP stack is that it is restricted entirely to applications which can be regarded as file transfers. In some cases this is only possible by 'fudging'. JTMP and (particularly) electronic mail sit uncomfortably above a file transfer protocol. More seriously, many applications are utterly unrelated to file transfer; these cannot be supported at all with the coloured book protocol stack.

So the academic community was faced with a major headache. Not only had new, OSI compatible, products to be phased in as a matter of some urgency, but all manner of conversion software was also required to cater for the situation where some sites had converted, and others had not. The Joint Network Team has produced a report[10] setting out the procedures which academic sites should adopt during this transition, which at the time of writing is now well under way. This is supported by various more detailed technical documents.

One final point should be made. Certainly the academic community could have continued to use the coloured books. After all they are proven products. Unfortunately, and this is the essence of OSI, unless the community converts to OSI products quickly, it will be denied the wider access which OSI compatibility brings. Fortunately many OSI products can be bought 'off the shelf'; the academic community had to do much of the development of the coloured book protocols itself. Clearly there is safety in numbers (at a cost).

9.6   References

1   'A Network Independent Transport Service' ('yellow book'), prepared by Study Group 3 of the PSS User Forum, SG3/CP(80)2.

2   'A Network Independent File Transport Protocol' ('blue book'), prepared by the FTP implementors Group of the Data Communication Protocols Unit, National Physical Laboratory, FTP-B(80).

3   'A Network Independent Job Transfer and Manipulation Protocol' ('red book'), produced by the JTP working party of the DCPU, DCPU/JTMP(81) (September, 1981).

4   'The JNT Mail Protocol' ('grey book'), C. J. Bennett, Department of Computer Science, University College London (January, 1982).

5   ARPANET RFC (request for comments) #680, 'Message Transmission Protocol'. See also ARPANET RFC #733, 'Standard for the Format of ARPA Network Text Messages', by D. H. Crocker et al.

6   The EPSS bridging protocol is discussed in the book 'Data Communication Protocols', by A. J. Swan, published in 1978 by NCC, Manchester. However, the information in this book is now out of date, having been overtaken by more recent events.

7   M. A. Johnson, 'Ring Basic Block Protocol', Computer Laboratory, Cambridge University (1980).

8   I. N. Dallas, 'Transport Service Byte Stream Protocol', Computing Laboratory, University of Kent (1980).

9   'Cambridge Ring Interface and Protocol Specifications' ('orange books' - two volumes), prepared by the JNT.

10   'Transition to OSI Standards', Final Report of the Academic Community OSI Transition Group (July, 1987), available from the Joint Network Team, Rutherford Appleton Laboratory, Chilton, Didcot, Oxfordshire OX11 0QX.

10 The ISO OSI Reference Model

10.1 Introduction

This chapter is concerned with basic concepts relating to the ISO Open Systems Interconnection Reference Model (OSI/RM) {7498}[1]. The model provides a common basis for the co-ordination of the development of structured protocols designed to facilitate open system interconnection. It is a framework for the design of standard protocols and services conforming to the various layer specifications, rather than as a definition of those protocols and services.

10.1.1 What is an open system?

An open system is one which is open to others for the purpose of information exchange, in the sense that all open systems use the applicable standards. A 'system' may be taken to include those components which, together, form an autonomous whole capable of performing information processing. This may include one or more computers, associated software, peripherals, terminals, human operators, physical processes, physical transfer mechanisms, and so on. In other words, the definition can be taken to include any set of resources which might use some underlying communication resource to communicate with another system or systems.

This definition may sound rather vague, and may even appear to beg the question, and indeed we will see that the entire reference model is couched in language which, at times, seems abstract almost to the point of incomprehensibility. This was a deliberate decision, as it was considered that any direct references to existing terminology (host, frame, packet and so on) could prejudice the generality of the model, and might lead some workers to assume some correspondence with existing protocols which was not the intention. We will return to the terminology issue later in the chapter.

OSI/RM assumes the existence of some physical medium connecting the systems, which is assumed to be of the telecommunication type. In effect, as far as this chapter is concerned, it can be assumed to be one or more WANs. Initially OSI/RM only covered WANs. More recently, IEEE 802 LAN standards were also adopted as an alternative for the lowest three layers of OSI/RM. These are discussed in chapter thirteen.

10.1.2 The purpose of the reference model

As indicated above, OSI/RM provides a framework whereby open system applications may communicate with each other, using the set of OSI resources. This communication is achieved, at least in the abstract, by providing application processes with a set of resources which are *layered* in order to provide a structured hierarchy, as will be described later. OSI/RM classifies application processes as manual, computerised and physical, and cites the following as typical examples:

- Manual application: a person operating a banking terminal.

- Computerised application: a FORTRAN program executing in a computer centre and accessing a remote database; also the remote database management system itself.

- Physical application: a process control program executing in a dedicated computer attached to some industrial equipment, and linked into a plant control system.

It is clear from the above examples that the potential scope of OSI/RM is far greater than can be catered for by just the protocols discussed in previous chapters. As well as virtual circuit and datagram access using wide and local area networks, many other types of access could be consistent with this very general definition of an application process. This however is not an issue which is of any concern in the definition of the reference model itself, which merely defines a framework for future progress in the definition of standard protocols. Where a particular access technique (virtual circuits, say) is required, it is for other workers to define a suitable service definition and supporting protocol at a later date, the only constraint being that any protocols so developed should be consistent with the basic requirements as set out in the reference model. In the absence of a framework such as OSI/RM, future development of protocols would inevitably have become even more chaotic than it has been until recently, with no prospect whatsoever of open systems ever interworking except in special, isolated cases.

Therefore a framework such as OSI/RM was needed, and needed urgently. Provided that complete abstraction can be maintained, it is not too difficult to define such a framework. There are two main problems however:

- One penalty of pursuing this abstraction to the limit is that the reference model has become littered with vague 'internationalese', which can become hard to relate to any real protocol or system. We will soldier on for a while using the abstract terminology, but we will in due course discuss real examples based on the terminology of HDLC and X.25.

- Another difficulty is that enormous effort was required to define (let alone get agreement on) suitable and consistent OSI/RM compatible standard service definitions and protocols. Although this process is now largely complete except for the application layer, it has been slow, and a set of services which will cover every possible type of open system interconnection still seems an impossible goal.

10.2 General OSI conventions

Before discussing any of the OSI layers, it is worth explaining the basic mechanisms which apply to, and between, all OSI layers, regardless of the function of the layer. These concepts are crucial to an understanding of OSI. The material in this section is mainly drawn from the reference model itself, and OSI Service Conventions {8509}.

10.2.1 Layering concepts

Before we can discuss the main features of OSI/RM, it is necessary to understand the concept of layering, and for the purposes of this discussion we will, for the time being at least, adhere roughly to the standard ISO terminology.

OSI/RM defines a *seven layer protocol hierarchy*. Starting at the bottom, the underlying physical medium provides a basic (and at this stage unspecified) transmission mechanism. This is successively *enhanced* by layers above it, so that the user's application process is logically situated above the highest layer. See figure 10.1. Details of the various layers are not yet shown, but the combination of several layers for successive enhancement in this way is often referred to as a *protocol stack*.

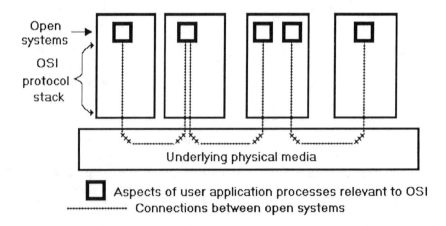

Figure 10.1 - OSI - basic reference model (RM)

This figure shows **connections** between application processes in open systems using some (unspecified at this stage) underlying telecommunication type physical medium. The means of providing this connection is structured, and the connection is achieved by co-operation between *adjacent layers* in a given open system, and between *peer layers* (i.e. equivalent layers) in the two end open systems, as shown in figure 10.2.

The initial version of OSI/RM was based on setting up, using and clearing down connections, where a connection has roughly the same significance as with YBTS, discussed in the previous chapter. This approach favours virtual circuit applications such as file transfer, but provides no support for datagram-based applications. The reference model was subsequently enhanced to include support for connectionless mode operation.

The connection is provided by these layers in co-operation, in the following way:

- Each layer, which we will refer to as layer n, provides a *service* to the layer immediately above it (layer n+1). The highest layer of all provides a service to the application itself.

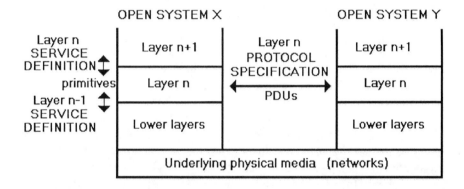

NOTE:
PDU   protocol data unit

Figure 10.2 - Communication between OSI layers

- Each layer provides that service by itself using the services of the layer immediately below it (the n-1 layer). The lowest layer uses the underlying physical medium. Therefore, for each layer, the service it provides to the layer immediately above it can be defined.

- Adjacent layers in the same open system communicate with each other using a defined interface. For example, layer n+1 communicates with layer n via a *n-service access point (SAP)*, and using a set of *n-service primitives*.

• This allows, for each layer, the definition of a *protocol* which governs how *peer entities* (i.e. implementations of a given layer in different open systems) communicate with each other in order to implement the service provided by this layer. *Protocol data units* (*PDUs*) are exchanged between the peer entities. Logically these travel 'horizontally' as shown in figure 10.2, but clearly in reality they have to be passed down vertically, layer by layer, along the physical medium, then up through the layers at the destination.

Primitives are in fact *abstractions* by means of which the functions of the service can be specified. It is common practice to refer to primitives when discussing a service definition in abstract terms, and to a *service data unit* (*SDU*) when discussing how particular service primitives map on to underlying PDUs. In subsequent discussions either term may be encountered.

• The net result of all of this is that, starting with the raw physical medium, each layer in turn will have provided some additional service, so that the application at the top has a means of communicating with a similar application on another open system (host), regardless of which or how many networks intervene.

To summarise, each layer (which may, according to the standard, comprise one or more sub-systems) provides a clearly defined service to the layer immediately above it. Corresponding layers (n) in different open systems communicate by means of the n-protocol, which is implemented using the services of the layer below (n-1). In other words the peer layer n-1 entities assist layer n in providing its service to the layer above, layer n+1. Layer n+1, the *service user*, may use any of the services provided by layer n, the *service provider*. In practice the actual service user may be a higher layer than n+1, and aspects of the n-service may be provided by lower layers. However the rationale behind OSI is that <u>the service user has no knowledge whatsoever of how the service is provided</u>; all it sees is a set of service primitives. Similarly the service provider has no knowledge of <u>why</u> the service user (or higher layers) is using its service, other than as expressed in the primitives passed to it. In particular, the meaning of any 'user data' passed with primitives is of no concern to the service provider.

The service provided by a given n layer may be tailored by choosing one or more *n-facilities*, which determine the attributes of the service. Where a layer entity cannot itself support a service required by the next highest layer entity, it may call upon its own peer entities to assist by means of a protocol. In order that peer entities at a given layer can co-operate, i.e. exchange information, an *association* must be established using the protocol of that layer; this association is known as an *n-connection*. These are provided between two or more n-service access points. Entities with a connection established between them are sometimes referred to as *correspondent entities*(although this term will not be used in this book).

10.2.2   Service primitive conventions

As indicated above, adjacent layers in the same open system communicate by means of service primitives and associated parameters across the layer interface. For example, layer n+1 uses the primitives of the layer n service, i.e. the set of n-service primitives.

Service primitives are in fact abstractions of the real physical data units which are exchanged over the interface, and service definitions merely provide details of what type of information should be exchanged, as *primitive parameters*. The primitive is in fact an abstraction of a real 'message' passed across the service boundary, which is known as a *service data unit* or *SDU*. For example in the network service we have NSDUs. At various times we will use the term SDU rather than primitive, in particular when discussing the mapping of these SDUs on to the underlying protocol as PDUs. Thus, for example, there will be some mapping between NSDUs and NPDUs (network layer), or between TSDUs and TPDUs (transport layer), and so on for each layer in the hierarchy.

For a given layer n, n-SDUs are transmitted to the peer layer n in the destination open system in n-PDUs, from where they are forwarded to layer n+1 at the 'other end', in n-SDUs. The means by which the primitive contents reach the other end is of no concern to layer n+1, but the layer n service definition defines which primitives (SDU types) are available to layer n+1, and how (if) the content of the parameters will be altered by the service provider (layer n or below).

As usual, the definition is rather dry and indigestible. The OSI service conventions standard {8509} is deliberately worded in a general manner, as the conventions are intended to apply to any layer service, thus imposing tight standardisation. In addition, the service definitions themselves are abstractions, in the sense that it is for the implementor to decide how, or indeed if, a particular layer interface will be implemented. The purpose of a service definition is merely to define what facilities must be provided (or may be provided if the facilities are optional), and that is all.

Primitive variants

Each primitive can have up to 4 variants, request, indication, response and confirm. The originator (layer n+1) issues a *request* variant to initiate some action. This is passed across the underlying network using the

198

underlying protocol, and is relayed to the peer layer n+1 as an *indication*. In some cases, it is possible that the service provider (the layer n protocol, or a lower layer protocol on its behalf) may alter the contents of one or more parameters of the n-request by the time it arrives as an n-indication. This typically occurs when layer n+1 has requested the use of some optional facility which is not available from the service provider (layer n or lower layers).

Two types of service are defined, as outlined in a moment. If no reply is required, that is the end of the matter, and the service is said to be unconfirmed. However if a reply to the n-indication is required, i.e. the service is confirmed, the remote layer n+1 is required to return a *response*, which in turn is passed up to the originating layer n+1 as a *confirm*.

Figure 10.3 should clarify how the primitives are used.

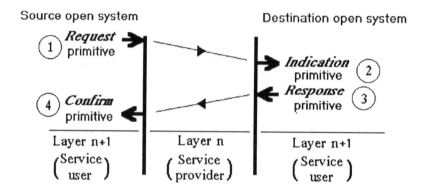

Figure 10.3 - Usage of service primitive variants

To be more precise, there are four main sequences of primitive which will be encountered, as follows:

 • In a *confirmed service*, a reply is expected from the remote layer n+1, so that all 4 variants are used.

An exception to this general rule applies in the case of Media Access Control (MAC) service primitives defined for LANs and discussed in chapter thirteen, where the response variant is not used, and the confirm is generated locally. In this case the confirm does not necessarily imply receipt of the indication by the peer, merely that the request appeared to have been transmitted successfully. The remote service user does not explicitly generate a response. Otherwise the receipt of a confirm implies that the indication was received, and the peer layer responded with a response. See chapter thirteen for more details of MAC service primitives.

- In an *unconfirmed service,* no reply is generated or expected.

In general, a service will be either confirmed or unconfirmed. Unfortunately odd cases exist in some service definitions where the response is optional. (This occurs for example in the session service, where confirmed synchronisation points are in effect subject to window acknowledgement.) For the time being however, you may assume that a confirm is either always expected, or never expected.

- Cases exist where an indication may be received which was *initiated by the service provider.* A typical example is where a network failure has occurred, and an indication to this effect is issued to both layers n+1. In this case there was no request.

- There is also the possibility of a *collision,* e.g. between a transmitted request and a received indication for the same primitive type. Particular cases are dealt with as they arise in the various service definitions.

Primitive notation and examples

In subsequent chapters where we discuss service definitions, we will usually base the discussion on the abstract service primitives provided. A special typeface is used for this purpose (12 point **bold Roman font**). Some examples follow; although these are real service primitives which will be encountered in later chapters, no attempt has been made to specify the actual parameters here.

T–DATA request, indication   parameter list

C–PREPARE unconfirmed   user data

These both represent an *unconfirmed* service. We tend to use the latter form for application services towards the end of the book, where a good understanding of service conventions can by now be assumed.

In the case of *confirmed* services, you may encounter any of the following three formats.

N–CONNECT request, indication   parameter list

N–CONNECT response, confirm   different parameter list

This form is used where there are important differences in the two sets of parameters, so that the two need to be discussed separately. In one or two cases each variant is discussed separately, so four definitions of this type will appear.

S–CONNECT request, indication,   parameter list
response, confirm

This is used where there are either no significant differences in the parameters in the request and the response, or such differences are either minor or will not discussed in detail. The latter applies in particular to some application service primitives with large numbers of complex parameters. Later in the book it is once more replaced by a shorthand version such as

A–ASSOCIATE confirmed   31 parameters

We will discuss individual primitives for the various service definitions in subsequent chapters. Unless a special case exists, an understanding of the concepts discussed in this section will be assumed.

10.2.3   Queue model of a connection

The queue model applies only to the **connection oriented** (**CO**) services, which are based on the idea of a **connection** between transport entities; in the case of connectionless (CL) services, no connection is defined, nor does any relationship exist between different SDUs, which are essentially transmitted on a 'send and hope' basis. It is discussed mainly so that you will get some feel for how ISO model service definitions and protocol specifications, and little further reference is made to it in the rest of the book.

A flow control function is provided between the two endpoints (users) of a connection, the purpose of which is to reconcile the abilities of the endpoints to send and receive data. This flow control is specified using a queue model, as shown in figure 10.4. Each queue represents a flow control function in one direction. Two such queues are considered to be available for each potential connection. The ability of the sending user to add items to the queue is controlled by the queue size, and also by the actions of the receiving user, which removes received items from the queue. Queue additions and removals take place at service access points (SAPs, in effect the interfaces between adjacent layers).

The sending user may place various types of information (referred to as *objects*) in a queue; each type represents a primitive and its associated parameters (if any). The receiving user may likewise place a comparable set of objects in the other queue. We will give an example for the network service in chapter fourteen.

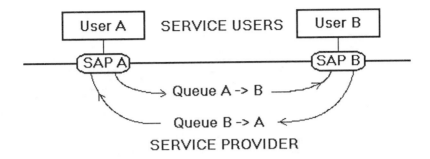

Figure 10.4 - queue model of a connection

10.2.4   Relay entities

Normally, the connection between two open systems requires the services of just two layers at any given level, one at each end of the connection (i.e. one in each open system), which communicate and provide services as described above. In some circumstances, where direct access between the peer entities is not possible, it may be necessary for two peer entities (layers), associated with the two endpoints, to communicate via a *relay*, i.e. intermediate peer entity. The relay is transparent in the sense that entities of higher layers are not aware that a relay is being used.

That all sounds very abstract. What it really means is that where two entities are associated with open systems (hosts) connected to different networks, they will be unable to communicate directly, and must do so via an intermediary (or intermediaries) which will be located at *gateways* between the networks. We saw an example of this type of usage when we mentioned the use of gateway YBTS stations in chapter nine.

Figure 10.5 shows how peer entities can communicate using a relay.

At this stage, a word of warning is necessary. It is most important, at least for the time being, that you should not attempt to rationalise YBTS (or any other protocol discussed in previous chapters for that matter) as if it represents a valid instance of an OSI/RM layer; not all of them can be accurately classified in this way. We will discuss the relationship of various existing protocols, including YBTS, to OSI/RM in due course.

10.2.5   Addressing concepts

Each layer entity has a global title, which uniquely identifies it throughout the entire OSI environment. In addition, within a naming domain (of which there may be one or several), its *service access point*

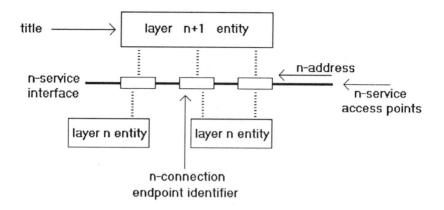

(*SAP*) can be referred to by a SAP address. For a given layer, this address may be used by the layer above to which it is either temporarily or permanently attached, to allow that layer to select the appropriate class of service required to implement its desired functions. The address of a 'remote' layer n may be used by the next highest 'local' layer n+1 as a means of accessing the peer layer n+1; an *n-endpoint identifier* is provided for this purpose. See figure 10.6.

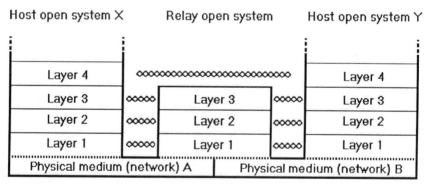

Figure 10.5 - communication through a relay

Figure 10.6 - use of addresses in OSI

Address mapping is used by a layer to transform from the global title to the locally significant address. This may take two forms. Where there is a one-one correspondence between adjacent layers, so that a layer address always maps on to a single next lowest layer address, a hierarchical scheme may be used. This would for example apply in figure 10.2; see also figure 10.7. Where there may be a one-many mapping, an alternative mapping using tables may be used.

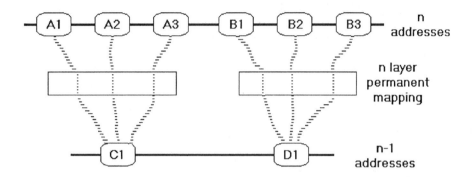

Figure 10.7 - hierarchical n address mapping

10.2.6   Quality of Service parameters

Quality of service (QOS) is an important OSI concept, and also one of the areas which causes the most difficulty for OSI designers. Each open system application may, in principle, specify the QOS which it requires from underlying layers in order to facilitate its communication with an application in another open system. The QOS is defined as a set of parameters, which fall into two basic categories:

    • Parameters expressing network service performance, which are sometimes referred to as network *grade of service (GOS)* parameters. These include the following aspects of a connection between two open systems: establishment delay, establishment failure probability (misconnection or connection refusal), throughput, residual error rate, resilience, transit delay, transfer failure probability, release delay, release failure probability. Since 1984, X.25 has included some GOS parameters which can be negotiated; see chapter fourteen.

    • Parameters expressing NS characteristics not directly related to performance, such as protection, priority and maximum acceptable cost.

The QOS requested by the application will in general be provided by more than one underlying layer, by a process of progressive enhancement, bottom upwards. A similar set of QOS parameters is defined at each layer, and many of the parameters will simply be 'passed down' by higher layers, for the attention of lower layers. We will discuss each QOS parameter fairly fully here, but in subsequent chapters we will normally simply refer to QOS in general, except where there is some specific point which needs to be made about a particular parameter.

The following discussion of QOS parameters includes, in some cases, references to various types of service primitive which have not yet been discussed. If this presents a problem, it is possible to relate these primitive types to setting up (connecting), using (data) and clearing down (disconnecting) X.25 VCs. Indeed X.25 classifies as a service definition in the OSI context. Where PDUs are mentioned, it is possible to substitute the term packet with minimum loss of information content.

A word of warning is necessary here. While it is in principle a good idea to be able to specify the required QOS in terms of a wide range of possible parameter values, in many cases hosts will be attached to a network which offers limited scope in the selection of QOS parameters, or over which only certain combinations of parameters are possible (e.g. low throughput with low error rate, or high throughput with high error rate, or whatever). Therefore in practice it will only be sensible to use certain QOS parameter combinations which it is known are consistent with what is available on the network(s) being used. Where a variety of routes is possible to the destination, it is possible that the QOS of the actual route may not be known in advance. (Applications, by definition, know nothing about the route through the underlying network.) This can pose problems in the transport layer, which will become apparent in chapter fifteen.

Connection establishment delay

This is the maximum acceptable delay (at the caller) between its issuing a connect request primitive and receiving a confirm in reply, including the time taken for the called user to generate a response.

Connection establishment failure probability

This is the percentage of connect attempts (in a representative sample of attempts) which will either fail, or which cannot be completed within the specified establishment delay. Such failures include misconnection and refusal (by the provider, possibly due to congestion in the underlying network).

Throughput

This is defined as the maximum rate at which the connection can sustain data transmission, in the absence of flow control constraints by the peer user, and is defined in terms of the effective transfer rate in bits per second sent or received, whichever is the lower. Furthermore, these bits must be delivered in the correct sequence and without error or loss. A separate throughput is defined for each direction of transfer.

For networks such as X.25, it may be defined in terms of some maximum data packet size, typically 128 octets.

Transit delay

This is the elapsed time between a data request primitive and the corresponding data indication primitive, based on successfully transferred PDUs. This is specified as 'target' and 'minimum acceptable' (i.e. lowest QOS) values. The values are generally taken to be averages based on a PDU size of 128 octets. Any increases which are a result of peer user flow control are not included.

Residual error rate

This is the proportion of lost, corrupted or duplicated PDUs resulting from primitives transferred across the service interface, again based on a representative sample.

Transfer failure probability

This is broadly the proportion of transfer failures during the life of a given connection. According to the standard, a transfer failure is deemed to have occurred when the observed performance of a representative sample of PDUs falls short of the desired performance. Broadly speaking, this can be viewed as the probability of a provider generated disconnect occurring, where the provider is reliably monitoring the QOS (whatever that means).

Connection resilience

This relates to the probability of provider issued disconnects and resets combined, during a specified time interval, on an established connection.

Connection release delay

This is similar to the establishment delay, and is the time from a disconnect request being issued by a user, to a matching reply disconnect confirm being returned to it.

Connection release failure probability

This is a measure of the proportion of release attempts which fail. A release fail is considered to have occurred if a new connection cannot be set up after the maximum release delay has elapsed following disconnection, provided that the service provider and not the user is at fault.

Connection protection

This measures the extent to which a service provider protects against unauthorised monitoring and manipulation of user data, and is specified from one of the following options, each of which deals with a particular type of security threat, and requires a different provider mechanism:

- No protection.
- Protection against 'tapping' (passive monitoring).
- Protection against unauthorised modification, playback, addition and deletion.

Originally an additional category of protection, message (PDU) authentication, was proposed for this QOS parameter. The idea of authentication is that safeguards should be built into the OSI stack which can provide some guarantee that a PDU is from the claimed sender, and is being sent to the intended recipient. It may be difficult, but it is not impossible for unscrupulous outsiders to intercept PDUs in transit and interfere with the address and other fields in a manner which cannot be detected by the transit network, thereby creating a serious security breach. This is in a sense a special case of unauthorised modification, but it is potentially much more serious than 'merely' altering the contents of a data field and suitably adjusting the FCS so that the change will go undetected. However the idea that this should be a QOS parameter implies that somehow the underlying network will be able to offer this type of protection. This is asking rather much of any network, and current thinking is that message authentication should be an application issue. It is of particular concern where the OSI directory is concerned. (This is discussed in chapter twenty three.)

This is not the only area relating to security which has ended up as an application layer issue, having originally been sited lower down the protocol stack. Encryption was originally perceived to be a presentation layer issue. Problems of this nature which prove to be too difficult to resolve in a reasonable time tend to become application layer issues. This is partly because the lower protocol stack has to be kept reasonably simple (and needs to become stable as quickly as possible), and partly because not all applications will require such things as authentication or encryption in any case, and the idea of the supporting protocol stack is to offer generalised rather than specific services. Unfortunately the dividing line between what is sufficiently generalised to be included in a lower layer, and what is sufficiently specific to be associated with a particular applications, is difficult to position.

Connection priority

The priority relates to a given connection in the context of other connections 'competing' for the same underlying resources. For example it may be used to determine which connections will be degraded or broken first, if this becomes necessary in an emergency in order to maintain some sort of service. This implies that some network management function will be available which can make this type of decision, although the nature of this management function is not specified. Whether an X.25 network which is on the point of internal collapse will be able to achieve this graceful degradation is open to question.

Maximum acceptable cost

This is a financial issue, but the cost units may be either absolute (real) or relative (comparative). The cost may include components from layers below the network layer.

10.3   Brief summary of the OSI layers

The standard is littered with other definitions, as well as those given above. Sufficient understanding of the basics of the model should however be gained from those discussed. These should give a feel for how entities communicate, and what functions are expected to be provided by each layer. The remainder of this chapter is devoted to a discussion of each layer in turn.

Figure 10.8 summarises the layer hierarchy, and figure 10.9 shows how relay layers may be present in a relay open system (gateway) where more than one physical medium (network) intervenes between the communicating open systems. Note that only the lowest three layers can be present in a relay. This is in part related to whether the layers are implemented in hosts, or form part of the 'underlying network'; this issue is discussed in more detail later on, and has important ramifications in the context of YBTS, as we shall see in chapter fifteen.

The sections which follow in this chapter deal with each layer in turn, starting at the lowest layer and working up. However, with the notable exception of the application layer, this chapter contains only statements of the general requirements of each layer, as defined in the reference model itself.

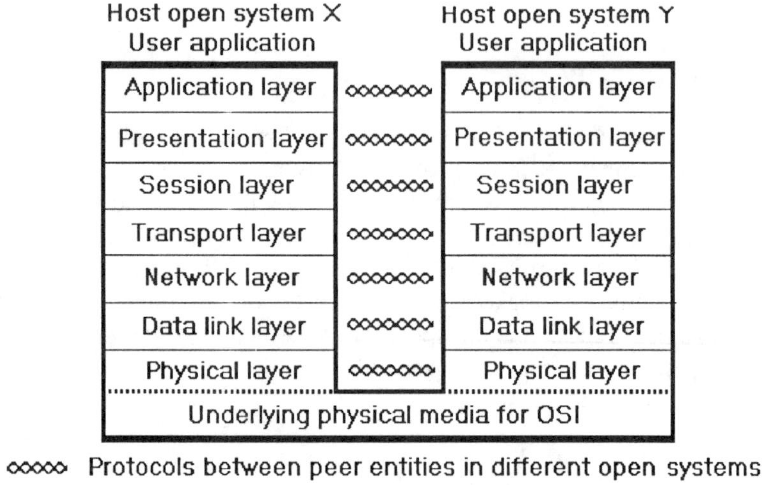

Host open system X User application		Host open system Y User application
Application layer	∞∞∞∞∞	Application layer
Presentation layer	∞∞∞∞∞	Presentation layer
Session layer	∞∞∞∞∞	Session layer
Transport layer	∞∞∞∞∞	Transport layer
Network layer	∞∞∞∞∞	Network layer
Data link layer	∞∞∞∞∞	Data link layer
Physical layer	∞∞∞∞∞	Physical layer
Underlying physical media for OSI		

∞∞∞∞∞ Protocols between peer entities in different open systems

Figure 10.8 - layers in OSI/RM

10.3.1   The physical layer

This covers the physical aspects of the communication, i.e. the transmission of raw bits over a communication channel. This includes the setting up, maintenance and clearing of physical connections. The data unit may be one bit (serial transmission) or 'n bits' (parallel transmission); the transmission mechanism may be either half duplex or full duplex. The definition of the physical layer is intended to be consistent with standard transmission techniques. Physical layer entities are connected by a physical medium. This is assumed to be 'of telecommunication type'.

The physical layer, as usual, provides services to the data link layer. These include the provision of physical connections, physical data units (bits), endpoint and circuit identification, sequencing (of bits), fault notification, and QOS parameters. Details of the physical layer are not covered in any detail in this book.

10.3.2   The data link layer

This layer provides the means to set up, maintain and release data link connections between adjacent nodes in a subnetwork (assuming a WAN mesh network), and to transfer I (the OSI term; they are usually referred to as *frames*).

Host open system X User application	Relay open system (if present)			Host open system Y User application
Application layer	∞∞∞∞∞∞∞∞∞∞∞∞∞∞∞∞			Application layer
Presentation layer	∞∞∞∞∞∞∞∞∞∞∞∞∞∞∞∞			Presentation layer
Session layer	∞∞∞∞∞∞∞∞∞∞∞∞∞∞∞∞			Session layer
Transport layer	∞∞∞∞∞∞∞∞∞∞∞∞∞∞∞∞			Transport layer
Network layer	∞∞∞	Network layer	∞∞∞	Network layer
Data link layer	∞∞∞	Data link layer	∞∞∞	Data link layer
Physical layer	∞∞∞	Physical layer	∞∞∞	Physical layer
Underlying physical medium (or media) for OSI				

∞∞∞∞∞∞∞∞∞ Protocols between peer entities in different open systems

Figure 10.9 - layers in OSI/RM with intermediate relay open system

The data link layer is also expected to detect errors occurring in the physical layer, and may also correct them, although this is not a compulsory function of this layer. Where the errors are detected but not corrected, they must be notified to the network layer. This is, however, subject to a residual undetected error rate, since no error detection algorithm can guarantee 100% success. The residual undetected error rate contributes to the overall QOS.

In general terms, the following services are provided to the network layer above (via the data link service interface):

• The service user is relieved of the need to know the details of the underlying physical layer. This is self-evident; it is simply stating the principle of layering.

• The provision of one or more data link connections between peer network entities as required; these will typically be between adjacent nodes in a subnetwork. These connections are established and released dynamically.

• The exchange of data units over data link connections. Typically these will be conveyed using HDLC as the data link protocol, and for this reason it is usual to refer to data link protocol units as frames, although it must be stressed that OSI/RM does <u>not</u>

imply the use of HDLC or any other specific protocol. The size of a frame is determined by the error rate on the physical medium, and by the link layer's ability to detect errors. This general issue was discussed in chapter two.

• The provision of endpoint identifiers by means of which a network entity may identify its peer, at the other end of a subnetwork.

• If appropriate, the data link may be split over several underlying physical connections.

• If required by the network layer, the sequencing (i.e. ordering) of frames must be maintained.

• The notification of detected but uncorrectable errors, as discussed above. The CCITT version of the standard (X.212(1988)) actually requires the transfer of data to be reliable, but this cannot be guaranteed, and in practice recovery from loss and corruption must be handled by higher layers.

• Frame flow control, as dictated by the requirements of the network entity.

• The optional selection of QOS parameters, for the duration of the data link connection. These include the mean time between detected (but not corrected) errors, and the residual undetected error rate (e.g. alteration, loss, duplication, mis-delivery or mis-sequencing of frames).

For WANs, the data link service is discussed in chapter eleven. For WANs, it is generally accepted that HDLC, or the X.25 (LAPB) or ISDN (LAPD) link access procedures, will normally be used in WANs to implement the data link protocol between adjacent nodes. In the case of LANs, the situation is rather different; see chapter thirteen.

10.3.3   The network layer

This layer provides a means of setting up, maintaining and clearing down a connection path (network connection) between a pair of transport entities. It also provides any necessary routing and relay (gateway) functions between intervening networks, where these are required in order to reach the destination. In other words it provides an end-end service over one or more underlying networks, controls the operation of the subnetwork(s), and is thus the highest OSI/RM layer which is network dependent. This layer is also responsible for the sequencing and flow control of *network PDUs* (which are generally referred to as *packets*) under the control of the transport entity.

The quality of service (QOS) is negotiated between network and transport entities at the time the network connection is set up. Where two or more subnetworks are involved, the QOS will be that of the worst case, unless it has been enhanced to that of a higher quality subnetwork, in which case the QOS of the overall network connection will 'approximate to' that of the higher quality subnetwork.

The following services are provided to the transport layer, each at known cost.

- Provision of network endpoint identifiers which are in effect network connection addresses for use by the transport entities.

- The means to establish, and subsequently to release, a network connection to exchange packets between communicating network service users (host transport layers); more than one connection may exist between the same pair of users. A network connection is point-point, i.e. between two and only two defined endpoints.

- A means of establishing the grade of service (GOS, a subset of the QOS) of the connection (including the residual error rate, service availability, reliability, throughput, transit delay, connection establishment delay).

- A means of transferring delimited packets on the connection. Packets consist of integral numbers of octets, and the contents of packets, and the integrity of, and boundaries between, them are preserved.

- If appropriate, the multiplexing of network connections, i.e. the use of a single connection for several different 'conversations' between the same pair of hosts.

- A mechanism whereby the receiving user may impose backward flow control, which may or may not be network service end-end.

- Error notification (for errors which cannot be recovered by the network service, or by a lower layer on its behalf). Upon notification (*signalling*), the transport entity above may elect to release the network connection, or may provide additional recovery mechanisms so that the error remains unnoticed by higher layer entities.

- Sequenced delivery of packets.

- Optional delivery confirmation (to the remote transport entity).

- Optional expedited data transfer.

- Optional resynchronisation of a connection, i.e. its restoration to a defined state, by means of reset (re-initialisation), with possible loss of data.

An important design issue in OSI/RM was whether the network nodes or the hosts should be responsible for ensuring that packets are correctly received at their destinations. In the early ARPANET, it was the network node (the IMP) which had this responsibility. In OSI/RM, the network layer makes best attempts to direct the to their intended destination transport entities in the hosts, but it is the transport layer's responsibility to recover lost packets. If delivery confirmation is provided, this confirmation of delivery is again to the host transport station. Thus, in the last resort, it is the responsibility of the host transport station to ensure correct receipt, and to take any necessary steps to achieve this.

Routing is another area where important design decisions had to be made. Although the precise means by which routing is to be achieved is not specified in OSI/RM, it is the responsibility of the network layer, where necessary using one or more underlying data links, to 'determine an appropriate route' to the destination host, this possibly involving two or more underlying networks and intermediate relay entities. Congestion control is also the responsibility of the network layer.

Some interesting comparisons with existing network routing algorithms may be drawn here. You will recall from part one that in the ARPANET, routing was considered to be a data link function, involving the transfer of IMP-IMP routing packets, and routing decisions by every IMP. As far as recommendation X.25 is concerned, the means by which routing is to be achieved is not specified, but the addressing facilities provided in LAPB are not sufficient to handle end-end routing, so that routing cannot be considered to be a data link function in X.25. Thus it can be concluded that the responsibility for routing in OSI/RM is closer to that in X.25 than to that in ARPANET. Any accounting which may be required in order to produce user billing is normally also associated with the network layer.

The apparently close relationship between the network layer requirements and what is offered by X.25 should come as no surprise, given that X.25 had already become widely adopted as a standard 'network protocol' by the time that OSI/RM reached IS status, and it would have made no sense to define the network layer in terms which were incompatible with X.25. In fact X.25 is a network service definition, not a protocol specification, as will be seen in chapter fourteen, and the network service definition was one of the earliest OSI layer standards to be developed. (In fact both the network service definition and X.25 had to be altered in order to ensure compatibility.) A corresponding network protocol was not initially defined, as (at the time) it was considered sufficient to rely on the (unpublished) internal workings of the various X.25 networks, and other tasks were more urgent, such as stabilising the higher layers. Standards defining suitable network protocols do now exist, however, including one for X.25 {8208, 8473, 8880}.

The extent to which X.25(1980) could be used to provide an OSI/RM compatible network service was an important issue for many years, and 'network convergence' studies played an important part in the definition of X.25(1984), with a number of documents published on this issue. The second edition of this book examined these convergence issues in some detail. The current edition concentrates on the current situation, as the problems associated with X.25(1980) have now been largely solved, and X.25(1980) itself will soon be of merely historical interest.

10.3.4   The transport layer

The purpose of this layer is to relieve higher layer host entities of any concern with (the details of) the transportation of data between them. In other words, the transport layer effectively hides any network-dependent details of the underlying network from higher layers, by providing *transparent* data transfer. All protocols defined for the transport layer have end-end (host-host) significance. In the context of a typical network, this means that the transport entity, and hence all higher layer entities, will be implemented in the hosts, not in the network.

The transport layer is also responsible for transporting this data in a *reliable*, cost effective way, as required by the selected QOS. It may optimise the use of the underlying network(s), if this is necessary to provide the required performance. The transport layer has the responsibility for ensuring that all data reaches the other end without error, loss or duplication, and in the correct sequence.

At least that is the theory. The crucial point is that the transport layer provides its service 'subject to the QOS required by the layer above it'. If the transport layer cannot maintain the required QOS, for example because of a serious underlying network failure, it will give up. So by itself the transport layer cannot guarantee reliability. We will return to this important issue several times.

Normally, a separate network layer connection is provided for each transport connection required by the session layer, but an option allows several transport connections to be *multiplexed* on to a single network connection. A further option is provided which permits the *splitting* of a transport connection over several network connections. Which (if either) is employed is dictated by considerations of cost or throughput. Multiplexing would tend to reduce cost at the expense of throughput, whereas the reverse would be true for splitting. The transport layer is however not concerned with routing or relaying issues, or for example the details of how the network connections(s) operate; these are the responsibility of the network layer.

The following services are provided to the user of the transport service, the session layer:

• The establishment and release of transport connections. Connections are established between session entities, which are identified by transport addresses as discussed earlier. Likewise, the transport entity is identified from the other end by its network address.

• Data transfer, in accordance with the agreed QOS. Both normal and expedited data units may be provided, although the expedited mode is a negotiable option, and therefore is not guaranteed to be available. While normal data units may be of any size, a size limit will be placed on expedited data units. The ordering of data units will be preserved.

• Recovery from transient failures in the underlying network(s), as required, subject to the requested QOS being maintained, and transparently to the service user. In practice this means that recovery must be possible within a time governed by the relevant GOS parameters. (See the earlier aside.)

• Notification of errors in the underlying layers which could not be recovered by the transport layer without unacceptable degradation of the QOS. This would include a failed network connection which could not be recovered within a certain time.

In order to provide these general services, the transport layer may incorporate the following functions, depending on the required :

• TC establishment and release (mandatory for COTS).
• Transport address to network address mapping.
• Multiplexing of transport connections to a single network connection.
• Splitting of a transport connection on to several network connections.
• End-end sequence control, error detection and recovery, QOS monitoring, flow control, and segmentation / blocking / concatenation and so on as necessary e.g. to optimise the use of underlying packets.
• Expedited data transfer.
• Supervisory functions.

10.3.5   The session layer

As far as the transport layer is concerned, the data is amorphous and unstructured. In other words it is effectively a transparent octet stream. The session layer is responsible for providing *structuring* and *organisation* of data, including synchronisation of the dialogue between the applications. Strictly speaking it is responsible for the management of the exchange of data between presentation entities[2].

The session layer is responsible for the creation and management of sessions on behalf of the presentation entities, as well as the termination of sessions when they are no longer required. A session might for example be created for the purpose of transferring a file, or to allow a terminal user to log into a remote timesharing service. Session entities use the services of the transport layer to implement a session connection (see below). However although the session layer provides various mechanisms for structuring and synchronising the dialogue, it has no knowledge of the meaning of the data, which still appears as a transparent octet stream.

The following services may be provided, in theory to the presentation layer, but in practice to application layer entities.

- The establishment and release of session connections.

- Normal and expedited (if available) data exchange. (There are other 'flavours' of data as well, as will be explained in chapter sixteen.)

- Interaction management. This service allows session service users to control whose turn it is to perform certain control functions, such as synchronisation the data flow and transferring data in a particular direction. It also allows them to relinquish their turn if so desired. Tokens are defined for these purposes. The interaction may be two way simultaneous (TWS, i.e. full duplex) or two way alternate (TWA, i.e. half duplex). Note that these are logical not physical concepts.

- Resynchronisation of a session connection. This provides for a facility rather similar to the NIFTP data marks, mark acknowledgement, and resumption facilities mentioned in chapter nine.

- Exception reporting. The session layer is required to report (to the presentation entity) any exceptional conditions which cannot be recovered by the session entity (or by a lower layer entity on its behalf). These include the irrecoverable loss of a session connection due to a network malfunction.

A quarantine service was originally envisaged for the session layer. In fact such a service is provided by the VT terminal service, an application (chapter twenty one), but not in the session layer itself.

In some implementations, it is expected that the session layer may be combined with either the transport layer or the presentation layer. In some cases, where sophisticated session management is not required, or where connectionless operation is being used (see §10.4) it may even be absent altogether.

10.3.6   The presentation layer

The session layer adds mechanisms for structuring the data, but at this layer the data is still treated as an amorphous stream of octets. However in reality the data is of several different types, and each will have some precisely defined data structure meaningful to the particular application. For example in a file transfer, there will be the actual file contents, possibly structured in some way (cf. a Pascal file of <record_type>). The receiver of the file needs to preserve both the structure and the meaning of the contents. Similarly there will be file transfer protocol control information, also structured but differently from the file itself. A means must be provided for distinguishing between different structures and representing them in an unambiguous manner.

At first sight there may seem to be an inconsistency here. We seem to be concerned with differentiating between the structure of file transfer control information and that of file data, whereas at lower layers we did not seek to make any distinction between protocol control information and user data. Why make the distinction here? At lower layers, there was always a user presenting data, and a protocol which had a uniquely defined structure. There were precise protocol encoding rules at each layer (which we have not discussed in detail, but are etched in stone). The encoding treated everything else as transparent data.

At the presentation level, we can certainly 'etch the presentation protocol in stone', but we can not do the same with the user data, because it can no longer be regarded as transparent. There may be several different application entities involved, each of which can have a different set of control and data structures. (This will become clearer in chapter eighteen.) The receiving presentation layer needs to know how to apportion the received data out among its various applications, and must also provide the structure and encodings which the sender placed there.

The problem is that all of the different types of information presented by the application layer need to be encoded absolutely on the connection between the open systems, but in a manner which allows the peer application to recover the meaning. In a sense we are 'multiplexing' several data streams from above, and the essence of multiplexing is that the different data streams can be recovered at the receiver. The function of the presentation layer then is to provide a means of representing these data structures in a consistent, network-independent manner. It provides facilities for the mapping ('presentation') of specific application-related structured data into a common network format, on behalf of the application entities. It is intended to represent information in a way which 'preserves meaning while resolving syntax differences'. In addition it resolves differences in format between hosts (e.g. where hosts use different ways of representing dates, floating point numbers and so on, or to provide network standard file formats, job transfer mechanisms, and terminal specifications). This is achieved by identifying some element of data to be transferred as a date (or whatever). The local representation may vary between hosts, but it must be encoded for transmission in a standard manner. The receiver can then decode it as it wishes. The fact that it is known to be a date, together with a standard means of representing it during transmission, is sufficient.

What is in fact provided is a mapping between an *abstract syntax* and a *concrete syntax*. The data presented to the session layer is defined in an abstract manner, rather like a Pascal declaration of data types and identifiers. An instance of such a data structure is known as a *presentation context*, of which there may be one or several in use over a presentation connection. The context defines the meaning and syntax of the data, but the precise means by which the application makes this available to the presentation layer for transmission are not defined. What is defined is a standardised way of transmitting it via the presentation connection, i.e. a set of *encoding rules*. The encoding rules also provide a means of distinguishing between several different presentation contexts in the currently *defined context set*.

Any number of abstract syntaxes could be defined. At the time of writing, only one has reached maturity. This is **abstract syntax notation number one (ASN.1)**, which allows the definition of simple data structures in a form which resembles programming languages such as Pascal. The structure of many application PDUs is defined in terms of ASN.1. Although ASN.1 {8824} and its rules for encoding as a concrete (transfer) syntax {8825} are not strictly part of the presentation layer, they are closely tied in with it from a logical viewpoint. Incidentally ASN.1 started life as part of the CCITT MHS(1984) recommendations. At the time there was no stable OSI presentation service. Most application protocols are now specified in ASN.1 terms, including MHS(1988).

Apart from encoding and decoding data, and managing presentation contexts, the presentation layer has few functions other than passing through session service primitives (with enclosed 'session user data' suitably encoded/decoded). For this reason the presentation service will often be treated as if it were a set of facilities available to the application (or session) layer, rather like a set of library routines, rather than as a layer of equal status to the others. Remember that OSI/RM says nothing about how the layers should be implemented; it is sufficient that an open system appears conformant to another open system, and there are may ways in which this might be achieved in practice.

The following services may be provided to the application layer:

• A request for the establishment of a session. This is a *pass through* service; i.e. the request will actually be dealt with by the session layer (see above).

• Data transfer (pass through, subject to syntax transformation of session service user data).

• The negotiation (and renegotiation) of the syntax to be used between the two application layers.

• Any necessary syntax transformation, formatting and 'special purpose transformations'.

Special transformations originally envisaged included encryption and data compression. If provided at all, they are now the concern of the application layer. No such transformations are currently defined.

• A request for the termination of a session (pass through).

Each presentation entity is associated with one, and only one, session entity. This means in practice that they may be physically combined in some implementations, although the logical distinction will remain.

10.3.7   The application layer

This, the highest of the seven layers, provides the means by which application processes may gain access to the OSI environment, for the purpose of exchanging information. Any interface above this layer is beyond the scope of the reference model, and is purely a matter for the host operating system, human user or whatever. This layer is responsible for communicating application process parameters, for each instance of an OSI communication.

The following services may be provided to application processes (by the application layer):

• Identification of the intended communication partners. OSI/RM is rather vague about this. Directory and registration services are being defined to assist in this.

• Establishment of the necessary authority to communicate using the OSI environment.

• Determination of the availability of the intended communication partners.

• Agreement on privacy mechanisms as required for the communication.

• Authentication of the intended communication partners.

• Determination of allocation of the cost of using the necessary resources.

• Determination of the adequacy of the resources available for the intended communication.

• Determination of an acceptable QOS.

• Synchronisation between co-operating applications.

• Selection of the dialogue discipline, including any logon and logoff procedures required.

• Agreement on who has responsibility for error recovery.

• Agreement on the procedures for ensuring data integrity.

• Identification of any constraints on syntax (e.g. character sets, data structures).

As can be seen, this represents a somewhat vague set of facilities, and nothing is said about any real application such as file transfer. OSI/RM's purpose is not to define specific applications, but to define a general framework into which conforming layer specifications can be fitted. In principle at least, the above set of requirements is consistent with any application.

Application layer structure

As this is the area of OSI which caused experts more problems than any other, and because fundamental changes in thinking took place between 1984 and 1988, it is worth devoting some time to this topic.

The original idea was that a service definition and protocol specification would be defined for each application (e.g. file transfer, job transfer, virtual terminal). It was soon clear that this was too simplistic. Two particular problems quickly became evident:

- Certain facilities which belonged in the application area would be required by more than one application. It would not be efficient to duplicate common requirements in several different application protocols.

- CCITT had, since 1980, been progressing standards for various telematic services (notably teletex and message handling systems, MHS). While it was always CCITT's intention that these would be OSI compatible, decisions had to be made before the presentation layer had reached stability, and at a time when there was no concensus even on how the application layer should be organised, let alone any stable applications. As a result, the first attempt at MHS(1984) ended up not matching the presentation and application layers (as they subsequently stabilised) very well at all. This in the major reason why there are important differences between X.400(1984) and X.400(1988), the latter taking into account the now stable OSI environment into which it fitted.

So it was clear from an early date that the application layer structure needed clarifying, and a further standard {9545} defining the application layer structure is nearing IS status at the time of writing. Although the standard regards the application layer as a single layer, it is convenient to view it as two sub-layers, which is the approach used here. The upper sub-layer contains *application specific* services, while the lower sub-layer contains various services of an *application support* nature. It follows logically that specific applications are the users of (i.e. are logically above) support applications. While the support applications will be discussed in more detail in chapter eighteen, it is worth looking at the historical development of support applications in a little detail here.

The 'application support sub-layer' (the author's term not ISO's) has had a somewhat chequered history. By 1984, ISO work was progressing in two areas, CASE and CCR. CASE stood (at the time) for Common Application Service Elements, which included a basic 'CASE kernel' for setting up and terminating application connections, known in the application layer as *application associations*. As well as the CASE kernel, a set of *Commitment, Concurrency and Recovery* (*CCR*) procedures was being developed {9804} to facilitate synchronisation and recovery between groups of applications co-operating over a potentially unreliable set of underlying connections. CCR was of particular relevance to applications such as job transfer, where several open system hosts could be involved, and it was necessary to ensure that all aspects of the job had been successfully completed. CCR was originally seen as an optional CASE functional unit. The CASE kernel was subsequently renamed *Association Control Service Elements*, or *ACSE* {8649}, and the CCR service elements were moved to a new standard {9804}.

Meanwhile CCITT had defined two related protocols for use in MHS(1984):

> • ROS (Remote Operations) provided an association between a message transferred to a remote message store, and the returned confirmation (or otherwise) of its delivery. In other words it supported a request/reply dialogue (paradigm).

> • RTS (Reliable Transfer) provided mechanisms for ensuring that the request and reply got through. We mentioned earlier how the transport layer could not guarantee delivery in the event of an underlying failure. RTS would repeat the attempt in this case.

It soon became clear that ROS and RTS had potentially much wider scope. MHS(1984) had built these general purpose applications into the specific MHS application out of necessity, as the application layer was in a state of flux at the time. By the 1988 revision of MHS, ROS and RTS had been moved to where they belonged, the application support sub-layer. In the process they had been modified to varying degrees, notably to reflect changes to CASE (now ACSE). They were also re-christened *Remote Operations Service Elements (ROSE)* {9072} and *Reliable Transfer Service Elements (RTSE)* {9066}. A further offering, *Transaction Processing (TP)* {10026} is currently under development by ISO.

The idea then is that the 'real' application services sit above this support sub-layer. The added complication is that the various ISO and CCITT application standards use differing combinations of support services, in a manner which defies neat classification. In particular, not all applications use ACSE, which appears at first sight to be essential in order to set up an application association. Without becoming to engrossed in the ramifications here, it is sufficient to comment that, in theory at least, any application service element may use any other, there being no implied hierarchy. In practice each application (file transfer, MHS, an so on) has its own, possibly rather eccentric, way of using some (possibly all) of the support services. We will defer further discussion until we discuss specific applications (chapters nineteen to twenty three).

10.4   Connectionless mode and OSI/RM

The original version of OSI/RM assumed that all communication would be by means of connections, i.e. using some form of session and underlying virtual circuits. This is the only mode of operation catered for in

X.25. However, we have seen that some applications are more amenable to a datagram type of communication. This is particularly relevant in the context of LANs, as we will see in chapter thirteen. Although an attempt to incorporate a datagram service in X.25(1980) was not a success, and the service was removed from the recommendation, this should not be seen as an indictment of datagram services in general. The decision was influenced in part by the fact that WANs are not particularly suited to this type of control, and also by the fact that nobody seemed interested in using that particular service at the time. Taking a broader view, ISO (i.e. its constituent members, ANSI in particular) felt that providing only connection-based communication in the reference model would unduly restrict its generality of application.

In consequence, ISO produced an addendum to OSI/RM {7498-1 ADD1} which provides a compatible framework for connectionless applications. The basic philosophy, and the terminology employed, are similar to those in OSI/RM itself. We will restrict this discussion to the main differences in functionality of the various layers.

Four basic cases are catered for:

• A connection mode (CO) application dialogue using underlying CO network protocols; this is the situation originally envisaged, and that normally used with WANs. It is suitable for bulk data transfer applications such as file or job transfer.

• A connectionless (CL) application dialogue using underlying CL network protocols (e.g. a datagram-based underlying network). This is suited to closely coupled process communication over LANs.

• A CO dialogue using underlying CL protocols, with mapping at the network layer. This could occur when transferring some types of file over underlying LANs.

• A CL dialogue using underlying CO protocols, again with mapping at the network layer. In theory this could also occur, but no CL applications have yet reached stability.

Where more than one underlying subnetwork is involved, a mix of connectionless and connection mode protocols between endpoints and relay entities may occur. As far as the layers are concerned, figure 10.10 shows the different types of 'vertical' interaction which it is felt should be catered for, in the two cases where the applications require connectionless and connection mode.

As can be seen from figure 10.10, a given type of service at the application layer implies the same service down to the transport layer.

Below the transport layer, four types of combination can be identified, as shown in figure 10.11. This also implies that two complementary sets of protocol/service will have to be defined at the application, presentation, session and transport layers, one set for each of the two cases.

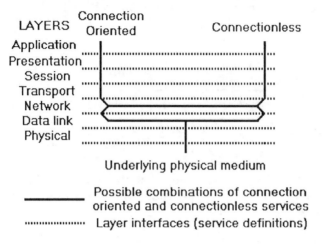

Figure 10.10 - service relationships at layer boundaries

Various combinations of service are possible at the lower layers, and in practice these will depend on the detailed operation of the particular underlying networks. In general, connectionless service definitions contain a subset of the corresponding connection oriented ones, omitting (obviously) those aspects concerned with setting up and clearing down a connection. Therefore unless mapping between connection oriented and connectionless modes is being discussed, the connectionless variant is not particularly interesting. Except at the lower layers, we will not discuss connectionless variants in detail.

Two final comments should be made on the connectionless variant of the reference model.

• Firstly, it should be noted that the session layer no longer has any real purpose in the context of a connectionless dialogue between application entities; the reference model preserves the layer mainly for reasons of consistency. A connectionless session layer is given only one task, that of mapping between session addresses and transport addresses. It is most unlikely that this layer will have a real, physical existence in any connectionless realisation of the model.

• Secondly, it should be noted that a realisation of a connectionless transport service over a connection mode network service implies a different usage of the set of (connection based) network service primitives. Those primitives which relate to the setting up and closing down of network connections are a particular issue. Details of this type of mapping will not be covered in this book.

type	layer n service	layer n-1 service	layer n functions	applicable layers
1	CO	CO	ISO 7498 (X.200)	all
2		CL	connection setup and release, sequencing	ND
3	CL	CO	control of n-1 connection, connection setup and release as dictated by layer n data traffic	ND
4		CL	mapping n data units to n-1 data units	all

ND: Network and Data Link layers

Figure 10.11 - connection/connectionless service combinations

10.5   References

1   A useful introduction to OSI/RM concepts may be found in the following article: P. A. Jenkins and K. G. Knighton, 'Open Systems Interconnection - an Introductory Guide', British Telecommunications Engineering, vol. 3, p. 86 (July, 1984).

2   S. Schindler and J. Schulze, 'Open System Interconnection - the Session Service', Computer Communications, vol. 4, no. 2, p. 43 (1981). This provides an interesting insight into early thinking on the session layer.

11   The Physical and Data Link Layers for wide area networks

11.1   Introduction

These are the lowest layers of OSI/RM. Therefore in a 'bottom up' approach, they must be the first to be discussed. However in the development of OSI, they were the last to become stable. At the time of writing, the Physical Service Definition {10022} is still at the DP stage, and will not be discussed in any great detail. The Data Link Service Definition {8886} has reached the DIS stage. Both have corresponding CCITT blue book recommendations, X.211(1988) and X.212(1988) respectively, but as we will see the CCITT versions discussed here have a number of grey areas. Both are still evolving, and some aspects of the Physical Service Definition were not fully defined at the time of writing.

The chapter starts by examining the Physical Service Definition. It is not the intention in this book to discuss this layer in any detail, but a few suggestions are made concerning how the properties of the underlying physical medium might be related to real physical transmission techniques. This chapter contains the only discussion of the physical layer in the book.

The Data Link Service Definition is discussed next. It defines the DLSDUs (data link service data units) which can be transferred across the service interface. These will typically be for transmission between adjacent nodes in a mesh network (such as a typical X.25 network like British Telecom's PSS network). At the time of writing, no generalised Data Link Protocol Specification exists, it generally being considered that HDLC in its various guises is sufficient for the time being. We discussed HDLC in some detail in chapter six, although not at that time in the OSI context. We first discuss the service definition, then relate the service primitives to specific HDLC X.25 LAPB) frame types. An understanding of HDLC will be assumed in this chapter.

The physical and data link layers described in this chapter are intended for application in WANs. Distinct physical and data link procedures have been devised for LANs. In chapter twelve we discuss some general properties of LANs, and some specific LAN architectures. In chapter thirteen we examine IEEE project 802, which has been adopted by ISO as the LAN variant of OSI/RM for the physical and data link layers {8802.2}. It is instructive to note that although OSI/RM was initially developed for WANs, it was the LAN variants of the lowest layers which were the first to be standardised. Pressure for standardisation is always most acute when there are several competing alternatives, which was the situation with LANs. Xerox, IBM and others all had vested interests in particular technologies, and all of these had the potential to become OSI-incompatible, but widely adopted, proprietary systems. If this had happened, the cause of OSI could have been set back by many years. This explains the urgency in stabilising the lowest layers for LANs. (In the event most of the competing technologies ended up being catered for in the standards, as we shall see in chapter thirteen.) In the WAN case, X.25 was the dominant protocol from the start, and since this was a CCITT recommendation, it was not proprietary, so that it could be used as a de facto model of the lowest layers until higher layers had been formalised; there was no significant proprietary competition which would make formalisation imperative. Furthermore what happens at the physical level has less impact on OSI in LANs than in WANs.

When we come to discuss the LAN data link service, a number of similarities with the WAN version will be seen. This is because the WAN version is to a large extent modelled on the LAN one, which (unusually for OSI) came first.

11.2   The physical layer

11.2.1   Introduction

This comprises a physical service definition, whereby data can be presented for transmission on the physical medium, together with a notional physical protocol. However no specific implementations are specified, nor are any constraints applied to the underlying physical medium, which is merely assumed to have some general characteristics typical of transmission media. In particular, there are no conformance requirements for the implementation of this layer.

The physical layer provides for transparent data transfer along a *physical connection* (*PhC*) between physical service (PhS) users. At this layer the service cannot be described as either connection oriented or connectionless. In addition, the QOS is predefined for a given underlying physical medium, and dependent on the particular characteristics of that medium.

11.2.2 General features of the physical layer

The physical layer can be simply described as offering a number of facilities which the service user can utilise, and providing access (via service primitives) to a physical medium with some standard, generalised characteristics.

Facilities offered

Basic features of the physical layer are as follows. In some cases, an attempt is made to relate the discussion to typical transmission services which are commonly available.

• The physical medium can be regarded as being continuously available, or as a resource which needs to be activated in order to use it. In the context of transmission via a modem, activation might entail raising the V.24 request to send (RTS) signal, to establish carrier on the line[1]. Without a carrier frequency present, nothing could be transmitted. A physical service primitive is provided (see §11.2.3) for requesting the activation of the medium (i.e. its enablement for transmission). There are circumstances, as we will see in a moment, where activation may be mandatory, and other circumstances where the service may be optional.

V.24 (CCITT) and the equivalent RS-232C (EIA) standard define the signals used with the familiar 25-pin computer-modem interface (D-connector), so hated by practitioners trying to make direct connections between pairs of micros, or between a micro and a printer. The author's experiences while attempting to interface his PC to a laser printer to print this book would be unprintable!

• The physical layer provides a means of transferring PhSDUs (service data units), which comprise either a single *bit* or a string of bits. (At this layer, the concept of characters and octets is entirely absent.) No constraint is placed on values which these bits may take (except of course that each bit must be either 0 or 1). Both the values and the ordering of bits are preserved (subject to the QOS of the PhC).

• A means is provided to identify individual PhCs available via a particular PhSAP (service access point). As an example, the layer may give access to several multiplexed channels. However no explicit service parameters are provided to achieve this.

- As with activation, it may be either compulsory, possible or impossible to deactivate the PhC when it is no longer needed. On a modem connection, deactivation could mean dropping RTS.

Other aspects of the physical service

The standard also provides some clarifications regarding how the above facilities should be interpreted in the context of typical physical media.

- The medium can be simplex (one way simultaneous, OWS), half duplex (two way alternate, TWA) or full duplex (two way simultaneous, TWS). This governs both whether one or two directions of transmission are available, and when they can be used. In the simplex and full duplex cases, the PhC may be available all the time (e.g. on a direct digital link), or at least may only need activating once, and deactivating when finished.

In the case of simplex and full duplex, the available direction(s) of transmission will always be (potentially) available, so that activation and deactivation may not be necessary in all cases. In the half duplex case, activation will always be required at some stage to turn around the direction of transmission.

- The physical layout of the medium can be point-point or multipoint (multi-endpoint).

- Synchronisation is assumed to be available on the physical medium. The transmission technique can be either synchronous or asynchronous. Although the service deals in individual bits, in practice these may be transmitted as characters framed by start and stop bits (asynchronous), or as groups of characters preceded by two or more ASCII SYN characters. In other words synchronisation (of some sort) may be assumed to be available.

Here is a classic example of the 'internationalese' which is encountered in standard documents. X.211 states that 'synchronisation is a veritable feature'. This means that it exists!

- The signalling rate may not match the PhSDU throughput due to inclusion of protocol control information, multiplexing, encoding mechanisms, or other transmission control functions.

In specifying the service available in practice (of which the primitives are purely an abstraction), the user basically needs to be aware of two principal characteristics of the medium:

- The type of synchronisation (synchronous or asynchronous).

• The mode of operation (simplex, half duplex or full duplex).

Model of the physical connection

The PhC is simply modelled as a pair of bit streams between the peer physical entities. (If transmission is simplex, there will only be one of course.) The standard recognises that there may be intermediate physical layer relays. (The standard is vague about what constitutes a relay, but it could typically be a repeater on a digital trunk circuit.)

Physical QOS

The main aspects of the QOS are twofold. First, the service user knows the actual value (of the various parameters), even if relays are involved (i.e. the perceived PhC spans several actual ones). Secondly, each physical medium will have a different QOS.

Strictly speaking this is the GOS subset of QOS; see chapter ten. However there is a problem here. The idea that there is a fixed (actual) value of the QOS is a nice theory, but it may well not work out that way in practice. There is no way in which it can be sensibly applied to ephemeral radio links such as those encountered in cellular radio. (See RLP, chapter six.)

The QOS (GOS) parameters which can be specified at the physical layer are as follows:

• Service availability. This relates to the physical availability for use of the medium.
• Error rate (from loss, alteration, creation, other causes). This is in effect the mean rate at which transmission errors causing bit corruption occur.
• Throughput. This relates to the line speed less overheads due to signalling, turnaround and so on.
• Transit delay. This is not normally significant except on satellite and radio links
• Physical connection protection. The standard cites encryption as an example.

11.2.3   Physical service primitives

Three basic services are provided, for activation of the physical medium, data transfer, and medium deactivation. Note that the standard refers to activation rather than connection. The medium usually exists physically (there are some exceptions), even if it is not actually being used at present. Contrast an HDLC connection, which has no physical meaning.

Activation service

This makes the physical medium available for transmission. A single service primitive is provided; this aspect is clearly causing the standard bodies some difficulty.

Ph–ACTIVATE request, indication   (parameters for further study)

As indicated earlier, this is an optional service, which may not be needed for simplex or duplex transmission. In the case of half duplex transmission via a modem, activation of one direction of transmission implies deactivation of the other, with possible turnaround delays impacting on the throughput and transit delay aspects of the QOS.

The QOS is beset with interpretational difficulties. In the half duplex case it depends on how often the direction of transfer is reversed. This cannot possibly be a fixed value known to the service user unless there are strict rules regarding turnaround. Unfortunately there are no rules which can be sensibly applied at the physical level..

Data transfer service

This service needs little explanation. Bits (or strings of bits) are presented for transmission. The only comment which needs to be made is that this is an unconfirmed service. The physical layer in general has no idea which individual bits may have got corrupted. This is for higher layers to determine, by applying error checking algorithms.

Ph–DATA request, indication   user data

The maximum data size which can be supplied with this primitive is a service provider option. The maximum permitted size is made known to the service user.

Deactivation service

This makes the physical medium unavailable for transmission. A single service primitive is provided; again this aspect is causing the standard bodies some difficulty.

Ph–DEACTIVATE request, indication (parameters for further study)

Once more this may be optional, as already discussed for the activation service. In the half duplex case, it is necessary (conceptually, that is) for one entity to deactivate its direction of transmission before the peer entity can activate the reverse direction. For example one end must drop the carrier on a half duplex modem line before the other end can raise its own carrier. This must be at the behest of higher layers, as there is no means of conveying a request to reverse the direction of transmission at the physical level. One begins to see why the detailed specification of the activation and deactivation services is presenting so many difficulties for the standards organisations, and why (at the time of writing), the physical service definition had still only reached the DP stage.

This implies that the blue book X.211 recommendation is also an early draft (and hence unstable) recommendation. CCITT have no formalised mechanism for indicating the status of their recommendations, in the sense that ISO have; see chapter five.

11.3   The data link layer

What is discussed here is the WAN variant of the data link layer. It has many similarities with the IEEE 802 LAN variant discussed in chapter thirteen, although there are a number of differences as well. The idea of the data link layer is that it masks the details of the physical medium from higher layer entities (specifically the network layer). The standard covers both connection oriented (CO) and connectionless (CL) services, although the latter functionality is minimal.

General provisions of the data link layer

This layer provides (in the CO variant) a data link connection (DLC) between peer DL entities (This can generally be interpreted as a connection between adjacent nodes in a communication subnet such as PSS, but this is not the only interpretation. The physical service can operate over multipoint lines, so that - in theory at least - multipoint applications are not excluded.) The general features of the data link layer are as follows:

• It provides independence from the underlying physical medium For example it is of no concern to higher layers whether the actual physical connection is point-point or multipoint, full duplex or half duplex.

Sadly, if the underlying physical medium is half duplex, this does impact on higher layers. There is a further aside on this subject in §11.2.3.

• The data link layer provides for the transparency of transferred information. No restrictions are placed on its content, format or coding, nor is any attempt made to interpret its structure or meaning.

• The layer provides reliable data transfer (subject to the specified QOS). In theory at least it relieves the service user (i.e. the network layer) from concern for loss, duplication, or corruption of DLSDUs. Optionally, if required by the network layer, it may also correct sequencing errors. Alternatively the network layer may perform this function.

While this is an interesting theory, there are many types of underlying data link protocol (such as BSC, and datagram services) which can in no way guarantee reliable data transfer. So the above statement should really be interpreted in the context of X.25 LAPB. Indeed the standard (X.212) admits that loss or duplication due to irrecoverable errors can occur.

• The data link service recognises various QOS parameters as discussed in the next section.

• A means is provided of identifying the appropriate DLSAP (if more than one available). However a global addressing structure is not considered to be appropriate at this layer.

Data link QOS

Various parameters are recognised, as follows; the detailed significance of these parameters was discussed in chapter ten:

- throughput.
- transit delay.
- residual error rate.
- resilience (of the DL connection).
- protection (none, protection from passive monitoring, or protection from modification, replay, addition and deletion).
- priority (somehow determining the order in which DLCs will be degraded or released in the event of network trouble).

11.3.1   Connection oriented data link service

Three services are provided in the connection oriented service, for data link connection establishment, data transfer, and connection release. We relate this service to X.25 LAPB in §11.3.3.

Connection establishment service

This is provided by a single service primitive. The usage of the variants differs, so they will be discussed separately. Only parameters of particular interest will be discussed.

DL–CONNECT   called address, calling address,
request, indication   QOS, user data

> • The *addresses* identify the two ends of the DLC. The *destination address* may in theory at least be a generic address (see responding address below), although this may well not be possible with many data link protocols.

> • As with X.25 call setup (chapter seven), the connect attempt may fail for various reasons. A DL-CONNECT request can result in a DL-DISCONNECT indication from the service provider (if a connection cannot be made), or a DL-DISCONNECT request (relayed as an indication) from the peer data link service user. The reason codes are discussed under the connection release service

> • Whether *user data* can actually be associated with the CONNECT is a function of the underlying protocol.

DL–CONNECT response, confirm   responding address, QOS, user data

> • In theory the *responding address* can be a specific instance of a generic address. However this is not appropriate if HDLC (LAPB) is used.

Data transfer service

Data transfer

This provides two primitives, for data transfer and link reset. Link reset was a later addition, included largely for compatibility with higher layer services, notably because X.25 packet mode has such a 'service'. The minimal subset of HDLC does not have a reset mechanism, nor does X.25 LAPB, although a new RSET un-numbered command has been added to HDLC and is also provided in the LAN version discussed in chapter thirteen.

A single primitive is provided for data transfer.

DL–DATA request, indication   user data

This conveys one or more octets of user data; the maximum permitted value is implementation dependent. (The standard states that it is known to the service user, which amounts to the same thing.)

It should be noted that although the data link layer is supposed to offer a reliable service, this primitive is *unconfirmed*. This begs the question of how the service user is to know that the data has reached its destination. This dilemma can be attacked in two ways:

- The simplest way is to argue that the service definition is an abstraction, and that an acknowledgement can be provided in some other way. That however is hardly a good explanation.

- More to the point, this the fact that there is a tacit assumption that HDLC will be used as an underlying data link protocol. This proceeds automatically, and it can be assumed that unless the link is disconnected (or reset), data so far has got through successfully.

Unfortunately this leaves the problem that if an unsolicited link reset or disconnect does occur, how is the sending service user to know which data got through and which did not? Therefore we must conclude that delivery confirmation is required. Unfortunately the standard is vague about how this can be achieved. In effect we are back to the first argument above.

Link reset

This is provided by a single service primitive. There are two cases of reset, where it is initiated by the service user (the data link layer), and where it is issued by the service provider, due to some problem with the underlying data link protocol (e.g. an HDLC I-frame transmitted the maximum number of times and still outstanding).

DL–RESET request   reason

As this is a request, it must originate from the service user. The *reason* in this case is always 'user resynchronisation'.

DL–RESET indication   originator, reason

This can either be a request from the peer service user, in which case the reason in the request is preserved, or it can be initiated by the service provider (in which case there was no request). In the latter case, the *reason* can be stated to be either 'DL flow control congestion' or 'DL error'. Where the reset was issued by the service user, it is not clear either how the reason and originator parameters can be conveyed by the underlying protocol. This problem will become clearer when we discuss how DL-RESET maps on to X.25 LAPB.

DL–RESET response, confirm   (no parameters)

The effect of DL-RESET is comparable to an X.25 reset, in that a complete cycle of primitives is required to flush data in transit. This can be best understood in terms of the queue model of the connection, as outlined in chapter ten (and as will be further discussed for the network layer in chapter fourteen).

It should be noted in this regard that if an underlying failure occurs, an indication will be issued to both users, each of which will reply with a response. In this case there will be no request or confirm primitives.

Connection release service

This is used to close down (disconnect) the DLC. It is used in three situations:

• Where it is not possible to set up the connection in the first place, i.e. as a reply to DL-CONNECT.

• If either service user no longer needs the connection. This is normal termination by the service provider.

• If some underlying failure renders the DLC inoperable. This is abnormal termination by the service provider.

A single primitive is provided as follows:

DL–DISCONNECT request   reason

The *reason* provided by the network layer may be normal termination, abnormal termination, connection rejected (permanent or transient), or unspecified.

By *transient* rejection, it is implied that it may well be worth the peer network layer entity trying again soon, i.e. the remote network entity is having some temporary problem which is not expected to be of a prolonged nature. If however the rejection is stated to be *permanent*, the peer network entity is expected to abandon the attempt to use this particular DLC, and either use another DLC or give up altogether. (Alternative links may be available, for instance if X.25 LAPB multilink procedures are being used; see chapter seven.)

DL–DISCONNECT indication   originator, reason

If this is a request being relayed to the peer as an indication (i.e. is user originated), the reason is the same as in the request. If however it is service provider originated, the *reason* may be permanent or transient failure, destination unknown, destination unreachable (either transiently or permanently), destination unavailable (again either transiently or permanently), or reason unspecified.

Once more it is far from clear how some data link protocols can convey the parameters of the disconnect.

11.3.2   Connectionless data link service

A single primitive is provided. Again this is an unconfirmed service.

DL-UNITDATA	source address, destination address,
request, indication	QOS, user data

Once more the user data is an integral number of octets, up to some agreed (implementation dependent) maximum value. This service is not supported in X.25 LAPB, and is included in the standard mainly for completeness. It differs in major ways from the connectionless service offered by the LAN variant {8802-2} discussed in chapter thirteen.

11.3.3   Use of HDLC LAPB as a data link protocol

Finally, in part to serve as useful 'revision' material on HDLC as discussed in chapter six, but more importantly to highlight some of the problems in interpreting the above service definition, the mapping of the connection oriented data link service on to an underlying X.25 LAPB data link protocol will be examined. This mapping uses all of the frame types defined in LAPB, namely SABM/SABME, DISC, DM, I, RR, RNR, REJ, UA and FRMR.

Connection establishment

This service maps on to LAPB link setup, as follows.

• The DL-CONNECT request is relayed as a SABM SABME frame as appropriate.

• The DL-CONNECT response is relayed as UA.

This is the standard HDLC link setup sequence. The called address is in the address field of the SABM command, and the calling address is in the address field of the UA response. These addresses are essentially redundant except in that they distinguish between commands and responses. Therefore the responding address has no significance in the LAPB case, although one can envisage link protocols over transmission media where it might have some significance.

The QOS parameter conveyed with the request may be used to decide which link to use, if there is a choice with different characteristics (e.g. a land line with low propagation delay, or a satellite link with high propagation delay). However the QOS parameter set is not relayed to the peer, as each link has a fixed QOS which is known to both data link entities.

Connection release

This service maps on to LAPB link disconnection, as follows.

• The DL-DISCONNECT request is relayed as a DISC if the link is already set up. This implies normal or abnormal termination of an established link, either by the service user or service provider.

• If a DL-DISCONNECT request is being returned by the receiving network layer to refuse a connection request, it is relayed as DM.

• The DL-DISCONNECT response is relayed as UA.

• In the case where the service provider aborts a connection (i.e. an indication is issued to both service users), in reality one data link entity will have sent DISC, and the other will have responded UA. Which data link entity actually issued the DISC is not of concern to the network layer.

The originator and reason parameters are not (cannot be) conveyed, and the standard states that they are of local significance only. Unfortunately all of this begs the question of how the receiver of a DISC (passed up as a DL-DISCONNECT indication) can distinguish between transient and permanent failures, or determine whether the service provider or peer service user was responsible. Ultimately this has to be left for higher layers to determine. Not for the first time, the facilities provided in the service definition are optimistic in the context of the actual underlying protocol.

Link reset

While HDLC now has a specific frame type which can be used to reset a data link (RSET, see chapter thirteen), it is not defined in X.25 LAPB. Therefore DL-RESET is mapped on to link establishment. This implies that either station can receive SABM(E) at any time while the link is established, and that this is not a protocol violation. In this context, the SABM/UA handshake purges all data in transit, and re-initialises the link (e.g. V(S) and V(R) are reset to 0, and all outstanding I-frames are discarded).

In the interests of proper division of responsibility, it would probably be better to use the new HDLC RSET command instead. The problem is that this was a late addition to HDLC, and existing PDNs such as PSS are committed to using a LAPB which has no such frame type. In a sense the difference is largely semantic, as the net effect is the same in either case.

- The DL-RESET request is relayed as SABM(E).
- The DL-RESET response is relayed as UA.

Provider initiated resets result in an indication to both service users, which are not aware of which station was responsible. The originator and reason parameters of the request primitive cannot be conveyed, and a received SABM contains no information which would allow any values to be specified in the indication parameters either.

Data transfer

As would be expected, DL-DATA requests are relayed in I-frames. In turn these are acknowledged via N(R) fields in returned I-frames or S-frames.

We pointed out in §11.3.1 that this service is not confirmed. As we will see in chapter thirteen, this is in marked contrast with the LAN service definition, where the corresponding service is confirmed. Indeed if LAPB is used as an underlying mechanism, I-frames are acknowledged via N(R) fields. Therefore it seems very strange that an unconfirmed service is specified. Nor is it valid to argue that a network entity can assume that all data has been implicitly acknowledged unless it receives a reset or disconnect, as in this case, I-frames can be lost, and the network layer has no means of knowing what has been acknowledged. Therefore any real implementation will certainly inform the network entity that I-frames have been acknowledged, even though no DL-DATA confirm is specified.

A further point to note is that the service definition makes no provision for flow control. Again the LAN variant has explicit flow control primitives. Once more it is clear not only that flow control is necessary between the data link and network entities, but also that the service definition is incompletely specified. In part this reflects the fact that the LAN standard is more mature. But it is also worth remembering that the service interface already existed between X.25 packet mode and LAPB. The abstract service definition does not have to be an exact mirror of a real implementation. In the LAN case, the service definition preceded implementations of HDLC over LANs, which is quite a different story.

11.4 Reference

1 Halsall (preface, background reading 1), provides a good discussion on V.24 and modulation techniques. See in particular chapter two.

12 Local Area Networks

12.1 Introduction

This chapter is concerned with the basic concepts relating to Local Area Networks (LANs). Some general characteristics of LANs are first discussed. The discussion then turns to topologies which have been successfully used, with particular emphasis on ring and linear bus. The relationship of LANs to OSI/RM is discussed in chapter thirteen, where the IEEE 802 LAN standardisation project is covered. At the end of that chapter, a further technology (slotted or Cambridge ring) is discussed, which has the support of ISO but not IEEE.

LANs are generally considered to have a scope which spans at most a few localised buildings, although there is ongoing study by IEEE of a standard for a Metropolitan Area Network (MAN[1]). Given the short distances involved, digital transmission techniques can be used, and very much faster data transmission rates are possible than would be the case if long-haul lines had to be used. In addition, LANs are likely to be very much more reliable than WANs, with very few detected transmission errors, and virtually no undetected ones.

It is generally agreed that basic requirements of LANs should include a single interface to the LAN for each attached host, a rapid interhost data transfer rate (to promote timely resource sharing), and a simple but effective broadcast facility. A *broadcast* is simply a frame which is transmitted automatically to all other hosts connected to the LAN, and which contains a special *broadcast address*. One use of broadcasts is to locate a resource whose physical location and network address are of no concern but may change, or to determine whether a required resource is currently available (or connected to the network). This is particularly relevant with the new breed of diskless workstations, connected by LAN to file servers, 'yellow pages' servers, and the like. Protocols based on broadcasts can be standardised regardless of where the server is located on the LAN. We will see in a moment that this restricts the choice of feasible LAN topologies. We will immediately dismiss the mesh network as a contender, and add the additional requirement that no alternative routes between hosts should exist within the LAN.

You will see that we have used the term frame rather than packet. This implies the use of data link protocols within LANs, and we will see that this is indeed the case. However some workers use the term packets instead, so you should be prepared to encounter either name used in the same context. This particularly applies to older, non-standardised, LAN protocols such as the original Ethernet ones. We will adhere to ISO/IEEE practice in this book, and always refer to frames.

Protocols on LANs will be substantially different from those on WANs. There will be less emphasis on error recovery and flow control, minimal concern with routing issues, and (in general) support for broadcasts, which also implies datagram support. It will come as no surprise to learn that a different structure in the lowest layers of OSI/RM will be appropriate for LANs. Furthermore, it is unlikely that a protocol such as X.25 packet mode will be appropriate, although HDLC remains a contender.

Another important consideration concerns the bandwidth available on a LAN. Attenuation and noise problems, which are a major constraint on transmission speed over long distances, are largely absent over the short distances encountered in LANs. If a very high bandwidth can be provided economically (far more, perhaps, than the traffic warrants) it is less crucial that the protocol optimises usage of the available bandwidth. On the other hand, WAN protocols need to use the limited bandwidth as efficiently as possible, and this can be restrictive. It may also mean that a simple protocol can be used when all is going well, at the expense of complex recovery procedures in the event of an occasional problem.

12.2 Local Area Network topologies

Before examining layering or protocols, we will first survey the possibilities for LAN topology, examining a few of them in more detail. This book is mainly concerned with protocol rather than hardware issues, and other books should be consulted for details of LAN architecture. A useful review of LAN protocols and architectures appears in an article by Stallings[2].

12.2.1 Parallel bus topology

This is a multi-bit highway, commonly used in internal processor architectures. For example a 16-bit data bus is required between the 80286 processor and the memory in an IBM PC/AT. This will often be merely a set of tracks on a printed circuit board. On a larger scale, parallel buses are commonly seen as multiwire flat cables, similar to those used to connect parallel printers to microcomputers.

Can this approach be used in the design of LANs? This would require all hosts to be connected to such a parallel bus. Figure 12.1 shows such a possibility, simplified to a 2-bit bus for typographical reasons. The simple answer is yes. The Manchester Computing Centre (MCC, formerly known as UMRCC) uses a closely related technique to connect its mainframes (Amdahl, 7600s, etc.). However there are two major problems, those of cost and complexity.

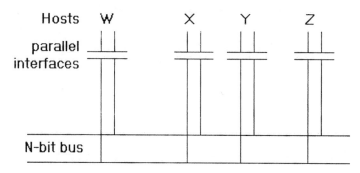

Typical bus widths: 8, 16, 32 bits

Figure 12.1 - simplified parallel bus topology

• **Cost**. Parallel cable is expensive, far moreso than serial cable. The cost of extending parallel cable round a building could be prohibitive.

• **Complexity**. There are several fundamental technical problems in implementing a highway network of this type. A detailed discussion of these problems is beyond the scope of this book, although some of the issues (particularly a timing problem) will be outlined later when we deal with a related topology, the coaxial cable. In the case of microcomputer connections, some interface between the microcomputer and the bus will normally be required, as direct memory access (DMA) is generally not possible to microcomputer memory. In addition, parallel interfaces of a suitable type can be hard to incorporate into microcomputers; although a serial to parallel converter is not excluded, it would add to the cost of the interface.

The combination of wiring cost and implementation complexity makes this a poor choice for connecting machines scattered around a building. This topology is generally restricted to connecting a number of larger computers in the same room, i.e. close together, as with the MCC example mentioned above.

12.2.2   Star network topology

Here, we envisage that all hosts will be wired to some central point. This is a very traditional network topology, which seems to be applicable to LANs. From the above discussion, we conclude that some form of serial transmission technique will be used rather than parallel. Again, this is a valid possibility. In the Department of Computer Science at Manchester University some years ago, a number of minicomputers and mainframes in the 'MU5 network' were connected together using a central intelligent switch known as the 'MU5 exchange'. This routed messages between attached hosts on the basis of the destination address. See figure 12.2.

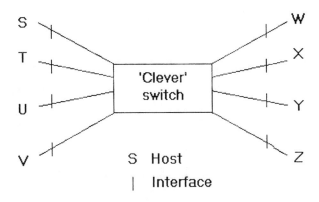

Figure 12.2 - star local area network topology

It is important to notice the distinction between this topology and the wide area star discussed in chapter two. In the wide area case, the 'hub' of the star was a fully fledged host, probably a mainframe with a front end processor. The central switch in the local area star is however just that, a device which exists purely to switch frames from one host to another, by interpreting and decoding the destination address. In contrast to the wide area star, nothing is routed to or from the hub, which is in effect a 'black box'.

There are a number of problems with this approach:

• **Reliability**. If the central switch fails, the entire network is lost. Thus the hub is a crucial element of the network, which cannot be allowed to fail. That is not to say that the problem cannot be overcome, but the switch will become complex and expensive if its reliability is to be guaranteed. It can be argued that the advent of ultra-reliable ISDN-compatible digital PABXs (Private Automatic Branch Exchanges) alleviates this problem, but as this type of LAN has yet to make any impact in the standards area, it will not be discussed further, except to say that there are bandwidth restrictions for connected stations which do not apply to the other technologies we will discuss.

• **Handling moving hosts**. One common LAN requirement is that the physical location of a host can be altered. If this happens, how is the switch to knows? This problem can be solved, together with the related problem of broadcasts, but again at a price. In the MU5 exchange mentioned above, all hosts were in fixed locations and dedicated to specific tasks, so that there was no requirement for broadcasts. (In addition, the network was used purely for research, so that reliability was not a major issue either, although in fact the MU5 exchange was quite reliable; it was MU5 which kept crashing!)

• **Wiring**. Wiring all locations to a central site is seldom the most cost-effective approach. As well as requiring longer cable runs than some other approaches, the cabling near the central switch can easily become a mess. Where there are several hosts in the same room, yet some distance from the central switch, there will be wasteful duplication of cables. Having said that, there is a school of thought which argues that ring (§12.2.4) wiring should be routed through a central patch panel between every pair of stations, to facilitate rewiring if part of the ring fails, and many standardised rings use this technique, despite the impact on wiring.

• **Flexibility**. Each time a new office (host) is to be connected, new wiring has to be laid to the central site. Possibly the switch will have to be reprogrammed as well, to include the new host. In an LAN environment, changes of this type are likely to be quite frequent, and too much seems to be required of the central switch. (Again it could be argued that, for a PABX, the necessary wiring will already be in place to provide a telephone service, and that the data service is the icing on the cake.)

• **Broadcasts**. As we shall soon see, each frame will be seen by every station with most LAN topologies, so that broadcasts are a 'natural' feature; with a star, multiple copies must be sent, which is inefficient and wasteful of bandwidth. Support for broadcasts is a crucial requirement of a LAN. With a star, they are inefficient and cumbersome.

To summarise, the MU5 exchange represented one of the few early applications for a star LAN; there were relatively few hosts (about 5), all were in the same room, the number of hosts was fixed and hosts were not 'moved around', reliability was not a major issue, and there was no requirement for broadcasts (hosts performed dedicated tasks). Like the parallel bus, it appeared until recently that this approach would not have sufficiently wide applicability. A digital PABX approach is admittedly now possible, but this still suffers from bandwidth limitations, inflexibility and inefficient handling of broadcasts.

Another area where a star is sometimes found is when a number of character terminals are connected into a terminal 'multiplexer' (more accurately referred to as a concentrator), which acts as a host on their behalf. However this is not strictly within the scope of this discussion, nor will it be discussed any further in this book.

This leaves us with two topologies which both minimise the wiring required to interconnect hosts, and are both suitable for LANs which extend (say) over all floors and rooms of a building. These are the *linear bus* and the *simplex ring*.

12.2.3   Linear Bus topology

In the *coaxial cable* (linear bus) approach, the cable is run through each room which has or may have a host, rather like a snake. Hosts and associated interface hardware (*interface* and *transceiver*; explained later) can then be 'tapped' into the cable at various points. There is no central point, and all connections to the cable will have equal status. The technique is in some ways similar to the parallel bus, except that a serial transmission technique is used, and coaxial cable is far cheaper (and less messy) than parallel cabling. See figure 12.3. If a single coaxial cable is insufficient, for example because it would need to be so long that attenuation problems would occur, several different *segments* can be used, connected together by *repeaters*. When a signal is placed on the cable, it will propagate in both directions, thereby (eventually) reaching every other station connected to it.

Repeaters are dumb devices, which simply transmit everything which reaches them on to the next segment. More sophisticated devices which check the destination address of the frame, and do not forward it if the destination address is on the segment the frame is being received from (thus reducing unwanted traffic on other segments) are known as *bridges*. Yet more sophisticated devices can perform protocol conversion, routing and other network layer functions. These are known as *routers*. You may also encounter the term *brouter*, which is sometimes used to describe a device which offers functions somewhere between those of a bridge and a router.

Linear buses immediately looks attractive. They have many advantages, the main one being their obvious flexibility. Special coaxial cable can be purchased which allows a host interface to be in effect 'screwed' into the cable at various points along its length. Thus host

246

interfaces can be moved around at will; they are in simply unscrewed from the coaxial cable and screwed in somewhere else on the cable. A host may also be disconnected merely by removing it from the interface, leaving the coaxial cable 'tap' in place.

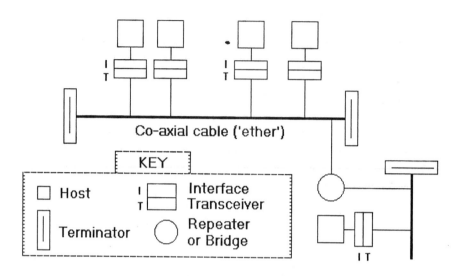

Figure 12.3 - coaxial cable topology

There is the additional advantage that broadcasts are trivially easy. Whatever signals are fed into the cable will automatically reach every other host (interface) which is attached. The interface will (among many other things) shield the host from signals intended for other hosts.

CSMA/CD bus (Ethernet)

This approach offers several advantages. It is in fact the most widely used topology world-wide. The most important implementation is based on the original one, *Ethernet*, which was originally designed by Xerox, and subsequently marketed by a consortium of DEC, Intel and Xerox known as DIX. We will discuss the IEEE 802 variant of Ethernet in the next chapter. It has become a de facto standard, particularly in the USA.

The standards recognise a number of different technologies, of varying speed and cost. They are mentioned only for completeness, as the hardware technology does not significantly affect the protocol concepts (except in the broadband case). The main technologies are as follows:

• The full specification system offers <u>10</u> mbps <u>baseband</u> (i.e. digital) transmission, with a maximum segment length of <u>500</u>m, known as *10base5*. Stations can be screwed directly into the coaxial cable at various tap points.

- A 'cut down' version uses cheaper coaxial cable which cannot be tapped into. Instead BNC connectors are used to connect stations to the cable. This has the disadvantage that it must be severed to add new stations. In addition, the maximum segment length is shorter. Normally, neither is a major handicap. This is referred to as *10base2*, or by the colloquial name *cheapernet*.

- A twisted pair variant has also become available, which can only support a transmission rate of 1 mbps, and is known as *1base5*.

- Broadband (modulated) systems are now becoming available, notably one known as *10broad36* {8802-3 DAD3}.

Protocols used over coaxial cable buses take advantage of two fundamental characteristics of this medium:

- Every station will receive all transmissions. The destination address must be examined to determine if the frame should be accepted or ignored. This is done by the *interface*.

- Every station can judge whether there is anything happening on the bus ('ether'), using a technique known as *carrier sense*. Thus a station can defer a transmission until the bus is inactive. This function is performed by the *transceiver*, which is between the interface and the tap.

Let us firstly assume that transceiver may transmit if the ether is free. This technique is known as *carrier sense multiple access* (*CSMA*). By itself, CSMA is no good, as there is a fundamental problem. The signal travels rapidly along the ether, but it will take a short but finite time (of the order of microseconds) for the signal to reach other transceivers. Clearly, the further away the other transceiver is, the longer it will take the signal to reach it. Once all transceivers have noticed the transmission, all is well, as they will all now defer until the transmitter has finished with the ether. This has the potential advantage that long frames can be sent. However there is a clear problem in that a **collision** will occur if two transceivers simultaneously (or almost simultaneously) decide that the ether is free, and both transmit. As the signals meet, they will interfere destructively with each other, and both frames will be irretrievably mangled.

Although collisions will normally be rare unless the loading is high, nevertheless something has to be done about this problem. The approach used in the standard Ethernet implementation is known as **carrier sense multiple access with collision detection**, or just **CSMA/CD**. The transceiver listens to the ether while it is transmitting. If what it 'hears' is not the same as it is transmitting, it knows that a collision has occurred, and takes recovery action. Firstly, it briefly *jams* the ether using a special signal. This will make sure that all other transceivers notice the collision, and it also stops them from transmitting. There are then three options:

- It can try again immediately. Used on its own, this is not a sensible algorithm, since there is another transceiver which will do exactly the same thing, giving the same collision again.

- It can wait (known as *backing off*) for a random length of time, then try again. Meanwhile, other transceivers may be using the ether, but this transceiver will not attempt to transmit until the specified delay has elapsed, even if the ether becomes free during this time (although of course it will still listen and receive). This is standard CSMA/CD. Note that the backoff time must be random, or the same collision will happen again.

If two transmissions collide and there is little or no other activity on the bus, this backoff will lead to wasted transmission opportunities, as no other station wishes to transmit at present. Some implementations therefore use a combination of these options (try again now, and wait) with a given probability. This can reduce the wastage of transmission capacity due to backoffs, but the probability has to be chosen with care to minimise the problems of the first option.

By backing off when a collision is detected, the loss of bandwidth due to collisions can be kept acceptably low, provided that the network does not become too heavily loaded. It may of course happen that the later retransmission also collides. When this happens, the delay period before a retransmission is progressively increased. After n attempts have collided, the transmission is abandoned, and an error condition is reported to the host. The transceiver now merely listens, and no attempt is made to transmit anything. One reason for this approach is that a transceiver fault could appear like a collision, and repeated un-necessary transmissions could cause the network to seize up.

Note that a break in the cable will also look like a collision, as the transceiver will see unwanted 'reflections' from an unterminated cable; normally these would be absorbed by the impedance matching terminator. Therefore if all frames from all transceivers appear to collide, it probably means that there is a cable fault. It is also possible for a faulty transceiver to jam the ether continuously, but the transceiver design aims to minimise the risk of this happening.

It should be noted that there is no guarantee that the frame reached the other host intact, simply because no collision was detected. It could have been corrupted by a transmission error, the receiving host may have crashed before it could be processed, or the host may not currently be connected to the network. This technique is further discussed in the next chapter.

Problems with the CSMA/CD technique

CSMA/CD is a simple, elegant technique. Unfortunately the collision problem impacts on its usefulness in several ways.

• One problem with collisions is that if they occur, the maximum time it will take to transmit a frame successfully cannot be predicted; in the worst case it may not get transmitted successfully at all. This is unacceptable in some applications such as process control. An instruction to a robot to perform some action needs to arrive predictably, otherwise chaos could result on a production line whose robots are controlled via a LAN. General Motors required a technique with a more predictable outcome, particularly in cases of high loading, and were one of the first organisations to attack this problem.

• In addition, attempts to load a CSMA/CD bus too heavily result in a progressive degradation of the service, as more and more frames collide and have to be retransmitted. Thus CSMA/CD is unsuitable if the network will be heavily loaded, although this is seldom perceived to be a problem in commercial Ethernets.

• A more fundamental issue is that the frame transmission time must exceed twice the transit time from one end of the network to the other (including segments joined by repeaters). This is to ensure that if two stations, one at each end, transmit at about the same time, the resulting collision will be seen by both stations. If transmission is simultaneous, the transmissions will need to last for at least the end-end propagation time for the collision to be detected by the receiver. But it also has to be detected by the transmitter, which means that the receiver's jamming signal must arrive back before the station has finished its transmission, otherwise the sender will not detect the collision.

What this means in practice is that there is a *minimum frame length* which will guarantee that collisions will be detected. The longer the ether, and/or the faster the transmission rate, the longer this minimum length needs to be. This leads to the necessity to pad out frames with short data fields, which is inefficient in some applications.

The original DIX frame format had to incorporate a long address field, which was necessary so that every station on every network in the world could have its own unique address. The idea that DIX should regulate addresses in this way was abandoned, as part of the standardisation tradeoff. However it is worth mentioning that the impact on efficiency is minimal, as more padding may be necessary if the length of the address field is reduced, with short data fields.

Because of these problems, other transmission algorithms were sought. One, known as *CSMA with Collision Avoidance (CSMA/CA)*[3] attempted to avoid the collision problem by using timeslots; each station was allocated a 'time window' during which it could transmit without risk of collision. But this leads to inefficient use of the ether, as many timeslots will be unused. Because of this, the technique allowed reversion to a free for all if no timeslots were used in a given cycle. Any resulting collision would result in the stations concerned giving up, and the timeslot phase would be re-entered.

One problem is that CSMA/CA is less efficient than CSMA/CD at low utilisations, and wastes too much bandwidth at high loadings if there are many stations connected to the bus, as each will have to wait for its timeslot. Furthermore, the minimum frame length restriction must apply in free for all mode. The technique has not proved popular, nor is it the subject of standards activity.

Token bus approach

Another way to avoid the collision problem is to ensure that collisions cannot take place (under normal operational conditions). This can be achieved by a *token passing* scheme. A token is a special frame which a station must receive (possess) before it can transmit any frames. In other words the token is a *permission to transmit*. In the simplest scheme, the token is passed round all of the stations on the bus in some predetermined order, so that in effect the linear bus is being used as if it were a logical ring. This has been developed by IEEE 802 into the **token bus** LAN standard. General Motors were the principal driving force behind this standardisation work, for reasons already mentioned. The technique will be discussed in more detail in the next chapter. Token passing eliminates the collision problem, and results in predictable performance at high loading. Token passing in a bus is only possible because all stations can see everything which is happening on the bus. The token is addressed to a specific station; all other stations see the token, and ignore it, but can possibly take special action if they fail to see the token being passed around the 'ring' (e.g. because it has been lost). However the technique introduces some compensating drawbacks:

- The overhead in passing the token round is appreciable when loading is very low. In this situation a station must waste time waiting for the token to arrive; in the case of CSMA/CD the station could almost certainly have transmitted immediately. (A similar problem arises with multidrop VDUs using poll-select procedures.)

- Once the logical ring is set up, token passing becomes a simple and elegant technique. However this is at the expense of complex initialisation and recovery procedures. Specifically, the logical ring has to be set up in the first place, new stations will wish to join the logical ring, stations will disconnect from the ring, and the token may become lost for this or other reasons. However if all stations could not see all activity on the bus, it would not be possible to implement recovery procedures at all, and the token bus scheme would be unworkable. It is also worth mentioning that the recovery procedures rely heavily on the use of broadcasts as part of the control mechanism.

12.2.4   Simplex ring topology

One problem with bus networks in general is that one new cabling technology, optical fibre, has still not been used with complete success. Optical fibre is largely immune to the attenuation and distortion inherent in electrical transmission, and thus gives the potential of very high transmission rates. However a satisfactory (and reliable) way of 'tapping into' optical fibre in the way required for bus networks is still sought, although some progress has been made. In any case, a CSMA/CD bus could not easily realise the full potential of optical fibre, due to bandwidth restrictions imposed by the collision problem. Other topologies (notably the ring) have no such problems in incorporating optical fibre wiring.

The ring topology is quite different from the bus topology, and is its principal contender at present. Whereas Ethernet interfaces are tapped into coaxial cable, in the case of a ring they are linked together into a circular structure, as shown in figure 12.4. Thus the interfaces, or ring stations, are an active part of the transmission medium (i.e. they are also repeaters), rather than being simply sources and (passive) sinks of data on the transmission medium. Data flows in one direction round the ring (i.e. the ring is simplex). The interfaces will need to contain buffers and logic, to identify and take copies of frames destined for the local host, as well as to relay frames on the ring.

A typical ring operates using four conceptually simple stages. We will discuss these stages in more detail later for the specific cases of token ring and slotted ring:

• A station wishing to transmit a frame must wait for permission to transmit to be received on the ring. Depending on the ring protocol involved, this may be that nothing is currently being received, the receipt of a token, or the receipt of an empty slot (proforma). We will discuss the token and slot approaches in more detail later.

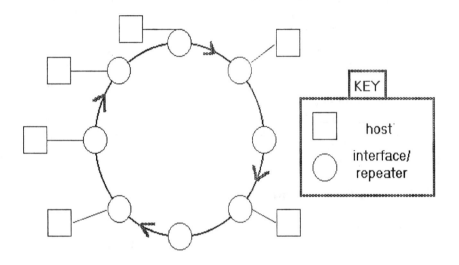

NOTE:

Repeaters may or may not have hosts attached

Figure 12.4 - simplex ring topology

• A frame is now transmitted. In the slot case, this will be inserted into suitable 'holes' in the slot, and the slot will be marked full. In other cases an entire new frame will be generated.

• Each station on the ring examines each received frame. If the destination address refers to this station, the frame may be copied to the local host. In some cases the frame contents may be modified to indicate that the station has (or has not) taken a copy for the local host. In all cases (except as below) the frame will be regenerated (possibly with some modification), and forwarded to the next station on the ring.

• It follows that the frame will in due course arrive back at the originating station. With most ring protocols, a simple algorithm is used to deduce that this station inserted the frame in the first place; this does not normally involve looking at the originating address.

When the frame returns to the sender, it is removed. In the case of a slot, it is simply marked empty.

There are one or two weaknesses in the ring approach, when compared with the bus topology. Firstly, repeater/interface boxes must be sited at all points where host are, or are considered likely to be, connected. Whereas Ethernet interfaces can be plugged in almost anywhere without significant disruption (at least in the full specification), installation of a new ring repeater requires the ring to be shut down, a cable to be physically severed, and some soldering to be done. (This may in fact even be an advantage, as it forces the network designers to consider carefully where hosts might be located before the cabling is laid.) A related problem is that adding a new repeater in the middle of an optical fibre section can be quite an intricate job, as special interfacing is necessary. This would have to be done outside operational hours. However the problems of disruption are often overstated, as careful management could ensure that new repeaters are only to be connected when the network is not supposed to be operational in any case.

Another problem is concerned with the fact that each repeater is on the ring itself, and must therefore actively regenerate the signals and forward them on the ring, as well as examine the frames to see if they are for the local host. This makes the integrity of the ring more dependent on the correct operation of a repeater than would be the case for a bus (although certain types of interface fault can ruin that type of network as well). Thus a fundamental ring problem is that of *reliability*. What happens if a repeater fails? Unless great care is taken in the design of the ring, the failure of a single repeater will effectively destroy the ring. The precise location of the fault may be hard to determine, and this could lead to a lengthy loss of service. There are a number of expedients which various designers have used to minimise this problem, some of the more notable ones being as follows:

• Duplication of the ring, e.g. two simplex rings, one in each direction. If one ring becomes severed, the reverse direction can be used as an emergency backup.

• A variant on this is to duplicate the ring in the same direction of transmission, with an automatic switchover in case a link is seen to have become severed.

• A repeater can fail because its power supply fails. One solution to this is to have several 'power supply units' (PSUs) on the ring, and to pass the voltage supply round the ring. This technique is used with the Cambridge Ring.

- To ease the problem of locating wiring faults, one technique which has been tried is to route all sections of the ring via a central monitoring point. This will contain a patch panel allowing faulty circuits to be located easily; 'broken' cables or repeaters may easily be bypassed by a simple wiring modification. However it is impracticable for some types of rings, e.g. the Cambridge ring (§13.5.4), although it is proving to be a popular technique for token rings.

A third problem with certain types of ring (including the Cambridge ring) is that a special *monitor station* is necessary to initialise the ring, to manage the ring traffic, to detect and remove mangled frames, and generally to keep the ring under control. In the absence of the monitor station, a fault can cause frames to circulate endlessly, or the token to vanish, with the result that the throughput possible on the ring can be seriously degraded. It is clear that the monitor must be designed carefully, and a backup may be needed.

To summarise, ring problems relate mainly to reliability issues. With careful design and reliable circuitry these can be minimised, but they cannot be eliminated.

It is sometimes claimed that bus networks such as Ethernet are better at withstanding cabling failures than rings are, because a break in the coaxial cable does not isolate all hosts. However it is not clear that the resulting cable will be correctly terminated. A non-terminated cable will produce reflections, which will interfere with the original signal. This supposed 'advantage' for bus networks is thus not as clear-cut as might at first be imagined.

The ring however has some compensating advantages when compared with the bus. Firstly, the potential transmission rate on a ring is restricted only by the available technology, and speeds of 100 mbps are quite feasible over quite long distances with optical fibre. Indeed a new standard entitled *Fibre Distributed Data Interface* (*FDDI*) {9314-2} is based on two optical fibre token rings operating at high speed in opposite directions. (The capability to interface other LANs to this 'backbone' is also provided.) The maximum throughput rate in a bus network is fundamentally restricted by the collision problem (or by the overheads required to eliminate the problem), and optical fibre can be used only with difficulty, if at all. In fact the collision problem is the 'Achilles heel' of the standard Ethernet. Rings cannot suffer from a collision problem, and the design is such that it is impossible to overload a ring.

On the question of broadcasts, there is little to choose between the two technologies. A frame sent by a host on either type of network will be seen by every interface, although ring interfaces will have more work to do, since they have to regenerate the broadcast at every point.

Two specific ring protocols have received significant support, and will be discussed further in the next chapter.

- The **token ring**, strongly supported by IBM and standardised by IEEE 802. This is now the dominant ring LAN. As its name suggests, transmission is controlled by a token which endlessly circulates the ring. There are however major differences from token buses, since in a ring, no station has a global view of what is happening; it cannot see what is being transferred between other stations on the ring.

- The **Cambridge ring** (CR), originally developed at the Computer Laboratory at Cambridge University, England, uses the **slotted ring** technique, where the ring is filled with endlessly circulating proformas, into which data can be placed as they pass a ring station. The CR was once very popular in the UK, and a set of protocols was devised to support the coloured book protocols discussed in chapter nine. Unfortunately the CR has no champion in the USA, and has therefore not been the subject of IEEE standardisation, although a variant of the original slotted ring access technique has been accepted by ISO {8802-7}.

12.3   References

1   IEEE P802.6, 'Distributed Queue Dual Bus (DQDB) Metropolitan Area Network (MAN)', current status draft for comment.

2   W. Stallings, 'Local Networks', ACM Computing Surveys, vol. 16, no. 1, p. 3 (1984).

3   W. Burr, 'Overview of the Proposed ANSI Standard for Local Distributed Data Interfaces', Commun. ACM, vol. 26, no. 10, p. 554 (1983).

13 IEEE project 802

13.1 Introduction

IEEE (the US Institute of Electrical and Electronic Engineers) project 802 was set up at the behest of various organisations in the USA, notably IBM, Xerox, Boeing and General Motors, who each had specific requirements and input to the standardisation process. The outcome was the definition of a LAN reference model for the lowest three OSI layers, together with service definitions and protocol specifications for various LAN topologies. Initial work concentrated on ring and linear bus topologies. We will discuss the IEEE standards in some detail. Most have also been adopted by ISO (fast track route).

Project 802 covers standardisation work by IEEE in four basic areas:

• The development of a LAN variant of OSI/RM to cover the physical, data link and network layers. OSI/RM in its original form was not specified for use over LANs.

• The definition of services and protocols for the new layers.

• For selected LAN technologies (CSMA/CD bus, token bus and token ring), detailed specifications of the internal workings of, and how to access, these LANs.

• An ongoing project which is attempting to define standards for a Metropolitan Area Network (MAN). Although this project has been under way for several years, it is beset with technical and other problems, and at the time of writing was still at the 'draft for comment' stage. It will not be discussed in this book.

13.2 The IEEE 802 LAN reference model

The project spans the lowest three OSI/RM layers, and the standards comprise a number of documents, as listed below. The relationships between the scopes of application of the documents are shown in figure 13.1.

• 802.1(A). Overview and architecture.

• 802.1(B). Addressing, internetworking and network management. We will not be discussing this area.

• 802.2. **Logical link control**. This uses a link service definition which resembles (in fact formed the basis of) the WAN variant discussed in chapter eleven, and defines a set of LLC PDUs based on a variant of HDLC ABME. A detailed knowledge of HDLC as discussed in chapter six will be assumed in the subsequent discussion. The HDLC implementation is intended as a common layer to be used above the following standards:

• 802.3. **CSMA/CD** access method and physical layer specifications.

• 802.4. **Token-passing bus** access method and physical layer specifications.

• 802.5. **Token-passing ring** access method and physical specifications.

• 802.7. **Metropolitan area network (MAN)**: see reference 1, chapter twelve.

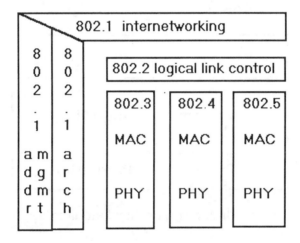

Figure 13.1 - relationship between IEEE 802 standards

The physical layer specifications for CSMA/CD, token-passing bus and token-passing ring are based on existing, well established technologies such as Ethernet, and we will not discuss these here. IEEE expect that additional architectures will be catered for in the future, but apart from MAN, these has been little or no progress to date. It can be inferred that this will depend on future LAN technology developments in the USA.

In this chapter, we will first discuss the logical link control procedures, and then proceed to examine the three established access methods, CSMA/CD, token bus and token ring. Issues such as architecture, internetworking and addressing, which are discussed in the overview documents 802.1(A) and 802.1(B) will be touched on in later chapters. The chapter concludes with a discussion of the slotted (Cambridge) ring.

13.3   Logical Link Control (LLC) (802.2)

Standard 802.2 {8802-2} defines *logical link control* (*LLC*) sublayer procedures for use above any of the four *medium access* standards 802.3 to 802.6, to perform services broadly corresponding to the 'upper half' of the OSI/RM data link layer, i.e. it is a data link sublayer, in that it uses the services of one of the underlying media to provide a data link service to the network layer above it. The functions of the network layer (such as it is) are covered by 802.1(B).

| IEEE 802 | ISO OSI/RM |
| {8802} | {7498} |

(NET)	Network layer
LLC	Data link layer
MAC	
PHY	Physical layer

Underlying physical medium

Figure 13.2 - relationship between IEEE 802 and OSI/RM

Figure 13.2 shows the broad relationship of IEEE 802 to the OSI/RM data link and physical layers. The network layer shown in the figure will not necessarily have a real, physical existence if spanning a single LAN, as its functions are minimal in the LAN context. (If more than one LAN, or LANs and WANs, are spanned, the network layer will perform routing and relay functions as discussed in the next chapter.) Communication between layers and sub-layers is defined in terms of primitives between the LLC sublayer and its peer(s) in other open systems, and also between the LLC and adjacent layers, as follows, and as illustrated in figure 13.3:

• LLC primitives, used across the interface between the network layer and the LLC sublayer.

• Medium access (MA) primitives for use across the interface between the LLC and MAC sub-layers.

• LLC protocol data units, exchanged between peer LLC entities, using a protocol very similar to HDLC.

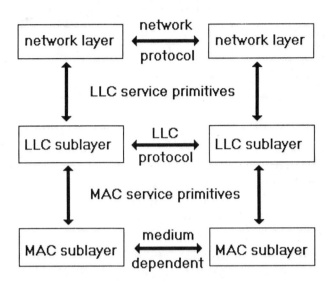

Figure 13.3 - communication to and between LLC sub-layers

Three types of LLC service are defined, as follows:

• *Unacknowledged connectionless service (type 1)*. This provides a minimal connectionless data link service, together with some management and test functions which will be discussed later.

• *Connection oriented service (type 2)*.

• *Acknowledged connectionless service (type 3)*. This is a recent addition {8802-2 PDAD2}, which enhances the unacknowledged service by adding delivery confirmation and some additional facilities. The reason for its inclusion was that there was felt by some to be a need for a connectionless service which could provide a predictable (fast) response. If no acknowledgement is returned within a set time, the data can be retransmitted. This was felt to be needed in process control type environments, since the unacknowledged connectionless service provides no delivery confirmation, which would therefore need to be provided by a higher protocol layer. It is only expected to be used over token rings (see §13.5.2). Having said that, by no means all experts feel that this additional service is needed at all.

The LLC service is provided to higher layers by means of a *data link service* defined, as would be expected, in terms of a set of service primitives. Four classes of service are provided, class I to class IV; figure 13.4 shows which service types are available in each class.

	Class I	Class II	Class III	Class IV
Type 1 (CL)	✓	✓	✓	✓
Type 2 (CO)		✓		✓
Type 3 (ACK CL)			✓	✓

Figure 13.4 - LLC service classes

It should be noted that an unacknowledged connectionless (type 1) service is always provided, but the connection based service is only provided by classes II and IV. This is the reverse of the situation in WANs, where the provision of a connectionless mode was almost an afterthought.

Data Link services are implemented as a protocol between peer data link entities, and consist of the exchange of LLC PDUs across the underlying network. We will see that the protocol is based on HDLC ABME (chapter six), and we will subsequently refer to PDUs as frames. We will first outline the interface primitives, and then go on to examine the protocol.

13.3.1   LLC services

The interface between the OSI network layer and the LLC sublayer is provided, in the usual way, by a set of primitives exchanged across the interface. The use of primitive variants (e.g. request, indication) is similar to that in OSI/RM services in general; see chapter ten for further details.

From this point familiarity with the basic concepts of HDLC will be assumed. The background required is in chapter six.

Unacknowledged connectionless (type 1) service

The unacknowledged connectionless (type 1) service is easily described. It provides for the transfer of frames to specified destinations on the network, or to a broadcast (group) address. The service is pure datagram in the sense that no indication of successful transmission is provided, and no acknowledgements are returned. This basic service provides only one primitive:

DL–DATA request, indication   source address, destination address, data, priority, service class

The *service class* indicates whether the transmission used an underlying MAC acknowledgement service. (This is not to be confused with the use of the term 'service class' to indicate which types of LLC service are available.) The *priority* relates to any priority mechanism which may be available in the underlying medium. When we discuss particular topologies later in the chapter, we will see that even if an acknowledgement can be provided, it is merely confirmation of delivery, not of acceptance, and in some cases no acknowledgement is possible at all. Similarly, not all underlying topologies support a priority mechanism. Hence these parameters may not be of much use.

When mapped on to HDLC, it is not possible to use I-frames to transfer this type of data, so a new un-numbered information frame (UI) had to be defined. The mapping on to HDLC frame types is briefly discussed later in this chapter.

Connection orientated (type 2) service

As would be expected, this service is more complex than the connectionless services, and primitives are provided for connection setup, connection orientated data transfer, reset, flow control and connection termination. Distinct primitive types are provided for data transfer.

DL–CONNECT request   source address, destination address, priority, service class

DL–CONNECT   source address, destination address, indication, confirm   status, priority, service class

These are used to set up a connection. There is no response variant of this or any other primitive. The data link layer is responsible for generating the indication. In part this is necessary since the destination may not even be present in the LAN context, in which case there would be no way in which a response could be generated. The service class indicates the priority requested, although this facility may not be available on the underlying network. The *status* in the confirm and indication variants indicates either success or the reason for failure. This primitive maps on to the underlying (HDLC) mode select command/response.

Once an underlying HDLC connection has been set up, data can be provided for transmission by means of the following primitive. The connect maps (in an abstract sense) on to HDLC I-frames.

DL–DATA–CONNECT request, indication	source address, destination address, data
DL–DATA–CONNECT confirm	source address, destination address, status

A different primitive is used from that in the connectionless case, because a confirm variant exists in this case, and also the mapping may differ in the underlying network. The status in the confirm is an acknowledgement indicating the successful delivery or otherwise of one or more previously transmitted data messages; this may be understood in the context of the HDLC I-frame acknowledgement mechanism. Several requests/indications may be sent before a confirm is returned which may acknowledge several at once. Again this reflects the HDLC window acknowledgement scheme.

DL–DISCONNECT request	source address, destination address
DL–DISCONNECT indication	source address, destination address, reason
DL–DISCONNECT confirm	source address, destination address, status

These are used to terminate a connection. In the indication, the reason indicates either a request by the peer entity, or a network malfunction. In the confirm, the status indicates whether the peer entity acknowledged the disconnection attempt, which it clearly will not have done if either it or the network has failed.

DL–RESET request	source address, destination address
DL–RESET indication	source address, destination address, reason
DL–RESET confirm	source address, destination address, status

A reset places a connection between two addresses in its initial state, as it was immediately after the connection setup. As usual, data loss may occur. In the indication form, the reason indicates whether the reset was requested by the peer, or was due to a network malfunction. Where the reset is due to a malfunction, both peers will receive an indication.

In the original version of HDLC there was no way of resetting a data link without disconnecting and re-connecting it. Therefore an additional un-numbered command, RSET was provided, which restores the data link to the state immediately after link setup. However, in common with LAPB, LLC does not make use of this frame type, instead mapping on to SABME.

DL-CONNECTION-FLOWCONTROL   source address, destination address,
request, indication   amount

This is used between peers using a given LLC (HDLC) connection to indicate the amount of data which can be outstanding between peer entities, as shown in the parameter of the request. This may best be understood in terms of the queue model of a connection discussed in chapter ten. If a zero amount is specified, this amounts to stopping the flow completely; this is realised by means of the HDLC RR and RNR frame types. Reducing the amount may also result in RNR. The standard allows the optional use of an amount 'infinity', which implies no flow control, other than that inherent in the underlying protocol (in the case of HDLC, a maximum possible window size). The amount specified in the indication from the underlying network is the maximum amount which can be sent while avoiding data loss. The precise interpretation of these primitives is implementation dependent.

Acknowledged connectionless (type 3) service

This service was not provided in the original draft version of the standard, and was included so that less work would need to be done by higher OSI layers in process control applications. It was introduced at the behest of IEC, to provide compatibility with IEC-defined protocols specified for the PROWAY-C industrial data highway {IEC 955}. It is specifically intended for use over the token bus. The rationale behind this service is that it provides the degree of control necessary in a process control environment without the overheads of setting up a data link connection. Although we will discuss this service in some detail, it should be mentioned at this point that not all practitioners feel that it is needed at all.

In fact this service offers more than its title would suggest:

- The basic service offers a confirmed datagram service, using an underlying HDLC handshaking mechanism which we will discuss later. This is distinct from, and far superior to, the type of acknowledgement returned with ring frames, which merely indicate that the frame reached the destination ring station, and which are implied by the 'service class' parameter in the various primitives. This basic service is known as the *data unit transmission* service.

- In addition, there are value added extensions which closely reflect the (somewhat eccentric) PROWAY protocol on which this service is based. As well as sending confirmed datagrams, a user may instruct its peer to prepare a reply to some request. This is the *data unit exchange* service. The key to understanding this service is to realise that on receipt of a 'prepare indication', the receiving service user is not expected to reply immediately. Instead, it is expected to 'go away and do something', and pass the outcome as data to its local service user, which will buffer the data. At some later time, the user will then demand the prepared reply. The peer uses the *reply data unit preparation* service to make the reply available to the local service provider, so that it can be immediately transmitted when demanded.

For even better understanding, these services should be related to process control applications such as a car production line (which is in fact a typical use). Consider an instruction from a controller to a robot to do something (e.g. weld a car door). The robot will reply either 'weld completed' or 'sorry I cannot do this', but cannot necessarily do so immediately, as it takes time to do the weld. However as soon as it has finished its task (or decided that it cannot do so), it makes the outcome available to the service provider, but the service provider does not send it yet, instead buffering it. The controller allows sufficient time for the robot to complete its task, and then demands information on the outcome. It is the intention of the service definition that the outcome will be available on demand, i.e. has already been made available for transmission. So both the instruction and the notification of the outcome are guarded by an underlying acknowledgement mechanism, and a short timeout can be set for returning the outcome, since it is presumed to be available already.

This effectively manages to provide two protocol layers in one. There are clearly some complications with this service which we will not discuss here. For example, how long should the initiator wait before demanding a reply, and what should it do (assume) if this reply is not available immediately? We will not attempt to examine the political background to this service.

The acknowledged connectionless service posed yet more problems for HDLC, as there was no existing frame type which could support this service, and yet more changes had to be made to accommodate this new service. Perhaps the most notable was alterations to the UI frame, to form two new U-frames, as will be discussed in §13.3.3.

Data unit transmission service

The basic data transfer primitive is similar to DL-DATA described above, but as it is acknowledged, it is given a different name to distinguish it:

DL-DATA-ACK   source address, destination address,
request, indication   data, priority, service class

Despite its name, this primitive is used to convey data not acknowledgements. Confirmation that the data was actually transmitted is provided by a separate primitive.

DL-DATA-ACK-STATUS   source address, destination address,
indication   priority, service class, status

This is generated by the source's service provider, and maps from explicit acknowledgement (or otherwise: status parameter). Therefore it contains explicit information from the peer service provider. This is why it is called an indication with a different primitive name, rather than a confirm of the same primitive.

Data unit exchange service

A service primitive is provided for requesting a previously prepared data unit from the peer. It can also be used to exchange data units. In the latter sense it is rather like DL-DATA-ACK, but the status indication (see below) may contain the prepared data which the peer user has (already) passed to its service provider.

DL-REPLY   source address, destination address,
request, indication   data, priority, service class

The *data* field is optional, which implies that the request for a reply may, in the absence of data, be capable of only one type of response. However what this means is of no concern to the service provider.

DL-REPLY-STATUS indication   source address, destination address, data, priority, service class, status

Again this informs the sender whether the DL-REPLY-REQUEST was accepted, and may contain parameters inserted by the peer service provider. In particular the *data* parameter contains the previously prepared information. (It is not inserted by the peer service user; the peer service provider already has the information required.)

Reply data unit preparation service

The final service element is used by the peer user to notify its (local) service provider that it has now completed the task specified in an earlier DL_REPLY indication. It should be noted that this request does not result in an indication (transmission); the data is simply held by the local service provider until the peer service user requests its delivery. Two primitives are defined:

DL-REPLY-UPDATE request   source address, data

This delivers the data to the service provider.

DL-REPLY-UPDATE-STATUS   source address, status
indication

The service provider uses this primitive to notify the service user that the data has/has not been recorded for later delivery.

13.3.2   LLC PDU structure

SERVICE TYPE	COMMANDS	RESPONSES
unacknowledged connectionless (type 1)	*UI XID TEST*	*XID TEST*
connection based (type 2)	I RR RNR REJ SABME DISC	I RR RNR REJ UA DM FRMR
acknowledged connectionless (type 3)	*AC0 AC1*	*AC0 AC1*

NOTE:
     Italicised frame types are not in the LAPB variant.

Figure 13.5 - the set of LLC protocol data units

IEEE 802.2 proposes a LLC PDU structure for bit orientated data transmission which is based on HDLC, and in the process reveals some interesting uses of the fields of HDLC frames. Figure 13.5 shows how the various data units are classified broadly in line with HDLC into commands and responses, and indicates which are comparable to standard (X.25 LAPB) HDLC facilities, and which are additions.

It is perhaps worth mentioning that what is discussed here is a a usage of HDLC procedures over existing MAC procedures; existing LANs such as Ethernet have entrenched frame formats, which IEEE were forced to accommodate in their standards. Therefore the HDLC address and control octets will be encoded as the first part of the data field in the medium-dependent frame format.

As can be seen from the list of data unit types in the figure, there are several differences from the version of HDLC discussed in chapter six. Before discussing the differences, we will outline the uses envisaged for the data units.

13.3.3   Types of data unit

- *I. Information frames* are used to convey connection orientated data. They will be acknowledged using N(R) and N(S) fields, in the usual HDLC manner, the window width being selected by flow control primitives.

- *UI.* These are *unnumbered information frames* (see below), used for unacknowledged connectionless data transfer, for which an acknowledgement is not possible.

- RR, RNR, REJ, SABME, UA, DISC, DM, FRMR. These perform the normal HDLC functions of mode selection (connection), disconnection, error recovery and flow control on connection based circuits, and will not be discussed further.

- *XID.* This is short for 'exchange identification', and is used between peer LLCs to indicate what services are provided, what window width should be used on a given connection, and so on. A response XID is expected in reply. This requires specific encoding of the information field, the details of which are of interest only to implementors.

- *TEST.* This is used for testing the transmission path. Regardless of the mode of the (HDLC-like) link, a TEST command solicits a TEST response at the earliest opportunity. No other characteristics of the link are affected.

TEST can be sent to multiple destinations, and one presumes therefore that it could therefore also be used (by higher layers) to determine which destinations are currently connected, although the standard makes no mention of this possibility. However the HDLC standard {4335} does state that the results of the TEST exchange 'may be made available to higher layers'.

- *AC0* and *AC1* are new frame types provided to support the acknowledged connectionless service type. The full name of the frame type is *acknowledged connectionless information, seq* 0 or 1. They are referred to as *ACn* frames. They are in effect extensions of UI frames, with the following enhancements:

  - AC0 and AC1 are distinct frame types (i.e. have different U-field values).

  - Each ACn frame is used in a command/response handshake. The P bit may be set in the command, and the F bit in the response; this, together with whether a data field is present, determines the function of the PDU.

  - The command relays the user request to the peer, and maps on to a request primitive. The response does not map to a response variant primitive, however. It is used for acknowledgement, and possibly to convey some data previously passed to the service provider by means of a DL-REPLY-UPDATE request.

  - The first octet of the I-field is used to provide two 4-bit fields indicating the success or otherwise of the command and response respectively. The remainder of the I-field is user data.

13.3.4   Differences from ISO 7776 HDLC (X.25 LAPB)

As you will have gathered, there are a number of differences from HDLC ABM as described in chapter six, of which the main ones are as follows:

- Extended format (ABME) is used, providing modulo 128 sequencing. This provides increased address and control field widths. (Although LAPB can use extended format, the usage of the address field is quite different.)

- The 16-bit extended format address field is used by LLC as shown in figure 13.6. This allows both source and destination addresses to be specified, and a group destination address if required. It is also used to indicate whether the transmitted frame is a command or a response. The use of group addresses with LLC ABME is more in the spirit of HDLC NRM, where multiple VDUs can be polled or selected on multidrop lines. However it is clearly also in the spirit of LANs, where the same logical link interconnects all hosts on the network, and the group address can be used to support broadcasts to all, or a selected group of, hosts.

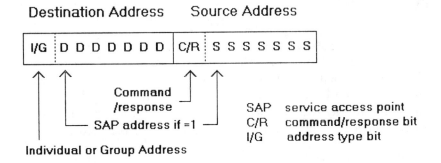

Figure 13.6 - use of HDLC address field in LLC protocol

This format appears to place an upper limit of 64 addresses per logical link. The standard does not appear to comment on this apparent restriction, nor does it suggest alternative uses for this field (for example, Ethernet incorporates a much wider address field width, which will be present in the frame as well as this HDLC-like address.)

• Several new un-numbered commands and responses have been added to those originally available in HDLC. These include UI (un-numbered information), RSET (link reset), TEST, XID, which are discussed above, and various new frame types to accommodate acknowledged connectionless mode. UI is just like an ordinary I-frame, except that it is un-numbered, so that it is not sequenced, cannot be acknowledged, and is not subject to window flow control. (Note that RNR has no effect on UI commands, which can still be sent; however, the receiver is at liberty to discard them without comment.)

• The XID command allows some negotiation, e.g. of window width, which is not provided in LAPB.

The control command SREJ is not provided. SREJ is hardly ever used except in specialised applications such as RLP (see chapter six). Although SREJ is in the base HDLC standard {4335}, it is absent from other derived standards {7776, 8802.2}.

13.4   Medium Access Control (MAC)

Communication with the underlying *Medium Access Control* (*MAC*) sublayer is provided in a medium-independent manner by the following primitives which are transferred across the LLC/MAC interface (see figure 13.3). Three primitives are provided, as follows:

MA–DATA request   destination address, user data, requested service class

One of these is generated for every LLC primitive which has to be transmitted on the network. The destination address may be a single address or a group (broadcast) address, according to context. The 'user data' will be an LLC primitive including its parameters. Again, the service class is the priority requested by the LLC user. What happens to this in the network, including any network additions, is implementation dependent.

MA–DATA indication   destination address, source address, user data, reception status, requested service class

This is the form of the primitive as it reaches the LLC from the peer MAC entity (i.e. from the network). The *reception status* indicates the success or failure (in the sense of requested function, or possibly in the sense of detected transmission errors) of the incoming frame. Frames with transmission errors, are not normally reported however.

MA–DATA confirm   transmission status, provided service class

This is used for local handshaking between the LLC and MAC. For example, the *transmission status* field indicates whether or not the last MA-DATA was successfully transmitted, and if it was, the *service class* indicates the priority at which it was transmitted. In the context of CSMA/CD, a failure could be signalled as a result of excessive collisions. Again remember that the receipt of a confirm reporting no error is no guarantee that the frame reached, or has been processed by, the remote host.

13.5   LAN technologies supported by ISO and IEEE 802

In chapter twelve we outlined the fundamental concepts of CSMA/CD, and introduced the concept of ring networks. In the remainder of the chapter, we will examine various aspects of interest for the IEEE 802 and ISO supported network topologies (CSMA/CD bus, token bus, token ring), and also the slotted ring (supported by ISO but not IEEE). Apart from slotted ring, they all operate under the LLC and MAC procedures described above.

13.5.1   CSMA/CD bus (802.3)

This standard covers access techniques such as those of standard CSMA/CD Ethernets, the basic concepts of which (including collision handling) were discussed in chapter twelve. The specification defines, as usual, the service provided to the LLC entity by MAC, and the means by which the underlying bus network is to be accessed (the physical access procedures).

The MAC service is broadly provided by the MA-DATA primitives already discussed, with the proviso that the service class parameters are not used, there being no way in which a priority based mechanism can be implemented using this access method. A MA-DATA request to a broadcast address will generate a corresponding MA-DATA indication at all network stations, including the sender.

The CSMA/CD frame structure

The format of a frame as actually transmitted on the network is shown in figure 13.7. This format, although it is not identified as such in the standard, is in fact similar to the original Ethernet frame format. This is inevitable, since if it is to be used, the standard must clearly be broadly compatible with current practice.

- The *preamble* is provided as a built in delay to allow the physical signalling (PLS) unit (and the ether) to reach a steady state.

- The *start frame delimiter* (SFD) is a defined bit sequence (10101011) which indicates the start of a valid frame.

- Two *address* fields are provided, which may be either 16 or 48 bits long. The decision on whether 16 or 48 bit addresses should be used is for the implementor. The destination field is transmitted first so that the receiver can determine whether to act on the frame at the earliest opportunity. More than one destination address may be implied if a group or broadcast address is being used.

- The first bit in the destination address is used to distinguish *individual and group addresses*, which may refer to none, some or all stations on the bus. In the case of 48 bit addresses, the second bit can be used to indicate whether the addresses are administered locally or globally; this is partly to accommodate Ethernet implementations which still use the global address registration scheme formerly imposed by DIX. The group address may be further categorised as follows:

FIELD	preamble	SFD	dest address	source address	data length	data	padding	FCS
OCTETS	7	1	2/6	2/6	2	variable	if reqd	4

NOTEs:

SFD   Start frame delimiter
LLC   Logical Link Control
FCS   Frame Check Sequence

Figure 13.7 - CSMA/CD frame format

• *Multicast* group address: this is an address associated by a higher level convention with a set of logically related stations.

• *Broadcast* address: this implies every station on a given LAN. This is defined as the address with all bits set to 1.

The address may also be partitioned into *fields* with local and global significance; all of this is in keeping with original Ethernet practice.

• The *length* field identifies the number of octets in the immediately following data field. As explained in chapter twelve, there is a minimum possible frame length for CSMA/CD, which is implementation dependent. Where the data field is not long enough to meet this minimum length, a *pad* field must be appended as necessary to the data field.

• The *frame check sequence* (FCS) at the end is 32 bits, which is twice as long as that normally used in HDLC. The end of frame is detected very easily; the sender simply stops transmitting.

Normal transmission and reception procedures

The normal transmission procedure is to wait until the ether is free, and then to send the data supplied by the LLC as a suitably formatted frame 'immediately'; sufficient padding will be added to avoid the undetected collision problem.

Assuming that the transmission was completed without contention (collision), the link layer is informed (via a MA-DATA confirm) of a successful transmission, and the PLS awaits the next transmission. Remember that the MA-DATA confirm is generated locally, and does <u>not</u> necessarily mean that the data reached the destination.

The normal reception procedure is for the PLS to synchronise with the preamble of any incoming frame which is detected, and forward all bits received to the 'medium access sublayer', which will read but discard everything up to the destination address, and retain the rest of the frame. When, but not until, the entire frame has been received, the destination address is processed. If the address is of no interest to the receiving station, the entire frame is then discarded, otherwise (subject to the FCS being valid, of course) it is passed on to the LLC; the source address, destination address and data become parameters of a MA-DATA indication.

13.5.2   Token Bus (802.4)

Overview

The token passing technique was introduced in chapter twelve; basically it works as follows:

• The station which possesses (has just received) the token now has control over the bus, i.e. is the only station permitted to insert one (or more) new frames. Thus collisions cannot occur during normal operation.

• The token is passed between various stations connected to the bus in such a way as to form a logical (not physical) ring. By this means, each station will in due course get permission to transmit.

• In the steady state, usage of the medium can be divided into data transfer and token passing phases.

• Ring maintenance functions are required, which include initialisation, recovery from the loss of a token, removal of deceased stations, addition of new stations, and general housekeeping.

The token passing bus may thus be viewed as a logical ring as shown in figure 13.8. The use of tokens rather than collision detection improves the performance of a bus in that it cannot now become overloaded under conditions of high presented traffic, which is a major drawback of

CSMA/CD. However, as we will see, there is quite a high overhead in passing tokens, handling new and 'deceased' stations, and generally maintaining the integrity of the logical ring. Thus this technique is not all advantages either.

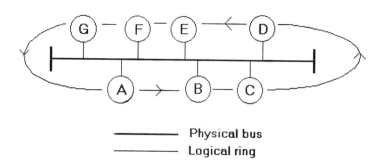

Physical bus
Logical ring

Figure 13.8 - physical bus viewed as logical ring

The operation of a station proceeds according to the following general rules. (It will become obvious that scope for more flexibility has been included in this specification than was the case with CSMA/CD; this is partly because there were fewer existing constraints.)

• A station should be prepared to receive frames, including the token, at any time. Any station may be sent a frame by the station which currently owns the token. As with CSMA/CD, all stations will see every frame transmitted by any other station, but will ignore those frames and tokens which are not addressed to them. However the use of tokens to control transmission means that the collision problem disappears in normal working, since it is not possible for two stations to transmit at the same time. This reduces the complexity of the bus interface.

• A station wishing to transmit may not normally do so until it receives the token, although there are a number of exceptions to this general rule, as will be discussed later. Once a station owns the token, it may then transmit as many frames as it has awaiting transmission, subject to certain constraints such as priority and a time limit for holding the token. Having transmitted any frames of the relevant priority, or after the time limit for holding the token has been reached, it must then transmit the token to the next station in the logical ring, after which it may not transmit any further data frames until next it receives the token. (Error recovery and other management procedures are discussed later).

The access method may be viewed as comprising a number of sub-layers, performing the following functions:

- A timer for handling loss of the token.
- Distributed initialisation procedures.
- A timer for token holding.
- Node address recognition.
- Frame encapsulation and preparation of the token for transmission.
- FCS generation and checking.
- Valid token recognition.
- Addition of new stations to the ring.
- Error recovery from node failures.

Frame types and format

Data frames, tokens and general management frames are all passed between stations using the standard frame format shown in figure 13.9.

FIELD	preamble	SD	FC	dest address	source address	data	FCS	ED
OCTETS	-------------	1	1	2/6	2/6	variable	4	1

NOTEs:

SD   start delimiter
FC   frame control
FCS   frame check sequence
ED   end delimiter
No data field length is present

Figure 13.9 - token bus frame format

- The *preamble* has the same significance as in the CSMA/CD case.

- SD is a *start delimiter*, and ED is an *end delimiter*. These are defined bit patterns used to indicate the start and end of frames. The SD has a similar function to the SFD in the CSMA/CD frame discussed earlier. In cases where the owner of the token is permitted to transmit more than one frame, the fact that there are more frames to send is indicated by setting a bit in the ED; another bit in the ED may be used by relay entities (if present) to indicate that an error had previously been detected in the frame, but it is being relayed anyway (although this may cause it to be discarded at a later stage). There may be up to 8191 octets between the delimiters. SD immediately followed by ED is used as a frame abort sequence. Unlike CSMA/CD there is no minimum frame length, so padding will not be required for short frames.

- The FC octet is used for *frame control*. This determines the type of frame, from the following list:

  - *Control frame*. This includes the following types of frame, most of which are discussed below under access control mechanisms:

    - Explicit token.
    - Claim token.
    - Set successor.
    - Solicit successor (2 variants).
    - Resolve contention.
    - Who follows?

  Control frames are used in cases where there has been some difficulty, or where changes are necessary to the token passing scheme.

  - *LLC data frame*. This is the normal user data frame. Some bits in the frame control octet are used for providing 4 levels of priority (out of 8 possible values), and others are reserved for possible future provision of acknowledgement and flow control.

  - *MAC management frame*. We will not discuss this.

- The *addresses* may be either 16 or 48 bits long; their use is similar to the CSMA/CD case, including the availability of multicast group and broadcast addresses.

- The *data field* contains an LLC PDU, a MAC management data frame, or a value related to one of the control fields (e.g. an address). There is no data length field, and there is also no need for padding, since there is no possibility of collisions (of LLC data frames), so that no minimum frame length is required.

- The *FCS* is the same as in the CSMA/CD case, but note that the ED which follows it is not protected by the FCS. This is necessary because the ED is used to report FCS errors. It is worth mentioning that this technique can only work because the overall error rate on the LAN is very low.

Access control mechanisms and token management

The mechanisms governing the passing of tokens are fairly straightforward. The complexity arises since tokens can become lost (e.g. because the station the token was sent to no longer exists), they can become duplicated, stations can fail, new stations have to be included in the token passing scheme, and administrative or other errors can result in two or more stations with the same address.

Token loss and duplication

The token loss and duplication function does not require a monitor station, as is necessary in simplex rings. Token management is distributed, and token loss may be detected by any station. It should also be added that not all stations need necessarily participate in the token passing scheme. For example, a station which is receive only need never own the token.

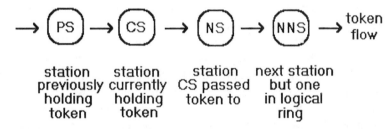

Figure 13.10 - handling of lost token in token bus network

The ring passing scheme operates by each station (CS) knowing which is the next station (NS) to receive the token; it can deduce (and remember) the previous owner (PS) from the source address in the token frame it receives. See figure 13.10. CS presumes that NS received it correctly if it 'hears' a subsequent valid frame (but see the note below). If CS does not see a valid frame within a given time, it sends the token to NS again. If the second attempt to pass on the token also appears to have failed, the CS assumes that the NS has failed, and sends a *who follows?* frame with the address of the NS. The next station but one in the sequence, NNS, should then respond by returning a *set successor* frame to CS, which can now send the token to the NNS, thereby effectively bypassing the station NS which (appeared to) fail.

There are two potential problems here. Firstly, if CS assumes that NS has failed when it has not, duplicate tokens will result, with chaos resulting and recovery being necessary. If on the other hand NS has indeed failed, but CS mistakes a delayed version of its own transmission for a subsequent valid frame, it may assume (incorrectly) that all is well, in which case the token will vanish. Either situation is highly undesirable, and the protocol designers (and implementors) went to considerable lengths to minimise the chance of this happening.

If n attempts to solicit a successor fail, then more drastic steps are needed. CS will be unsure what has happened, so it will wait until it has data to transmit, then attempt a *claim token* and retry the entire procedure. As a last resort, the station will give up altogether, and merely listen passively to the ether. In fact the recovery procedures are rather more complex than that, in that each station maintains a 'no traffic detected' timer, and inactivity (which would result if the token vanished) may trigger a claim token from (in principle) any station.

Ring initialisation

Initialisation is triggered by inactivity on the ring; this inactivity could be the result of the owner of the token failing, or because the network has just gone live and the token does not exist yet. One or more stations may then try to gain the token by sending a *claim token* frame. The token passing order is based on address value (normally descending order), and the claim token frame lengths are adjusted to be a function of the station's address. The highest address station will be the one which 'wins' the contention to own the token. At the risk of yet another oversimplification, this is rather like a collision. The station detecting silence after it has completed its transmission thus knows that it has the highest address of those present, and therefore now owns the token. (Others will continue to hear the longer transmissions after they have finished their own transmissions, and will defer.) Note that in this case the collision must be allowed to proceed for the token ownership algorithm to work.

In fact the algorithm is more complex than the above discussion suggests, and involves several stages based on different parts of the address. Procedures are also incorporated to prevent two stations with the same address (not allowed of course) from both thinking they have 'won', as if this occurred there would be two tokens, which would not work. The algorithm used ensures that either both lose out, or only one is admitted, in which case the other one (with the same address) will detect the error when it sees a transmission from another station with the same address as itself.

Initialisation is not yet complete however. There is only one station on the 'ring' at the moment. Others (with lower addresses) will be solicited using the solicit successor technique discussed below, until the ring is completed. This could take some time if there is a large number of stations.

Adding new stations

The addition of new stations presents a different type of problem. A new station must wait until some other station which is in the token scheme issues a *solicit successor* frame. This gives potential new recruits within a given address range (normally between CS and NS) a chance to get into the scheme, by replying with a frame requesting to be the next station in the ring. The sender of the solicit successor waits for a certain length of time (the response window) to see how many stations will respond. If stations do respond, it examines all responses, and decides which will be nominated as its successor.

There is of course the possibility that more than one station will respond, in which case the station will see garbage (a collision). In this case it initiates a procedure for sorting out the mess, using a *resolve contention* frame. There are some similarities to initialisation; again the procedures are somewhat complex and will not be discussed here.

The outcome of all this is either than no new stations wish to join (the usual case except just after initialisation), or that a single station will be selected. If so, this station is then passed the token, together with the address of the new NNS (the station which was previously NS), and the new member of the ring therefore becomes NS. Other potential new recruits will have to wait for another opportunity at a later time.

The reason for having two variants of solicit successor is that two address windows are required for the station with the lowest address, as in this case the current NS will have the highest address, so that a single address range would be inappropriate; the new address could be lower than the lowest, or higher than the highest currently in the ring.

Some of you may be wondering how General Motors can claim that the token ring gives a predictable response time when there are so many strange and timeconsuming procedures such as initialisation and solicit successor. In fact although these are complex, it is possible to define the maximum possible time they will take, so that a worst case response time can still be defined for a token ring, even though this must be relatively long to take into account worst case conditions (heavy loading, frequent loss of the token, and so on). In CSMA/CD, the sender will give up indefinitely if repeated collisions occur, whereas with the token bus the transmission will succeed (eventually, barring a major catastrophe).

Priority handling

Four levels of priority (MA access class) are possible. The algorithm is simple. A station owning the token will transmit its highest priority frames first. If it has time (and there is an upper limit on the length of time a station may retain the token) it may then transmit low priority ones. The time limit is based on the concept of a *target token rotation time* for each priority. Each station starts a timer when it transmits the token. When it next receives the token, it may transmit frames of a given priority provided the time since this station last transmitted the token is still less than the target rotation time. If the token arrives too late, it must be passed on immediately. The outcome is that while there are high priority frames awaiting transmission, lower priority ones will have to wait.

The priority scheme is optional. If it is to be used, the priority depends on the requested service class in the MA-DATA request. If not, the highest priority will be assigned to all frames. It is clear that excessive use of the highest priority may indefinitely delay the transmission of frames of lower priority. Therefore if the scheme is used, the highest priority must be used with great care.

13.5.3   Token Ring (802.5)

The token idea originated in ring networks, and the philosophy is very similar to that of the token bus. A token, which constitutes a permission to transmit, is circulated round the ring, and a station which receives the token may convert it into a frame(s), transmit the frame(s), and then re-insert the token. The main difference in philosophy from the token bus stems from the fact that this is a real, physical ring, and not merely a logical ring protocol imposed on a physically broadcast medium. This has important implications. The techniques which were used with token buses for initialisation and control cannot be applied, since they rely on all stations seeing, and thus being aware of, all traffic on the bus. Clearly this cannot apply in the context of a ring, since a ring station can only see what arrives on the ring, and has no knowledge of what is happening elsewhere. Thus a different set of control procedures must be applied, and control of the ring must rest with a single station. All stations have a built-in *monitor* function, and one station will be designated as the currently active monitor station, while other stations will have the potential to take over this function as necessary, i.e. their monitor functions are on standby (see below under ring maintenance). The use of a monitor station is also necessary with the Cambridge Ring, for similar reasons, although in this case the monitor is a special station.

Once the ring token has been converted into a frame, the frame thus inserted must do a round trip of the ring before it is removed by the sender; the intended recipient has the opportunity to insert response bits at the end of the frame, indicating whether it copied the frame. But the token will not be re-inserted into the ring until the sending station sees the start of its transmitted frame return, or has finished transmitting the frame, whichever occurs later. (Clearly, which occurs first depends on whether the entire frame will fit in the ring, which is implementation dependent.) In principle, a station could insert the token when it had finished transmitting, even if the start of the frame had not yet returned, but this could cause problems for error recovery.

Once the transmitting station has finished with the token, it forwards the token to the next station, which then itself has an opportunity to transmit. If the station receiving the token has nothing to send, it simply forwards the token, and takes no other action.

Ring token format

There are two basic formats, that of the token, and that of a frame. The token format is shown in figure 13.11.

| start delimiter | access control | end delimiter |

Figure 13.11 - token ring token format

- The *delimiters* are defined bit patterns, including binary 0 and 1, and two 'non-data' states. This is related to the Manchester encoding used for the transmission, which allows four different encodings per bit duration, two of which are 'illegal'. All frames and tokens must start with the defined SD sequence, otherwise they will be regarded as invalid. The ED contains a different, but again fixed, bit sequence.

- The *access control* octet is present in both tokens and frames, and contains the following fields:

    - *Priority* field. This allows up to eight different priorities. In this case it is used to indicate the current priority of the token. See also the reservation field below.

    - *Token* bit. This indicates whether what follows is a token or a frame.

    - *Monitor* bit. This is a bit used by a monitor station, the purpose of which is to ensure that frames and (certain types of) tokens do not illegally circulate for ever around the ring. In the case of a frame, the function is very similar to the Cambridge Ring monitor bit discussed in the next section. A discussion of its use with tokens is beyond the scope of this book.

• *Reservation* field. This is used to request high priority tokens; a station may request several priorities, and these requests will be stacked, and are serviced by receiving a token of a suitable priority. Further details may be found later.

Token ring frame format

The frame format is shown in figure 13.12.

FIELD	SD	AC	FC	dest address	source address	information	FCS	ED	FS
OCTETS	----	1	1	2/6	2/6	variable	4	1	1

NOTEs:

SD	start delimiter	AC	access control octet
FC	frame control field	FCS	frame check sequence
ED	end delimiter	FS	frame status
			(not protected by FCS)

Figure 13.12 - token ring frame format

• The *addresses* are transmitted destination first in the usual way. They are either 16 or 48 bits long. Their use includes universal or local significance, and individual or group destination addresses.

• The *frame control* field includes the following:

• The *frame type*, which may be a user (LLC) frame, or a ring control (MAC) frame.

• The *priority* (LLC frames) or *control information* (MAC frames); see below for a discussion of the priority algorithm.

• No maximum *length* is specified for the information field, which may also be of zero length. In practice, the maximum length is restricted by the time a station is allowed to hold the token, which is limited on a per station basis. In a MAC control frame, the information field is formatted according to special rules.

• The frame *status* field follows the FCS, and is therefore not error protected. It is placed at the very end of the frame so that the receiving station can use it to set *address recognised* and *packet copied* fields, to indicate what action (if any) the receiving station took, from the following list:

• The station is inactive/does not exist (initial settings).

- The station exists but the packet was not copied.
- The packet has been copied.

• There is also a facility for any station to indicate to the sending station that an error was detected. This bit will be set if any station detects that the FCS appears wrong, or that the frame was otherwise invalid (e.g. the priority was incorrect). Once set by a station, this bit will remain set, even though subsequent stations may detect no further errors.

Priority handling

This is rather more complex than for token buses, but again the idea is to get the higher priority frames transmitted before lower priority ones. Each AC octet has two fields, a priority field and a reservation field.

• The *priority field* indicates the current priority of a token or frame. 8 levels of priority are provided.

• The *reservation field* may be used for requesting a token of a <u>higher</u> priority than that of the token just received.

If there are frames to transmit at the current token priority, they may be transmitted now. If the station wishes to transmit higher priority frames, it increases the value in the reservation field of the token to the required priority, and *stacks* the original priority. When the token returns with this priority, appropriate frames may be transmitted. At this point the priority may possibly be 'cranked up' again, until it reaches the highest value.

In order that the token priority does not remain for ever at the highest value, each station which cranked up its priority must return it to the (lower) stacked value after use. Although it sounds complex, this provides a fair, distributed, priority scheme. Further restrictions are that there is a time limit on token holding, and only frames at the current priority of the token may be transmitted. This latter restriction ensures that no lower priority frames may be transmitted by any station until the token priority returns back to the lower value. Again it is clear that excessive use of high priority frames will prevent the transmission of lower priority ones.

Token ring maintenance

Maintenance is concerned with three basic conditions which could cause the system to fail. These are loss of the token (including failure of the station currently holding the token to release it), a 'break' in the network, and failure of the monitor station. We will briefly discuss each of these aspects.

MAC control frames.

These perform various housekeeping functions. The complete list is as follows; most are discussed below.

- *Claim token* .
- *Standby monitor present*, transmitted periodically by standby monitors (but not using up more than 1% of the available bandwidth).
- *Beacon*.
- *Purge*, used after claim token, and for reinitialisation.

Loss of the token

The monitor station detects the loss of the token by means of a timeout. It will then reissue the token. Thus, under normal conditions, the monitor will issue a new token, and other stations will not be required to take any special recovery action.

The token could have been lost due to a failed station, which failed to re-issue the token. A station which has failed, or which no longer wishes to be part of the ring, can be bypassed using special relay circuitry. This means that, in effect, the ring is connected around, rather than through, this station.

If a station fails to remove a transmitted frame and re-insert the token, the monitor station will detect this via the monitor bit, and perform this action itself, thus preventing the frame from circulating endlessly.

Breaks in the network

Where the ring is physically severed, be it due to a node failure or to the transmission medium becoming damaged, the station immediately 'downstream' from the failure will transmit a *beacon* MAC control frame. This is a standby monitor function. This frame will be received by the monitor station, and the source address of the frame gives a useful indication of the location of the fault.

Failure of the monitor station

If the monitor fails, nothing unusual will happen until the token becomes lost. Then, some other station will notice that the monitor has not re-issued it, and will enter a 'claiming token' state. It will transmit a *claim token* MAC control frame, and this may result in this station becoming the new active monitor. The procedures are rather complex, and may be found in the specification itself. They are aimed at ensuring that only one station becomes the new monitor as a result of this action.

13.5.4   Slotted (Cambridge) Ring

The principles of the slotted ring technique, where proformas which can be filled with data and addresses endlessly circulate the ring, were outlined in the previous chapter. The prime example is the Cambridge ring, which contains several types of device, as follows. See figure 13.13.

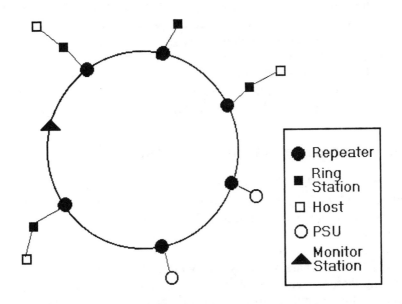

Figure 13.13 - devices on the Cambridge Ring

• *Repeater*. Repeaters are responsible for forwarding slots round the ring. The slot is regenerated at each repeater, and the contents may be examined (copied), and/or modified (patched), as the slot passes through the repeater. Therefore there must be some built-in delay in each repeater to allow this to happen; this also serves to increase the 'length' of the ring, so that a useful slot length can be achieved. Repeaters may or may not have devices attached to them. When a host is attached, it will be connected to a repeater via a ring station.

• *Ring station*. This device can buffer data from a host pending its transmission on the ring (ready to be inserted into a free slot), and also has a second buffer for data received on (copied from) the ring, and destined for the host. A ring station may be plugged into any repeater, and has defined interfaces with the host and the repeater, which will be discussed later. One type of ring station is special. This is the

• *Monitor station.* This is a special type of repeater responsible for ring initialisation, general maintenance of slots, and generation of diagnostic information on certain ring problems.

• *Power supply unit* (PSU). It is a design aim that repeaters can function with or without ring stations attached. To this end, they are powered via the ring itself, rather than from an attached ring station, and separate PSUs may be connected to the ring at suitable points. For additional reliability, more than one PSU can be provided, so that the ring will still operate if a single PSU fails. PSUs are plugged into repeaters rather like ring stations. Clearly, there can be no host at a PSU point, and a PSU repeater will never modify the slots which pass through it.

Basic ring principles and the monitor station

The ring works by using endlessly circulating *slots*, which are filled and emptied by ring stations. These slots are initially generated, and maintained, by the monitor station, whose responsibilities include cleaning up damaged slots, and freeing slots where the source station has not done so (e.g. because it failed). The monitor can also perform error checking of its own, by filling passing empty slots with random addresses and data, and checking these on return (if the slot has not since been used). Note that a mangled slot will still be freed by the originator, even if the addresses are corrupted (provided that the slot structure is not lost), since the station recognises a returning slot by counting slots, not by looking at the address fields of the slots. It will then check the data in 'its' slot, notably to determine what (if any) response was returned (see later), but it will perform these checks on a copy of the slot, not on the slot itself (there would be insufficient time before the slot had passed by).

In the Cambridge Ring, slots are known (for historical reasons) as *minipackets*. To avoid possible terminological confusion, we will use the generic term slot in this discussion.

There has to be an exact number of slots in the ring, for obvious reasons. The monitor station includes a variable length shift register, which in effect adds sufficient delay to round up the 'length' of the ring to a multiple of the slot length. (Short gaps are inserted between slots for synchronisation purposes.) It may also be necessary to adjust the transmission speed slightly from the nominal speed (which in the original

Cambridge ring was 10 mbps, although speeds of up to 100 mbps are now feasible using optical fibre), to ensure that an exact number of bits is in circulation, and so avoid potential transmission timing problems.

The slot structure means that stations cannot simply be 'patched out' as they can in a token ring. Doing this would leave the ring too short to hold the slot structure. It would then be necessary to 'lengthen' the monitor station (by adding more delay there) to compensate.

The standard length of a slot in the CR-82[1] standard (used with the coloured book standards discussed in chapter nine) was 40 bits, although implementations with 37 or 38 bits, based on earlier standards, were also permitted, and were supported by some manufacturers. Much longer slots are now possible due to technological advances which allow much faster data rates, and hence many more bits may be present in the ring at any time, than was originally possible. The discussion here is based in the main on the CR-82 format, ignoring any fields or options which are not part of the basic access technique. You should be aware that the data (and address fields) can be longer than those shown here.

It is also worth mentioning one or two other problems with the CR-82 approach. The main one was that broadcasts were prohibited, even though they had been allowed in earlier CR protocols. This was because a virtual circuit YBTS-compatible service was all that was being offered, and there was no place for broadcasts in this scenario. Another restriction was to ban multiplexed slots arriving from different source stations, which necessitated a new response 'not selected' to senders who were banned from transmitting for the time being. Implementing YBTS over a CR required the specification of four layers of protocol, known as the Ring, Packet, Virtual circuit and Network layers. The current status of CR protocols above the ring access (MAC) technique is somewhat inadequate, and only the access technique has been standardised (and even then, not by IEEE).

Slot format and fields

The format of a slot on a standard slotted {8802-7} ring is shown in figure 13.14. It should be noted that this description is based on the minimum slot length; some fields may be longer than this.

FIELD	start of slot	in use bit	monitor bit	dest address	source address	data	type	ACK	parity
BITS	1	1	1	8	8	16	2	2	1

Figure 13.14 - Standard Cambridge ring slot format

• The *start of slot bit* is set to 1, and follows the (logic 0) inter-slot gap. It is simply used for framing purposes.

- The *in use bit* is set by a ring station when it inserts its data, to mark the slot as full. It is also known as the full/empty bit. Setting this bit makes the slot unavailable to other stations until it has been cleared. Stations will examine slots for contained information only if this bit is set. The bit is reset by the sending station when the slot returns to it, the now empty slot then being forwarded not re-used. This bit thus determines whether the slot is free.

- The *monitor passed bit* is for the use of the monitor station in preserving the integrity of the slot structure. When a station inserts its data into a free slot, it clears the monitor passed bit (as well as marking the slot full). This station then has no further interest in this particular bit. However the monitor station will set the bit whenever a full slot passes it. Thus, under normal conditions, all full slots reaching the monitor will have this bit clear, and it will be set. The full slot should never reach the monitor station with this bit set, since it should have been marked empty by the sending station on return. See figure 13.15. However, if the sending station fails to free the slot (e.g. because it has failed), the full slot will reach the monitor station a second time, this time with the monitor passed bit set. The monitor station will mark any such slot as free. This mechanism is required so that a slot will not remain permanently full (and hence unavailable for use) in cases where the sending station has failed and is unable to free the slot on its return.

STATION	ACTION
monitor	slot not in use, no action
sender	clear monitor bit, set in use bit
receiver	possibly copy contents, set ack bits
monitor	slot in use and monitor bit cleared, set monitor bit
sender	(a) normal: clear in use bit (b) abnormal: fails to clear
monitor	(a) slot not in use, no action (b) slot in use and monitor bit set, clear in use bit

Figure 13.15 - use of full/empty and monitor passed bits by stations

- The *destination address* field is at least 8 bits long. (It can be longer, but this discussion assumes this length.) This allows 254 distinct stations on the ring, addresses 1-254. (Addresses 0 and 255 are special; see below.) Not all addresses need be present on the ring. The destination address comes first so that the receiver can know whether to act on this slot as soon as possible. Two addresses are special:

• *Address 255* was traditionally used as a broadcast address, and slots with this destination address could be copied by any station. Use of broadcasts is not supported by CR-82; see the earlier aside.

• *Address 0* is the address to which error notifications are sent. It is the address of a special 'diagnostic node', which could be a special node dedicated to this purpose. It is implied that the repeater with address 0 has connected to it some sort of diagnostic 'host' which merely listens for error reports and generates an error log.

• The *source address* is again (at least) 8 bits long, and is that of the sending station. It is passed on to the destination host by the receiving station (if the data is copied), so that the host will know where to send any reply. This address may again be in the range 1-254.

• In the original design, a slot had room for two *data bytes* only. This restriction was a consequence of the slot technique and (at the time) restricted transmission speed, the slot length being constrained by the requirement to circulate slots continuously. This meant that a host wishing to send a frame 128 bytes long had to do so in stages, using 64 separate slots to send the entire frame. This of course made the protocols more complex than they would need to be with other technologies, where an entire frame can be sent at once.

Two data bytes was generally considered to be a poor utilisation factor. (At most 16/40 or 40% of the slot would be user data.) Implementations with more data bytes per slot are now allowed.

• The *type bits* had specific uses in CR-82, including locating the first slot of a sequence comprising a frame.

• The two acknowledgement or *response bits* are used by the receiving station, to indicate the action (if any) which it took on the packet just received. These are used to indicate whether a copy of the slot was taken at the destination. As usual for simplex rings, if the initial value remains unaltered, this means that the station was either not connected or 'deaf'.

• The *parity bit* is set so that the slot as a whole has even longitudinal parity. Each node checks and sets the parity bit. Parity

---

errors are notified to address zero, at the first available opportunity, i.e. before any data queued for transmission. The monitor passed bit will not be cleared in such slots, nor will it need to be freed on return. It contains no data, the only significant information provided being the source address, which can be used to determine the location of the error.

Usage of slots

Gaps between slots are a few bits long, with logic 0. The first bit of the next slot must always have logic 1, thus easily allowing a station to identify the start of a slot. A station wishing to transmit selects the next available free slot. It marks the slot full, inserts addresses and data, and sets response bits. The destination ring station (if present) may or may not copy the slot, and will alter the response bits to reflect the action (if any) it has taken. The slot then returns to the sender. The sender can only 'own' one slot at a time. When the slot returns, it is checked for errors (a nominated station is notified if any are detected), and the response bits are examined. If unaltered, this means either that the destination ring station never saw the slot (e.g. it did not exist), or that it had been instructed by its host to ignore all received slots. In other cases, it may have been accepted, rejected or ignored by the destination. The usage of bits in a slot is covered later in more detail.

When the slot returns, it must be marked empty before it is forwarded to the next station. It may not immediately be re-used by the same station. This *anti-hogging algorithm* aims to ensure that no single station can gain unfair access to the ring resource. If the response bits indicate that the data in the slot was accepted, the station may send the next part of the data (to the same station) as soon as it wishes (but not in the same slot immediately). However if the destination did not accept it, it may not try again to this destination until one ring cycle has been completed (e.g. 3 slots have passed, and the same slot returns, although this particular slot may by now have been filled by another station, of course). If a second attempt fails, a backoff algorithm comes into play, causing a delay of 15 ring cycles. Again, this algorithm is designed to allow the most effective use of the medium, and to prevent a station from flooding the ring with useless (i.e. undeliverable) data.

Performance

The parity bit was optional in early implementations, and in any case clearly provides very poor error detection capabilities, as 50% of errors will not be detected. This, coupled with the fact that a typical HDLC-style frame will need many slots to be fully transmitted, leads to messy recovery problems if critical fields in the frame (e.g. the data length) are mangled because an individual slot was corrupted. There is also the possibility of individual slots being delivered to the wrong destination, or associated with the wrong originator, due to address field corruptions. This does not prejudice the integrity of the frame as a whole, as it will contain an FCS field (transmitted in the last slot). Unfortunately it can however cause the receiver considerable grief, as it can end up waiting for slots which do not exist (the frame is not as long as the receiver expects), or prematurely detecting the end of a frame (in which case the receiver may be confused when the rest of the frame arrives).

In particularly bad cases the slot structure itself may be damaged (e.g. the start of slot bit could be mangled), in which case recovery action will be necessary by the monitor station. In the extreme, the entire slot structure has to be regenerated by the monitor station. It is true that in practice errors will be rare, but when they occur, recovery tends to be much more messy than is the case with most other technologies.

To summarise, the slotted ring technique is interesting but rather eccentric in nature. The main difficulties relate to throughput limitations due to the slot overheads, the potentially chaotic effects of undetected errors in slots, and the need for an extra protocol layer to associate several slots with a single frame. Although the access technique has been accepted as an ISO standard (which at one time this author considered most unlikely), there is still no standardised protocol infrastructure which can be used above it. In particular, the interim YBTS-compatible protocols for which CR-82 was designed are now obsolete, and in any case are not OSI-compatible. The fact that Ethernets have been installed in the Cambridge University Computer Laboratory, the very heartland of slotted rings, perhaps says it all.

13.6   Priorities and expedited data

NETWORK TYPE	NO OF PRIORITIES	EXPEDITED POSSIBLE?
CSMA/CD bus	1	no
token bus	4	yes
token ring	8	yes
slotted ring	1	no (see note)

NOTE:
> No OSI support is is provided for slotted rings. A priority
> mechanism would in theory be possible, but it would be very
> messy to implement given the slot structure used.

Figure 13.16 - Priorities and expedited data in LANs

It can be seen from the above discussions that some technologies allow priority schemes, whereas others do not. Figure 13.16 summaries what (if any) different priority levels are available. By implication, if more than one is available, *expedited data* may in principle be used over the network.

13.7   Reference

1   J. Larmouth ed., 'Cambridge Ring 82 Protocol Specifications' (second orange book), prepared by the JNT.

14   The OSI Network Layer

14.1   Connection oriented network service definition

The principal aim of this chapter is to explain the *Connection Oriented network Service* (*CONS*), and to explain how it maps on to X.25. This standard {8348} defines the services provided by the network layer to the transport layer, subject to the requirements set out in chapter ten. The network service definition was one of the first OSI support standards to be developed. This was because there was an urgent need to map to X.25 (at the time, the 1980 version), before work could proceed at higher layers of OSI/RM. As usual there are two flavours of the network service, the Connection Oriented version (CONS), which is suitable for use over virtual circuit networks such as X.25, and the connectionless mode variant (CLNS), which provides a datagram service with no connection setup or cleardown facilities. The basic standard concentrates on CONS, and addenda cover the CLNS, addressing issues and 'additional features'. For the time being we will concentrate on CONS, as this is the dominant service. We will then go on to discuss its use over X.25(1988) networks.

A chapter could be written on the problems which were encountered in mapping CONS to X.25(1980), and the effect this had on both CONS and X.25. However in the interests of space, and because X.25(1980) is becoming increasingly obsolescent, this aspect will not be discussed. There are only minor differences between X.25(1984) and X.25(1988), notably the definition of some additional facilities in the latter, so that what is discussed here can be taken to apply to X.25(1984) as well.

The network service (NS) provides a definition of the service provided to transport entities, which influences the facilities offered by the transport protocol {8073, 8602}. It also forms the basis for a definition of a network protocol, which is discussed later in the chapter. See figure 14.1.

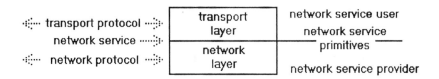

Figure 14.1 - scope of the OSI network service

The network service (NS) is defined, in the usual way, in terms of a set of *NS primitives*, their parameters, and the order in which they can be transferred across the interface between the network layer and the transport layer. The service definition is not intended to be an implementation guide, but rather seeks to define the nature of the service. As we shall see later, there are constraints on which of the services defined can actually be used in a real case.

The NS provides for the transparent transfer of transport protocol data units (TPDUs) between its users (transport entities). The way in which supporting communication resources are used to this end is transparent to the transport entities. The NS offers the following types of support to the transport layer:

- The NS relieves the transport layer of any concern for the details of the underlying resources, i.e. it allows the transport station to be network independent. The one exception to this is that the QOS of the underlying network(s) is made known to the transport entity, so that it can be enhanced, if this is required by the transport users.

- The NS provides for the end-end transfer of network service data units (NSDUs). In the case of CONS, it involves the setting up of a *network connection* (NC) between the two endpoints. This may involve the use of intermediate relays, or the use of several network connections (NCs) in parallel as dictated by the required QOS; the details are not made known to the transport layer.

- The NS provides for the transparent transfer of data as two octet streams, one in each direction. The content, format and coding of the data are neither restricted nor interpreted by the network layer.

- The NS provides a means for requesting and negotiating the QOS required from the underlying resource, by means of the GOS parameters described in chapter ten; this may allow the NS suitably to tailor its use of the underlying data link service.

- The NS allows users to refer to each other unambiguously, using a suitable addressing system {8348 ADD2}.

14.2   Network service primitives

The service, as defined in the above queue model, is implemented in practice by the transfer of network service primitives (objects) across the transport/network layer interface. The primitives defined below are for use with CONS. As an illustration of the queue model discussed in chapter ten, Figure 14.2 gives a list of the types of object which may be placed in a queue by a network service user. As you can see as you compare the list with the primitive types discussed below, the categorisation as queue objects adds little to the discussion, except that you should be aware that a queue implies delays and a possible inability to issue primitives due to the queue being full (a 'blockage').

Connect requests.
Normal data octets.
End of data unit (packet) markers.
Expedited data packets (optional).
Received data acknowledgements.
Reset requests.
Disconnect requests.

Figure 14.2 -NS queue model object types

14.2.1   Connection establishment phase

The establishment of a NC is a confirmed service. It will be seen that there is a close parallel with the call setup packet sequence in X.25. Because of the significant differences between the variants, we will break with the usual practice and consider each variant separately.

N–CONNECT request   called address, calling address, receipt confirmation selection, expedited data selection, QOS parameter set, NS user data

This primitive is issued by the initiating transport entity wishing to set up a network connection; on receipt of this primitive, the network layer sets up a pair of queues as discussed above. These queues will remain associated with the NC until a 'disconnect object' is either entered into, or removed from, a queue. At this point, we will abandon this somewhat obscure ISO terminology. While the standard refers to objects being entered in, and removed from, queues, this does sound rather abstract, and for convenience we will henceforth use a less precise, but perhaps more readily understandable, terminology.

A number of parameters are associated with this primitive, as follows:

• *Called address*. This is the address of an endpoint, the called user, and is used to locate a remote transport entity. The addresses of any intermediate network relays, which might be used to reach the peer transport entity, are of no interest to the calling user, and will not be discussed here (although they are relevant to the network protocol).

• *Calling address*. Similarly, this is the address of the calling user. Note that both addresses refer to host open systems, with possibly several networks intervening; for example, the addresses are <u>not</u> those of X.,25 network endpoints.

• *Receipt confirmation selection* and *expedited data selection*. Both of these services are <u>optional</u>, and will not necessarily be provided by the NS. An expedited data service will not necessarily be required by the transport users in any case. Whether or not receipt confirmation is required depends on the class of transport protocol being used, as discussed in chapter fifteen. The parameters are used by the calling user to indicate whether the services are *required* or *not required* by it. When used over X.25, the D-bit (see chapter seven) must be set in data packets if the receipt confirmation facility is to be used.

• *Quality of service parameter set*. The calling user provides two sets of QOS parameters, the *target* which is the QOS desired by the caller, and also a QOS which is the *lowest acceptable* to the calling user. The QOS was discussed in chapter ten.

• *NS user data*. A limited amount of user data, between 0 and 128 octets, may be included. This data will not be delivered if the NS setup attempt fails.

N-CONNECT indication   called   address,   calling   address, receipt   confirmation   selection, expedited data   selection,   QOS parameter set, NS user data

This primitive is used by the destination network entity to pass the connection setup attempt to the called user (transport entity). The same set of parameters is provided as in the connect request, but their usage differs as described below:

• *Expedited data selection* and *receipt confirmation selection*. Again two values are possible in each case, but the notional names *used* and *not used* are now used to reflect the change in usage. Where the caller stated that the facility was required and it cannot be provided by the network service, it is altered to not used, and the called user is not informed that the caller requested the facility. Where the facility is requested and also available, the called user will be informed using the value used, but the called user still has the option not to use it; see under response below.

• *QOS*. The actual QOS provided by the NS may be anywhere between the target and minimum acceptable values of the parameter sets indicated by the calling user. Where the best QOS which can be offered lies between the two, the different value *available*, and the caller's lowest acceptable value, are passed to the called user. If the NS cannot provide a suitably high QOS (at least the lowest acceptable), the NC setup attempt will fail, and a disconnect will be returned to the caller by the network service (see below). The called user will not be informed of the connection attempt in this case.

N-CONNECT response, confirm   responding   address,   receipt confirmation, selection, expedited data selection, QOS parameter set, NS user data

The called user uses this primitive to indicate that it is agreeable to the transport communication, as defined in the parameters of the indication as received by it (which are not necessarily those placed in the request issued by the caller), but possibly on its own terms, as set out in the parameters of its response. (If the called user is not agreeable to set up the connection on any terms, it will issue a disconnect, as discussed below.) The parameters are the same as for the indication, except that only one address is provided, the responding address. The parameters are used as follows (or their use is obvious if not stated):

    • *Responding address*. This is the address of the remote NSAP to which the NC has been established. This will normally be the same address when returned to the calling user in a confirm (see below), but it may be different in some cases (e.g. if the call has been redirected, which is an optional facility in an X.25 underlying network, or if generic addressing is being used. Generic addressing was discussed in chapter nine).

    • *Optional service selection*. The optional facilities will be marked as used only if the caller requested the facility, the NS can provide it, and the called user also wishes to use it. In all other cases, the value not used is returned. This allows the called user the option to refuse to use an optional service requested by the calling user, for example to *negotiate down* an optional facility which it cannot, or does not wish to, support. [Note that since the facility is optional, the calling user must be able to operate without it, and it would be invalid for the calling user to object to this.]

    • *QOS parameter set*. Where the called user is agreeable to a QOS parameter set lying somewhere between the available and the lowest acceptable values, a single QOS, *selected*, will be returned by the called user, indicating the QOS which it wishes to use. This value will be relayed back to the calling user. The value must of course be in the range specified by the caller, although it may well be less than the target value, and therefore it must be acceptable, even if not ideal, to the calling user. If the called user is not prepared to accept a QOS in the stated range, the connection attempt will fail, and the called user will return a disconnect.

Any difference between the selected and target QOS must be made up by enhancement within the transport layer, as will be discussed in chapter fifteen.

The response is relayed to the calling user as a confirm, which is in the same format as the response. The service provider does not alter any of the parameters which were placed in the response.

When these primitives have been exchanged, the NC is considered to be set up, and the communication enters the data transfer phase.

14.2.2   Data transfer phase

Several primitives may be sent during this phase, but many relate to the optional expedited and receipt confirmation services, and may not be used if these facilities are not selected.

Normal data transfer

As far as *normal data transfer* is concerned, there are four primitives (two unconfirmed services), as follows:

N–DATA request, indication   NS user data, confirmation request

N–DATA–ACKNOWLEDGE   (no parameters)
request, indication

These bear a similar relationship to each other as the connection establishment primitives. Note that the confirmation request parameters in the n-data primitives, and the acknowledge primitives, may only be used if it was agreed during connection establishment that the optional receipt confirmation facility would be used.

The standard does not set any limits on the size of the user data, except that at least one octet must be present. This is an issue for the network service, based on the packet size available in the underlying network. Any data unit markers of significance to an application or other higher layer entity are transparent to the network service. Any data in transit may be destroyed by a disconnect or a reset (see below).

One noteworthy feature is that what is offered is not a confirmed service, in which each TSDU is individually acknowledged, but an 'asynchronous' service where several TSDUs may be outstanding at any given time. In a way this reflects the origins of CONS in X.25, where TSDUs map on to data packets, and the window acknowledgement technique used would make a confirmed data service hard to use, and inefficient. The service definition says nothing about when data should be acknowledged, and offers no recovery procedures in the event that an acknowledge is not received. However three additional points must be made in this regard:

• The underlying network protocol may include acknowledgement procedures which attempt to ensure receipt confirmation. There is also a N-RESET primitive which the network service provider can issue in the event that there is a problem. As we shall see, receipt of N-RESET implies loss of data (what has not been acknowledged if receipt confirmation is being used, and an unknown amount otherwise).

• What should be done if no acknowledgement is received within some timeout period, when receipt confirmation is being used, is a transport layer issue.

• It should also be noted that the definition of N-DATA does not include any means of uniquely identifying the NSDU, nor does N-DATA-ACKNOWLEDGE indicate what is being acknowledged. This is not a mistake in the service definition. It is important to remember that the service definition is an abstraction; in practice mechanisms are (must) be provided to associate N-DATA-ACKNOWLEDGE and prior N-DATA NSDUs. The point is that how this is achieved is for the implementor to decide. This is further discussed in §14.3.2.

Expedited data transfer

In addition to the above primitives, two additional data primitives relate to *expedited data* transfer, but these may only be used if use of this optional facility was successfully negotiated in the connection establishment phase:

N-EXPEDITED-DATA   NS user data
request, indication

Between 1 and 32 octets of user data may be sent in an expedited primitive. This restriction closely parallels what can be sent in an

X.25(1988) interrupt packet, but as will be discussed later, this does not necessarily mean that this primitive can easily be mapped on to an X.25 interrupt packet.

Expedited data transfer, if available, bypasses normal flow control. In particular, it may still be possible to send expedited data if the normal data flow is blocked (e.g. by flow control imposed by an underlying network). However as neither ISO nor CCITT consider that its provision should be made mandatory, difficulties can be encountered in implementing it over some networks, and it cannot even be provided over some other networks, it is not generally considered to be a particularly useful facility. In particular, no application can rely on its availability, although some (e.g. VT, chapter twenty one) can make use of it if it is available.

It is also worth noting that if network expedited data is not available, it may still be possible for applications to use expedited data, in which case the transport layer will send it as network normal data, with a flag (transparent to the network layer) which identifies it as 'expedited'. Clearly any such 'expedited data' will get no preferential treatment in the network layer, as It would violate OSI conventions if a given layer were to be aware of the significance of data passed to it by higher layers. This also means that although a Q-bit is defined in X.25, it has no use in OSI. In particular it cannot be used to distinguish between normal and expedited application data on the same network data channel; this distinction is an internal transport layer matter, of no concern to the network layer.

Resynchronisation

The third type of primitive in the data transfer phase relates to *resynchronisation*. Four primitives are provided to implement a reset function, as follows:

N-RESET request, indication   originator, reason

N-RESET response, confirm   (no parameters)

A reset may be initiated by either a user or the service provider. A user can use reset to resynchronise the NC. The service provider can use it to report an irrecoverable loss of data, where the loss is not serious enough to warrant a disconnection of the NC. The philosophy of this service is very similar to that of the X.25 reset. Where either reset or disconnect (see below) is issued by the service provider to notify internal network problems, it is referred to as a *signalled error*. The parameters in the request and indication are used as follows:

> • *Reason*. This gives the cause of the reset. A user may issue a reset for the purposes of user resynchronisation, as dictated by its own needs, or as requested by a higher layer entity. The network

service may issue a reset because of congestion or for 'other reasons'.

• *Originator*. This will be either the 'NS user' or the 'NS provider', i.e. it identifies where the reset was issued. There are four cases to consider, the outcomes of which depend on where the reset originated (assuming a NC between two users X and Y, either of which may have been the calling user, for the purposes of this discussion):

    • Where the reset is issued by user X, the sequence of primitives exchanged is once more similar to that shown in figure 10.3. The originator is set to 'NS user'.

    • Where the reset is initiated by the service provider, an indication will be sent to both users, and a response is returned by each user. In this case, no request or confirm variants are required. Note that unlike YBTS, no attempt is made to give the precise location within the underlying network, as this information would not be of use to the service user.

    • Where both users simultaneously issue reset requests, they will both receive a confirm from the network service in return, and in this case no indication or response variants are involved.

    • In the case where user X requests a reset, and simultaneously the network service provider also issues a reset, user X will receive a confirm in return, and user Y will receive an indication, for which a response will be returned.

14.2.3   The connection release phase

Only one primitives is involved in this phase. The service is unconfirmed (but see also §14.3.2).

N–DISCONNECT	originator, reason,
request, indication	NS user data, responding address

These are used to release the NC in any of the following cases:

    • By either (or both) users in the data transfer phase, to terminate the NC.

    • By the service provider in the data transfer phase, as a result of some failure in the NC.

• By the called user during the establishment phase, to refuse a connection attempt by the caller (i.e. to reject a connect indication).

• By the service provider during the establishment phase, if it is unable to establish the NC (i.e. to reject a connect request).

The parameters are used as follows:

• *Reason*. This indicates why the NC has been disconnected, from a list of permitted values.

• Where the user disconnects, the reasons include disconnection (normal and abnormal) and connection rejection (required QOS not available, invalid user data, reason unspecified).

• Where the service provider issues the disconnect, the reasons include disconnection (normal and abnormal) and connection rejection (unknown address, unreachable address, required QOS not available, reason unspecified).

• *Responding address*. This is present only if the disconnect is issued in lieu of a connect response, i.e. the called user is refusing the connection attempt. Again, if the call has been redirected or generic addressing is being used, this will not necessarily be the same as the called address.

• *User data*. Between 0 and 128 octets of user data may accompany a disconnect issued by a user, but any such data will be lost if the service provider simultaneously issues a disconnect itself. For this reason, use of this field has not been recommended for use by UK implementors.

14.2.4   Connectionless service

A single primitive is provided. As usual this is an unconfirmed service.

N-UNITDATA   calling address, called address, QOS,
request, indication   NS user data

Each data unit must be individually addressed, and there is no certainty of delivery. This normally maps directly on to the corresponding data link service primitive. The calling address maps to the DL source address, and the called address to the DL destination address. In some cases, the underlying data link service may be connection oriented. We will discuss CO/CL combinations briefly at the end of the chapter. In general we will not discuss WAN connectionless services or CO/CL mappings in detail.

14.3 Use of X.25 to provide the CONS

14.3.1 Historical introduction

X.25 was not originally designed with OSI/RM in mind, nor could it have been, of course. The original motivation behind X.25 was purely to provide PTTs with a standard means of defining how users of their packet switching networks should interface to them. This was originally its only aim. However this aim proved too restrictive, and many changes were made to accommodate the requirements of the users (hosts), of which the provision of fast select, an increased interrupt packet data field length, and delivery confirmation are among the most important.

X.25 in its 1980 form posed major problems for OSI, and indeed there are still some unresolved issues. Would it not have been better to abandon it in favour of a new protocol, something more 'OSI-friendly'? Unfortunately this would not have been feasible. Worldwide, there are so many interested and committed parties that it would have been absurd to contemplate abandoning the recommendation. Therefore it was enhanced. Discussion on the relationship between X.25 and the OSI/RM network layer (and below) has gone on for some years, and interim proposals were produced whereby X.25(1980) could be made to provide a rather cut-down CONS. Ultimately X.25 was modified to become more compatible with CONS, culminating in the production of an standard defining the use of X.25 packet mode {8208} to provide CONS {8878}. To cover the interim period when X.25(1980) implementations were still widespread, ISO recommended a strategy which aimed to provide two basic approaches:

- The definition of a direct mapping of X.25(1988) on to CONS primitives.

- The definition of a separate subnetwork dependent 'Convergence Protocol'[1], which indicated how X.25(1980) can be enhanced to provide the CONS, as an interim measure until all PDNs implement the 1984 version (which is to all intents and purposes the same as the 1988 version).

Both of these approaches were published together in June, 1984, the intention being to issue them as a DP as soon as possible. The convergence protocol was however withdrawn before it left DP status, and the whole area has now been overtaken by events. Therefore we will restrict the discussion in this book to the current standards.

14.3.2   Mapping of X.25(1988) to CONS

This mapping {8878} defines how the X.25(1984) packet mode procedures (referred to by ISO as the X.25 packet level protocol, or PLP) {8208} packets are used to map network service primitives, and is therefore the packet layer version of the corresponding data link mapping to LAPB discussed in chapter eleven. This mapping proved far harder to achieve, as we saw in the previous section. However it is now essentially stable, and it is mapping of X.25 (1988) which we will discuss here. A detailed understanding of X.25 (chapter seven) is assumed in the following discussion.

Network connections essentially map on to X.25 virtual circuits (calls). (Permanent virtual circuits (PVCs) have no direct parallel in the OSI network service.) This is in principle straightforward for two reasons.

• X.25 existed when the CONS was being defined. Therefore it would have been surprising if the CONS had not suited a mapping to X.25. Changes to X.25 between 1980 and 1984 indeed made it possible to produce a quite close mapping.

• Despite the ISO name referred to above, X.25 is not a protocol, as it defines how to interface with an X.25 network, and is therefore by nature a *service definition*.

Since the new (1984/88) versions of X.25 can be mapped reasonably well on to NS primitives, many of the problems with the 1980 version have disappeared, allowing us to discuss the mappings to standardised X.25(1984/1988) packet types. We will discuss each service primitive in turn. Where necessary we will discuss individual variants.

There were many problems in mapping the CONS to earlier versions of X.25, which variously did not support fast select, had inadequate space for the peer NSAP addresses, were unable to support or negotiate delivery confirmation or the use of expedited data, had inadequate user data fields, and so on. Although the second edition of the book discussed these issues in some detail, we will not deal with them here. The great majority of the difficulties were resolved with X.25(1984), although the area of QOS still presents some difficulty.

Connection establishment

The N-CONNECT primitives map on to the corresponding X.25 call setup packets. However as you will have seen in §14.2.1, the parameters for the different primitive variants are quite different, and negotiation is also involved. Therefore this particular mapping will be discussed in some detail.

N-CONNECT request

This maps on to the *call request* packet. The parameters are handled as follows.

• The *called address* and *calling address* are mapped into the address fields of the X.25 header. These are the NSAP addresses of the endpoints. (The service user is in the host open system.) It was necessary in X.25(1984) to cater for extended formats for address fields, since the original X.25 fields catered only for a single X.25 network, whereas a NC may span several underlying networks. Clearly not all of the called address is relevant to the current X.25 network, but we will not discuss the ramifications of this here.

• The *receipt confirmation selection* is mapped by setting the *X-bit* in the GFI, if the caller proposes to use the facility.

• The *expedited data selection* is mapped on to an entry in the facilities field, proposing the use of expedited data if appropriate.

• X.25(1988) includes *GOS* parameters for end-end *transit delay* and minimum *throughput class*. These are encoded in the facilities field. This in part provides for the *QOS parameter set* parameter.

• *Expedited data selection* also maps to an entry in the facilities field.

• The *NS user data* is encoded in the *data field*. This requires the use of *fast select*, which is mandatory, since otherwise the call request packet can only contain 16 octets of call user data, which is insufficient to convey the parameters of the N-CONNECT request. (The call accepted packet would not have a called user data field at all.)

. (Fast select is requested in the facilities field.) There is clearly a limit on the amount of user data which can be provided.

N-CONNECT indication

This maps on to the *incoming call* packet. The parameters are the same as in the request, but those parameters which are negotiated may have been altered (downwards) by the underlying network as follows:

• If *delivery confirmation* was requested but cannot be provided by the network, the X bit is reset to 0 in the incoming call packet.

• If the *QOS* (GOS) requested cannot be met, the reduced value available will be reflected in the facilities field. In theory if the minimum acceptable value cannot be achieved by the network, the call attempt will fail. In practice this will not happen however, as the QOS of real X.25 networks are known (specified), and it would make no sense to attempt to use a network which it was known could not meet the required QOS.

• If the network does not support *expedited data*, again the caller's request to use it will be removed from the facilities field. (A network which does not support the full 32-bit interrupt data length is considered to be unable to support expedited data transfer.)

N-CONNECT response

This maps on to the *call accepted* packet. The parameters are handled as follows.

• The *recall address* may differ from the calling address for such reasons as call deflection or redirection by the called DTE, or for other reasons. If the called address is a relay (gateway), it is in theory possible for the call to be redirected to an alternative gateway from which the required destination can be reached. However addressing issues are too complex to be discussed in detail here.

• The called user may elect to reduce the *QOS* (further), provided it does not fall below the minimum acceptable value. This then becomes the value available (which the network will leave well alone on the way back).

• If the incoming call packet indicated that *receipt confirmation* or *expedited data* were requested and available, the called user (or relay) may either agree to use them, or refuse. This could reflect either whether the called host wishes to use the facility, or whether the next network after the relay can support the facility. Note that once a facility has been negotiated out, it can never be negotiated back again, nor will a facility ever be proposed if the calling host did not request it.

N-CONNECT confirm

This maps on to the *call connected* packet at the originator. The parameters in the call accepted packet are delivered unchanged.

Data transfer

N-DATA request maps on to *data packets*, which generate N-DATA indications on valid receipt (in order). Unless delivery confirmation has been agreed, any P(R) numbers returned to the sender do <u>not</u> necessarily imply that the associated data has been delivered, which can cause problems if a reset occurs, as an unknown (to the network layer) amount of data may have been lost.

- The *confirmation request* maps onto the D bit set in the corresponding data packet, but unless delivery confirmation has been agreed, this bit must not be set. Similarly if it has been agreed, it must always be set.

N-DATA-ACKNOWLEDGE maps on to the D-bit and P(R) fields in received packets. Note that the primitive merely specifies the abstract service.

- The peer packet mode entity updates P(R) to take into account data packets correctly received, and passes these on as N-DATA indications to the service user (the transport layer). The user replies (notionally) by returning a N-DATA-ACKNOWLEDGE request. This is an implicit concept, since this primitive does not actually correspond to any real transaction. X.25 itself returns the updated P(R) as appropriate; it does not wait to be 'instructed' to do so by the service user.

- When the sending network entity (X.25 DTE or DXE) receives an N(R) which acknowledges one or more transmitted data packets, this (notionally) results in a N-DATA-ACKNOWLEDGE indication to the sending user.

This will typically result in less throughput than if the D-bit is not used. However, in theory, in the event of an unsolicited reset or disconnect, the service users have a clear idea which data has reached the destination, and therefore how much has to be retransmitted. But this is only a theory. Higher level procedures are needed to ensure that the data has been 'safe stored' as opposed merely to having been received correctly.

Expedited data

A N-EXPEDITED-DATA request maps on to an X.25 interrupt packet. This places a notional limit of 32 octets on the user data field size. Expedited data is not available unless its use was agreed at connection establishment time.

It should be noted that there is a mismatch with the service definition, in that the X.25 interrupt packet is a confirmed service, whereas the N_EXPEDITED service is not. It is not a requirement for receipt of the DCE interrupt confirmation packet to be notified to the service user, although in practice it may well so be reported.

This is largely of academic interest, as only the VT application standard (chapter twenty one) has so far found any use for expedited data. In any case any connection between open systems which encounters an X.25(1980) implementation en route will automatically lose the ability to select expedited data transfer. (See under connection establishment above). So any application which requires expedited data (as opposed to possibly finding it useful) will have to wait until all X.25 networks have been upgraded to at least the 1984 version, as well as ensure that no network (such as CSMA/CD LAN) is used which cannot support it either. In practice, as the VT application may have no knowledge of which underlying networks it will use, or may be implemented on a host attached to a CSMA/CD LAN, this makes the use of expedited data problematical to say the least.

Resynchronisation

It is transparently obvious that N-RESET must map in some way on to the X.25 reset packets. However it is not as simple as that. RESET primitives have always caused a problem when mapped on to X.25 networks. In theory the X.25 reset packet reason code field can provide sufficient information to supply all of the reasons in the request and indicate primitives. The problem is that resets can arise not only because the service user issued a N-RESET request, but also either because of internal X.25 network problems resulting in a service provider issued N-RESET indication. If two X.25 resets collide, one from each source, any reasons encoded in the reset packet may be lost. Therefore it will not always be possible to supply the service user with the correct cause in the indication.

YBTS (chapter nine) had a similar problem. The solution adopted there was to encode the parameters of a YBTS reset in data packets immediately following the completion of the X.25 reset exchange. The Q-bit was set in these data packets so that the receiver would know that what was encoded therein was parameters of the reset, not than user data.

Unfortunately use of the Q bit in this way is not consistent with OSI principles, which dictate that meaning of NS user data (in whatever packets or primitives it occurs) is of no concern whatsoever to the service provider (in this case the network layer). Therefore there is no way in which the network service can use the Q-bit to identify service primitive parameters, which in fact makes the Q-bit redundant where X.25 is being used to realise the OSI network service.

As well as obsoleting YBTS, this restriction also obsoletes X.25, which makes a similar use of the Q-bit, as well as any protocol (X.29 and YBTS included) which make use of the data field of the first data packet for protocol identification purposes.

Connection release

N-DISCONNECT clearly maps on to X.25 clearing packets. As with N-CONNECT, there are four cases to consider.

N-DISCONNECT request

This maps on to an X.25 *clear request* packet. There are two cases to consider.

    • If the N-DISCONNECT request is to refuse a N-CONNECT indication, the *originator* is the receiver of the incoming call packet.

    • Either user may issue the primitive at any time during the data transfer phase to terminate the virtual call (NC).

    • In either case the *reason* can be suitably mapped on to the clearing cause and diagnostic code fields of the clear request packet. (The reason is only relevant in the indication; see below.)

    • The *user data* is encoded in the clear user data field, which is available as the call must be fast select.

    • The *responding address* is significant only if the X.25 call was redirected or deflected, the call setup was refused, and the initiator of the call specified the CLAMN facility (in which case address fields are available in the clearing packet).

N-DISCONNECT indication

This maps on to an X.25 *clear indication* packet. The parameters are the same as in the request. The indication may be a relayed request from the peer user, or may be issued by the service provider; this will be clear from the clearing cause and diagnostic code, which will specify the *reason* for the disconnection. Remember that the service provider can reject the initial call setup (clear indication to the caller only) or at any time during data transfer (clear indication to both parties).

As with N-RESET, in cases where a provider initiated DISCONNECT collides with a user initiated DISCONNECT, the reason parameter and *user data* may be lost. For this reason it is not recommended to send user data with N-DISCONNECT.

Negotiated release services are available in higher layers, where agreement to disconnect is reached by the peer applications before issuing a primitive which maps to a N-DISCONNECT. Unsolicited N-DISCONNECTS are either recovered from by the transport protocol (chapter fifteen) or result in a session provider abort (chapter sixteen).

Response/confirm handshake

These primitives are not defined in the service definition, but as the request/indication results in the X.25 network returning *clear confirmation* packets, the service is effectively confirmed, although it is purely a handshake, it not being possible to convey any user data in the clear confirmation packets. The service user does not need to be explicitly notified of the release. The action to be taken if the release failure probability or release delay QOS parameters are not met is a management issue. It clearly does not affect the service user, except in the sense that it may be impossible to set up a net connection (for some time).

Discussion

To summarise, X.25(1988) in effect provides something very close to the OSI/RM network layer, and there are few major problems in realising the network service in this way. It should, however, be mentioned that the discussion document4 leaves some areas open for further study. These 'temp-notes' mention, among other things, the problems of how the network layer entity is to police compliance with optional service and QOS negotiation requirements, and how a default QOS throughput parameter is to be catered for. At the time of writing, these problems had not been completely resolved, but they are mostly minor.

14.4 Connection oriented / connectionless mapping issues

The prime aim of this chapter was to explain the network service, notably the CONS. However the internal organisation of the network layer may be far more complex than this. In this section we will briefly discuss mapping issues; in the next we discuss addressing, internetworking and related issues.

There are of course four mappings possible between the network and data link layers.

• The CO to CO mapping is between the CONS discussed in this chapter and the CODLS discussed in chapter eleven. It is the standard WAN mapping. The NC uses a succession of underlying DLCs.

• The CL to CL mapping is trivial. It simply maps the N-UNITDATA primitive to the DL-UNITDATA primitive. All required addressing is contained within the parameters.

• The CO to CL underlying service mapping in effect disregards the connection setup and release phases, and transmits N-DATA as DL-UNITDATA. This requires additional procedures in the network protocol to maintain the integrity of the connection as seen by the user, as the underlying CL service will not be confirmed, and is therefore prone to loss or mis-sequencing of PDUs.

• Mapping a CLNS on to an underlying CODLS is frankly to be avoided if possible. As N-UNITDATA primitives are not related, they would have to be mapped individually on to connections, involving both complex management procedures and inefficiency.

14.5   Some network layer issues

One crucial aspect of the network layer does not appear in the network service definition, since this only defines the interface with the transport layers in the end-users (hosts). This is the issue of *internetworking*, the use of *relays*, and the impact on the QOS. Where only one network intervenes there is no difficulty, but if a number of intervening networks are involved, the QOS provided by these networks may differ widely. In this case, the QOS which the network service imparts to the called user as that 'available' will normally be that of the worst case intervening network. The transport service may well have to enhance the QOS itself, if it is going to be able to provide the required QOS to its own users, since it would clearly not be acceptable for every NC setup to be allowed to fail for this reason alone, as effective communication would then be impossible.

A second issue relates to the facilities offered by different underlying networks. The issues in relay (gateway) design are complex, and involve protocol conversion in the general case. Where, in addition, different facilities exist in the various networks as well, it is not simply a case of mapping between data encodings, and it must be accepted that some facilities simply cannot be made available to end users unless every intervening network can provide them. For the use of facilities such as expedited data and delivery confirmation to be possible, all underlying networks must be capable of supporting them. The network service definition acknowledges this to an extent, by making receipt confirmation and expedited data delivery optional. There were major difficulties in using the X.25(1980) interrupt service for expedited data transfer, and even now the X.25 interrupt packet is confirmed, whereas N-EXPEDITED-DATA is not a confirmed service. In addition, delivery confirmation cannot be supported using X.25 implementations which do not support the D-bit used in conjunction with P(R).

Such difficulties in providing the same service to the transport layer regardless of which network(s) intervene imply that the differences between networks will inevitably percolate upwards to higher layers. Although, as we will see in the next chapter, five different classes of transport protocol are defined to cater for different types of underlying network, only such a limited number of different classes can sensibly be provided. A transport layer which attempted to hide every possible difference between underlying networks from the user would become unbelievably complex. Therefore, until all underlying networks conform at least broadly to the OSI requirements, it will be hard to achieve true network independence at the session and higher layers. This has influenced the development of OSI in two ways:

> • As the underlying layers are not entirely trustworthy, upper layers (notably RTSE in the 'application support sublayer'; see chapter eighteen) must incorporate additional procedures in case the lower layers 'let them down'.

> • Applications may need to avoid using certain network facilities which are either not essential for provision of the OSI network service, or are inherently unsuitable for this provision. Expedited data generally comes under this heading.

In addition to these problems, it is clear that the network service definition is very abstract, and leaves implementors with considerable room for manoeuvre. Considerable work still has to be done, for example in the areas of addressing, routing and charging. The best hope for the future is that OSI/RM, in particular the network service definition, will mature into a consistent and compatible set of protocol implementations which can interwork in a way which really is transparent to the users.

Finally, it is worth mentioning a number of standard documents which exist in this area, although some were still at the DP stage at the time of writing:

> • Protocol combinations to support the network service (CONS and CLNS) {8880-1}.

- Provision and support of the CONS {8880-2}.
- Provision and support of the CLNS {8880-3}.
- Protocol for providing the CLNS (connectionless internet protocol) {8473}.
- X.25 relay function {TR 10029}.
- End-intermediate system routing protocol to support X.25 implementation of the CONS {9542}.
- End-intermediate system routing protocol for use with the connectionless internet protocol {9542}.
- Intermediate-intermediate system routing protocol for use with the connectionless internet protocol {10030}.

14.6   References

1   ISO DP 8472, 'Network Convergence Protocol'. This was subsequently withdrawn, as it had been overtaken by events.

Part four

The Host Application Support Layers

In part three we introduced the basic concepts of OSI, starting with the reference model, and then covering the lowest three layers, physical, data link and network. We discussed both the WAN and LAN variants. In fact the CONS was the only aspect of these network-dependent layers which received early attention. Early effort on defining services and protocols centred on building a framework above the CONS, with the urgent aim of defining a framework for use over X.25 networks; such areas as the data link service definition only recently received detailed consideration.

In this part we discuss the host layers: transport, session and presentation, together with the 'application support' sublayer. Together, these aim to provide both network independence and a resilient framework for use by the various applications which have been, or are currently being, defined. We will look at specific applications in part five.

The astute reader will have noticed that an application sublayer is referred to. In fact the application layer has a split personality. According to the application layer structure (draft international) standard {9545}, all application service elements (ASEs) have equal status, and any can make use of any other. In practice however, some have no useful role on their own, and are intended to provide support for 'genuine' ASEs such as file transfer, which implies that they are logically below such applications. We will examine this issue in more detail in chapter eighteen. Suffice it to say that much difficulty was encountered with the application layer structure, in part due to differences of opinion between experts, and also because existing CCITT telematics standards somehow had to be accommodated (some with difficulty). We will avoid describing interim proposals such as CASE which have now been superseded, and concentrate on the current position, even though some areas are still unstable.

15 The transport layer

15.1 Introduction

The transport layer has two main functions, related to *reliability* and *network independence*. Its prime function is to relieve the service user (the session layer on behalf of an application) of any concern either for how particular underlying networks operate, or for any transient problems which may arise from malfunctions or inefficiencies of such networks. In other words, the session layer can use the same procedures regardless of which networks are being used. As usual in OSI, the session layer has no knowledge whatsoever of what lies underneath the transport layer, nor how the transport layer operates. For most of the chapter we will concentrate on the connection oriented variant, where a *transport connection* (*TC*) is set up between the two hosts, spanning all of the intervening networks.

Stated more formally, the transport layer is responsible for providing the QOS required by the session layer, and this may mean that the transport protocol needs to provide additional facilities (*enhancement*) over and above what the underlying networks can offer. This could include additional error detection and correction features, transparent recovery from underlying network signalled errors (network service resets and disconnects), throughput improvements, cost reduction, and so on.

15.2 Connection oriented transport service

15.2.1 Services provided by the transport service

Before discussing the various *COTS* primitives in detail, this section summarises the general facilities which the transport service {8072} provides to the session layer.

Connection setup

This covers the establishment of a TC with another TS user for the exchange of transport service data units (TSDUs). More than one TC may be set up between the same pair of users.

QOS selection

A means is provided for requesting, negotiating and agreeing a QOS when the TC is set up. The transport layer optimises the use of the available communication resources as required in order to provide the requested QOS at minimum cost. This QOS is selected using a parameter set including the GOS parameters throughput, transit delay, residual error rate and the probability of failure of the transport connection.

Depending on the requested QOS and what can be provided by the underlying network(s), the transport layer will select a suitable transport protocol class which provides (at least) the necessary enhancement. *Five classes of transport protocol* have been defined, and they will be discussed later in the chapter. It is for the transport layer itself to decide, based on the requested and available QOS, which class of transport protocol to use (i.e. how much enhancement to provide) in order to achieve this QOS, and this is (in theory at least) an internal transport layer matter.

Reliable transmission

It is a requirement in some cases that errors signalled to the transport layer by the network layer (reset, disconnect) should where possible be corrected, transparently to the user. Errors which remain undetected at lower layers should also be corrected. This is subject to the requested QOS, and implies the selection (transparent to the users) of the appropriate transport protocol class, depending on the type of underlying network. *Three types of underlying network* have been identified.

Independence from underlying communication resources

The TS hides from its users any differences in the QOS provided by the network service; these differences may arise from the use of a variety of communication media by the network layer when providing the network service.

End-end significance

The TS provides for the transfer of data between users in end open systems. Neither the users nor the TS have any involvement in, or knowledge of, any intermediate relays which may exist in the underlying medium for the purpose of connecting different underlying networks; these are the responsibility of the network layer.

Transparency of transferred information

A means is provided for transferring TSDUs on a TC. The TS provides for the transparent transfer of user data and/or control information, which is sent as a stream of octets. A TSDU consists of an integral number of octets. Boundaries between TSDUs are preserved by the TS provider, and their content is not constrained. No restriction is placed by the TS on the coding, formatting or content of this information, nor is its structure or meaning interpreted by the TS.

TS user addressing

The TS uses a system of addressing which is mapped into the addressing scheme of the supporting NS.

TC release

A mechanism is provided for the unconditional (and hence possibly destructive) release of a TC.

15.2.2   Transport service primitives

As would be expected, a TS user communicates with the TS by exchanging a set of primitives and associated parameters across the interface. This technique should be well understood by now. The primitives will be discussed in turn, with a brief explanation of the parameters, based on the three phases of operation, connection establishment, data transfer and connection release. This discussion closely parallels that provided in chapter fourteen for the NS.

The connection establishment phase

Four primitives are used in this phase, the purpose of which is to establish a TC between end users, subject to a given QOS. The primitives (and their parameters) closely parallel the comparable NS primitives, and discussion will be restricted to the more significant differences.

T-CONNECT request, indication   called address, calling address, expedited data selection, QOS, TS user data

T–CONNECT response, confirm   responding address, expedited data selection, QOS, TS user data

The following aspects are most notable:

- The *quality of service* is specified as a *single set of parameters*, whereas two sets are provided to the network service. In the connect request, it is the QOS requested by the calling user, and any defined value is allowed. The TS may specify to the called user (in the connect indication) an equal or lower QOS, except that the requested TC protection must be the same as that requested by the calling user. The called user may once more reduce this QOS if desired (this time including the TC protection), and the value placed in the connect response by the peer transport user will be returned unchanged (by the TS) in the connect confirm.

Where the QOS is reduced by the TS provider, it may mean that

- the delay becomes longer;
- the throughput becomes lower;
- the error rate becomes higher;
- the priority becomes lower;
- the probability of failure becomes higher

than the calling user would like. The TS will only reduce the QOS if the requested one cannot be provided. Once the QOS has been agreed, it then applies for the duration of the TC.

The transport layer will indicate both 'target' and 'minimum acceptable' QOS parameter sets to the network layer, as explained in chapter fourteen. This is of no concern to, and is transparent to, the TS users, with the obvious proviso that the minimum acceptable QOS must be at least that indicated to the TS users.

- The called user (or the TS) may refuse the connection request; see below under the termination phase.

- An *expedited data selection* option is provided, as with the network service, and the mapping on to lower layers which also may provide this option should be clear. Its availability (or otherwise) is negotiated between peer users. If the calling user requests it, the called user may either accept or refuse the request, but the called user may not request the option if the calling user does not wish to use it. A different QOS may apply to expedited data. If the service is declared (by the TS) to be unavailable on the connection, it may not be used, and any subsequent expedited data primitives will be treated as normal data.

• TS *user data*. Up to 32 octets of user data may be included in T-CONNECT primitives. This compares with up to 128 octets in the equivalent network service connect primitives. This difference seems at first sight to be inconsistent. UK users are recommended to restrict the N-CONNECT user data field to a maximum of 32 octets as well.

• The *responding address* is, in the current standard, expected to be identical to the called address. The use of a different address (e.g. where generic addressing is used by the caller, and a specific instance of this address is returned by the called user) is for further study.

You will have noticed that no mention is made of a receipt confirmation option of the kind provided by the network service. How then can this option be requested, in the absence of a suitable parameter? The answer is that it does not need to be requested. The reason lies in the fact that the TS user is not concerned with whether or not the TS provider gets this confirmation; it is only interested in passing data to the TS, and knows that its correct delivery is guaranteed by the TS, except of course in the case of irrecoverable failure of the underlying network. The use or otherwise of receipt confirmation is therefore again an internal TS issue, and is of no concern to the users. On the other hand, an expedited data service may well be of interest to the users, which is why the service is provided (but again see below).

The data transfer phase

Two primitives are defined, providing normal and (optional) expedited data transfer, as follows:

T-DATA request, indication   TS user data

T-EXPEDITED-DATA   TS user data
request, indication

T-DATA primitives contain *Transport Service Data Units* or *TSDUs*. Requests are issued by the sending user, and these are transmitted to the receiving user as indications, with the same data content. Since the TS undertakes to preserve the integrity, sequence and boundaries of TSDUs, no acknowledgement functions are provided for the TS users.

Recovery from data loss, duplication or corruption is an internal TS matter, except that the TC may be disconnected as a last resort if the underlying NC cannot be recovered without violating the requested QOS (e.g. within a certain time; see under termination phase below). Where a N-

DISCONNECT or N-RESET originating from the service provider is received, either the loss is recovered transparently to the service user, or a T-DISCONNECT is issued. This depends on both the QOS and protocol class.

It should also be noted that T-DATA is an *unconfirmed* service, whereas the equivalent N-DATA primitive was confirmed. This is again consistent with the idea that the transport layer either guarantees delivery or will notify irrecoverable failure..

The length of a TSDU is not restricted by the standard. The requested QOS applies to complete TSDUs. The boundaries between TSDUs are preserved by the TS, so that the use of short TSDUs over networks such as X.25 could result in increased costs if the full X.25 packet length is not utilised, since the TS provider will be inhibited from applying optimum cost reduction mechanisms (such as ensuring that full X.25 packets are sent where possible).

Since any necessary underlying flow control is also an internal TS issue, the queues on which the TS is modelled are of 'unknown size', which implies that a TSDU may always be placed in a (local) queue by a TS user, with no concern for windowing issues. In practice, such a flow control mechanism will normally be needed, and this matter is discussed later. Issues not in the aegis of the TS will also restrict the flow of TSDUs, since most high level protocols involve a dialogue, and the flow of TSDUs will eventually cease pending a response from the peer user. In other words the user protocol (e.g. the session protocol) may elect to include its own peer flow control which operates above, and therefore is of no concern to, the TS. Furthermore, the impact of any underlying flow control constraints will be reflected in QOS parameters such as transit delay and throughput; at this layer, these are defined in terms of what the users see, which is not necessarily what can be achieved in the absence of flow control. The TS will lower a QOS request (such as throughput) which cannot be achieved using the underlying mechanisms in conjunction with any enhancement provided.

Expedited data transfer is again an option. The expedited primitives are unavailable unless their use has been agreed by both users during the connection establishment phase.

The connection release phase

Two disconnect primitives are used, which closely parallel those provided by the network service:

T-DISCONNECT request   TS user data

T–DISCONNECT indication   disconnect reason, TS user data

- The *request* may be issued by either user wishing to terminate the TC, or by the called user to refuse a connect request.

- The *indication* is transmitted to the peer user in response to a disconnect request, or may be issued to the calling user in response to a connect request, if the TS itself is unable to set up the TC. If the TS is forced to terminate the connection in the data transfer phase (see under reasons below), an indication will be sent to both users. In the case where the underlying network fails catastrophically, this will be after the best attempts of the TS to restore the connection have failed. (How hart the transport entity tries depends on the agreed QOS, which in turn determines the transport protocol class used.)

It should be noted that the connection release service is unconfirmed. There is no need for a reply confirmation from the peer, as both users will be aware of the disconnection. If the disconnect request becomes lost or garbled in the network, it is the responsibility of the TS to take the necessary steps to recover the associated TPDU. If this proves impossible, the transport layer will eventually issue a disconnect indication to the peer for a different reason (network failure).

This does not preclude both users from simultaneously issuing a disconnect request. Neither will be relayed to the peer users, since the other user would gain no additional information from receiving a disconnect indication. This implies that the reason provided by the user will be lost.

The *disconnect reason* indicates why the TC has been closed, from the following list:

- Invoked by the remote TS user.

- Invoked by the TS provider. This may be at connection setup time, or at any time in the data transfer phase if, despite its best attempts, the transport entity is unable to establish or maintain the connection for any of the following (or other) reasons:

  - No TS resources are available (local or remote).

  - The obtainable QOS is below the minimum level acceptable to the user(s).

  - The TS provider (i.e. an underlying network) has 'misbehaved'.

  - A reset has been received, and the protocol class in use has no facilities for recovering any lost data. (It is invalid to pass the reset to the service user.)

- The called TS user is unavailable or unknown.

- Unknown reason. (This is a somewhat unhelpful category which is generally included in such cases for completeness).

In practice, the transport and session layers will normally be implemented in the same host, and they may also be combined in a real implementation. In this case, it is most likely that if a TS user fails, this will have an impact on the local TS as well. This is however an implementation issue.

15.3 Connection oriented transport protocol

15.3.1 Introduction

The **COTP** {8073} operates between peer transport entities, and uses the facilities of the underlying network service, in particular the set of network service primitives. The transport protocol is designed to provide users with consistent procedures when using underlying networks of different qualities, and to this end *five protocol classes* are defined. The class of protocol to be used is negotiable between peer transport entities, based in part on the QOS requested by the transport service users, but is transparent to these users, and therefore does not form part of the transport service discussed above. This discussion relates to the connection orientated transport protocol {8073}; a companion connectionless protocol exists {8602}, but performs only one function, that of providing additional error checking and detection. The transport protocol also defines the structure of *transport protocol data units* or **TPDUs**. TPDUs are exchanged between peer transport entities, and these may be transmitted using packets or frames depending on the underlying network.

15.3.2 Types of underlying network

The transport layer is envisaged as being capable of operating over three different *types of network connection* (i.e. types of underlying network), which are distinguished by the way in which they handle (or do not handle) various types of error:

- **Type A**. The residual error rate (i.e. errors not signalled by reset or disconnect) on this type of connection is deemed to be acceptably low, so that special procedures to handle them are not required. The rate of signalled errors is also *acceptably low*. This could be said to constitute a 'reliable' network which does not generate (a significant number of) unsolicited resets or disconnects.

• **Type B**. The residual error rate is again acceptably low, but the rate at which errors are signalled (by reset or disconnect) is unacceptably high, so that procedures will be required to recover from these. This could be said to constitute a reliable network with an acceptably low undetected error rate, so that additional error detection procedures are not required, but one which nevertheless signals a sufficient proportion of errors to the transport layer to require the provision of additional facilities to recover from network generated resets and disconnects.

• **Type C**. The residual error rate on these connections is unacceptably high, and additional error detection and correction facilities will therefore normally be required. In this context, the rate at which detected errors are signalled is irrelevant, and recovery procedures will be needed as well. This covers 'unreliable' networks which fail to report a significant proportion of errors. Leaving aside the connectionless issue, pure datagram networks which simply discard corrupted packets without comment could be said to exhibit type C characteristics.

In the second edition of this book it was stated that LANs could be classified as type A, X.25 networks as type B, and datagram networks as type C. After all this seems sensible, as LANs are very reliable, and X.25 networks can generate signalled resets and disconnects. Unfortunately this is not how many practitioners see things. The crucial issue is precisely what 'acceptably low' means, particularly for such things as resets from networks such as X.25. Unfortunately, like QOS, this is a grey area which defies neat classification. Partly for historical reasons, CCITT telematic services (e.g. MHS, teletex) operate over X.25 as if it is a type A network. Protocols over LANs generally treat them as type C, not because they are unreliable, but because of the tendency to use connectionless services in LANs (i.e. for them to be used as datagram networks). Operational practice thus distorts the above classifications. So it may be better simply to think of the facilities provided by the various protocol classes, rather than attempt to relate these to network types as defined in the standard. In addition there is an application entity (RTSE; chapter eighteen) which can recover from signalled errors if the transport protocol fails to do so. There is a further aside on this matter in §15.4.3.

A given network (service) can be classified as belonging to one of the above types using QOS criteria. (Or as the above aside suggests, little or no notice can be taken of this.) It is assumed that either the transport station can deduce which type a given network connection is, and make an appropriate choice of protocol class (if more than one network is available), or that it will be connected to a specific network and use a specific class as agreed in some

OSI profile (see chapter twenty three). In fact the class of protocol is in theory negotiable between transport entities.

15.3.3   Transport protocol classes

Five protocol classes are provided, as follows:

- Class 0 (TP0): simple class.
- Class 1 (TP1): basic error recovery class.
- Class 2 (TP2): multiplexing class.
- Class 3 (TP3): error recovery and multiplexing class.
- Class 4 (TP4): error detection and recovery class.

What follows is a brief outline of the functions of each protocol class. It is not the intention in this book to discuss the transport protocol in great detail. Some aspects are very complex, and some decisions seem to have been made for political or historical, rather than technical, reasons. In any case there is not the space to do the subject full justice. A summary of the facilities provided by the various protocol classes is provided in §15.3.4.

TP0 - simple class

This is the simplest class, and hence the easiest to describe. It is assumed that the underlying network is inherently reliable. Therefore TP0 is intended for use over type A network connections, and no additional error handling facilities are provided over and above those available in the network service. This class of procedure is compatible with CCITT Teletex recommendation T.70. (The teletex service is briefly discussed in chapters twenty two and twenty three.)

TP0 provides for transport connections using only the underlying network flow control mechanisms. Disconnection of the transport connection relies solely on the underlying network service disconnection primitives, and unsolicited disconnects and resets will be rare. In the event of either disconnect or reset, the connection will be terminated.

It is a general requirement that TP0 must be provided by all open system implementations. (Other conformance requirements tend to depend on the country involved.)

TP1 - basic error recovery class

TP1 provides a basic transport connection with minimal overheads. The main facility provided is *recovery from unsolicited network disconnects or resets*, as far as possible without involving the users. This class was originally intended for use with type B network connections (which in theory includes X.25), but few implementations of this class exist, TP0 being more commonly used.

Where recovery from loss of data (due to a network reset) or a failed network connection is necessary, this is done without involving the transport user (the session entity), except that the user must be informed if recovery proves to be impossible even after the best attempts of the transport entity.

TP2 - multiplexing class

This class provides a means of *multiplexing* a number of transport connections on to a single network connection. Like TP0, it is intended for use above type A network connections. In the context of X.25, several application 'conversations' between the same pair of hosts could share the same VC.

This class may provide optional *explicit flow control*, as may be necessary to avoid congestion at endpoints or on the network connection. The intention here is to optimise response times and resource utilisation, particularly when traffic is heavy, or multiplexing is intensive. Where explicit flow control is provided, a *credit mechanism* is defined whereby the receiver may inform the sender precisely how much transmitted data may be outstanding (unacknowledged) at any time, during the data transfer phase. Once the transport connection has been set up, TPDU sequencing and a window mechanism, coupled with transport end-end acknowledgement TPDUs, are used to control the flow of data in each direction.

The philosophy behind this scheme owes much to HDLC, although again the parallel is in the technique rather than in the scope of application. A reject TPDU is also available, which may be used in a manner analogous to the HDLC REJ; it requests the retransmission of one or more outstanding TPDUs. Again following X.25 practice, there is no transport protocol equivalent of the HDLC SREJ supervisory command. An initial credit (in each direction) is provided at transport connection setup time; this credit may be zero, but provision is made for the credit to be varied if required, during the data transfer phase.

Expedited data transfer is permitted, but only if explicit flow control is provided.

TP3 - error recovery and multiplexing class

TP3 combines TP2 facilities with those of TP1. In other words, it provides for multiplexing over type B network connections, with recovery from unsolicited resets and disconnects. Neither TP2 nor TP3 has many implementations at present.

TP4 - error detection and recovery class

This class combines the characteristics of TP3 with *error detection*, and is for use over type C network connections. The errors which can be detected by the transport service include the loss, mis-sequencing, duplication and corruption of TSDUs, of both data and control types. Recovery from unsolicited resets and disconnects is of course provided as well.

This error detection may be achieved by the use of sequence numbering as provided in TP2 and TP3, by timeout mechanisms, and by 'additional procedures'. A *checksum* mechanism is available as a means of providing error checking, but its use is an option, negotiable between peer transport entities.

Additional facilities provided include *splitting* of a TC over several NCs, which can provide greater resilience over networks which cannot be relied on not to lose connections. This is in effect the reverse of multiplexing as offered by TP2.

15.3.4   Implementation of the transport protocol

The elements of the transport protocol are now briefly, and somewhat incompletely, discussed in relation to the network service primitives already discussed.

The protocol relies on the use of a number of **transport protocol data units (TPDUs)**, which have standard abbreviations. We will not be discussing these in any great detail, but a list is provided in figure 15.1 for reference in the following discussion.

Assignment to network connection

This assignment mechanism is used in all classes of procedure to assign transport connections (TCs) to NCs. A CR is relayed to the called transport station, which may respond with a CC (success) or a DR (failure). The underlying network primitives for setting up a NC are used to convey these TSDUs. Where appropriate (depending on the class), an existing network connection may be used for this purpose.

TPDU NAME	PARAMETERS
CR connection request	credit, DST_ref, src_ref, class/option, parameters, user data (note 1)
CC connection confirm	credit, DST_ref, src_ref, class/option, parameters, user data (note 1)
DR disconnect request	DST_ref, src_ref, reason, [checksum,] user data (note 2)
DC disconnect confirm (not used in TP0)	DST_ref, src_ref, reason[, checksum]
DT data	[DST_ref,] seq number, end of sequence marker, [parameters,] user data
ED expedited data (note 3)	DST_ref, seq number, [checksum,] user data (max 16 octets)
AK data acknowledge	credit, DST_ret, ack, parameters
EA expedited ack	DST_ref, ack[, checksum]
RJ reject	credit, DST_ref, ack
ER TPDU error	DST_ref, reject cause, invalid TPDU [,checksum]

NOTEs:
1   User data not allowed in TP0, otherwise max 32 octets.
2   User data not allowed in TP0, otherwise max 64 octets.
3   ED unavailable unless service selected. Not available in TP0 or in TP2 without explicit flow control.

Figure 15.1 - transport protocol data units

TPDU transfer

This is possible once the connection has been completely set up. DT, ED, AK, EA and RJ TPDUs are sent using network service data and expedited primitives, but of course ED and EA TPDUs may only be sent if the expedited option is being used. Since all TPDUs have defined formats and parameters, including a length parameter (which will however not be discussed here), they can be concatenated. TSDUs may also be segmented, i.e. spread over two or more TPDUs as necessary.

Transport connection release

The TC will be released when it is no longer required by the session entity. The release can be either normal or as a result of an error. There are two ways in which a connection can be released, as follows:

• *Normal release* is used by all classes, and there are two variants, depending on the class.

• *Implicit release* is used only for TP0, and only a N-DISCONNECT is used, since no additional facilities are provided in this class of procedure.

• TP1-4 rely on *explicit release*, where DR and DC TPDUs are first exchanged using N-DATA primitives. The subsequent release or otherwise of the associated NC (using N-DISCONNECT primitives) is at the discretion of the transport station, and does not concern the user of the transport service.

In theory at least, the session entity user can re-use the transport connection for a new session connection. There are however some problems in relation to this, which are discussed in the next chapter.

• *Error release* is required only in TP0 and TP2, and occurs if a network reset or disconnect is received, since there is no provision for recovery of the transport connection for these classes.

Credit and flow control (TP2)

During connection setup, each station proposes an *initial credit*, which determines, in effect, the maximum window width which will apply. Data and expedited data TPDUs are sequenced. Data and expedited acknowledgements contain a field, referred to in figure 15.1 as 'ack', which (as in HDLC) refers to the next expected data (or expedited data) TPDU. Imposition of credit in effect imposes an HDLC-like window limit, which can be reduced (subject to various constraints) during the life of the TC.

The standard gives the sequence number fields strange-looking names, TPDU-NR and EDTPDU-NR, which may be confusing as here the NR is an abbreviation of 'number', representing a send sequence count, quite the reverse of the similar sounding N(R) used to represent receive sequence counts in HDLC. Acknowledgements in the transport protocol are given equally strange names YR-TU-NR and YR-EDTU-NR. (YR is short for 'your'.)

Checksum mechanism (TP4)

In figure 15.1, you will see that every primitive has either an optional checksum field, or a 'parameters' field. Where no explicit checksum is indicated, this will be one of the optional parameters, of which many are defined. TP4 allows any TPDU to be protected by an additional checksum field, which is in addition to anything similar which may be provided by the underlying network. Note that this is an option, and it would be pointless specifying checksums over an ultra-reliable LAN with a good FCS check, as nothing would be gained. However there would be every reason to use checksums over a BSC network.

Negotiable options

Various options may be negotiated during connection establishment, of which the checksum facility mentioned above is only one. There are various constraints on negotiation, some of which are inherent in the protocol class to be used, and others in what is required by the application (e.g. use of expedited data) or available in the underlying networks (e.g. whether the error detection algorithm is adequate). Figure 15.2 summarises the main negotiable options, including the valid protocol classes in which they may be used. (Negotiation of protocol class is covered in §15.4.3).

Negotiation of options follows a familiar pattern:

- In the CR (connection request), the initiator may propose the use of some optional facility.

- If use of the facility is proposed, the recipient may either agree, or refuse, to use the facility, and this decision (which is binding on the initiator) is returned to the originator in the CC (connection confirm).

- If the facility is not proposed in the CR, it cannot be specified in the CC. In other words negotiation is always downwards.

- In the case of the *checksum* and *explicit flow control* optional facilities, the negotiation is to agree not to use the facility rather than to agree to use it. In other words the facility is assumed to be required unless the peer transport entities agree otherwise. The reason for this in the case of the checksum is that over networks with weak error checking, failure to add a checksum could result in the connection request or confirm TPDUs being corrupted unknown to the transport entity. It would therefore be prudent for the transport entity to protect at least the connection request.

OPTION	APPLICABLE PROTOCOL CLASSES
transport expedited data transfer	1 2 3 4
use of receipt confirmation	1
use of network expedited	1
checksum use (note 2)	4
explicit flow control (note 2)	2
use of extended formats	2 3 4

NOTEs:

1   If the network expedited option is not used, any transport expedited data will be sent in normal network data packets, and will thus get no priority in the network.

2   Negotiate not to use; see the text above.

Figure 15.2 - negotiable transport protocol options

15.4   Transport service supporting addenda

The following notable additions were made to the standard, and were subsequently incorporated as addenda.

15.4.1   Connectionless mode

This addendum {8072 ADD1} defines a minimal unacknowledged datagram service. The service definition offers a single primitive type as follows:

T-UNITDATA request, indication   called address, calling address, QOS, TS user data

In addition there is a minimal protocol specification {8602} which offers a single value-added service, checksums. This can improve the error detection on TPDUs (datagrams) which arrive, but as it is an unconfirmed service, there is no guarantee that TPDUs will arrive at all, or in the same order in which they were transmitted. In this context, checksums can only improve the chance that what arrives is error free; they cannot increase the proportion of arrivals.

15.4.2 Network connection management sub-protocol

The aim here {8073 ADD1} is to provide for greater flexibility in the re-establishment of failed network connections than was possible using the original standard, which specified only rudimentary procedures for handling such failures. Further details will not be provided.

15.4.3 Conformance issues and protocol class negotiation

The fact that five different protocol classes exist has potentially serious implications for network designers, particularly when it is also realised that some classes include various options as well (not all of which have been discussed above). This raises an obvious question. To what extent will the various transport layer implementations, each possibly providing a different selection of classes and options, be able to interwork? ISO has of course long been aware of this potential problem, and the protocol specification includes rules which allow the initiating transport entity to specify (in the CR PDU) both a *preferred class* and an *alternative class*. The alternative class is optional, but if it is provided, a certain amount of *negotiation* of protocol class is possible, the *agreed class* being returned in the CC PDU. While the rules are quite complex, the net effect of implementing the full negotiation rules is to define two mutually incompatible protocol class subsets as follows:

- Any implementation supporting TP1 must be capable of negotiating down to TP0.

- Any implementation supporting TP3 or TP4 must be able to negotiate down to TP2.

This appears to leave the way open for incompatible implementations. In fact the rules governing which alternative classes can be negotiated down to are more complex than that, and if a given class is stated to be preferred, any lower class (or none at all) can be specified as the alternative. However this does not necessarily mean that any protocol class lower than the preferred one can be used. For example, if TP3 is preferred and TP2 is the alternative, either TP3 or TP2 can be used, but not TP1 or TP0. However if TP1 is specified as the alternative, any of classes TP3 down to TP0 can be used.

This seems to be getting rather out of hand, and additional guidance was required. For this reason, the transport protocol specification now includes a *conformance statement* {8073 DAD3}, since it is clearly desirable to have a class and options set which all implementations can be guaranteed to support. The conformance requirement basically states that any conforming implementation should support either TP0, or TP2 with explicit flow control, or both (these being the two most popular choices of ISO member organisations). A choice of maximum TPDU size is also made available, conforming implementations being allowed to select from maximum sizes of 128, 256, 512, 1024, 2048, 4096 and 8192 octets; they must also being able to support any TPDU length less than the chosen maximum value. The conformance statement further requires the following:

- If TP1 is implemented, then TP0 must also be implemented.

- If TP3 or TP4 is implemented, then TP2 must be implemented as well.

These are not really restrictions, as TP4 incorporates the functionality of TP3 and TP2, and TP0 has minimal functionality.

- Suppliers of transport systems must state explicitly which class(es) of procedure, and options, are supported, be they implicit or explicit.

This leaves just two mutually incompatible implementation groups, those which support TP0 (with or without TP1), and those which support TP2 (with or without TP3 and TP4). It may also be possible in some cases for incompatible endpoint transport stations to 'negotiate down' to a lower, mutually acceptable, class of service, e.g. from TP3 to TP0.

But that is not the end of the matter. While this is better than a free for all, it is clearly not entirely satisfactory. In 1984, ITSU published a technical guide[1] in which it was recommended that UK implementors should provide both TP0 and TP2 in transport service implementations. In the event this advice was overtaken by events. For a historical discussion of what happened in practice see the following aside (which makes numerous forward references to material not yet covered). Transport protocol class negotiation is in effect now superseded by the requirements of various *OSI profiles*, including TOP, MAP, and the UK and US Government OSI Profiles (GOSIPs), all of which are discussed in chapter twenty three. These define the services and protocols required throughout the OSI protocol stack, including which transport protocol class should be used, to support various applications. In this context, only those class(es) need to be implemented which are consistent with the applications to be used on that host for the relevant OSI profile. In practice only TP0 and TP4 have received significant support. (If you read the aside which follows, you will see that there is still scope for incompatibilities.)

CCITT developed telematic services before the transport and upper layers were stable. MHS (chapter twenty two) and Teletex usage is consistent with TP0, even though it is used over X.25 networks, because no transport layer was catered for in the original MHS and Teletex proposals, and this is in effect tantamount to using TP0. Indeed TP0 was designed to be compatible with the (rudimentary) Teletex transport protocol. This left MHS with a problem. If an X.25 network decided to issue a reset, this could not be corrected by TP0, and the application would be unceremoniously disconnected. (There is no T-RESET primitive). But even if a transport protocol class is used which can recover from unsolicited disconnects, there are some severe errors which no transport protocol could recover from. In short, MHS cannot rely on the integrity of the underlying connection, and additional procedures are required. CCITT's solution to this dilemma was to define what they termed 'reliable transfer' (RTS) procedures in the application layer, which subsequently matured into the RTSE ASE {9066} discussed in chapter eighteen. Therefore RTSE is used as an application layer guarantee of delivery. In case of failure, RTSE will recover the failed underlying connection and try again, and will only give up as a last resort. Other applications such as FTAM (chapter nineteen) are also being implemented in the UK and some other countries over TP0 and X.25 (although FTAM uses CCR rather than RTSE). Unfortunately that is not the end of the matter. There are notable differences in philosophy between Europe and North America on whether connection oriented or connectionless mode procedures should be the norm, as well as what protocol classes should be used over different types of network. Thus US GOSIP advocates the use of TP4 over X.25 for FTAM, leaving TP0 only for MHS.

15.5   General transport layer issues

The release of a transport connection, be it by the user or the service provider, is not graceful. When a disconnect request is issued (or a disconnect indication is received), any data in transit will be lost, as will any user data in a disconnect primitive which has not been completely received. It is for the higher layer protocol (e.g. the session layer using negotiated release; see the next chapter) to ensure, by means of any necessary handshaking, that the data has all reached its destination, before issuing a disconnect request. (For example, see the session service negotiated release, discussed in the next chapter.) Facilities for negotiated release are used by several applications.

Another issue relates to the transmission of expedited data. The TS guarantees that any expedited data will be delivered before any normal data received after it, although it will not interrupt a normal data TSDU which is in the process of transmission across the interface to the user. Where possible, preferential treatment will be given to expedited data by (logical) reordering of TS queues. Unfortunately, we have seen that the service may well not be available at lower layers. Therefore all that this really means in many cases is that expedited data will not be overtaken by normal data, and where there is no underlying expedited mechanism, expedited data may well get no preferential treatment at all below the transport service. In fact there are three possible scenarios, depending on whether expedited data was requested, the class of protocol selected, and the characteristics of the underlying network, as follows:

- It is not required, or was requested and is unavailable. In this case it cannot be used.

- It was requested and the protocol class can support it, but the underlying networks cannot. In this case it will be distinguished by using ED TPDUs, but these will use the underlying normal data channel. In this case EA TPDUs must rely on the normal acknowledgement procedures (e.g. X.25 P(R) numbers), which can be a problem as only one EA can be outstanding at a time (in a given direction).

- Only in the most favourable case can an underlying expedited channel be used for ED TPDUs.

At this point, you may well argue that expedited data can 'jump the queue' in the transport station. Possibly this might be the case, but the queue is a logical rather than a physical entity, and in practice the 'queue' might be physically distributed throughout the underlying network, making a generalised definition of queue jumping rather difficult. In cases where the interface between the user and provider consists of host buffers, then clearly the provider may be able to extract expedited units out of sequence. In practice however, an effective expedited data service is difficult or impossible to implement in most underlying networks, and therefore the service is not likely to be very useful. UK users have been advised to avoid using the expedited data transfer option where possible.

This also implies that it will be meaningless to request expedited data transfer over a TP0 transport connection, and indeed this is not allowed. However this class may be appropriate if it is known that the users will never request the expedited data service. Apart from the VT (Virtual Terminal) standard (chapter twenty one), no specific use has been found for expedited in application standards. This is probably just as well, since using TP0 over X.25 means that no use of X.25 interrupt packets is possible, as TP0 does not permit expedited data transfer.

No flow control mechanisms between the user and its local TS are specified in the transport service definition. It is felt that these cannot be suitably specified in an abstract manner without placing undue constraints on implementors. However flow control is possible within the transport protocol, and local flow control over the user-provider interface will normally be required, and this can be exercised in a number of ways, for example:

- By a 'stop-go' mechanism (similar to RR and RNR in HDLC) across the interface.

- By restricting the buffer space available in the TS provider for user data awaiting transmission; when the buffers become full, it will become physically impossible to issue any more primitives until buffers become free.

- By requiring local acknowledgement of TSDUs (primitives) exchanged across the interface, and applying a window mechanism to these local exchanges.

Which if any of these can be applied in a real case depends on internal host implementation issues, which are beyond the scope of the reference model (and of this book).

15.6   The transport layer compared with YBTS

In chapter nine we briefly examined the UK academic interim Yellow Book Transport Service (YBTS). Given its name, it is instructive to compare it with the OSI transport service, to see to what extent it may be compatible. It is not worth devoting too much time to this comparison however, as we shall soon see that it is utterly incompatible. YBTS was conceived before any significant work on OSI/RM, let alone the OSI transport service, had even begun, and there is therefore no reason why it should have been compatible.

YBTS had the specific task of providing an interface to X.25(1980) and the Cambridge Ring (CR) which would appear the same to NIFTP above it, regardless of which network was actually being used. In fact, despite its initial claim to be 'network independent' (the original name was Network Independent Transport Service, NITS), it was closely tied in to what could be provided by X.25(1980), which was currently being specified by CCITT. When YBTS is compared with the OSI transport service, a number of fundamental differences are immediately apparent:

- There is no connectionless variant. In itself this is not an incompatibility, as there was no connectionless version of the OSI transport service initially.

- While an expedited data service is in theory available in YBTS, there is no way in which it can be negotiated, which implies that it is always available. But no expedited data service is available in CR, and the interrupt packets in X.25(1980) could only contain a single octet of data, and had to be acknowledged before the next could be sent, so that they were of little or no use in any case. Therefore the expedited service was never used.

• YBTS also makes use of features of X.25 which are not OSI-compatible. It uses the M-bit to link together transport service data primitives, and the Q-bit to distinguish transport service data from other primitives. Neither is a valid OSI transport service function.

• YBTS does not just operate between end hosts. In addition it is implemented in gateways (relays) between networks. This is definitely a network layer function. Initially YBTS contained an address primitive, so that YBTS addresses could be transformed at gateways between naming domains. It ultimately operated over a single naming domain controlled by NRS (the Name Registration Service), making this primitive redundant. However YBTS never provided genuine endpoint (TSAP) addressing in the OSI sense.

• YBTS in theory supports the QOS concept, but in practice it was never defined, and no means was specified for QOS negotiation. This resulted in a 'default' value always being specified, which was not useful.

• Perhaps the most fundamental flaw however was the failure of YBTS to provide any enhancement of the underlying network QOS. In the OSI sense, it is a very badly behaved transport service. It passes resets directly to the layer above via a reset primitive, which is absolutely banned in OSI. It provides no mechanisms for recovering from disconnects from the service provider, a facility which is available in most transport protocol classes. It also offers no recovery procedures whatsoever for handling data loss, so that delivery confirmation is impossible. In the X.25 context, it cannot make use of the D-bit negotiation provided in X.25(1984/1988).

Having said that, we have already seen that if TP0 is used over X.25, the same will happen there, except that reset will be converted to disconnect. The difference is that there is an OSI application service (RTSE) which is specifically provided for this purpose. It is not left to the OSI equivalent of NIFTP (FTAM).

The best that can be said for YBTS is that it provides something close to TP0, but even then it misbehaves, as TP0 converts a received reset into a disconnect, whereas YBTS passes on the reset. It appears that YBTS is little more than a thin shell over the network service. But even as a network service it is deficient, as the network service allows negotiation of receipt confirmation and expedited data, and also supports QOS negotiation; YBTS does none of these.

In the OSI context, YBTS is therefore an irrelevance, and we had better forget about it, as indeed the UK academic community decided to do some years ago. We will compare NIFTP with the OSI FTAM application in chapter nineteen, where it will become apparent that the inadequacy of

YBTS forced NIFTP to perform functions belonging to every OSI layer from the transport layer upwards. It is already becoming obvious that NIFTP will not be OSI-compatible either.

15.7 Reference

1   'Intercept Recommendations for the Transport Layer', TG 102/1, UK Department of Trade and Industry (March 1984).

16   The session layer

16.1   Background

The *connection oriented session service* (*COSS*) {8326} provides a *session connection* (*SC*) between peer presentation entities, providing various degrees of enhancement over the underlying transport connection which will be discussed in the next section. This layer is particularly involved in providing various mechanisms for *structuring* the data sent on a transport connection. It can segment the data stream into *activities* with defined bounds, and can provide *synchronisation points* (data markers) which can be acknowledged, and to which the session can be 'rolled back' in the event of problems arising. The session layer can also provide for negotiated release of a session, i.e. only with the prior permission of both applications on the connection. We will discuss the COSS in some detail in this chapter.

In theory the session service user is the presentation layer. In practice, the presentation layer has few functions of its own other than those concerned with the encoding of application data and control information, and 'passes through' most session service primitives to the application layer. Therefore the presentation layer may be considered to be rather like a library of data encoding routines, applying various prearranged formats to the application data. Therefore in practice it is the application layer which is the effective user of the session service.

The enhancement which COSS provides over COTS is implemented by the *connection oriented session protocol* (*COSP*) {8327}. This is even more complex than the transport protocol, and will only briefly be examined.

A connectionless variant also exists {8326 DAD3, 9548}. However this has no value added functions, its only purpose being to map presentation service unitdata primitives on to the corresponding transport service primitives. Therefore we will not discuss this any further. In a typical implementation it will probably not even exist in its own right.

The evolution of the session layer was a somewhat painful process, involving adaptation of previous work by both ECMA and CCITT, together with input from ISO and the need to provide session services which would be useful to applications, most of which had yet to be specified! Not surprisingly the result is a somewhat motley assortment of facilities, rather like a menu from which applications can select what is appropriate to their needs. Two addenda, unlimited user data and symmetric synchronisation, discussed later in the chapter, had to be developed because the original session layer specification proved inadequate for some applications' needs. A very interesting technical guide published some years ago[1] provides an insight into the decision making behind the provision of the various mechanisms, and why some of the facilities provided by the session layer may seem either strange or restrictive. A technical guide published by ITSU[2] in 1989 contains further clarifying information. As a general rule, it is unlikely that any particular host open system will need to provide every session layer function; this is dependent on which functions are required by the particular applications to be supported, and different applications use different subsets of the session service.

16.2 The session service

The session service (SS) {8326} provides the means for organised and synchronised data exchange between SS users (e.g. presentation entities). Means are provided for users to:

- establish a *session connection* (*SC*) with another user, to use it to exchange data in a (possibly) synchronised manner, and to release the connection in an orderly manner when it is no longer required;

- negotiate the ownership of tokens which are may be used to control the direction of data flow, to insert synchronisation points, to effect synchronisation, and to propose the release the connection;

- establish synchronisation points within the dialogue and, in the event of errors, resume the dialogue from an agreed synchronisation point;

- interrupt a dialogue and restart it later at a prearranged point.

16.2.1 General concepts

This outline of functions clearly requires considerable further explanation. The basic concepts discussed in this section are crucial to an understanding of the session service. It should be noted that what are described here are merely a set of *mechanisms* which a particular application may, or may not, wish to use. We will go on to discuss the service in more detail in §16.2.2.

Functional units

The facilities offered by the session service are grouped into *functional units* (*FUs*), which can be combined to provide services tailored to the requirements of particular applications. A number of FUs are defined in the standard, and their functions are summarised below.

The original draft standard also defined *subsets* of FUs, including *basic combined subset, basic synchronisation subset* and *basic activity subset*. No subsets are defined in the current standard, which (implicitly) leaves it for particular implementations to decide on what subsets to define, based on which applications will be used on that particular host. This is mainly because each application in effect requires its own peculiar subset.

- **Kernel**. This provides the basic (and minimal) session service functions of SC establishment and release, and also handles abort conditions where the connection is abruptly terminated. This FU must be used.

- **Half duplex**. This provides for *two way alternate* (*TWA*) data exchange, when required.

- **Duplex**. This provides for *two way simultaneous* (*TWS*) data exchange. Either the half duplex or duplex FU must be used, but not both on the same SC.

- **Negotiated release**. This provides for agreement between the users on the release of an SC. One user will propose release; if the other user does not agree, the SC remains connected.

- **Minor and major synchronisation**. This allows the specification and acknowledgement of synchronisation points, placed in the data stream as determined by the application.

- **Resynchronisation**. This provides for agreement on the use of a previous synchronisation point as a restart point.

- **Activity management**. This provides for identifying, starting, ending, suspending and restarting activities. The concept of an activity is discussed in detail below.

- **Expedited data transfer**. Expedited data will, in theory, be able to overtake normal data. In practice this depends on whether the underlying network(s) can support expedited data. If not, it may still be possible to specify expedited data, but it will be indistinguishable from normal data in the network layer, and will therefore be subject to the same flow control blockages as normal data. This matter is discussed in more detail in §16.3.3.

Some session service primitives, e.g. those of an 'urgent' nature, are sent (using the connection oriented session protocol, COSP) as transport expedited data whenever possible. The main reason for using expedited data in this case is so that any flow control blockages which may be suffered by normal data can be bypassed; it may be these blockages which triggered the need to send the 'urgent message' in the first place. What happened if 'urgent' SPDUs got blocked as well, due to the unavailability of expedited data transfer mechanisms, caused much discussion among experts.

- **Exceptions**. This FU provides for the reporting of exception (i.e. error) information from the service provider (the transport layer). It could for example report the receipt of an unsolicited T-DISCONNECT when TP0 was being used by the transport layer.

Tokens

Tokens are attributes of SCs which are dynamically assigned to (i.e. become the property of) one SS user at a time. *Ownership of the token* confers the *exclusive right to perform some action* on the owner, which retains this exclusive right until it passes the token to the peer station. The station may voluntarily relinquish one or more tokens (or all tokens it currently owns), or it may be instructed to do so by its peer.

Four tokens are defined, as follows:

- The *data transfer* token, required to send normal data in half duplex mode.

- The *release* token, allowing this station to propose the release of the SC.

- The *synchronise-minor* token, allowing this station to issue minor synchronisation points.

- The *major/activity* token, allowing this station to issue major synchronisation points, or to start or end (or otherwise alter the status of) an activity. (The concept of an activity is discussed below and in §16.2.2.)

A token will always be in one of two states:

- A token is said to be *available* if one of the users possesses it. In this case it is said to be *assigned* to that user, and *not assigned* to the other user. For example in half duplex data transfer, the data token will be assigned to each user in turn. Hence the data token controls the direction of data transmission in half duplex (TWA) mode.

- The token is said to be *not available* if it is not assigned to either user. This can mean one of two things, depending on which token is involved.

- In the case of the *data transfer and release tokens*, both users may now use the service without restriction, i.e. data transfer can be full duplex, and either station may unconditionally release the SC.

- In the case of the *synchronisation and activity* tokens, the service itself will be unavailable unless and until the token is assigned to a user.

Synchronisation and dialogue units

The session service provides a number of mechanisms which allow the connection to be *structured*. Figure 16.1 shows the different ways in which an SC can be structured.

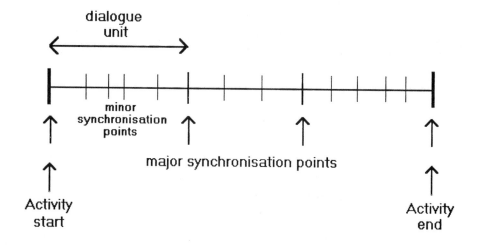

Figure 16.1 - activities, dialogue units and synchronisation points

Provided that the synchronise FU has been selected, the user owning the relevant token may insert synchronisation points into the data it is transmitting (a technique similar to that used in NIFTP, discussed briefly in chapter nine). Each synchronisation point is identified by a **Synchronisation Point Serial Number** (abbreviated in this chapter, though not in the standard itself, to *SPSN*), which is maintained by the session layer. There are two types of synchronisation point:

- A **major synchronisation point** is used to structure the data exchange into **dialogue units**. Communication within a dialogue unit is entirely separate from that of other dialogue units. (For example a dialogue unit might be used to transmit an entire file in a file transfer; it is for applications to decide how to use them). Each major synchronisation point separates two dialogue units (or ends the last dialogue unit in a session), and must be explicitly confirmed before a new dialogue unit can be started.

- On the other hand a *minor synchronisation point* is used to provide a *data marker* within a dialogue unit, by means of which the data exchange may be structured (in a manner which is entirely determined by the application layer). There may be several minor synchronisation points within a dialogue unit. They are not necessarily confirmed explicitly, i.e. acknowledgement windowing can be used, with several SPSNs outstanding at any time. (Clearly the acknowledgement of a major synchronisation point must mean that all preceding minor ones are acknowledged as well.)

Activities

An *activity* is a concept much favoured by CCITT, and used for example by the MHS application (see chapter twenty two). An activity may be considered to be some distinct logical operation which the SS user wishes to perform. Only one activity may be in progress on a given SC at any time, although an activity may consist of any number of dialogue units. For example in MHS, an activity is used to encapsulate a message transfer together with the return of the delivery confirmation. In this case the message and its delivery confirmation each comprise a dialogue unit within the activity. A major synchronisation point occurs at the start and end of an activity, as well as at the end of each dialogue unit.

Symmetric synchronisation

One problem with using minor synchronisation points in duplex mode is that although the data transfer itself is not under token control, the right to synchronise the data streams is controlled by a token, and this synchronisation affects both directions of transmission. It needs no great imagination to see that this is a clumsy approach. In addition, it makes it hard to implement some types of application which need both full duplex data flow and independent minor synchronisation for each direction of data flow (e.g. FTAM extensions currently under study; see chapter nineteen).

For this reason addenda have been added to the service and protocol standards {8326 ADD1, 8327 ADD1} which allow each end to synchronise independently in duplex mode, i.e. not under token control. The concepts are otherwise basically similar to normal synchronisation.

For half duplex (TWA) mode, which the great majority of applications use, the token-controlled synchronisation is entirely adequate.

Resynchronisation

Either user may resynchronise, subject to ownership of the token. Resynchronisation is typically used by applications when it appears that data may have been lost, or some error has occurred, although as usual the reason is of no concern to the session layer. The SC is reset to a defined state, tokens are reassigned, and the SPSN is set to a new value. All undelivered data is purged and is therefore lost. Three options are provided:

- *Abandon*. the SPSN is set to an unused value (e.g. higher than any used so far). This implies that the current dialogue unit is being aborted, and a new one may now be defined. This could result in discarding everything back to the last major synchronisation point, the start of the current activity, or the start of the current session (connection) according to context.

- *Restart*. The SPSN is set to any used value which is in, or at the start of, the current dialogue unit. In other words rollback cannot take place past the last major synchronisation point. In some applications, rollback may be well be to the last acknowledged (minor) SPSN, this being the latest point in the data it is known that the peer application has definitely received. In theory the SPSN to which rollback takes place should have been acknowledged (confirmed), but like the confirmation itself, this is not policed by the session layer.

  The draft version of the ISO standard contained an unfortunate typesetting error at this point which made the wording meaningless, causing some confusion at the time. This error has been corrected in the final version.

- *Set*. The SPSN may be set to any desired value. The standard does not suggest any restrictions on the new SPSN value, nor any possible usage for the facility. It is presumed that the choice of the new (next) SPSN will be of significance to the applications.

Negotiation

Negotiation between peer users is possible during SC establishment, for the following cases:

- **Functional units**. The kernel FU is always used, since this forms part of the minimal session service. Other FUs may be used subject to peer user agreement, which is negotiated in a manner broadly similar to that in the transport protocol discussed in the previous chapter. This allows peer users to 'tailor' the session service subset used to the particular needs of a given application. Some FUs are mutually exclusive, e.g. duplex and half duplex, one of which must be selected in addition to the kernel.

• **Initial token settings**. The ownership of tokens is negotiated where an agreed FU requires the use of a token. This determines if the token is to be available, and if so which user will initially own the token. In the latter case the initiator may specify that either it or the recipient should initially own the token, or it may leave the decision to the recipient.

• **Initial SPSN**. This is required if a synchronisation FU is in use (but see below), in which case negotiation is used by the users to agree an initial value for the SPSN.

Quality of service

As with any other layer, the users may specify a required QOS. This is the QOS which the transport layer must provide. The usual set of parameters is provided. In theory the transport layer will disconnect if it cannot sustain the required QOS, but in practice it can be difficult to determine whether certain aspects of the QOS are being met. The connection will certainly be lost if the transport protocol cannot re-establish a failed network connection.

Proposed quarantine service

OSI/RM included provision for a 'quarantine service' as part of the session layer function. The idea here was that the receiving session entity should be able to store received SSDUs, and these would not be released to the receiving user (application) until the sending user gave its permission.

The quarantine service never got further than an idea in OSI/RM however. There are a number of reasons. One is that there have always been more pressing issues. Another is that the session layer is already something of a 'hotch potch' of ill-assorted facilities, and adding an optional quarantine service on top would merely make it more messy still. A third, and perhaps more convincing explanation, is that the application layer contains mechanisms such as CCR (see chapter eighteen) which provide a more powerful service, so that the quarantine service is not really needed in the session layer.

16.2.2   Session service details

As with the network and transport services previously described, the service is implemented by passing S-primitives in SSDUs across the interface between the session and presentation layers. The approach used here in this chapter is to base the discussion broadly on the FUs, introducing new primitives as necessary to support the discussion. Although all primitives are covered, a number of detailed aspects of the service are 'glossed over' in the interests of space and clarity. In addition, only primitive parameters of particular interest will be discussed, although all will be listed.

Connection establishment and release, and exception reporting

This is the prime function of the *kernel* FU. SC *setup* is by means of the following primitive:

S-CONNECT request, indication, response, confirm
    SC identifier, session address(es), result, QOS, session requirements, [initial SPSN,] initial token assignments, SS user data

• The *session addresses* are the calling and called addresses in the request and indication, and the *responding* address in the response and confirm. The responding address may be a specific instance of a generic called address. Generic addressing was a later addition to the standard.

• The *session requirements* comprise the required FUs, which are subject to negotiation.

• The *result* indicates whether the connection was successfully set up, and if not, why not; this appears only in the response and confirm. (If it failed due to network problems, there may well be no response.)

• The *SS user data* length was originally restricted to 512 octets in this and many other primitives. In addition SS user data was not permitted with certain other primitives. As applications were developed which had specific PDUs which had to map on to these primitives, using SS user data to pass parameters, this upper limit became increasingly restrictive, notably given the number and complexity of parameters in the ACSE A-ASSOCIATE primitive (see chapter eighteen). Therefore addenda {8326 ADD2, 8327

ADD2} were produced allowing the transfer of ***unlimited user data*** with such primitives, and the use of the SS user data parameter with certain other primitives where previously it was not permitted. (In this chapter we show the primitives as they existed prior to unlimited user data.)

- The *initial SPSN* field allows any starting value to be proposed. It is not present if activity management is being used, as in this case it must be 1. This is one of many rather strange restrictions you will encounter in this service definition.

Similarly the primitive used to ***release*** the session connection is

S-RELEASE request, indication,   result, SS user data
response, confirm

- The *result*, present in the response and confirm only, indicates whether the release was granted. As mentioned in the previous section, if the negotiated release FU is being used, the request may only be issued by the holder of the release token, and in this case it may be refused by the recipient. If this FU is not being used, the release request may come from either service user, and must be granted.

It is also important to note that <u>the session connection is not disconnected - it is released</u>. This is because the procedure now involves more than just terminating the connection; negotiation may be required as well. In addition, release of the SC does not necessarily mean that the underlying TC will be disconnected; under certain circumstances it can be used to establish another SC (to the same destination host, of course). As we shall see in due course, when we reach the application layer the connection itself becomes known as an association, because the term now implies far more than merely a fancy virtual circuit.

The kernel is also responsible for handling ***aborts***. Either the service user (in effect the application) or the service provider (the session service) may unilaterally terminate the connection if some condition arises which makes it impossible to proceed. The application may have detected a procedural error and elected to give up, or the underlying transport connection could have been lost. Two primitives are provided; note the variant(s) used in each case:

S-U-ABORT request, indication   SS user data

S-P-ABORT indication   reason

The user data in the user abort is relayed to the peer, and may be used to inform the peer of the reason for aborting. There is no way in which the peer can reply in the same connection, as it no longer exists. The reason code in the provider abort can be 'transport disconnect' or 'protocol error'.

The other type of error handling is *exception reporting*. Two primitives are provided:

S-P-EXCEPTION-REPORT   reason
indication

S-U-EXCEPTION-REPORT   reason, SS user data
request, indication

The service provider may report either a 'protocol error' or a 'non-specific error' as the *reason*. The service user may include a reason from the following list, or may omit to specify a reason (non-specific error):

- Local service user 'receiving ability jeopardised' (could result in incorrect handling of received data).

- Local service user error.

- Sequence error (e.g. out of sequence SPSN received).

- Demand data token (e.g. the other user failed to reply to S-TOKEN-PLEASE, or never received it).

- Unrecoverable procedural error.

The receiving user acts on the exception report by resynchronising, aborting, releasing the data token or abandoning the current activity, as appropriate for the current status of the connection and the reason given. The error has to be cleared before normal service can resume.

Data transfer and primitives

We have already implied that there are both 'normal' and 'expedited' data types. It may come as a surprise to learn that there are in fact *four flavours of data* primitive. The standard format for the primitive is

S-<DATATYPE>-DATA   SS user data
request, indication

where *<DATATYPE>* has four variants, which are discussed below; as you will see, they all have defined and distinct scopes of application, and there are some very strange features indeed in some of the data types. With the exception of capability data they are all unconfirmed services.

- **Normal data** (S-DATA). This is controlled by the data token in half duplex mode. Only if the data token is held by a user can it send this type of data. In duplex mode, either user can send normal data in unlimited quantities at any time.

- **Expedited data** (S-EXPEDITED-DATA) may be sent at any time provided the underlying transport expedited option has been successfully negotiated (see chapter fifteen). The standard restricts the data field length to 14 octets (a somewhat strange limit). Unfortunately, since it is also possible for some classes of transport protocol to use network normal mode to transfer expedited data, this data will not necessarily get any preferential treatment in lower layers, and could therefore also be blocked by flow control on normal data. This issue was discussed in the previous chapter. There is an additional problem that some service primitives (e.g. for resynchronisation) are mapped on to T-EXPEDITED where possible, and implementations are generally advised to use expedited data with care.

- **Typed data** (S-TYPED-DATA). This is a somewhat eccentric service. Typed data is similar to normal data except that it can be sent when the data token is owned by the other station, i.e. against the normal data flow in half duplex mode. This is useful for applications which may wish to send a limited amount of 'control data' against the normal half duplex data flow. It is used by the VT protocol (chapter twenty one). Although the session layer cannot prevent it, it is generally considered to be unwise to attempt to use typed data in order to 'defeat' data token control. This is because some implementations may attach lower priority to it than to normal data in the interests of overall efficiency, on the basis that priority should be given to the most frequently used facilities. (VT is an exception to this general rule; see chapter twenty one.)

- **Capability data** (S-CAPABILITY-DATA). This is even more eccentric than typed data. Unlike the other data types it is a *confirmed* service, and it has the severe restriction that it can be used only if the activity FU is selected and an activity has not yet been started. There was also originally a limit of 512 octets on the data field length (which did not apply to normal or typed data, although unlimited user data removes this restriction anyway). The reason for the inclusion of capability data is basically that CCITT favour the use of activities, and they envisaged that capability data could be used to determine the capability or otherwise of the two stations to participate in an activity. The data in the response is a 'reply' to that in the request; the confirmed nature of this service implies a 'question-answer' dialogue.

To emphasise the eccentric nature of this data type, the standard even says that the data field is optional, so that it appears to be possible to issue the primitive without any data! One presumes either that this is an error, or that the mere fact that the primitive is being used might mean something to the recipient. Alternatively, it could be that a null reply to transmitted capability data is acceptable, although this is not consistent with the data being optional in the request variant as well. This data type has all the hallmarks of a fudge which was necessary in order to get the standard accepted by all interested parties. However the author is not aware of any application which actually uses S-CAPABILITY-DATA, so perhaps it doesn't really matter after all.

Token management

Initial token assignments take place at connection establishment time. Which tokens are assigned at this stage depends on which FUs are to be used on this SC. There are one or two other occasions as well when tokens can be reassigned; these are discussed in the text. At other times, tokens may be passed from one user to the other by means of various unconfirmed primitives, as follows

S-TOKEN-GIVE   tokens
request, indication

This passes one or more tokens to the peer user.

S-TOKEN-PLEASE   tokens, SS user data
request, indication

This primitive is used by a service user to request that the other user pass one or more tokens to it. Although it is called 'please', it is in fact an order which the peer must obey. It is a protocol violation to ignore the indication, if the requested token(s) are not received within a given time, an S-U-EXCEPTION-REPORT request will be issued by the peer user.

S-CONTROL-GIVE   (no parameters)
request, indication

This primitive is used when, for some reason, a service user wishes to transfer all of the tokens it owns to the other user. This is part of the *activity management* FU, but can only be used outside an activity. (This restriction is the same as that applied to capability data.) It is used by the ROSE application support service discussed in chapter eighteen.

It is worth noting that only the S-TOKEN-PLEASE primitive could originally carry data. The unlimited user data addendum removes this somewhat illogical restriction; applications might for example wish to provide some reason parameter with the S-CONTROL-GIVE.

Dialogue, synchronisation and activity management

This is perhaps the most complex aspect of the session service. Basically the data stream can be structured in two ways:

- Using *synchronisation points* (*SPs*), which may be *major* (delimiting dialogue units) or *minor* (inside dialogue units).

- Using *activities*. These are identified by activity identifiers.

Synchronisation and dialogue control

Each SP is given a unique sequence number, the SPSN discussed in the previous section. Two primitives are used to define and acknowledge SPs, as follows:

S-SYNC-MAJOR request,   SPSN, SS user data
indication, response, confirm

S-SYNC-MINOR request,   type, SPSN, SS user data
indication [,response, confirm]

In general each SP is given an incremental SPSN, and an acknowledgement window technique is applied to minor SPSNs, so that more than one may be outstanding. This is reflected in the *type* parameter of S-SYNCH-MINOR, which specifies whether an acknowledgement is required. This is why the response and confirm variants are in brackets; it is an 'optionally confirmed' service. (A strange inconsistency is that even if an acknowledgement is stated to be required, whether one is actually returned is not checked by the session layer.)

Major SPs must be acknowledged as soon as possible, and there are severe restrictions on what primitives can be issued while an S-SYNCH-MAJOR confirm is awaited. In order to issue synchronisation points the appropriate token must be owned, except in the special case of minor synchronisation points in duplex mode when symmetric synchronisation is being used.

Resynchronisation is achieved by the following primitive:

S-RESYNCHRONIZE request,   type, SPSN, initial token settings,
indication, response, confirm   SS user data

- The *type* field specifies abandon, restart or set, as discussed in the previous section.

- The *initial token settings* (called just 'tokens' in the standard) permits the assignment of tokens in the same way as in S-CONNECT.

No, the author is not being inconsistent in his spelling! ISO use resynchronize, which is also standard practice in the USA, whereas common UK practice is to write resynchronise. Although both spellings are allowed in UK English, this difference once resulted in incompatibility between UK and US versions of a standard, when a typist decided to 'correct' the spelling of the ISO document when producing the 'identical' BSI standard; the corresponding ANSI typist made no such change!

Activity management

Activity management has all the hallmarks of an additional feature 'grafted' on to something which is otherwise fairly self-contained. Indeed it was added at a relatively late stage, in order to provide compatibility with certain CCITT telematic standards (notably Teletex and MHS). There are some odd features of activities, such as the use of capability data, but not inside an activity, and various restrictions the use of other primitives inside or outside activities. We will not attempt a detailed discussion here, instead concentrating on basic concepts.

There was much discussion on how activities should be used. The view held by CCITT was that S-CAPABILITY-DATA should be used for negotiation (i.e. to determine the 'capability' of the co-operating applications to start the activity). Then everything else in the session would be enclosed in (*bracketed* by) an activity. This is sometimes referred to as the 'pure activity' approach. CCITT-originated standards such as MHS use activities, whereas ISO-originated ones such as FTAM do not.

Two primitives are used to start and terminate an activity:

S-ACTIVITY-START   activity identifier, SS user data
request, indication   [SPSN=1 implicit]

S-ACTIVITY-END request,   SPSN, SS user data
indication, response, confirm

The start of an activity is automatically given the SPSN value 1, so that there is no need for an SPSN parameter. The end of an activity is however identified by an SPSN, the sequence number being provided as a parameter. Each activity is assigned a unique *activity identifier* which can be used to *resume* the activity if it has to be *interrupted* due to an error. Activities may be interrupted by either user as follows:

S-ACTIVITY-INTERRUPT   reason
request, indication

Possible reasons for interrupting include local service problems, sequence errors and failure to receive (be assigned) the data token on request; in fact they are the same as those for S-U-EXCEPTION-REPORT discussed earlier. The user issuing the interrupt is assigned all tokens. Interrupting an activity is not destructive; previous work in the activity will be intact, and it can be resumed later.

To resume an interrupted activity, the following primitive is issued:

S-ACTIVITY-RESUME   new and old activity identifiers,
request, indication   SPSN, old SC identifier, SS user data

The failed activity is re-established, by providing both the identity of the interrupted activity and that of the session connection involved. (Activity identifiers are only unique for a given host-host association.)

Resumption is not possible if the activity was *discarded*. If this happens, any data currently in transit will be lost. In this sense it is rather like an unsolicited disconnect, but discarding the activity does not cause the session connection to be released. The primitive is as follows; the *reason* is from the same list as for S-ACTIVITY-INTERRUPT:

S-ACTIVITY-DISCARD   reason
request, indication

16.3   The session protocol

16.3.1   General features

Whereas the session service definition defines the facilities offered by each service primitive, it does not provide any details of how these primitives will be mapped on to the transport layer below. The session protocol specification {8327} covers this aspect, and while there is considerable duplication of technical content between the two standards, the protocol is specifically concerned with three basic areas. As usual, we will concentrate on the *Connection Oriented Session Protocol* (COSP), as the connectionless version has no significant functionality.

- The mapping of SSDUs on to different types of SPDU.

- The detailed encoding of these SPDUs.

- The usage of the transport service by COSP, including which COTS primitives are used, and the rules for concatenating SPDUs on to TSDUs.

16.3.2   Primitive to PDU mapping

In principle, the mapping of SSDUs on to SPDUs is simple, although the majority of the standard document is concerned with such unexciting matters as the detailed encodings of SPDUs, and also defines numerous state variables which together define the operational rules for the session connection. We will not cover these aspects here.

There is normally a simple relationship between SSDUs and SPDUs. For example, the S-TYPED-DATA SSDU maps on to the TYPED DATA SPDU. For confirmed services, the response/confirm generally maps on to a separate SPDU with ACK appended to the name (e.g. RESYNCHRONIZE, RESYNCHRONIZE ACK).

The main exception to this general rule is where the response/confirm can be either positive or negative. Hence S-CONNECT maps on to CONNECT, ACCEPT and REFUSE SPDUs, and S-RELEASE maps on to FINISH (request/indication), DISCONNECT (accepted response/confirm) and NOT FINISHED (refused response/confirm) SPDUs.

16.3.3   Use of the underlying transport connection

We end the discussion of the session protocol with some comments on the use of the underlying TC by COSP. This usage raises some important OSI issues, not all of which have yet been resolved to everyone's complete satisfaction.

Transport connect and disconnect

Connection and disconnection of the underlying transport connection is effected by the use of T-CONNECT and T-DISCONNECT as would be expected. However there is no direct relationship between S-CONNECT and T-CONNECT, or between S-RELEASE and T-DISCONNECT. S-CONNECT and S-RELEASE (and their variants) are transported in T-DATA TSDUs. This implies that the transport connection is either already set up, or will be set up by COSP before it issues the CONNECT SPDU. The TC also remains connected after the DISCONNECT SPDU has been sent\received. This implies that an existing transport connection may be used to set up a new session connection (between the same pair of hosts), and that releasing the session connection does not necessarily mean that the underlying transport connection will also be disconnected; it may be re-used by another session connection.

In order for the session service provider to be able to re-use the underlying transport connection, it must request this in the ABORT or FINISH SPDU which is used to terminate the session connection. There is one further restriction, which is that the transport connection cannot be re-used if the use of network expedited data has been agreed on the underlying transport connection. The reason for this is that any S-EXPEDITED data sent at the very beginning of the new session could conceivably overtake the FINISH and CONNECT SPDUs which have just been transmitted to end the old session and start a new one, since these SPDUs use the network normal channel. There is thus a risk that the expedited data would be received at the end of the previous SC, rather than at the start of the new one! (There is no problem if normal and expedited data both use the network normal channel.) It is possible that an addendum will be progressed to overcome this problem.

Use of transport normal and expedited data

You will have deduced from the above discussion that most SPDUs are sent on the transport normal data channel. If use of the transport expedited data channel is possible, it will of course be used by S-EXPEDITED-DATA, i.e. by EXPEDITED SPDUs. It is also used by S-RESYNCHRONIZE. There are a few other SPDUs which will use *transport expedited* if possible; these include the ABORT SPDU (which is mapped on to by S-U-ABORT and S-P-ABORT primitives), and the ABORT ACCEPT SPDU (which is used by the session protocol to acknowledge the ABORT, but does not result in a confirm primitive).

If the transport expedited channel is available, it will also be used by the *PREPARE* SPDU, which the session protocol uses to notify its peer of the 'imminent arrival' of an SPDU representing one of the following, which is destructive of data: major synchronisation point acknowledgement, resynchronisation, activity interrupt, activity discard, activity end, and acknowledgement of any of these. PREPARE is sent immediately before such an SPDU; since it is expedited, it may overtake data which has recently been transmitted. This allows any data received between PREPARE and one of the above SPDUs to be discarded. Of course if transport expedited it not available, there would be no point in using PREPARE as it would be unable to overtake anything. Hence PREPARE may only be used if transport expedited is available.

There are two particular problems with expedited data.

- The obvious problem is that the underlying network may not be able to support it. In this case there are two possibilities. One is that it will be negotiated out altogether. The other is that transport expedited data will share the network normal data channel (and will be only be distinguished from transport normal data by the TPDU type). In the latter case there is a further potential problem as well as the one just discussed. Any flow control blockage on the normal data channel will now halt expedited data as well. If, say, a resynchronise is issued in an attempt to recover from a flow control blockage (by purging the data streams), the RESYNCHRONIZE SPDU will get blocked as well. In the extreme case there will be a lockup which can only be solved by each user (or service provider) unilaterally aborting the session connection. As will be seen in subsequent chapters, this will require the invocation of recovery procedures in the application layer.

- If expedited data is supported by the underlying network but is used 'excessively', throughput restrictions (such as those in X.25 for interrupt packets) could result in long backlogs of expedited data in hosts. Any RESYNCHRONIZE SPDU which was generated would go to the back of the expedited queue. (The network layer has no way of knowing that this expedited data is 'special'.) It would then have to wait its turn behind other expedited data, thus defeating the object of using expedited for such primitives, as well as making expedited data slower than normal data.

Because of these potential problems, the use of expedited by applications is generally discouraged except in special cases.

One such case is in the VT service, where expedited can be used to get through a 'shut up'-type command to a remote host which was listing a long file (at the terminal user's expense).

Flow control

One final issue concerns flow control. There are no procedures for flow control in the session layer. As we have seen, excessive use of expedited data, or a network flow control blockage, could result in a backlog of SPDUs awaiting transmission. In particular no procedures are provided in the service definition to prevent S-DATA primitives from being issued, or to limit the amount of data in such a primitive.

This is a problem which requires resolution of course, and there are two possibilities.

• The first possibility is to make use of the flow control in the transport protocol (using the credit mechanism; see the previous chapter). Unfortunately this is not available in TP0, and since most implementations over X.25 use TP0, this effectively rules out this option in most cases.

• The real solution to the problem in fact lies outside the scope of the standard documents, and has to do with the fact that the service definition is abstract. In order for the service user to issue a primitive, there must be sufficient buffer space in the session entity to store its contents. Since both the service user entity and service provider entity reside in the same host, they must compete for buffer space, and in practice implementing the service primitive may simply amount to altering the assignment of a block of memory. In this case memory shortages could well mean that the primitive cannot be issued in the first place. Alternatively, explicit flow control across the session service boundary is not excluded by the service definition. This gives considerable freedom to implementors, including combining layers into a single software module. Indeed the acid test is that a peer open system, or the underlying network, receives valid PDUs or SDUs, not precisely where in the sending host they were generated. Few implementors would write self-contained, distinct modules, one for each layer, just because that is how OSI/RM defines the procedures. In practice this would be cumbersome and inefficient.

16.4 References

1   J. Larmouth et al, 'An Introduction to the Technical Content of OSI Layers 6 and 7', prepared for the UK Ministry of Defence by Smith Associates (September 1984).

2   'Guide to the Upper Layers', Department of Trade and Industry, Information Technology Standards Unit, TG 200/1, first published January 1989.

17   The presentation layer and ASN.1

17.1   Introduction

In the previous chapter we discussed the salient features of the session layer. It provides a rudimentary means of *structuring* the data flow, by inserting various types of data mark (major and minor synchronisation points, and activity boundaries), and various mechanisms for acknowledging data marks, and resynchronising the data stream in the event of a problem arising. What the session layer does not do is provide any means of interpreting the data which is passed in its various data primitives. As far as the session layer is concerned, user data is merely an octet stream with 'markers' inserted into it at various points. How the data is interpreted, and what the structure means, are entirely up to the layers above to decide.

The presentation layer is concerned with *interpretation* and encoding of data. To illustrate why this is an issue which needs a layer devoted to it, consider a typical interpretational problem:

Imagine that I had attempted to telephone a colleague in the USA, and for some reason my call had been misrouted, and I found myself speaking to someone who could only speak Chinese. I would have no idea what he was trying to say, and no doubt vice versa. Even though I could perform a Fourier analysis on his speech waveform, or encode it digitally on a compact disk, I would still not be able to deduce the meaning of the information he was imparting. A solution exists to this dilemma, which is to teach everybody in the world to speak Esperanto.

Esperanto was never a great success; human beings are surprisingly good at learning foreign languages if they have to, so there was never a strong perceived need for the language. With dumb computers however, the provision of the equivalent of Esperanto is vital. The problem with OSI is that a similar problem exists if two (computer) users communicate via a session connection, and they each transmit a bit (octet) pattern which means everything to them, but nothing to the recipient. There are various obvious problems. Consider the problem of representation of a date. Firstly the receiver has to be aware that this sequence of octets is supposed to represent a date in the first place. Having achieved this, both sender and receiver have to agree on how the date is to be interpreted. For example if it is transmitted as the ASCII character string '010391', what precisely does this mean? Sadly it depends on which side of the Atlantic you live. So we don't simply need to say that what follows is a date, we need to say that *what follows is a date represented in an unambiguous format.*

The encoding of a date is only one such example. Other more esoteric examples include machine-dependent ways of representing character strings in general (e.g. is the first byte to be interpreted as the length byte, or is the entire string to be interpreted as text up to the first zero byte; both interpretations are used by different systems), different internal representations of floating point numbers, and so on. The list is almost endless.

ISO's solution to this dilemma was to specify a language known as an *abstract syntax notation number one (ASN.1)* {8824}, which contains various Pascal-like data types (including Boolean, integer, ASCII string, and so on) and constructs which allow the *meaning* of their data to be specified by applications, rather than any specific encoding. This abstract syntax is derived (generated) from a particular application's idiosyncratic view of how data should be represented internally. The problem is, as we have seen, that this view will not be the same in different hosts. The advantage of using ASN.1 is that the ASN.1 definition of the data structure, the *abstract syntax*, can be converted into a standard way of representing the information in the session data stream, known as the *concrete syntax* or *transfer syntax*, which can similarly be unambiguously decoded by the recipient. How the ASN.1 representation of the data is mapped internally in a host is of concern only to that host. For example a date represented as '010391' at one host may end up as '910301' or '030191' at another. The point is that there is no ambiguity, since neither host cares about how the date is represented internally in the other host. Specific *encoding rules* {8825} are defined for the actual transfer over the presentation connection. The fact that a concrete syntax is being used means that the recipient can translate this (via ASN.1) into its own (possibly different) idiosyncratic physical representation.

You may be wondering if there are other ASNs, given that this is by implication the first. The answer is 'not yet', but ISO are aware both that different ASNs may be needed in the future, and also that it may be possible in the future to provide more abstraction than is the case at the moment. When or if ASN.2 will actually appear is an open question at present. ISO have far more pressing matters to attend to at the moment. More rigour is felt to be necessary in the specification of services and protocols, and for this reason two formal description techniques have been developed, known as LOTOS {8807} and ESTELLE {9074}. These will be briefly examined in chapter twenty three.

By itself, ASN.1 is merely an interesting concept. It is rather like a set of Pascal declarations with no supporting code. What ASN.1 needs is additional support. This is done by defining *abstract syntaxes*. An abstract syntax is a set of data representations, expressed in ASN.1 terms, which may be used by an application to define the structure of information it will send to another application. The key here is that an application may wish to make several different abstract syntaxes known to the presentation layer, for example to define several different types of data structure. The application will then negotiate with the presentation layer a *presentation context*, which is a specific abstract syntax to transfer syntax mapping. In practice more than one will normally be required to support an association between applications, as there will be a need to distinguish between (for example) application protocol commands, data in a file, and various application support protocol commands (see chapter eighteen). Each will have its own distinctive 'language', which must be distinguished from other languages used on the presentation connection. Therefore a set of presentation contexts, known as the *defined context set* (*DCS*), applies on the presentation connection at any given time. Any context in the DCS may be used on the presentation connection (PC). Each presentation context is assigned a unique (for a particular application) name, so that the receiver is in no doubt as to which context should be applied to the received data.

The value added functions of the presentation layer are then as follows:

- It allows various presentation contexts to be defined.

- It allows applications to select the presentation context(s) they wish to use during an association, i.e. the DCS, and also provides facilities for altering the current DCS during an association.

It follows of course that the abstract syntax currently selected by an application from the presentation context in use must also be made known to the other application; the encoding rules also cater for this.

Strictly speaking, ASN.1 and the encoding rules are not presentation layer standards at all. They are two of several application-related standards defining the structure and encoding of information. We will encounter others in part five. The reason that ASN.1 is discussed here rather than in part five is that nearly all application protocols are specified in terms of ASN.1, and the conversion to concrete syntax is a presentation layer function. Other standards of this type tend to apply to particular applications (such as teletex and facsimile).

17.2 Presentation service

As already suggested, the presentation layer provides a passive mapping of all session service primitives to the application layer, merely applying encoding rules to presentation service primitive parameters encoded using ASN.1. This aspect is essentially the same as the session service. In addition it provides the value-added functions of definition and negotiation of use of presentation contexts, for which new primitives are provided. These aspects will be discussed in turn.

17.2.1   Pass through session services

The pass through service primitives are exactly the same as the session service primitives discussed in the previous chapter, except for the prefix. Hence we have P-CONNECT, P-RELEASE and so on. There is little point in discussing these again, as the presentation layer performs no value added function in these cases, apart from encoding any user data parameters which may be present.

17.2.2   Specific presentation services: functional units

Those presentation functions which are not pass-through session services are controlled by three *functional units* (*FUs*); pass-through services are in effect under the control of session service FUs.

Kernel

Negotiation of the presentation context to be used on the PC is achieved by means of the P-CONNECT primitive. This forms part of the kernel FU, and is similar to S-CONNECT discussed in the previous chapter, except that additional parameters are provided for context negotiation. The full form of the primitive is shown below; the following parameters are of particular interest.

> • The *multiple active contexts* parameter is only present if an application would like to have more than one presentation context active at once. This would be unusual. If used, an additional parameter is provided, the *presentation context reference*. This is a sequence of presentation context identifiers, each of which may be used by the application to identify which particular context is being used at present. This is provided by the presentation layer, and is only present in the indication and confirm.

P-CONNECT request, indication   connection identifier, called address, calling address, [multiple active contexts, presentation context reference,] presentation context requirements list, protocol name, class of service, QOS, service requirements, initial SPSN, initial token settings, PS-user data

P–CONNECT response, confirm   connection identifier, called address, responding address, [multiple active contexts, presentation context reference,] protocol name, class of service, QOS, service requirements, initial SPSN, initial token settings, result, PS–user data

• The *presentation context requirements list* is a set of abstract syntaxes which the application requires the presentation layer to 'register', so that subsequent use by the application can be handled (distinguished) by the presentation layer. It should be noted that this information is also passed to the receiving application (and its presentation layer), but there is no right of reply. It is therefore implied that co-operating applications must agree (by means of their definition) which abstract syntaxes will actually be used. This parameter can only restrict usage to a subset of what a 'complete' instance of the application could handle. Such matters are of course of no concern to the presentation layer itself.

• In theory the *protocol name* allows the application to decide which presentation protocol to use. The availability of different protocols (mapping in different ways on to the session service) is 'for further study'.

• The *service requirements* parameter identifies which (presentation service) FUs are required. Most correspond to session service FUs such as kernel, duplex, and so on.

If only the (presentation) kernel FU is used, what is negotiated at connection setup time remains in force for the duration of the PC, and cannot be altered. All further presentation service functions are then pass-through session service ones. In order to alter the active context set, and to be able to recover an earlier one after a change, two further presentation service FUs are needed, as follows.

Context management

This FU provides for changes to be made to the defined context set during the life of the PC. The following additional primitives are provided for presentation context management during the presentation connection (application association). They allow the addition and removal of presentation contexts, and changes to be made to the set of context sets from which applications may currently choose. Precisely how these are used is for the applications to decide, and in practice few applications defined so far make use of these facilities. This is merely an abstract facility which many applications may not in fact require.

P–DEFINE–CONTEXT   presentation context id, presentation
request, indication   context requirements, user data

P–DEFINE–CONTEXT   presentation context id,
response, confirm   result, user data

These allow an application to create a new presentation context definition during the PC, subject to the agreement of its peer.

> • The *result* indicates whether the request was accepted by the peer, rejected by the peer, or rejected by the presentation layer (in which case the peer will not receive the indication, the confirm being generated within the presentation layer).

P–SELECT–CONTEXT   context amendments list, user data
request, indication

P–SELECT–CONTEXT   result, provider reason,
response, confirm   user data

These allow an application to alter the defined context set, i.e. to select a different one. Again this attempt may fail for reasons as discussed above.

P–DELETE–CONTEXT   context name
request, indication

P–DELETE–CONTEXT   result, provider reason,
response, confirm   user data

These allow context sets which are no longer required to be deleted. Again this must be by agreement between the applications and the presentation layer. Curiously, no user data parameter appears in the request.

Context restoration

This unit is provided to allow the recovery of context sets after session resynchronisation. The idea is to restore the defined context set to that which applied when the SPSN to which resynchronisation has taken place was first issued. In order to do this, the presentation layer needs to keep a log of defined context sets each time a synchronisation point is issued to, or received from, the layer below. The presentation protocol allows the defined context set to be restored to either the value current at the time, or that in force at connection setup. Context restoration is clearly not required unless context management is being used.

17.3   Presentation protocol

In theory a variety of presentation protocols may be available, one of which will be selected at PC setup time. In practice only two are currently standardised, the basic connection oriented {8823} and connectionless {9576} presentation protocols. We will discuss the presentation oriented protocol briefly, but will pay scant attention to the connectionless variant.

Figure 17.2 shows the PPDUs which are used in the kernel and context management FUs.

FUNCTIONAL UNIT	PROTOCOL DATA UNITS USED
KERNEL	connect presentation (CP) connect presentation accept (CPA) connect presentation reject (CPR) abnormal release - user (ARU) abnormal release - provider (ARP)
CONTEXT MANAGEMENT	define context (DC) define context ack (DCA) context delete (CD) context delete ack (CDA)

Figure 17.1 - kernel and context management PPDUs

Most protocol functions associated with P-primitives are in fact carried out by the underlying session protocol, and therefore do not appear (explicitly) in the presentation protocol. Figure 17.2 shows the other PPDUs defined in the standard, which are associated with data transfer and resynchronisation.

• The *data transfer* PPDUs are there to make available the (session service) data transfer functions to the application. The data transferred is subject to the appropriate encoding rules.

• The *resynchronisation* PPDUs allow the presentation entities to co-operate in restoring the correct active context set after rollback. A *restore indication* parameter is used to determine whether the initial context set will be used, or that which applied at the point which is being rolled back to.

FUNCTION	PROTOCOL DATA UNITS USED
DATA TRANSFER	transfer presentation typed data (TTD) transfer presentation data (TD) transfer expedited data (TE) transfer capability data (TC) transfer capability data ack (TCC)
CONTEXT RESTORATION	resynchronise (abandon) (RA) resynchronise (abandon) ack (RAA)

Figure 17.2 - miscellaneous PPDUs

It is clear that many other presentation service primitives exist than just those mapped on to PPDUs. The point is that PPDUs are only provided in cases where the presentation layer has some value added function. To summarise, the value added areas are as follows:

- Establishing the active context set at connection time.

- Recovering the active context set after resynchronisation.

- Altering the active context set during the connection.

- Applying the context to application data. This includes any 'user data' parameters of presentation service primitives, in which case (conceptually at least) a PPDU for the user data parameter will be embedded in a SPDU for the session layer function.

In cases where the presentation layer has no value added function, no PPDUs are provided, the P-primitives mapping directly on to S-primitives beneath, and serviced by SPDUs. This covers the majority of P-primitives, with the proviso that session service unlimited data makes S-primitives fall into the fourth category above.

17.4 Abstract syntax notation 1 (ASN.1)

ASN.1 and its encoding rules started life as part of the CCITT MHS recommendations; initially both appeared in X.409(1984). As they were clearly of wider applicability than just MHS, ISO and CCITT decided to separate these and develop separate standards for each. The intention was that the ISO and CCITT standards would be technically identical. Thus ASN.1 itself became {8824} and X.208(1988), while the ASN.1 encoding rules became {8825} and X.209(1988). The CCITT numberings thus now place them in the OSI (X.200) series rather than the MHS (X.400) series.

At this point it is worth explaining the numbering scheme used in the CCITT OSI-related recommendations. The X.2xx series covers general OSI standards. X.200 itself is OSI/RM, and X.210 covers OSI service conventions. We have just mentioned X.208 and X.209. Otherwise X.20[1-7] are general layer definitions, while X.21[1-7] and X.22[1-7] represent layer service definitions and protocol specifications respectively (X.217 and X.227 cover ACSE), while X.2[1-2]8 and X.2[1-2]9 cover the application support RTSE and ROSE definitions, these again having their origins in MHS. (Apologies to the uninitiated for using Unix-type wildcard conventions.) At this point CCITT ran out of suitable numbers, so that the newer application support standard CCR uses X.2[3-4]7. Specific applications use different numbering schemes altogether, such as X.4xx (for MHS) and X.5xx (for the Directory). It has to be said that the CCITT numbering scheme is at least logical, which is more than can be said for that of ISO. Lists of relevant ISO standards and CCITT recommendations may be found in appendices B and C.

We suggested above that ASN.1 was something like Pascal, in that it provided a set of data types. In fact there are similarities and differences. It may be helpful to compare what Pascal offers with the corresponding ASN.1 facilities, although the analogy should not be taken too far.

Pascal offers a basic set of *data types*, from which more complex ones may be formed. For example from the basic types of INTEGER, REAL and BOOLEAN, more complex types such as ARRAY, SET, RECORD and FILE can be constructed. ASN.1 provides a directly comparable facility, although the details are different.

Pascal allows identifiers to be defined based on these data types, the intention being to generate object code which performs some operations on (i.e. transforms the values of) the identifiers. In ASN.1, the intention is rather different. Instead of modifying the elements of a data structure, ASN.1 has the rather more limited aim of allowing an abstract definition of a *data structure* which is both unambiguous, and also capable of being mapped by an application on to a real data structure. The intention is merely to get the structured data to the peer application intact.

A typical Pascal program consists of source code which will be complied into machine dependent object code, and it is this object code which is then executed. The precise nature of the object code is normally of no concern to the human user (provided that it works properly), and is dependent on the underlying hardware; it is the source code which is (in theory) portable. ASN.1 can be viewed similarly. The abstract ASN.1 data structure representation is rather like 'source code', which any user (application) can understand. It is 'compiled' into a 'object' form which is what is actually transmitted across the network(s). The precise encoding on the network (presentation connection) is of no concern to the application, provided that it can be 'de-compiled' into a form which can be understood unambiguously by its peer. So the software which implements the ASN.1 encoding rules can in a sense be viewed as a compiler, the encoded octet stream being in effect the 'object code' of the ASN.1 program. Indeed there could in theory be any number of different encoding rules, although only one has so far been defined.

17.4.1 ASN.1 data types and structure

ASN.1 offers basic 'building blocks', together with various means of using these to create various types of data structure of any desired complexity. The data structure may define the internal ordering of a file, or the format of a mail message. This is of concern to the application but not to the presentation layer. This is why applications are allowed to define their own context sets, so that they can agree on what types of data structure can be used over the presentation connection.

ASN.1 provides the following basic facilities.

- A small number of *primitive data types*. These include such things are Boolean and integer.

- Various *construction rules* for combining data types to form *constructed data types*.

- A means of identifying types by means of *tags* which can have various scopes, such as unique for any ASN.1 use, or specific to a given application.

- Pascal-like semantics for defining data types. This includes the ability to include comments, aimed at improving readability, but not processed by the 'compiler'.

The definition of ASN.1 is in BNF. A few examples of possible ASN.1 constructs will be included from time to time. These are in something similar to ASN.1 format, but we will not always adhere precisely to this format, and in some cases the syntax in the examples will be incomplete.

As the above aside implies, it is not the intention here to provide a rigorous definition of ASN.1, but rather to introduce the reader to some of the more important concepts, so that more detailed examples of ASN.1 usage can be provided illustrating its use with individual applications in later chapters. The crucial thing to remember is that ASN.1 and its encoding rules are required because applications operate on data (and application protocol control information) of defined and agreed (between applications) data structures, and peer applications need to be able to extract both the context and the content from the underlying (concrete syntax) octet string.

Primitive data types

There are several distinct data types, plus a null one which can be used as a 'place marker' indicating that the corresponding data element is not present on this occasion. The primitive data types are as follows:

- **Boolean**. This can take the values TRUE or FALSE, which are ASN.1 *reserved words*. (Whether this requires one bit or more on the underlying data stream is for the encoding rules to decide. Reserved words are discussed later in the section.)

- **Integer**. In principle this is any integral value between plus and minus infinity. In practice the encoding rules used may restrict this by specifying a maximum number of octets which are available for its representation.

- **Real**. In principle this is any value between PLUS-INFINITY and MINUS-INFINITY. It contains three components, the Base, Exponent and Mantissa. Bases 2, 8 or 16 are supported for binary values, and base 10 for character representations.

- **Bitstring**. This is an ordered sequence of bits, any of which may be 0 or 1. There is no implied limit to the length of the bit stream, although applications may wish to specify minimum and maximum permitted lengths (as comments).

- **Octetstring**. This is like a bitstring, but applies to octets (bytes) instead. A string length of zero is permitted. Construction rules discussed below allow more specific string types (such as ASCII strings) to be defined.

- **Null**. This is the place marker referred to earlier. It may be used at any point where alternatives exist but none applies in this case. It will be encoded as a specific value which is distinct from any of the valid alternatives.

- **Object identifier**. This is a recent addition, and allows registered named objects to be specified. A complex standard {9834-1 to 9834-11} is being progressed specifying procedures for registration authorities; this is briefly discussed in chapter twenty three. Although the standard is not well advanced at the time of writing, it is envisaged that object identifier names will be registered.

- **External**. These are types whose encoding is unknown to ASN.1, but can be understood by the applications which are co-operating.

- *Enumerated*. Values of this type are given distinct identifiers as part of the type notation.

Construction rules

Using primitive types alone would not allow a particularly rich repertoire of data structures. Rather than attempting within the ASN.1 standard to define as many data structures as applications may conceivably need, which could not be feasible, the approach adopted is to allow applications to build their own more complex data types using a relatively small set of rules. The principal *construction rules* are as follows:

- *Sequence*. This allows a new type to be defined as a fixed ordering of elements of various different types. While the order and the number of elements must always be the same, it may contain various different types. This is similar to the idea of a Pascal RECORD containing, say, two Booleans and three integers, in that order. A simple ASN.1 example is shown in figure 17.3.

```
EMPLOYEE-DETAILS::=
      SEQUENCE            -- this is a comment --
      {NAME               [1] name-type,
      ADDRESS             [2] address-type,
      DATE-OF-BIRTH       [3] date-type,
      SEX                 [4] sex-type OPTIONAL
      }
```

Figure 17.3 - a simple ASN.1 data structure

- *Sequence of*. This is more restrictive than sequence in one sense, and less so in another. The elements must now be all of the same type, but the number of elements in the sequence is not fixed. This is comparable to the Pascal ARRAY. (More strictly it is analogous to conformant array parameters.)

- *Set of*. This allows a type to be constructed which contains zero or more elements of a single type. There is again a clear analogy with Pascal. For example a Pascal SET OF [1..11] may contain between 0 and 11 integers, ranging from none at all to one each of all of the possible values. A hand of cards can be regarded as a set of cardtype, as the hand may contain any number of cards between zero and the number in the pack, and every card has a different value.

- *Set*. This is discussed after 'set of' because there is no direct equivalent in Pascal. All elements which may be present in a 'set of' must be of the same type (integer in the example above). In a set, the values can be of different types. This construct has no simple application in programming, but is an important feature when defining data (e.g. document) structures.

- *Choice.* In a sense this can be viewed as a special case of 'set of' which must contain exactly one element from the set. A simple choice example for the SET OF [1.11] above is that the value must be a single integer in the range 1..11, although a choice is not necessarily restricted to a single type of course.

Tags

It is all very well being able to define exotic types, and indeed some very complex ones indeed can be formed from just these relatively simple rules. The next essential task is to provide a means of referencing these new types. Pascal has the TYPE declaration for this purpose. Having defined TYPE FANCY = ARRAY [45..987] of BOOLEAN (or whatever), the name FANCY can subsequently be used unambiguously to refer to this type. ASN.1 uses the essentially similar concept of *tags*. Four types of tag are defined; as usual with standards which precede the applications which will use them, one is in effect an escape route in case the study group has overlooked something which will be needed in the future. The tag types are as follows:

- *Universal.* Tags of this type are reserved for the basic ASN.1 primitive types such as Boolean, integer and so on. ASN.1 also assigns universal tags to a few construction rules and simple constructed types which are considered to be of general utility. These include certain character set types and time types. Any application can use any universal tag. In effect they are *global* types.

Figure 17.4 shows the list of universal class tag assignments; those not shown are currently unassigned (reserved).

- *Application.* Implementations of applications such as FTAM are based on international standard documents. Each application standard may include the definition of types peculiar to that application. Since they appear in the standard, they can be used in any ASN.1 definitions contained within that standard, and have a unique meaning only in the context of that particular application. They are given the application tag. Other applications may use precisely the same tag identifiers for something quite different; this is of no concern to the presentation entity. This entity knows precisely what UNIVERSAL 2 means, but it is left to applications to decide whether something declared as APPLICATION 3 is correctly encoded. That is an application conformance matter.

TAG	ASSIGNMENT
0	reserved
1	Boolean
2	integer
3	bitstring
4	octetstring
5	null
6	object identifier
7	object descriptor
8	external
9	real
10	enumerated
16	sequence, sequence of
17	set, set of
18-22	character sets (ASCII, teletex etc.)
23-24	time types
25-27	character sets (ASCII, teletex etc.)

Figure 17.4 - ASN.1 universal class tag assignments

• *Private*. These are tags which are defined neither in ASN.1 itself nor in an application standard. They are intended for private agreement between 'non-registered' applications, and it for the applications themselves to ensure that they are used consistently. As PRIVATE is never used in ISO or CCITT application standards, there is no possibility of conflict with data structures defined in such standards.

• *Context-specific*. This is subject to no restrictions whatsoever, and can be used for virtually anything.

Other constructs

Like Pascal and other similar languages, ASN.1 has a set of *reserved words*. These include all of the primitive types and construction rules, together with some others which come into a 'miscellaneous' category. TRUE and FALSE were covered under BOOLEAN; others are now briefly discussed. (They should strictly be typed in uppercase, but we will not always adhere to this.)

Componentsof

In a set or sequence type, this can be used to reference the name of another type where the actual component types are defined, rather than having to duplicate its type definition. Thus a sequence may be a sequence of various types followed by, preceded by or including, an entire sequence defined elsewhere.

Default, optional

DEFAULT allows a specific value to be used where a specific value is not included in the data. It is appropriate as a space-saving convention where only a minority of instances will have a different value. On the other hand OPTIONAL means that if this element is left out, no value is implied. So for example PET::= CHOICE {CAT, DOG} DEFAULT DOG and PET::= CHOICE {CAT, DOG} OPTIONAL have different meanings. The former defaults to DOG if the species is not specified; in the second case, failure to specify the species implies that it is unknown.

Implicit, any

These can be applied to tags. IMPLICIT means that the tag need not be explicitly identified during data transfer. How this is interpreted depends on the encoding rules. ANY means that no tag is associated with the data which follows. There are some restrictions on the use of ANY which we will not discuss here.

External

. This allows references to be made to other abstract syntaxes. By implication this requires access to some registration authority. Registration is discussed briefly in chapter twenty three.

17.4.2   ASN.1 encoding rules

The encoding rules standard {8825} defines how the data structure defined by ASN.1 is physically encoded in the presentation connection octet stream. The rules of themselves are not particularly interesting, and only a few brief comments will be made here.

Each data element is represented as four fields, as follows:

- *Identifier octets*. These encode the tag (class and number) and the type (structured, unstructured, choice, any, and so on) of the data element. The encoding allows for both short and long formats, depending on whether the tag can be encoded in a single octet or requires two or more. (This applies to some other fields as well.)

- *Length octets*. The length may be in long or short format. The long format ends with a special terminating octet, allowing (in principle) data items of unlimited length.

- *Contents octets*. These are encoded as required for the particular data type. Booleans map into an entire octet, zero meaning false and any other value meaning true. (This is inefficient, but is in keeping with the normal tendency to make fields multiples of one octet long, which we referred to in chapter six.) Integers are transmitted as a twos complement binary bit string.

- *End of contents octets*. This field is required only if specified in the length field. In some cases the length is explicitly stated, in which case this field is not required.

Further details of encodings may be found in the standard document itself. They are mainly of interest to implementors.

17.5   Other issues

A few final comments should be made. According to OSI/RM, the presentation layer has responsibility for *encryption* and *data compression*. At present there is no support in the presentation layer standards for either. Provision of these is clearly possible in almost any layer, although this layer is the most logical place to provide them. There is little doubt that further abstract syntaxes and encoding rules will ultimately be provided which support encryption and data compression, although at the time of writing, no new work item has yet been raised. It is worth noting that application standards such as the Directory have specific security requirements which have led to the inclusion of cryptographic facilities.

Further developments which are expected include support for new character sets. A separate standard {2022} concerns the classification and registration of character sets.

18 General application layer functions

18.1 Structure of the application layer

In OSI/RM, there has been much discussion of application layer functions, but almost from the start it was realised that there were three distinct aspects of applications:

- Some aspects of the application layer would provide *common services* to more than one application. We saw this in the UK interim protocol hierarchy (chapter nine), where NIFTP provided a common service to JTMP and JNT mail. Unfortunately the common service that NIFTP provided was not compatible with OSI. However it is clear that in the OSI application layer, at least one common service is necessary, a *kernel* which is responsible for setting up 'connections' between applications.

- Some aspects of the application are *application specific*. Thus procedures for file transfer should be entirely distinct from those for job transfer or terminal handling.

- However the chief difficulty is in deciding where the upper limit of the application layer should be placed. Of course everything above the presentation layer is application-related. But many aspects of an application will be *beyond the scope of OSI*. For example, details of how files are stored on disk for a given operating system is clearly of no concern to OSI, whereas provision of a virtual filestore model which allows a common mapping of different aspects of filestores certainly is within the aegis of OSI.

So where does this leave us? Initial work assumed that there would be 'common application service elements', or CASE, in what would effectively have been a lower application sublayer. Specific application support would be provided above this, e.g. for file handling, and a series of such application-related services would then form, in effect, the upper sublayer. By 1984, a CASE kernel, responsible for 'application connection' setup and cleardown had been specified, together with Commitment, Concurrency and Recovery (CCR) procedures. The idea was to select the CASE kernel plus (optionally) one or more of the other CASE elements such as CCR.

This is very similar to the selection of a kernel plus some other functional units in lower layer services. On the face of it this seems entirely logical. Selection of CCR would then be comparable with (but obviously unrelated to) selecting session activity management from the CASE menu.

Unfortunately this simple scenario proved to be too simplistic in the context of the application layer. Between 1984 and 1988, the entire application layer philosophy was rethought, the result being something which is quite unlike what happens in lower layers.

The main obstacle to this new approach was CCITT's Message Handling System (MHS) recommendations, the X.400(1984) series. MHS is discussed in chapter twenty two, although it is the more recent 1988 version which is discussed there. MHS provides generalised support for message switching between hosts, and can support (although it is not itself) an electronic mail service. Many PTTs such as British Telecom wished to offer electronic mail services over PDNs, hence the haste to standardise MHS. Developed as it was before the upper layers of OSI had become stable, this first version of ended up violating a number of emerging OSI conventions. MHS(1984) effectively bypasses the presentation layer (which was only in an early stage of development at the time), and uses the 'wrong' transport protocol class, TP0 above X.25 networks (since it was based on even earlier Teletex 'transport service', defined before even the OSI transport layer had become stable). Using TP0 over X.25 leaves the MHS application vulnerable to unsolicited disconnects due to internal X.25 problems. (Resets are converted by TP0 to disconnects as well.) Clearly MHS procedures were left vulnerable to underlying failures, which is reminiscent of the way NIFTP is left to recover from underlying X.25 resets (chapter nine). To alleviate this problem, CCITT defined what it called the *Reliable Transfer Service* (*RTS*). This resided in the application layer, and provided end-end acknowledgement and recovery from underlying failures. In addition, a second application service, known as *Remote Operations* (*ROS*) was defined to operate above RTS. Its function was to co-ordinate a message transfer with the return of its delivery confirmation. Optionally, RTS could protect both the message and the returned confirmation.

TP1 can recover from resets and disconnects, but a serious failure cannot be recovered by this layer, as the QOS could not be maintained. Sophisticated applications such as MHS therefore need something like RTS over any transport protocol.

Both RTS and ROS were in effect application support services, but unfortunately their usage did not fit in with current ISO thinking on CASE. In particular in X.400(1984), the MHS procedures used ROS over RTS directly over a dummy presentation layer, bypassing the CASE kernel altogether. In order to accommodate MHS into OSI, both MHS and the application layer structure had to change. In this respect, there were two glaring incompatibilities in the application layer.

- ISO assumed that all applications would use the CASE kernel, combined with one or more optional extras such as CCR.

(At the time that was the only optional extra available.) But MHS did not use the CASE kernel at all. This is clearly not consistent with the concept of a kernel as something which must be used by all applications.

• More disturbingly for ISO, MHS(1984) used ROS above RTS, i.e. RTS as a user of ROS. This flew in the face of ISO thinking at the time, which was that a specific application would use a combination of CASE functional units of equal status. Here, one application support service was using another one below it.

Clearly something had to be done. In the event both MHS and the application layer structure changed significantly. We will discuss the MHS changes in chapter twenty two. In this section we discuss the new ISO *application layer structure* standard {9545} which emerged as a result of convergence between the ISO and CCITT approaches; this standard was at the DIS stage at the time of writing. A corresponding CCITT recommendation (X.207) is also in preparation, but was too late to be included in the blue book (1988) recommendations.

Application entities, service elements and associations

The current thinking is that the application layer consists of a number of *Application Service Elements* or *ASEs*, each having some defined service which can be used either by other ASEs or by the real application 'above' the application layer. Nominally, each ASE is therefore of equal status, so that any ASE can be the service user of any other ASE. An *Application Entity* or *AE* is then defined to perform some task (e.g. MHS, file transfer), in terms of a set of ASEs and the way in which the use each other's services.

This introduces a new concept, the *application association*. This is established between exactly *two* AEs in different open systems, and can be viewed as the application layer's equivalent of a *connection* at lower layers. An association is however far more than simply a connection. It defines the co-operation between specific AEs (i.e. the collection of ASEs, for example for the purpose of file transfer) in two or more open systems, but it does far more than just this. It also specifies which supporting applications will be used, the hierarchy of ASEs which will be used (e.g. FTAM over CCR over something corresponding to the old CASE), and the context in which a given ASE will use the services of another in the same or the other open system.. An application association cannot be directly related to an underlying presentation connection, although the transactions which take place between the co-operating AEs will use one (unless connectionless underlying services are to be used, a scenario which we will not consider). A full interaction between several open systems, e.g. to transfer a job, enquire of its status, and return the output, may require several different associations to be established at different times. For example if a job is submitted on Monday, processed on Tuesday, and the output returned on Wednesday, the submission and output are clearly part of the same application (JTM), but several different associations are required. It would be absurd to maintain an underlying presentation connection for two days, just so that it could be used to return the job output.

The discussion in the previous paragraph begs the question of what happened to the CASE kernel. It is becoming clear that the CASE kernel (or something like it) will need to handle the establishment and termination of application associations. The most fundamental change to MHS which took place between 1984 and 1988 was its modification to use application associations. It is now a requirement for associations to be established between AEs. As we shall see, this is done by something which is essentially the old CASE kernel, but under a new name (ACSE). This clearly leaves MHS(1984) out in the cold, and it must therefore be viewed as obsolescent.

The detailed relationship between ASEs in the same and peer open systems is complex. Various parts of application dialogues may use different ASEs within the same AE. It is not possible to generalise at this point, as we have not yet fully discussed the establishment of application associations, and different applications use different ASE combinations. But it is clear that there are two types of ASE:

  • Some ASEs must have an OSI service user. For example CCR by itself would have no application to manage, and must therefore have a defined user ASE, such as FTAM. We refer to these as application support ASEs. (This is not an ISO term.)

  • On the other hand FTAM's user is above (beyond) the scope of OSI. FTAM entities in different open systems can co-operate to do something specific (transfer a file in this case). We sometimes refer to FTAM and the like as application specific ASEs.

So what happened to the CASE kernel? To cut a long story short, CASE was renamed *Association Control Service Elements* or just *ACSE*. It is one of several application support ASEs which may be called on by application specific ASEs such as FTAM, MHS and JTM. However it is special in two senses. First, it must be used at the start and end of an association; no other ASE is compulsory in this sense. Secondly, that is (at the time of writing) the only time that ACSE can be used. During the association, ACSE is effectively bypassed (except if an abort occurs). In this chapter we discuss ACSE and the other application support ASEs. In later chapters we examine application specific ASEs. The principal support ASEs, which receive most attention in this chapter, are as follows:

- **ACSE: Association control** service elements. These provide a mechanism for setting up an association (co-operative linkage) between a pair of AEs on different open systems, and for releasing it when it is no longer needed.

- **CCR (CCRSE): Commitment, concurrency and recovery** service elements. These provide mechanisms for co-ordinating associations (dialogues) between various AEs where the entire set of dialogues is to be viewed as an atomic action. A two stage commitment procedure is provided which seeks to ensure that either the entire atomic action (set of dialogues and their outcomes) proceeds to completion, or it is abandoned with no trace of its existence remaining.

- **ROSE (ROS): Remote operations** service elements. These provide a means of controlling request/reply dialogues, which are common in application associations. The reply can be the results of some remote processing (rather like a remote procedure call), or it can simply be confirmation of delivery of a message. As an application support ASE, ROSE has no interest in why it is being used.

- **RTSE (RTS): Reliable transfer** service elements. The request and reply dialogue units associated with each other by ROSE may need safeguarding. ROSE itself does not ensure their delivery; if necessary it uses RTSE to do this. The basic aim of RTSE is to keep on trying until delivery has been achieved. This caters for loss of the underlying presentation (session) connection; RTSE will re-connect and try again. RTSE must of course be a confirmed service, and the confirmation of delivery of the dialogue unit (the RTSE confirm primitive) is taken by ROSE as confirmation of delivery of the request or the reply.

This point is made as there is the possibility of confusing the reply dialogue unit controlled by ROSE with the delivery confirmation provided by RTSE. Delivery of both the ROSE request and reply may be confirmed by RTSE. It is also possible to confuse the request in the ROSE request/reply paradigm with the request variant of a service primitive. For this reason we sometimes use the terms enquiry and response rather than request and reply.

We deal with these in the order in which they were outlined above. Unfortunately their functions are closely intertwined, and it is not possible to discuss them without introducing forward references at various points. You are advised to read the material twice to gain full benefit from the descriptions.

18.2 Association Control Service Elements (ACSE)

18.2.1 Introduction

As discussed earlier in the chapter, ACSE matured from the earlier CASE kernel. The purpose of ACSE is to set up and maintain an *application association* between two co-operating *application processes* (*APs*), or more specifically between the *application entities* (*AEs*, set of ASEs) which are responsible for communication between the APs, on different open systems. We will see examples of combinations of ASEs in this and the following chapters. At present, the standard assumes that a single ASE in each open system will use ACSE, possibly on behalf of 'superior' ASEs in the same open system. The use of ACSE by more than one ASE is for further study.

An application association is a co-operative relationship between two AEs, and defines their terms of reference. The association determines which application protocols will communicate, and how they will do so, including their use of the presentation service.

18.2.2 ACSE service

As is usual with OSI service elements, various services are defined in terms of service primitives. ACSE offers four services, for handling the setup of the association, graceful termination of the association, and abnormal terminations. At present, each service is associated with a single service primitive, although mechanisms fo the provision of additional facilities for altering the association details during its currency are currently under consideration.

Associate service

This sets up the association. A single primitive is provided. As can be seen from the number of parameters, it is exceedingly complex, and we will only attempt to discuss a few classes of parameter in general terms. In this and succeeding chapters, we will refer simply to 'confirmed' or 'unconfirmed' in cases where we do not wish to discuss the variants in which various parameters are used, or differences in parameters between variants.

A-ASSOCIATE confirmed   31 parameters

- Various parameters are included to *identify the peer application process* (AP). For both the calling and called open system, the AP title, AE qualifier, and the AP and AE invocation identifiers are specified in the request. This identifies both the application and the specific instance to be used in this association. The latter is necessary since (for example) FTAM may be running simultaneously in association with several different open systems and files; in the event of failure, we need to identify which instance of FTAM is to be recovered. This is similar in concept to the recall address used in YBTS (chapter nine).

- The *responding* values are returned in the response variant. Whereas the called values identify the intended acceptor, the responding values may indicate that a different one has actually been used. One possibility is that a generic acceptor was requested, and the responding details indicate a specific identity.

- Various parameters are included which allow the *presentation details* to be established. These include the responding presentation address, presentation contexts, and a default presentation context (which may be used if there is no defined context set).

- In addition, *session requirements* are specified, including initial SPSN and token assignments.

The standard specifies three **association classes**. These define the relationships between the entities, in terms of which entity or entities can invoke remote operations of the ROSE type (see §18.4).

- **Class 1** association. Only the AE *initiating* the association may invoke operations.

- **Class 2** association. Only the AE *responding* to the association may invoke operations.

- **Class 3** association. *Either* AE may invoke operations.

Both the presentation and session requirements map on to the appropriate parameters of a P-CONNECT, which in turn maps on to a S-CONNECT. Other parameters (including many which have not been mentioned) map on to user data. ACSE use of the presentation service has a defined presentation context which is different from that of other ASEs' control information or ASE data. It is clear that, in general, several different presentation contexts will be required. Procedures are being developed for registering context sets {9834}, and this will ultimately result in some simplifications by being able to refer to standard names for common types of association. (It is proving to be a difficult area to standardise.)

Release service

This terminates the association. The primitive is much simpler than the associate:

A-RELEASE confirmed   reason, user information, result

• The *reason* may be normal, urgent or 'user defined' in the request. In the response, it may be normal, not finished, or again 'user defined'.

• This of course implies that *the release is negotiated*. The *result*, which appears only in the response, indicates whether the release was accepted (affirmative) or rejected (negative). An affirmative response coupled with a not finished result indicates that the association is terminated, but that the recipient of the request was in some way 'unhappy' about this, generally because it still had information to send or receive.

Abort services

There are two abort services, *user abort* and *provider abort*. These map on to the presentation (and hence session) abort services discussed in chapter sixteen.

User abort

This is at the request of either service user, which is the ASE nominated as the *sole user* of ACSE. (Only one ASE may use the services of ACSE.) It is also possible for ACSE to issue an abort on its own initiative, in which case it relays a request to the peer open system (where it becomes an indication), and an indication to its own service user. The association is released with possible loss of information. The primitive is as follows:

A-ABORT request   user information

A-ABORT indication   source, user information

• The *user information* (which is optional) is presumably understood by the peer ASE and/or the ACSE service user. As usual if abort requests from both open systems collide, this information will be lost.

• The *source* indicates either that ACSE itself has aborted (in which case there was no request), or that the service user (some nominated ASE) requested the abort. (This will be conveyed to the peer application by means of the A-protocol, which we will not be discussing.)

Provider abort

This is reported by the presentation service, and was discussed in chapter sixteen (session layer). A single primitive is used:

A–P–ABORT indication   reason

This could result from some underlying failure which cannot be recovered by the transport protocol without unduly degrading the QOS, or because of some protocol violation detected by an underlying layer.

18.3   Commitment, Concurrency and Recovery Service Elements (CCR)

18.3.1   Introduction

Historical development

Procedures for commitment, concurrency and recovery (CCR) {9804, 9805} were initially developed by ISO for use by the JTM application (see chapter twenty), which (in its full operational mode) allows the co-operation of several OSI hosts in performing job processing. In this situation, careful control is needed to ensure that all participating hosts have actually completed their tasks, and all have a clear and consistent view of what has been achieved by the association. DP versions of the CCR service definition and protocol specification were available as early as 1984. {They were numbered 8649-3 and 8650-3, and were originally associated with the CASE standard, although 8649 and 8650 now deal only with ACSE, the successor to CASE, discussed in the previous section.} Indeed the original service definition was briefly discussed in the second edition of this book. Subsequent development of CCR proved difficult however, and it was not until the end of 1990 that it finally reached IS status. The documents were rewritten and were also re-numbered {9804, 9805}, reflecting the major changes in thinking on CCR which took place between 1984 and 1988.

The main problems for CCR resulted from the decision to use it under certain other application standards (RDA and TP, discussed in chapter twenty three), which necessitated major changes to CCR, notably to the responsibility for commitment. The original version of CCR was considered to be too complex for such new applications as TP, and while its basic philosophy survived, much of the detail was changed, and in many cases simplified. This had the effect of causing problems for JTM, which was built on the old version of CCR. The changes to CCR resulted in a 'defect report' being issued for JTM.

The CCR philosophy

This discussion of CCR takes into account the changes made to accommodate RDA and TP, and reflects the 1990 standard which had just reached IS status at the time of writing, but not draft amendments which were under consideration at that time. (These are mentioned later.) Certain aspects of CCR have had to be simplified in the interests of keeping this discussion at the appropriate level.

Co-ordination between co-operating application entities is necessary in many applications. A typical example is an update applied to a distributed database, which may result in records at several different physical locations being updated by a single transaction originating at yet another location. In this case it is clear that we want all updates to be applied, not just some, and if for some reason problems occur which make an update impossible at one location, the entire update will have to be either abandoned or attempted again from scratch. Another example which we encountered in chapter nine, and will see again in chapter twenty, is that of a complex job which requires partial processing at several sites. Again it may be of little use if parts of the job get executed while others do not.

It was for situations of this type that CCR was devised. The set of database updates mentioned above has the characteristic that it must either proceed to completion, or be abandoned with no trace of its existence remaining. Thus the set of updates, taken as a whole, may be regarded as an *atomic action*. The controlled completion of an atomic action is achieved in CCR by means of a *two stage commitment* procedure. Each entity indicates that it has completed its contribution to the atomic action, but does not actually apply the changes until it is told to do so by a controlling entity, whose responsibility is to ensure that all contributions from other entities have been completed as well.

In fact the set of database updates has 'granularity', and CCR incorporates mechanisms for handling pasts of atomic actions within the whole, as we shall see in due course.

CCR has what are sometimes referred to as *'ACID' properties*. This is an acronym of Atomicity, Consistency, Isolation and Durability. This is really just a rather fancy way of saying that the atomic action must either be performed completely or not at all, all aspects of the atomic action must be performed reliably and consistently, and any other application entities involved will only be informed of results on a 'need to know' basis. In fact despite its name, CCR does not actually offer any concurrency mechanism. According to a tutorial annex to the service definition {9804 Annex C.4}, 'the preservation of the atomic action requires that the implementation considers concurrency'.

18.3.2   The CCR management philosophy

Entity types and the commitment tree

CCR provides mechanisms for controlling a set of (components of) atomic actions which form part of a whole, and potentially involve many different open systems. CCR defines three types of entity, which relate to each other as follows:

> • The *master entity* is the open system which has responsibility for controlling (co-ordinating) the entire activity for the atomic action. This atomic action may comprise several components, which may be viewed as a tree-like hierarchy. Each component is itself treated as an atomic action in its own right. In effect therefore, the commitment procedure is recursive. In the context of a tree of components, the master is at the root, and therefore there can only be one master entity. See figure 18.1.

> • For each component in the hierarchy, i.e. each branch of the tree, there is a *superior entity* which initiates that component of the atomic action, and a *subordinate entity* (on of the superior's children) which co-operates with the superior in whatever dialogue constitutes this particular component of the atomic action. The highest superior in the tree is also the master.

At first sight it would seem that the subordinate is being told to do something, and is required to confirm its completion to the superior, but this is to take too simplistic a view of matters. During the atomic action, there is in general a two way dialogue between the superior and subordinate, which is user data as far as CCR is concerned. It is presumed by CCR that either the superior or subordinate, or both, will know when the dialogue relating to the atomic action is complete, and in fact either can signal its completion, as will become clear in the next section.

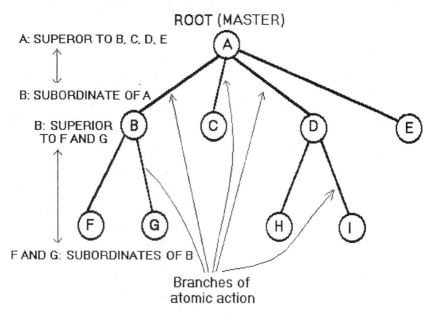

Figure 18.1 - The CCR commitment tree

In the general case, a superior may have more than one subordinate, each of which has a part to play in the overall subset of the atomic action for which this superior has responsibility; each subordinate may of course itself be a superior lower down the tree, and have its own subordinates, so that in the general case, CCR can be viewed as recursive in nature.

The standard does not define precisely what constitutes an atomic action, except to the extent that it is a sequence of operations which progress without interference from external actions, and which must either all complete successfully, or all terminate with no change to the associated (external to the OS environment) data. 'Without interference' can be interpreted in the database update context as meaning that no other updates will actually be applied to the records in question until the atomic action has completed, as will become clearer in a moment.

Stages in CCR

For any given (component of an) atomic action, there are a number of stages, which can be summarised as follows:

• The master notifies the subordinate that the atomic action is about to BEGIN. What happens during the atomic action is of no concern to CCR.

• When the master's service user has completed whatever dialogue constitutes the atomic action, it may signal this to the subordinate by inviting it to offer commitment (PREPARE).

• Assuming that nothing has gone wrong, the subordinate will then offer commitment (READY). Alternatively it may do this without receiving a PREPARE, if the subordinate's service user can determine that the dialogue constituting the atomic action has been completed. Hence the PREPARE above is optional.

• The crucial point to note here is that the subordinate has merely *offered* commitment; it has not yet committed. This is the essence of two stage commitment. Other parts of the atomic action may fail, so that the offer may not be taken up. Therefore the subordinate must now be in a position either to *proceed to completion*, all changes having been applied, or to *rollback* to the initial state, forgetting all about the previous dialogue. For example if the atomic action was an update replacing the contents of an database record, the subordinate must be able either to keep the old copy or replace it with the new contents. But the subordinate does not know yet which action to take. It is merely notifying the superior that it <u>can</u> complete the atomic action if subsequently ordered to do so.

In the general case, a superior entity may have more than subordinate, and it may also be a subordinate itself (i.e. it is not the master entity). In this case, this entity will collect all of the READYs from its subordinates. Once they have all been received, the READY passed to its own superior will imply that all aspects of the atomic action which this entity has responsibility are also READY.

• Again assuming all is well, all of the READYs will reach the master. Once the master is satisfied that all branches of the tree are capable of commitment, it may then *order commitment* by issuing a COMMIT. This in turn passes back down the tree, each subordinate passing it on to all of its subordinates in turn.

- It may also happen at any time that an entity anywhere in the tree runs into difficulties of such a nature that there is no point in continuing with the atomic action. In this case it can issue a ROLLBACK, which will have the effect of causing the entire atomic action to be abandoned.

The presume rollback paradigm

That is then normally the end of the matter. Unfortunately things can go wrong at any stage in the proceedings. One of the crucial differences between the old and new versions of CCR is in regard to what happens when things go wrong. There are two aspects to this, relating to the keeping of a *log* of the progress of the atomic action, and the *presumed action* in case of a failure of one of the branches.

- The *old version* of CCR used a *presume nothing* paradigm. What this means in effect is that if a failure occurs, the master makes no assumption as to the state of the atomic action. So the master had to find out, and this involved some rather ugly and asymmetric handshaking using C-RECOVER and C-RESTART primitives, which no longer form part of the standard. In addition, the master had to open a log of activity for the current atomic action when it started it (issued the BEGIN), so that it could keep track of the status of each branch.

- This was considered to be adequate for JTM, the first user of CCR. However when it was considered for use with TP, the TP designers felt that the procedures were too cumbersome and inefficient. In particular they wanted to minimise the number of disk accesses which would be involved in maintaining the log. Therefore in the *new version*, a different approach is used. The master delays producing a log for as long as possible, in fact until it issues a COMMIT to its subordinates. The subordinate opens its log when it offers the READY. In the event of any failure before the log has been opened, each entity *presumes rollback*, which is another way of saying that until the entity has a log, it assumes that if a failure occurs, the entire atomic action will roll back and be abandoned. Therefore there is no point in an entity issuing an explicit ROLLBACK primitive if it has not yet created a log. Further simplifications were also made to the procedures, including the elimination of primitive parameters relating to the level of commitment.

Figure 18.2 outlines the various stages in CCR, for dialogues between a superior and a subordinate.

- This considerably eases the recovery problem, but leaves two main cases to be considered. One is where the subordinate has a log, the master has issued a COMMIT, and the commit is lost. Another is where a subordinate has issued READY, then fails. Any entity encountering difficulties of this type may attempt to RECOVER, based on its copy of the log.

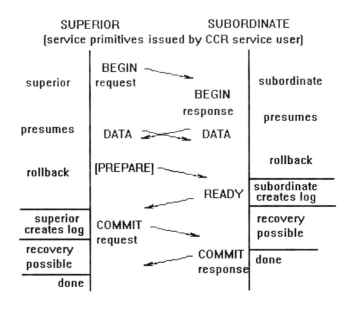

Figure 18.2 - stages in normal CCR dialogue

The above procedures simplify considerably if only one subordinate is involved, of course. In this case the master STARTs, and optionally PREPAREs. The subordinate indicates that it is READY, and the superior can immediately COMMIT, as it is also the master. However we have discussed the more general case, as only by examining a tree can the full complexity of the mechanism be appreciated, and some applications such are TP require this type of tree structure.

That then is the philosophy of the new version of CCR, and reflects the current IS. In a moment we will elaborate on the service, relating it to specific service primitives. However it is worth mentioning that a number of *amendments* (addenda) are currently under consideration. One is called 'heuristics', and concerns the means by which the subordinate notifies the superior of its intention to commit following communication failure after it has issued a READY. Others are concerned with mapping to the session layer, and with which entity has ultimate responsibility for the ultimate COMMIT. We will not be discussing these.

18.3.3   CCR service primitives

The CCR service is provided by means of a set of *C-primitives*. It is not the intention here to provide a detailed discussion of this service; the following examples of primitives are included to give a feel for how the service operates, and the list is not complete. Full details may be found in the standard document.

C-BEGIN optionally confirmed   atomic action id, branch id, user data

This is issued by a superior to a subordinate, to initiate an atomic action, and hence establish a *CCR association* between the application entities.Typically after the BEGIN has been issued, possibly on several different branches of the 'commitment tree', various transactions will take place which are transparent to, and of no concern to, CCR. These comprise the atomic action, which is again significant to the CCR user rather than CCR itself. Once all aspects of the atomic action have been completed, the superior may optionally ask each subordinate whether it has successfully competed its part of the atomic action, and *invite* each subordinate to *offer commitment*, as follows:

C-PREPARE unconfirmed   user data

On receipt of the PREPARE, the subordinate replies as follows if it is prepared to commit. (If it is not in a position to offer commitment, it may simply ignore the request, and the superior will presume rollback; this is one of the major differences between the current version and the old one.)

C-READY unconfirmed   user data

Assuming that all subordinates have returned READY rather than refuse, the superior may then require all subordinates to commit by issuing the following primitive to all of them:

C-COMMIT confirmed   user data

As this is a confirmed service, the C-COMMIT response confirming committal is mandatory. Receipt of all of the C-COMMIT confirms signals the end of the atomic action.

The new version of CCR still has a primitive for rollback:

C-ROLLBACK confirmed   user data

In fact ROLLBACK can also be issued if the superior encounters difficulties before the PREPARE stage is reached. In situations where there is a tree structure of atomic actions, with upper branches depending on the success of lower branches, the superior at any level may pass a ROLLBACK back up the tree to its superior, and so on up to the master (root). In any case where a ROLLBACK indication is received, the subordinates will release all resources before responding with the response variant.

One final primitive is provided:

C–RECOVER maybe confirmed   recovery state, atomic action id, branch id, user data

This is to cater for the situation where a subordinate has offered commitment but, due to a failure of the application association, it is unaware whether it is required to commit. Similarly, after issuing a C-COMMIT request, a loss of the association may mean that the subordinate does not confirm the commit.

- C-RECOVER is a confirmed service if it is *issued by the superior*. In this case the *recovery state* may be either ready (commit), retry later or unknown. In the case of retry later, the subordinate retains its atomic action details and attempts another RECOVER at a later time. (Precisely when this might be is of no concern to CCR itself.)

- If C-RECOVER *issued by the subordinate*, the *recovery state* is always ready. In this case the primitive is optionally confirmed.

One final point worth noting is that the old version of CCR had primitive parameters to support three commitment levels. This allowed the subordinate CCR service user to indicate partial or full commitment. The view now held is that how the offer of commitment is to be interpreted is nothing to do with CCR, and therefore should not be a specific CCR parameter. Any implied degree of commitment is now conveyed as user data, and is for the service user to worry about. In fact the full class JTM service (discussed in chapter twenty) made use of all three levels of CCR commitment (and was hence 'defective'), and the basic class used two (and was also defective).

18.4 Remote Operations Service Elements (ROSE)

18.4.1 Introduction

ROSE provides a protocol to support interactive services. It supports enquiry/response dialogues. In many ways it has the characteristics of a remote procedure call (RPC), a function commonly provided on client/server LANs. An ASE, known in ROSE as the *invoker*, passes a task specification to an ASE in the other open system known as the *performer*. The performer performs some operation as indicated in the task specification and returns the result to the invoker. This is a technique which is common in LAN distributed operating systems. There will normally be a requirement for the performer to perform the operation within some time limit, or to advise the invoker of failure.

In the example above it was implied that the response would be the result of some request. As we will see in a moment, the original use of ROSE had nothing to do with this type of dialogue. This merely serves to emphasise the often made point that ROSE, like other OSI support services, simply provides a mechanism, and it is for superior ASEs to decide what use to make of it. In that sense ROSE is more generalised than RPC.

ROSE started life as part of the X.400(1984) MHS recommendations. It was then known as ROS, which differed in detail from ROSE, notably in that it did not make use of ACSE (CASE kernel), which was not sufficiently stable at the time. In the MHS context the task is typically a mail message which requires to be stored in a remote mailbox. The function of ROSE in this case is to associate the message and a returned delivery (non-)confirmation. If required, ROSE may use the underlying RTSE discussed in the next section to provide a guarantee that both the message and the confirmation get delivered successfully. At present MHS is the principal user of ROSE.

It is important to note that, by itself, ROSE is not viable. There has to be some association between superior ASEs which have an understanding of the nature of the request and reply, and only they can generate the request and reply in the first place. Without service users, ROSE is merely an abstraction, which is why it is referred to in this book as an application support service. It is for the ROSE user to specify what remote operation is to take place, supply any associated parameters, and determine how the results are to be formatted. Most of this is user data as far as ROSE is concerned.

ROSE offers two alternative mechanisms, which are termed *synchronous* or *asynchronous*. (These terms are also used in the context of certain other applications such as VT.)

   • In the *synchronous* case, there is a tight *binding* between the request and the reply. In effect the request and the reply form part of the same application association. A reply must be received, and in general the reply must be received before the next request can be issued. In the synchronous case, ROSE always reports either success or failure.

   In this context success is to be interpreted as a result, and failure as an error.

   • In the *asynchronous* case, there is no such binding. In this sense it is rather like a datagram service, and any combination of reporting, success or failure, success only, failure only and none at all is permitted. (In a sense this is analogous to the connectionless modes in LLC; see chapter thirteen.)

ROSE can also operate *recursively*. In this case the performer may initiate a further ROSE association with a third entity (a 'child' entity) which will actually perform the operation. The outcome of this subsidiary ROSE association will be reported back on completion (or failure). This can in theory operate to any level of recursion. Again the ROSE user determines if and how this will take place.

Two mappings are permitted on to underlying services. ROSE may either map on to RTSE, which is the MHS usage, or may map directly on to ACSE and the presentation service. If mapping is to RTSE, either RTSE or the ROSE user will be responsible for managing the application association. (As mentioned earlier, ACSE can only have one user.)

18.4.2   ROSE service

Overview

The ROSE service is best explained in terms of the sequence of operations which ROSE controls. Basically this consists of establishing an application association (*bind*), sending a request (*invoke*), possibly getting a reply (*result*), and terminating the association (*unbind*). Each of these has service primitives associated with it, and as usual we will concentrate on the service primitives available rather than the underlying protocol mechanisms. Figure 18.3 illustrates a typical ROSE association, showing the usage of ACSE, RTSE and the session service.

Bind and unbind services

These are used to establish and terminate a ROSE association. Two service primitives are involved. The details are complex and will not be provided; basically the services map to ACSE services already discussed. If ROSE is not the sole user of ACSE, these services cannot be used.

RO–BIND confirmed   various parameters

This establishes the association. Parameters include those which are passed to the A-ASSOCIATE primitive, including details of the application and presentation contexts. A ROSE association must be bound (established) before it can be used.

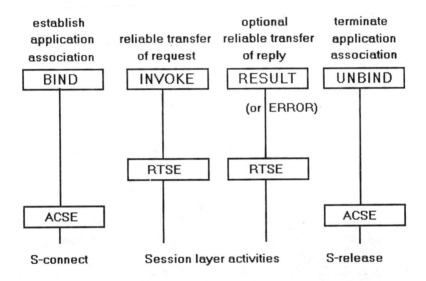

Figure 18.3 - ROSE phases and use of underlying services

RO–UNBIND confirmed   various parameters

This terminates the ROSE binding, i.e. ends this association.

Request-reply services

In order to avoid terminological confusion between the request service and the request primitive variant, we will sometimes refer to the request-reply as an enquiry-response. Separate primitives are provided for the enquiry and the associated response. The request variant of the primitive mapping the enquiry specifies whether the dialogue is to be synchronous or asynchronous. In the asynchronous case, a parameter associated with the enquiry specifies whether a response is expected, and if so, under what circumstances (success and/or failure). It should be noted that the primitives are unconfirmed. If ROSE needs to be certain whether the primitive 'got through', RTSE (see §18.5) may be used as an underlying mechanism. RTSE either confirms delivery, or reports a failure, in which case an error is reported to the ROSE user.

Each enquiry and response may be handled by RTSE, in which case the RTSE turn (see §18.5) must be passed to the peer RTSE entity once the enquiry has been received, in order to be able to transmit the response. If RTSE is not used, ROSE may use the session service data token directly rather than the RTSE turn, which implies that the RTSE turn itself maps on to the session service data token.

An enquiry (*request*) is passed to ROSE using the RO-INVOKE primitive, as follows:

RO-INVOKE unconfirmed   operation value, operation class, argument, invoke and linked identifiers, priority

• The *operation value* is an identifier whose meaning is significant to the ROSE user (e.g. MHS; see chapter twenty two).

• The *operation class* is either synchronous or asynchronous. In the asynchronous case, it is also specified whether a response is required. If so, it must be received within a certain time as dictated by the requested QOS, subject also to the priority parameter (see below). In the case of asynchronous (unco-ordinated) requests, the peer ROSE entity may wish to optimise the use of the underlying RTSE turn in order to minimise un-necessary 'shuttling' of the session service data token. However any such optimisation must not prejudice the QOS and priority requirements. (This is in effect a decision for the implementor.)

• The *argument* contains the contents of the enquiry.

• The *invoke and linked identifiers* are used by ROSE to correlate requests and replies. In this context, it should be noted that in the asynchronous case, requests and replies may be interleaved.

• The *priority* is for use by the peer ROSE entity, and indicates the degree of urgency which should be applied to formulating a response. *Eight levels of priority* are provided. It is for the ROSE user to determine which requests are urgent and which are not. MHS makes use of all eight priorities for various purposes.

If a response (*reply*) is to be provided, the peer ROSE user will provide this by means of a RO-RESULT primitive as follows:

RO-RESULT unconfirmed   operation-value, result, invoke
identifier, priority

> • The *result* contains the text of the response. The *invoke identifier* associates the result with an earlier invoke. The other parameters have similar meanings to those in the INVOKE.

It may of course be that a response was not required, in which case a RESULT is not expected. If used, RTSE will use its best efforts to deliver requests and replies. However if this proves to be impossible (within the required time, or subject to the required QOS), RTSE will notify ROSE of an exception condition, which will be reported to the ROSE user by means the RO-ERROR primitive:

RO-ERROR unconfirmed   error-value, error-parameter,
invoke-ID, priority

> • The error-value and error-parameter are values which are meaningful to the ROSE user. The other parameters are similar to those of the INVOKE or RESULT.

> Note that there is a clear distinction between RO-ERROR and an RO-RESULT containing (say) a notification of failure to deliver the RO-INVOKE. For example if the INVOKE was a message, the RESULT could say that the message could not be delivered to the user, as his mailbox was full. The implication is that the INVOKE did get there; ERROR in reply means that it did not.

Exception reporting

Situations can arise where the peer ROSE entity receives an INVOKE, RESULT or ERROR indication, but for some reason is unable to handle it correctly. For example, it may have lost its association with its user, and cannot deliver an INVOKE or RESULT. In this case the REJECT-U primitive is issued to the sender:

RO-REJECT-U unconfirmed   reason

> • The *reason* indicates either why the INVOKE or RESULT has been rejected, or in the case of ERROR, it notifies some

illegality in the ERROR PDU (such as an unknown error code, or an invalid invoke identifier reference).

It is important to note in the latter case that implementations must ensure that situations cannot arise where the receipt of an invalid ERROR PDU will lead to the return of another ERROR which itself is invalid, as this could lead to an endless (and useless) exchange of such notifications. Such problems were also identified in early email protocols.

A second kind of exception condition is rejection by the service provider. In this case the ROSE user receives a RO-REJECT:

RO–REJECT–P indication   invoke–ID, returned–parameters, reason

- The *returned parameters* are those of the primitive which could not be delivered due to some illegality such as invalid type, format or encoding; the *reason* specifies the nature of the error. This indication may be returned for any primitive issued by the user which requires something to be sent to the peer user.

18.5   Reliable Transfer Service Elements (RTSE)

18.5.1   Introduction

The purpose of RTSE is to 'protect' some message (i.e. application PDU relevant to the service user) being transferred between applications, i.e. either to confirm its successful delivery or to notify that this proved to be impossible within the requested time. For example MHS may use RTSE (via ROSE, discussed in the previous section) to supervise (e.g. email) messages and delivery confirmations (see chapter twenty two).

At this point you may well argue that the transport layer is supposed to ensure reliable delivery, but this is insufficient for two reasons, as indeed we suggested in an aside in chapter fifteen:

- No class of transport protocol will recover from a failure of the underlying network(s) which results in the required QOS not being met; under these circumstances the underlying connection will be lost.

- For historical reasons, MHS was designed to operate over TP0 which provides no recovery at all from signalled errors (including X.25 resets). In the event of either an X.25 reset or a disconnect, TP0 would again terminate the underlying connection.

Therefore RTSE is required, if only to re-establish the underlying failed connection and repeat the transmission attempt, transparently to the user. But even RTSE cannot guarantee delivery, and if success cannot be achieved within a given time, RTSE will report failure. This may occur for example if there is a catastrophic failure either of the underlying network or of the peer application, which clearly neither RTSE nor any other ASE can do anything positive about.

It should be clear that QOS means different things at different layers. A QOS requirement which is too high to allow the transport connection to be re-established is not necessarily too high to allow RTSE to make another attempt. QOS is a somewhat elusive concept.

Like ROSE above it, RTSE is not viable on its own, as it has no knowledge of the context of the PDU which it is attempting to deliver, nor indeed would it have anything to deliver. Therefore again there must be a *RTSE user* which understands what RTSE is being used for, typically a MHS(1988) service element using ROSE, as discussed in §18.4 and in chapter twenty two.

Another feature of RTSE is that it uses *session layer activities*, a common feature of CCITT-originated applications. Each PDU (e.g. message) and the response confirming (or otherwise) its successful delivery are encapsulated within an activity; the PDU and its delivery confirmation are further encapsulated within *dialogue units* (major synchronisation points). RTSE may also insert *minor synchronisation points* at suitable intervals during the activity, as it sees fit. An activity may be *interrupted* in the event of minor errors occurring, and can be resumed later. In case of more severe errors, such as loss of the application association itself, the activity may need to be *discarded*, and in this case the transaction will start again from scratch at a later time, in a new activity. Only if recovery proves impossible (within a specified time) will the activity be abandoned altogether and failure be reported to the user.

It is not for RTSE to specify what the maximum time should be. It may be of the order of minutes, hours or even days, depending on the application concerned.

The standard mapping of RTSE on to the underlying protocol stack is via ACSE and the presentation service. This is the mapping defined as standard for MHS(1988), and intended to be used by any new applications using RTSE. Unfortunately this poses problems for MHS(1984) implementations which use neither, so an additional mapping is permitted (as an interim measure) which bypasses ACSE and uses a minimal (default) presentation service. We discussed the reasons for this in §18.1. We will exclude considerations relevant only to MHS(1984) from the discussion.

18.5.2   RTSE service

Overview

RTSE is organised into various services. The RTSE user (e.g. ROSE; see §18.4) must first use the *open* service, which uses ACSE to establish an application association. At the end, the user invokes the *close* service to terminate the association. Unless using the special MHS(1984) backward compatibility mode, RTSE must be operated over an application association.

As well as graceful termination of the association, RTSE includes the usual *abort* services, associated with user and service provider aborts, which we will not discuss any further.

Once the association is set up, RTSE operates by means of sending some 'message' via the *transfer* service. Each message TRANSFER is confirmed, the response variant indicating success or failure, and each transfer and the response is encapsulated within a session activity. In the case of failure, the transfer can be repeated. Failure is to be interpreted as meaning that the transfer was not successfully completed within a specific time, as specified by the required QOS. It is therefore possible that failure was reported but delivery was actually achieved, but 'too late'. Session minor SPs may be issued as required during a transfer.

The other main feature of RTSE is the concept of the *turn*. This closely parallels the *session service data token* in half duplex mode, in that the turn gives permission to transfer a user PDU to one RTSE entity at a time. Requesting the turn maps on to S-TOKEN-PLEASE, and surrendering the turn maps on to S-*CONTROL*-GIVE (not S-TOKEN-GIVE, as all tokens will be passed to the peer RTSE entity). This allows RTSE to be used under ROSE, the turn being passed to the peer ASE when the request has been received, in order to transmit the reply.

Figure 18.4 shows diagrammatically the different phases in an RTSE association, and how the underlying ACSE and session services are used.

Open service

A single service primitive is provided, which typically (but not necessarily) maps upwards to the RO-BIND primitive discussed in §18.5.2. It always maps downwards to the A-ASSOCIATE primitive discussed in §18.2.2.

RT–OPEN confirmed   28 parameters including mode, initial turn, application protocol

Most of the parameters are mapped on to the underlying A-ASSOCIATE primitive discussed earlier. Other parameters of particular interest are as follows:

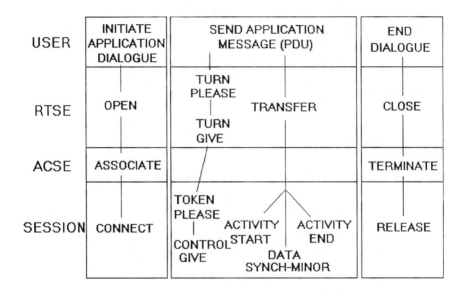

Figure 18.4 - RTSE phases and usage of underlying services

• *Application protocol*. This identifies the RTSE user. Typically this is ROSE (the BIND service as discussed in the next section). However in principle any ASE can make use of RTSE. Remember that RTSE cannot operate in isolation; a user must be specified.

• A *mode* parameter is provided for backwards compatibility with MHS(1984) implementations. This determines whether full use will be made of underlying services (the MHS(1988) standard), or a 'retrofitted' service using a minimal presentation service, and not using ACSE, is to be used.

• *Initial turn*. This determines the direction of transfer of the first 'message' to be handled by RTSE. This is determined by the ACSE class, as discussed in §18.2.

Close service

A single service primitive is provided, which typically (but not necessarily) maps upwards to the RO-UNBIND primitive discussed in §18.5.2. It always maps downwards to the A-RELEASE primitive discussed in §18.2.2.

RT–CLOSE confirmed　　　　　　　reason, user data

- The *reason* and *user data* are those passed to the underlying ACSE RELEASE service.

Transfer service

In order to request the transfer of a message (APDU), the following primitive is used:

RT–TRANSFER confirmed　　　　APDU, transfer–time, result

- Where ROSE is the user, the *APDU* will typically contain a request, reply or error notification, as discussed in the next section. The standard use of RTSE is to protect ROSE transactions, although this does not preclude other uses.

- The *transfer time* is the maximum time allowed for confirmation of successful transfer. This leaves the possibility that the transfer succeeded, but the confirmation was not received in time, so that failure was reported in the *result* parameter.

Turn services

In order to use RT-TRANSFER, the RTSE entity must own the turn, i.e. the session service half duplex data token. Furthermore, since each TRANSFER maps on to a session activity, each RT-TRANSFER is bounded by S-PRIMITIVES to set up and terminate the activity. Although we will not discuss these in detail, the activity must be successfully terminated before the turn can be exchanged. Two primitives are provided so that the RTSE user may gain control over transmission of PDUs; these map on to session service token primitives:

RT–TURN–PLEASE unconfirmed　　　priority

This maps on to S-TOKEN-PLEASE, requesting the data, sync-minor and major-activity tokens.

- The *priority* indicates how urgently the peer should act on the received indication. This in turn reflects the priority assigned by the user (typically ROSE on behalf of a MHS service). Maximum priority is reserved for tokens requested so that the association may be terminated.

On receipt of a RT-TURN-PLEASE indication, the peer RTSE user must relinquish all (i.e. all relevant) tokens within a time determined by the requested priority. It issues:

RT-TURN-GIVE unconfirmed   (no parameters)

This passes control to the peer, which will now either initiate a new TRANSFER or request that the association be terminated, as appropriate.

Part five

OSI applications and management

We conclude the book by examining what might (inaccurately) be described as the 'upper half' of the application layer. We devote by far the most space to the four principal applications, File Transfer, Access and Management (FTAM), Job Transfer and Manipulation (JTM), Virtual Terminal (VT) and Message Handling Systems (MHS). Other applications are discussed as well, albeit in much less detail, including Office Document Architecture (ODA), Manufacturing Messaging Systems (MMS) and Remote Data Access (RDA). As far as OSI management and control are concerned, the Directory is covered, as well as other topics including OSI profiles, conformance statements, and the formal description techniques LOTOS and ESTELLE. The book concludes with a few comments on likely future developments.

19   File Transfer, Access and Management (FTAM)

19.1   Introduction

Ever since networks existed, there has been a need to ship files between machines. Early attempts at file transfer protocols (FTPs) were between machines of similar type, and provided a simple mapping from the physical filestore of machine X to that of machine Y, implemented directly over some link protocol such as BSC. This was efficient in this context, in that only the filename and mode of access (read, write, append...) had to be specified. Since both X and Y understood the physical layout of both filestores, and both hosts implemented the underlying protocol, there was no problem.

More recently, a variety of FTP programs of similar philosophy has emerged for the IBM PC / MSDOS environment. Both PCs have the same view of the internal organisation of the filestore, and the same filename conventions. You do not even need a network. All that is required is to connect the serial ports of two PCs together with a cable, and run the program on both machines. Typing the relevant commands on each PC is all that is required. The well known *Kermit* program from Lancaster University is one of the most popular of this type, and also incorporates terminal emulation functions.

If things are so simple, why bother going to the trouble of standardisation? Why not simply run Kermit everywhere? There are two main problems with programs of this type:

> • Kermit is tied into the facilities of a particular operating system (in this case MSDOS). Therefore Kermit can only guarantee to interwork successfully with other MSDOS machines which have the same view of the filestore. When using Kermit between a MSDOS machine and a UNIX machine, it is possible to request file transfers which are guaranteed to fail, because the file naming conventions of MSDOS and UNIX are fundamentally different; those of UNIX are far more flexible. In order to be able to use Kermit, the user must make decisions on what can and cannot be achieved. This is clearly against the whole spirit of OSI. No (human) user can be expected to know the filestore conventions of numerous different operating systems and hardware configurations. Assistance is needed which programs such as Kermit cannot provide.

- Equally importantly, Kermit is tied into using its own private protocol. In effect it is implementing a rather rudimentary FTP directly over a proprietary link protocol. It is therefore highly network dependent, and it is not clear how, or if, it could be used over (say) an X.25 network.

Within its limitations Kermit is extremely useful, as this author can testify. But in the OSI context what is required is a much more generalised framework, something which will provide standardised mechanisms which will work between any pair of physical filestores, and independently of the underlying networks. ISO has already solved the second problem by providing OSI/RM, and the support layers discussed in previous chapters. Now what is required is a framework which can form the basis of an OSI file handling application.

The UK academic interim NIFTP (see chapter nine) introduced the concept of a *virtual filestore* (*VFS*), which is an abstract representation of a physical filestore by means of a set of *attributes*. This should by now be a familiar concept. The hosts *negotiate* the set of attributes to be used, and this defines what subsequent operations can be performed on the file, and the effects these operations will have on the real filestore can be predicted, even though the physical details of the real filestore are hidden behind the attributes. Unfortunately while NIFTP is on the right lines, it still fails the test as an OSI protocol, for reasons which we will discuss at the end of the chapter.

NIFTP is, by its very nature, a *file transfer* protocol. It has no other function than to provide a mechanism for the transfer of an entire file from host X to host Y, where the direction of transfer and mode of access are negotiated prior to the transfer. Although various session-service-like mechanisms are provided for data marks, rollback and restart, the philosophy of NIFTP is that the entire file will be transferred, although it is possible to abort a transfer part way through.

While it is true that transferring entire files is, and will remain, important, other functions are required as well which NIFTP cannot support. FTAM, as the name implies, is far more than merely a glorified file transfer protocol. As well as file transfer, it provides more powerful mechanisms.

- *File access*. FTAM provides mechanisms whereby the internal structure of a file can be defined, so that parts of it may be accessed independently. A file is considered to be a structure of *File Access Data Units* (*FADUs*). Although the ordering of FADUs within a file is defined, operations on one FADU (i.e. on the data units inside it) do not necessarily affect other FADUs in the file. FTAM provides a variety of mechanisms for combining FADUs into a file structure, which are based on a hierarchical model. FTAM also provides mechanisms such as locking to support shared access to files. We will examine file structures in more detail later in the chapter.

• *File management.* FTAM provides mechanisms for the management of virtual filestore access rights (e.g. read, write) and filenames (e.g. rename). It does not yet possess filestore management capabilities, but these are currently under consideration.

In short, FTAM is more powerful than NIFTP, and provides facilities which have a potentially wide range of applications. Since it provides facilities both for transferring entire files, and for manipulating parts of files, it could ultimately replace proprietary systems such as Sun's NFS, to handle downloading of files from fileservers to diskless workstations, as well as allow several workstations to share a file. It goes without saying that FTAM can handle the kind of file transfers for which Kermit was devised, although it should be equally clear that terminal emulation aspects of Kermit are of no relevance whatsoever to this discussion.

Some experts currently feel that further work is required before FTAM can be considered as a viable contender in an LAN environment. There appears to be no immediate threat to Sun's NFS from FTAM at the time of writing.

19.2   Basic features of FTAM

NIFTP was an unbalanced protocol between two hosts, One host (P) initiated the file transfer, and the other (Q) had to decide whether the transfer request from P was acceptable. Similarly FTAM has an *initiator*, which has a need to run FTAM, and a *responder* which either has (or may have) some file to which the initiator requires access, or is the intended recipient of some file. Unlike NIFTP however, FTAM permits 'initiator only' and 'responder only' implementations. The initiator only mode would be appropriate for a diskless workstation which needs to obtain files from time to time, but the file server could not operate in this node, as it would not be able to process incoming requests, only generate its own. But if the file server was entirely passive, merely servicing received requests, it could be implemented as a responder only.

A second parallel between FTAM and NIFTP is that, once access to a file has been agreed, FTAM refers to the *sender* and *receiver*, either of which may be the initiator.

Expressed in rather formal terms, FTAM offers a number of generalised services:

- Access between open systems offering some form of information storage facility.

- File transfer between these information stores.

- Access to a file in an information store, for the purpose of adding, removing or altering parts of a file.

- File management in the information store, including the ability to create and erase files, and to alter their attributes.

These facilities are more generalised than those offered by NIFTP (the blue book), but include facilities of the NIFTP type. The FTAM service definition makes provision for one system to control file operations between other systems, and provides support for more generalised file access and file management operations, with the intention in the future of including operations on groups of files (e.g. file directories: filestore management).

As usual in OSI, FTAM is based on *functional units*, and it is for peer applications to negotiate which functional units are to be used for a particular FTAM association. We discuss the functional units available in §19.4.

19.3   The virtual filestore

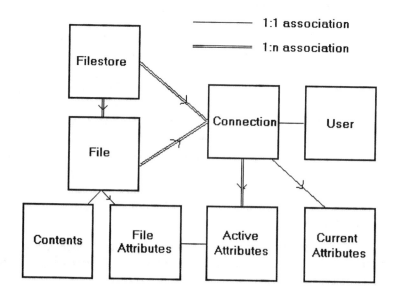

Figure 19.1 - FTAM virtual filestore schema

The operation of the file protocol is based on the concept of a virtual filestore, i.e. a model defining files and their attributes in a way which is sufficiently abstract to be general. The virtual filestore provides a means for describing a variety of attributes of a file. Figure 19.1 illustrates the relationships between the user, the file and the filestore, as depicted in the standard document.

19.3.1   Attribute types

Two types of attribute are defined, *file attributes* or *activity attributes*. Use of these attributes is subject to negotiation as discussed in §19.3.3. A complete list of attributes of each type will be provided, and selected attributes of each type will be discussed in more detail.

File attributes

These relate to the current status of the file, and can only have a single value at any one time. A complete list appears in figure 19.2. The following are among the most important.

- **Filename**. The actual name of the file. There are many system-dependent restrictions on filenames. For example in MSDOS systems, only an 8-character name and 3-character extension are permitted, separated by a period (and optionally preceded by a path through the directory tree). However this is of no concern to FTAM, except in the sense that specifying an illegal filename will certainly cause the FTAM file association to fail. FTAM allows filenames to be composed of one or more strings of 1 to 8 uppercase letters or numbers, each starting with a letter.

  It is not immediately clear how this caters for filenames which are case sensitive.

- **Access control**. This indicates the conditions under which the file is to be accessed, as follows:

  - *Permitted actions* define the required access, from read, insert, replace, erase, extend, read file attributes, change file attributes and delete file.

  - *Identity, password* and *location* of initiator. The aim here is to provide some form of user authentication, a difficult area to police at the best of times.

  Provided that the requested access is allowed, select, open, locate, close and deselect operations may always be performed on the file, as discussed in §19.6. (These operations do not alter the contents of the file.)

ATTRIBUTE	ASN.1 TYPE
Filename	Vector of Strings
Permitted actions	Boolean vector
Contents type	Abstract syntax or reference
Storage account	String
Date and time of creation	Date and time
Date and time of last write	Date and time
Date and time of last read	Date and time
Date and time of last attb change	Date and time
Identity of creator	String
Identity of last modifier	String
Identity of last reader	String
Identity of last attb modifier	String
File availability	Subset of defined values
Filesize	Integer
Future filesize	Integer
Access control	See text
Legal qualifications	String
Private use	Unconstrained

Figure 19.2 - FTAM file attributes

• **Storage account**. This identifies the accounting authority responsible for any file storage charges.

• **File availability**. This indicates whether the file is available now, which will not be the case if there will be a delay opening the file, for example if the file is archived on magnetic tape.

• **Filesize** and **future filesize**. Before getting a copy of a file, it is advisable to have sufficient room to be able to store it. Similarly, if writing or adding to a file in a filestore, it is useful to know in advance that there is room for any changes which will be applied. The FTAM association will fail if the recipient will not have room for all of the necessary changes, or if a file to be read will not fit in the receiver's filestore. This is negotiable, although FTAM will not be interested in <u>why</u> the negotiation failed.

The MSDOS operating system used on the author's PC regularly irritates him by attempting to copy files from the hard disk to a floppy disk when it could easily have determined in advance that there was insufficient room. After all, MSDOS knows both the size of the file to be copied and the space remaining on the floppy disk! The problem is not just one of irritation in the OSI context however, as the useless file transfer would have to be paid for.

• **Legal qualifications**. The UK has a (somewhat ill-conceived) Data Protection Act. This parameter is intended to be used in the context of such national data privacy legislation.

Activity attributes

These reflect the current status of the FTAM association, i.e. what is currently happening to the file, who is currently using it. Again many different attributes are provided, and the full list is shown in figure 19.3. (Locking style is discussed in §19.6.)

• **Initiator identity** and **location**. These are intended for use with authentication services when these are finalised.

• **Password**. A host may require password permission to access files or particular parts of files. FTAM merely provides a mechanism.

ATTRIBUTE	ASN.1 TYPE
Active contents type	
Access request	Boolean vector
Initiator identity	String
Location (in file)	Node Descriptor
Processing mode	Boolean vector
Calling application entity title	Application entity title
Responding application entity title	Application entity title
Account	String
Concurrency control	Vector of enumeration
Locking style	Boolean
Access passwords	String (or octet string)

NOTE:
All of these refer to the current status of the FTAM association. The full name has the prefix 'current' in each case (except for active contents type).

Figure 19.3 - FTAM activity attributes

• **Account**. This refers to the 'account holder' of the file currently being operated on.

- **Concurrency control**. One application of FTAM is to support shared access to a file held by a file server by several workstations (connected via a LAN). If more than one user may update all or part of the file, concurrency control is needed so that the file's contents are always in a consistent state, and to avoid access conflicts. The parameter may take the values 'exclusive access' and 'shared access'.

How the open system implements concurrency control is of no interest to FTAM, which merely provides a means of requesting and agreeing to use it. The RDA standard (chapter twenty three) is also concerned with concurrency control.

19.3.2   Attribute groups

When NIFTP was designed (see chapter nine), it was realised that not all attributes would be required in all implementations, and therefore minimal implementations were permitted. Unfortunately this also meant that two implementations picked at random could not be guaranteed to interwork, and values such as 'no value available' could be returned in the attribute negotiation stage. In FTAM, a more systematic approach has been adopted, and various negotiable *attribute groups* have been defined, Within each group, either no attributes are supported, or all are either partially or fully supported. The response to a partially supported attribute again includes 'no value available'.

The attributes contained in each group are listed below without further comment.

Kernel group

File attributes: filename, permitted actions, contents type.

Activity attributes: Active contents type, current access request, initiator identity, location, processing mode, calling and responding application entity title.

Storage group

File attributes: storage account, date and time of creation, last modification, last read access and last attribute modification, identities of creator, last modifier, last reader and last attribute modifier, file availability, filesize, future filesize.

Activity attributes: current account, concurrency control, locking style.

Security group

File attributes: access control, legal qualifications.

Activity attributes: current access passwords, active legal qualification.

19.3.3 Attribute negotiation

This is one of those areas which is simple in principle, but complex in detail. The mechanism is rather similar to that used in NIFTP. Basically the initiator proposes a set of attributes, subject to the attribute group constraints. The responder either returns the same value (agreement), suggests an alternative value (e.g. to reduce the future filesize), rejects the attribute (e.g. no such file), or responds 'no value available'. (This implies that this attribute does not have sufficient support at the recipient for it to be able to confirm the proposed value.)

Precisely what happens then depends on how the initiating FTAM user reacts to the set of returned attributes, which is beyond the scope of FTAM. Attribute negotiation occurs at various stages, as will become clear when file services are discussed in §19.6. In addition, file management allows interrogation of specific attributes and modification of attributes, which do not count as negotiation.

19.4 Functional units and service classes

19.4.1 Functional units

FTAM is a complex standard, providing a variety of services of varying complexity. In order to provide some rigour in implementation, it is necessary to group the services into *functional units* (*FUs*). The means by which functional units can be negotiated is simplified by defining various *service classes*. For a given service class, some FUs will be mandatory, while others will be *optional* (i.e. negotiable), and yet others may not be permitted. The *QOS* required for the FTAM association may also influence the implementation of some FUs. This is an internal FTAM issue which is not visible to the user, and will not be discussed in this book.

19.4.2 Functional units provided

The following FUs are provided.

- **Kernel**. This is responsible for setting up the FTAM association, and selecting the file to be operated on. This FU must obviously be provided in all implementations.

- **Read** and **write**. These allow transfer of data to and from the initiator respectively. Note that this only refers to the *direction* of file data transfer, not to what is transmitted, which depends on the agreed access to the file. In addition, it does not imply that a file is being read from or written to. This function maps on to the session service data token service.

- **File access**. This allows data structures in files to be manipulated. In the absence of this FU, only the entire file can be accessed.

- **Limited file management**. This covers reading file attributes, and creating and deleting files.

- **Enhanced file management.** This adds the capability to alter file attributes.

- **Grouping**. This is related to efficiency considerations within the FTAM protocol, such as concatenating FTAM PDUs. We will not be discussing the FTAM grouping service.

- **FADU locking**. This allows part of a file to be 'locked' against user access during concurrent operations on the file. This is relevant when a user is in the process of updating that part of the file, and other users must not be allowed to access the potentially unstable data until the first user has finished. Further details of the locking technique are provided later.

- **Recovery**. It is possible that the FTAM association will be lost due to the irrecoverable failure of the underlying network (or for other reasons). If this FU is used, it may be possible to recover the association at some agreed point at a later time. This is very much like the NIFTP resumption facility.

- **Restart**. Again NIFTP offers rollback to a previously acknowledged data mark. While NIFTP data marks as such are effectively the same as session service synchronisation points (which are a general OSI service), FTAM offers an additional service which is specific to FTAM.

19.4.3　FTAM service classes

FTAM defines six specific service classes, to handle the various categories of FTAM usage. In addition there is a so-called 'unconstrained' class. These are as follows:

Transfer class

(Class T.) For simple file transfers, this class suffices. It must include either the read or the write FU, together with the grouping FU. Optionally, both read and write may be used, together with limited or enhanced file management.

Management class

(Class M.) This is for applications which need the full management facilities, but do not wish to transfer any files. Therefore limited file management (and grouping) are mandatory, and enhanced file management is optional.

Transfer and management class

(Class TM.) This combines the functionality of the above two classes, FUs which are mandatory are those in both of the above classes. The others are optional.

Access class

(Class A.) This allows file transfers plus access to parts of files. Read, write and access FUs are mandatory, and the following FUs may also be used: grouping, limited file management, limited and enhanced file management (but not enhanced file management by itself), FADU locking.

Combined classes

It is also possible to specify transfer, management and transfer and management (T,M,TM), or all four of the above classes (A,T,M,TM).

Unconstrained class

This is a class in name only, since only the kernel FU must be provided. It is provided for flexibility. Which FUs will actually be used is the subject of negotiation during association establishment. Clearly the use of this class only makes sense between FTAM entities which are co-operating in some known way, and a successful association with a FTAM entity which is not 'in the know' cannot be guaranteed. The unconstrained class can only be requested in addition to one of the above defined classes.

19.4.4   Service class and functional unit negotiation

Service classes (apart from recovery and restart; see the aside which follows) are negotiable during association establishment.

Negotiation basically consists of the initiator proposing one or more service classes, together with which optional FUs it can support with the service classes proposed. The responder will indicate from the set of optional FUs those which it can support, but will not propose any additional classes or FUs. The class and FUs to be used is therefore as returned by the responder.

In the case of the unconstrained class, all FUs (except the kernel) have to be negotiated in this way. Where the two FTAM entities are not related by sharing an interest in some common cause, it may well be that negotiation of an unconstrained service class will not result in a sensible set of FUs being agreed.

It will have been noticed that the recovery and restart FUs do not appear in any of the above service classes. Their use is not negotiated either. The reason has to do with the internal structure of FTAM, which includes an *internal service* and an *external service*. This is a complex area which will not be discussed further.

19.5   File structure

19.5.1   FADUs and DUs

Files are specified as containing one or more *File Access Data Units (FADUs)*. A FADU is the smallest unit of a file which FTAM can access and manipulate. This may cover any desired 'granularity' range, depending on the intended access to the file:

  • In the case of a simple transfer of an entire file, the FADU will correspond to the entire file.

• In the case of remote access to, and/or update of, elements within the file, FADUs define those parts of the file which can be accessed, and for the purposes of file accesses, they are independent. In the context of concurrent operations, the FADU locking FU allows access to FADUs to be controlled on an individual basis.

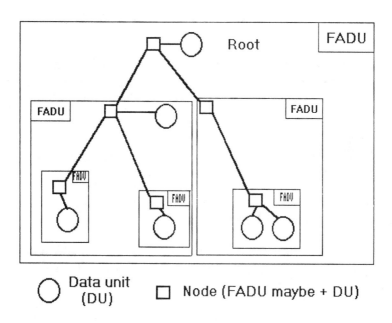

Data unit (DU)   Node (FADU maybe + DU)

NOTE:
> Each node in the tree is a FADU containing itself and any subordinate levels of the tree. (Root is level 0). An unstructured file consists only of the root.

Figure 19.4 - FADU and DU structure

FADUs may be structured, and each may contain zero or more **data units (DUs)** with defined structure. FADUs are related in a logical fashion; the current version of the standard uses a hierarchical (tree structured) model as illustrated in figure 19.4. It is important to note the distinction between FADUs and DUs. The physical file contains DUs, the structure of which can be represented in ASN.1 as a presentation context. FADUs define a hierarchy of collections of DUs which can be accessed. In effect a FADU represents any node in a generalised tree, together with all subordinate nodes; each node may or may not contain DUs. The subordinate of a FADU is itself a FADU, albeit with a distinct name. This provides a generalised way of defining the structure of many different types of files. As far as FTAM is concerned, a single file transfer is of a single FADU, the root, containing one DU.

FTAM defines four structures, which further assists in understanding the concepts of FADUs and DUs.

- The **file access structure** defines the hierarchy of FADUs comprising the file.

- The **presentation structure** on the other hand describes the structure of the DUs in the file.

- The **transfer structure** is concerned with how the FADUs are ordered for transmission purposes, which in a sense is similar to asking whether a binary tree is preorder, inorder or postorder.

- The **identification structure** is concerned with how a given FADU in the hierarchy can be identified, i.e. the names assigned to FADUs in the file. As indicated above, a FADU can represent a single node or an entire branch of a tree.

19.5.2   Constraint sets

While the tree structure is very generalised and potentially powerful, it is too generalised to be of much practical use without the application of constraints which place restrictions on the tree structure (which would otherwise be limitless). These are known as *constraint sets*. As usual in OSI standards, commonly encountered simple file structures are catered for, together with more esoteric options allowing the full functionality of the structure to be exploited. The principal constraint sets are as follows:

- **Unstructured**. This is a single FADU, the root. As there is only one, it does not need to be named, as it represents the entire file. Although this maps on to transfer of (access to) a complete file, it is merely a special case of the more general tree structure.

- **Sequential flat**. This is a sequence of unnamed FADUs. Although they are not (and do not need to be) named, the fact that they are in a ordered sequence means that they can be referred to by position.

- **Ordered flat**. This is in effect an extension of sequential flat, where names are allowed. Duplicate names may appear.

- **Ordered flat with unique names**. This is the same as ordered flat, except that duplicate names for different FADUs are not permitted.

- In addition, constraint sets allowing more structure are provided: *ordered hierarchical*, *general hierarchical*, and *general hierarchical with unique names*.

19.5.3 Documents

This is clearly becoming rather complex. We can define the hierarchy of a file in terms of FADUs, the structure of the data contained in terms of DUs, and a presentation context which is an ASN.1 definition of the contents of the DUs. But it would be cumbersome to have to specify each of these separately every time. For this reason, various common *document types* have been defined. A document type specification includes all of the above and more, and FTAM users can thus simply specify a document type rather than all of the fine details on structure and so on. Ultimately these (and possibly many others) will be registered according to procedures currently under development {9834}. In the interim, the FTAM standard includes a number of standard document types (file types) as follows:

- **Unstructured text file** (FTAM-1). This consists of a single FADU containing a number of character strings. It can only be transferred or accessed as a single unit. It can represent a text file of any type, and is mainly intended for simple file transfer.

- **Sequential text file** (FTAM-2). This consists of a sequence of FADUs, each of which contains a number of character strings. Individual FADUs can be accessed, and the order is significant. This would be suitable for remote access to, say, a data file containing a sequence of records such as employee details, although FTAM itself is not concerned with what the contents of the character strings <u>mean</u>, and it may well be that in this case a different application would be more appropriate.

A standard problem with OSI applications which taxes the experts is what to include in a standard, and what to omit. The line between inadequate provision and un-necessary duplication is very thin.

- **Unstructured binary file** (FTAM-3). This consists of a single FADU, i.e. it is similar to an unstructured text file, except that it contains binary strings. This could, for example, be a code file which is only useful when transferred as a single unit.

- **Sequential binary file** (FTAM-4). This is like a sequential text file, except that it contains binary strings. It could (perhaps) represent a concatenation of several object modules, although as usual this is an interpretation which a user may apply, but which is of no concern to FTAM itself.

- **Simple hierarchical file** (FTAM-5). This file type has a hierarchical structure, with individual FADUs named. Thus access by name to each FADU is possible.

NIST (see chapter five) has identified a number of other document types, and these will no doubt eventually be registered. It is probable that most FTAM implementations will be restricted to such common document types in the interests of minimising complexity and assisting interworking.

19.6   FTAM service

19.6.1   Overview

The FTAM standard {8571-1 to 8571-5} includes a virtual filestore definition, service definition and protocol specification. We have already touched on some aspects of the virtual filestore. In this section we will adopt the usual approach of explaining FTAM in terms of the services provided and the primitives used. Unfortunately to do so in a complete manner would take far more space than is available, so here we concentrate on the principal facilities available. The discussion is based on the various services provided by FTAM which are visible to the user.

There is also a protocol specification, which is bound up with various recovery aspects of FTAM which are far too complex to be discussed here. A detailed discussion of the protocol specification would serve to confuse rather than add to the understanding of FTAM.

19.6.2   Service types

FTAM offers various *file transfer* options. These include the ability to send partial or complete files between hosts, to share access to files (e.g. in a LAN environment between a server and multiple workstations), and to transfer files between workstations and file servers.

The level of service provided is determined by the QOS requested by the initiating user. The user may specify varying degrees of reliability which 'trigger' additional recovery functions inside FTAM.

As discussed in §19.4, the file service may be customised from combinations of FUs to produce a number of service classes. In this section, we examine in more detail the services provided by selected FUs, basing the discussion on the service primitives provided.

19.6.3 Regimes, phases and services

The standard refers to various *regimes*, associated with which various *services* may be used. Regimes are in a sense nested, in that a given regime must have been entered for a 'child' regime to be activated. See figure 19.5. In order of priority, the regimes defined are as follows:

• **FTAM** regime. This establishes and terminates an FTAM association. Termination may be orderly, or by abortion by either the user or service provider. A draft addendum to the standard {8571-# PDAD1} proposes *filestore management*. This is not shown in the figure, but it is envisaged that this will be possible after establishment of the FTAM regime, and before file selection.

• **File selection** regime. This identifies the file to be referenced (SELECT) or creates a new file (CREATE), which will be the file to be acted on during the association. Only one file may be referenced at a time. Once a file has been either DESELECTed or DELETEd, a different file may be selected.

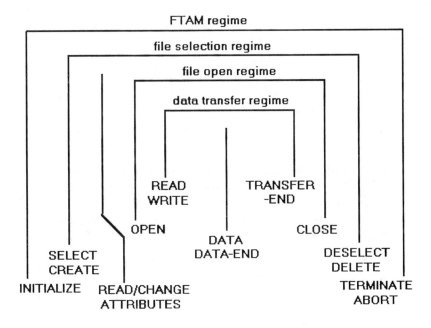

Figure 19.5 - Scope of regimes in FTAM

• **File open** regime. This OPENs the specified file for data access. Before this is done, file attributes may be examined or altered. The file is CLOSEd to end this regime. The (same) file may be opened again, possibly after further attribute accesses.

• **Data transfer** regime. Each data transfer is preceded by a READ or WRITE, which determines the direction of data transfer (to or from the initiator). One or more data units may then be transferred in that direction. CLOSE terminates this particular direction of transfer. This corresponds closely to ownership of the data token in the session layer.

Associated with the regimes are *phases*. In general there is a phase for entering and leaving each regime; each phase has one or more associated *services*, and it is the services which will be described in the rest of this section. Full parameter lists are given in almost all cases for the *F-service primitives*. Some parameters appear in several different primitives, and the standard explains the usage of such parameters in a separate preliminary section. The approach used here is to discuss such parameters when they are first encountered, but not subsequently.

This discussion is of necessity oversimplified in some areas and incomplete in others. The aim is to provide a basic understanding only. Reference to figure 19.5 may prove helpful. In this context, please note in particular the following specific omissions:

• No attempt has been made to distinguish between parameters which appear only in request or response variants; all parameters which can appear are shown. In some cases it is obvious when they can be used (e.g. an action result can clearly only appear in a response). A complete discussion is not possible in a book of this length.

• The FTAM entity is in fact layered, with an *external service* which is visible to the user, and an *internal service* which is not visible. Some additional parameters are used by the internal service; these are concerned with recovery aspects, depending on the requested QOS. Recovery issues are far too complex to cover here.

• The standard specifies whether the initiator, responder or either may issue each service primitive type. This depends on the primitive concerned. This aspect is not covered here, although in some cases it is obvious. For example only the initiator can issue the INITIALIZE or TERMINATE primitives, and only the authorised entity can issue the DATA primitive; which one depends on whether there was a previous READ or WRITE.

FTAM regime establishment service

This is responsible for establishing the application context and the initial state of the FTAM regime. Its functions are to ensure that the application association links to the correct address, to negotiate the service class and FUs to be used in this association, and to obtain any necessary accounting and authorisation information needed for subsequent file operations. There is a single service primitive.

In the following discussions, rather than writing 'request, indication, response, confirm' or whatever, we will simply state that the service is either confirmed or unconfirmed. This is consistent with the decision not to distinguish between parameters which are present in different variants. Only parameters of particular interest, referencing features not already discussed, will be explained.

F–INITIALIZE confirmed   22 parameters including state result, action result, association and presentation details, service class and FUs, attribute groups, account, filestore password, diagnostic

* The *state result* appears in several primitives, but is only present in the response and confirm variants. It indicates in this case whether the initialise was successful, i.e. whether the regime has been established. More generally it specifies which state has now been entered (which may represent 'no change' if the primitive failed).

* The *action result* is again present in several primitives, and indicates that the result was either success, a transient error or a permanent error.

* The *diagnostic* is an explanation of the failure.

FTAM regime termination services

There are two services. The orderly service handles termination by agreement between the two applications. The abrupt service handles abnormal termination, after which the state of the file is left in an indeterminate state. On completion, the FTAM regime is terminated.

Orderly termination

F–TERMINATE confirmed   shared ASE information, charging

This terminates the association, which is released, together with accounting and identification information.

> • The *shared ASE information* is again present in several primitives, and is information which is not directly relevant to FTAM, but will be used by another ASE which forms part of this association. In the context of FTAM this may be taken to be CCR. In the simplest case, F-TERMINATE implies commitment of the atomic action which contains all of the actions which have been performed on a file or its attributes.

Abrupt termination

F–U–ABORT unconfirmed   action result, diagnostic

This implies that there has been some service user problem which makes continuation impossible. This could be for example some mechanical failure of the real filestore such as a disk head crash. The diagnostic will provide further details. This maps on to S-U-ABORT in the session layer.

F–P–ABORT indication   action result, diagnostic

This is a service provider abort which maps on to S-P-ABORT in the session layer. It implies some catastrophic failure either in the session layer or some underlying layer, typically the failure of an intervening network.

Filestore management service

This is the subject of ongoing study, and currently appears only in a draft addendum. The idea is to provide enhanced management, for example of directories. The current FTAM standard can only handle individual files. It will be possible to manage the filestore only while no file is currently selected.

File selection service

A file may be specified either by selecting an existing one or creating a new one.

The aim of the file selection service is to nominate a specific existing file on which future actions will be performed. This file remains selected until it is explicitly deselected or FTAM terminates. While it is selected, all actions are implicitly on that file. In the current version of the standard, selection is made on the basis of the filename. Future extensions may allow selection to be made on the basis of other attributes as well. A single service primitive is provided; in order for this to work, the file must clearly exist. On successful completion, the file selection regime is entered.

F-SELECT confirmed   state result, action result, attributes, requested access, passwords, concurrency control, shared ASE info, account, diagnostic

• The *requested access* may be read, insert, replace, extend (i.e. append), erase, read attribute, change attribute or, delete.

• The *concurrency control* parameter is used to determine whether FADU locking facilities are required for this file; these are further discussed in the file open service below.

File create service

As an alternative to selecting an existing file, a new one may be created. There are options, similar to but more powerful than those in NIFTP, for deciding what to do if a file of that name already exists. A single primitive is provided.

F-CREATE confirmed   state result, action result, override, initial attributes, create password, requested access, concurrency control, shared ASE info, account, diagnostic

• The *override* parameter specifies what action should be taken if the file already exists. The options available are to fail the request, to select the existing file, or to delete it and create a new file. In this last case, there is the further option of either using the old file's attributes or those proposed for the new one.

File deselection service

The result is that the file selected regime is terminated. No file is now selected, and a different (or the same) file may be selected, or the association may be terminated. (In future versions of the standard, filestore management will be possible at this point.) There is a single service primitive.

F-DESELECT confirmed

action result, charging, shared ASE information, diagnostic

File management services

Once a file has been selected or created, but before it is opened, its attributes can be examined or altered. Two primitives are provided, to read and write attributes. The usage of these primitives is obvious in principle, although precisely what can be done depends on the particular attribute.

F-READ-ATTRIBUTE confirmed

action result, attribute names, attributes, diagnostic

F-CHANGE-ATTRIBUTE confirmed

action result, attributes, diagnostic

File open service

A selected or created file must be explicitly opened before its contents can be accessed or updated. On successful completion, the file open regime is entered. The data transfer regime may now be entered and left as many times as appropriate. Again a single primitive is provided:

F-OPEN confirmed

state result, action result, processing mode, contents type, concurrency control, shared ASE information, enable FADU locking, diagnostic

This establishes the data transfer facilities required, including the presentation context(s) for the DUs within the file.

• The *processing mode* determines which of the set of possible actions agreed in the SELECT can be applied to this file, specifically whether read, insert, replace, extend and/or erase may be applied to the FADUs in the file (and by implication to the DUs contained within the FADUs). Remember that for a simple file transfer, the entire file is a single FADU, so the above list can apply to the entire file or any individual section of it.

• The *contents type* references a description of the file, including structuring information. It may well be a reference to a document type.

- The *concurrency control* allows locks to be applied on one of the following bases: not required (I will not do this), shared (anyone may do this), exclusive (only I may do this), no access (nobody may do this). This provides support for access control for shared files.

- The *enable FADU locking* parameter specifies whether this concurrency control is to be applied to the entire file or on a per FADU basis.

File close service

This makes the file unavailable for data transfer, i.e. terminates the file open regime. However the file remains selected, and can be re-opened if necessary. In particular the file still exists, although it may well have different contents from when it was opened. Not until the file is deselected is the association with this file lost. A single primitive is provided.

F-CLOSE confirmed   action result, shared ASE information, diagnostic

- The *shared ASE information* is used in conjunction with CCR, for example if the file open phase is to be regarded as an atomic action which must now commit. The use of CCR is implementation specific, in the sense that the 'granularity' of the FTAM association in terms of atomic actions and commitment can be varied to suit particular requirements. For example if commitment was required at this stage, the action result, coupled with the shared ASE information, could indicate the success or failure of this commitment, and the diagnostic could give the reason for failure.

File delete service

This deletes the nominated file, and again the file open regime is ended (as it must in this case). Again the file remains selected, and one presumes that a new file of the same name could then be created. More likely, the file has been deleted after a NIFTP-style 'read and remove' operation, the original copy no longer being required. This is in effect moving the file from one open system to another. If appropriate, the file will only be deleted if commitment has been offered in the CCR context, otherwise both copies could be lost. The primitive is as follows:

F-DELETE confirmed   action result, shared ASE information, charging, other parameters

Data transfer regime

Once the file is open, file data may be transferred in either direction. Data is transferred to or from FADUs; although FADUs may contain several DUs, these DUs are not individually accessible. Depending on the transfer class selected, either a single operation (e.g. read the entire file) or multiple operations (on individual FADUs) may be possible. Each data transfer operation is under the control of the **bulk data transfer (BDT)** service. Before the operation takes place, details of the operation type and the identity of the FADU to be accessed must be provided. This is done by means of either a READ or a WRITE primitive, one of which must precede every data transfer operation. Each data transfer operation must be explicitly terminated by a TRANSFER-END primitive. In other words each data transfer is encapsulated, the encapsulation being the data transfer regime.

FADU locate and erase services

A number of control operations are provided as commands and responses. These include locating a FADU and erasing a FADU. Two primitives are provided.

F–LOCATE confirmed   action result, FADU identity, FADU lock, diagnostic

   • The *FADU lock* can toggle between 'no access' and 'not required', or between 'shared' and 'exclusive'; the meanings of these terms were discussed above under the file open service.

   • The *result* says whether the FADU was located.

F–ERASE confirmed   action   result,   FADU   identity, diagnostic.

This erases the FADU concerned. All data in the FADU will be lost unless it has previously been copied.

Bulk data transfer service

As mentioned above, data transfers are encapsulated in READ/WRITE and END-TRANSFER primitives. The data transfer is initiated by means of either a READ or a WRITE primitive:

F–READ confirmed   data specification

This specifies a data transfer *from the responder*.

F-WRITE confirmed   data specification

This specifies a data transfer *from the initiator*.

> • The *data specification* is the bulk data transfer (BDT) specification, and provides either the FADU identification, access context and FADU lock for READs, or the FADU operation, FADU identification and FADU lock for WRITEs.

It is a restriction of the current version of FTAM that only one F-READ or F-WRITE may be current at any time, and the direction of data transfer will remain fixed until F-TRANSFER-END. This in turn determines which entity will hold the session layer data token, using the half duplex FU. This is considered restrictive for some LAN applications, in particular when the standard session layer synchronisation service is used. The net effect is to impose a structure which may well be adequate for most WAN applications, but appears cumbersome and inflexible in the LAN context. As a result an addendum is being progressed in FTAM for *overlapped access* {8671-# PDAD2} and a supporting addendum has already been agreed in the session layer for 'symmetric synchronisation' {8326/7 ADD1}.

The data transfer is accomplished by means of the following primitive:

F-DATA unconfirmed   data

where the context of the data is as defined in the preceding READ or WRITE. The end of the data unit is explicitly indicated by means of

F-DATA-END unconfirmed   action result, diagnostic

Should the READ, WRITE, DATA or DATA-END fail for some reason, the entire current invocation of the data transfer regime will be cancelled by means of

F-CANCEL confirmed   action result, shared ASE information,
                                      diagnostic

Unless cancelled, this particular bulk data transfer ('guarded' by the previous READ or WRITE) will be explicitly terminated by means of

F-TRANSFER-END confirmed   no parameters

The previous READ or WRITE no longer applies; another may be issued, e.g. to reverse the direction of data flow or to reference a different FADU.

Other services

The *grouping* service is intended to allow various FTAM PDU combinations to be made in the interests of protocol efficiency. Regime *recovery* and *restart* services are also provided, but these are internal to FTAM. Neither will be discussed here.

19.7   FTAM use of underlying services

19.7.1   Use of ACSE

It is a requirement that establishment and termination of a FTAM association be under the control of ACSE, which was discussed in chapter eighteen. At the time of writing, ACSE offers no other mechanisms, but it is anticipated that future releases of ACSE will provide a framework whereby FTAM can make use of ('refurbish') an existing application association. Use of FTAM, with or without other applications, is an application context as discussed in chapter eighteen. The specific case where FTAM is the sole application involved on the association is catered for in the file protocol specification {8571-4} by defining a specific application context for this purpose.

It is a further requirement of the file protocol that only one file activity at a time is allowed per association. Therefore in order to handle multiple file (activities), multiple associations must be established. Although they will be between the same pair of open systems, they are entirely independent instances of FTAM. Clearly they cannot reference the same file at the same time.

19.7.2   Use of CCR

We have seen many examples above of shared ASE information. This is primarily to allow file transactions, or groups of file transactions, to be treated as atomic actions, by passing parameters for the action of CCR as an underlying mechanism. Typically all operations on a file from opening to closing it would be regarded as a single atomic action which must either commit (all be applied) or fail (none applied). Any necessary C-primitives to control the commitment procedure are beneath FTAM, and therefore not visible to the user, which sees only the result, as success or failure. That sounds simple and elegant, but the situation is in fact far more complex particularly when shared access, including reads and writes to different parts of the same file, may occur in any order. Further details are beyond the scope of this book.

19.7.3   Use of presentation and session services

As explained earlier, ASN.1 is used to describe the structure of DUs in the file. Each host supporting FTAM will establish a set of presentation contexts, one or more of which can be used during a FTAM association. As far as the session service is concerned, FTAM must police the ownership of the data and synchronise/minor tokens. Session service symmetric synchronisation is being progressed to provide some freedom from these restrictions.

19.8   NIFTP compared with FTAM

NIFTP, discussed in chapter nine, was devised by the UK academic community so that University and Research Council sites could exchange files over the PSS network and Cambridge Rings. As such, the idea was to use the underlying YBTS to 'hide' the eccentricities of X.25 from NIFTP. Being developed before even OSI/RM itself was stable, it comes as no surprise to learn that NIFTP is not compatible with OSI.

NIFTP contrives to break all manner of OSI rules:

• It is asked to handle X.25 resets, which is a transport layer function. (If TP0 is used, it will convert the reset to a disconnect, from which RTSE or CCR can recover.)

• It incorporates data marks, rollback and restart facilities which, in the OSI context, are session layer functions.

• While NIFTP attempts to provide a limited amount of presentation layer type support, this mainly consists of being able to specify which transmission code is currently being used. It can say nothing about the structure of a file, which in the case of FTAM is represented (in ASN.1) as a presentation context.

• NIFTP not only serves as a framework for transmitting files, but also as a vehicle for transmitting JTMP job decks and JNT mail messages. It even has modes of access such as 'take job input'. In these cases the result is a somewhat unhappy marriage between a file transfer service and objects which in many ways are quite unlike files. A job deck is something which is executed, not (necessarily) placed in a filestore. Similarly a mail message being directed to a mailbox defies neat description in terms of writing a file to a filestore. In OSI terms file handling, electronic mail and job handling are all applications of equal status. The NIFTP approach is inappropriate.

Having said that, OSI is not without its little eccentricities. TP0 was not originally intended to be used over X.25 networks, as it cannot recover from unsolicited X.25 resets or disconnects. And according to the application structure standard {9545}, it is in theory possible (although not necessarily sensible) to combine JTM and FTAM in the same application association.

20 Job Transfer and Manipulation (JTM)

20.1 Introduction

JTM is an ISO standard designed to support the submission of batch jobs between OSI sites. Unlike many OSI applications which seem somewhat esoteric, this one at least can easily be understood in principle by the layman. For many years remote job submission has been an important feature of the UK academic community's use of the JANET network, with many University sites wishing to run jobs at the large Regional Computer Centres in London, Manchester, Edinburgh and Bath. The result was the 'Red Book' Job Transfer and Manipulation Protocol (JTMP), discussed briefly in chapter nine. This in fact served as a model for ISO work in the area, which was just starting as JTMP was becoming stable. As a result, JTM is very similar in philosophy to JTMP, although there are significant differences in detail.

Warning. The acronyms JTM (the ISO standard) and JTMP (the UK academic interim standard) are very similar. Be careful not to confuse the two, both of which are referenced at various points in the discussion.

Work on ISO JTM is now well advanced, and a full class service definition {8831} and basic class protocol {8832} reached IS status in 1989. Briefly, the job service seeks to provide a means for transferring job descriptions between OSI hosts (JTM entities), together with certain facilities for controlling and monitoring job progress (manipulation). JTM does this by providing a standardised means for specifying the work to be done on one or more open system hosts, and for monitoring and modifying the execution of work previously specified. The aim is to provide a framework, not to attempt to standardise JCLs, which is neither necessary nor feasible. Indeed precisely what happens when the job description arrives is of concern only to the JTM service user. Only the general nature of the task (execution, document disposition, status enquiry, and so on) is understood by JTM itself.

20.2 JTM Concepts

In this section, we examine briefly some general features of JTM, before looking in more detail at the service definition.

20.2.1   JTM service classes

Two *classes of service* are defined in the JTM standard {8831}.

> • The *full class* offers a full 'bells and whistles' service, allowing participation of multiple sites (application entities), and several stages in job execution, including the collection of program and data files en route. In this sense it is similar in many respects to the JTMP protocol on which it is modelled. Unfortunately the full class JTM is very complex, many would say excessively so. For the full class, only the service definition exists in final form, and although work is progressing on a full class protocol specification {8832 PDAD1}, its future is by no means certain at the time of writing.

> • In practice, all that most organisations want is to be able to submit a job to a remote site, and have the output 'disposed' to a third site (in many cases the originator, e.g. to a results file or lineprinter). This *basic class* is more restrictive than the full class, but has the advantage of relative ease of implementation and much wider international support. The basic class protocol specification {8832} is essentially complete. Despite the doubts about the future of the full class service, we will discuss it, even though it has no (stable) protocol support at present. We will discuss the restrictions imposed by the basic class subset in §20.4.

20.2.2   Documents and work specifications

Fundamental to JTM is the concept of a *work specification*. This comprises details of the job to be performed by the receiver, together with instructions on what action the receiver should take when its contribution to the job processing is complete. Thus it could specify that the receiver is to 'execute' the contents (which in effect means treat the machine-specific JCL, program code, data, and so forth as a conventional batch job). The receiver might then be required to forward the results of this batch job to another site as a new work specification. (This concept is very similar to a JTMP task descriptor, as discussed in §9.4.2.)

In JTMP, task descriptors were transferred between hosts using an underlying file transfer protocol (NIFTP). In the case of JTM, the standard OSI protocol stack is used (ACSE over presentation), with the additional backup of CCR to manage the set of work specifications as a single atomic unit. The use of CCR ensures that if a job has to be abandoned part way through (perhaps because some intermediate site has failed with loss of job details), any associated data which was modified by the job so far can be restored to its initial state, exactly as if the job had never started. This is one area which JTMP never addressed, as at the time no suitable mechanisms such as CCR existed.

While JTMP pretended that its task descriptors were files, using NIFTP to transfer them, JTM makes no similar use of FTAM. Instead, JTM uses its own protocol, together with underlying session layer services, to transfer work specifications. These are transferred between JTM entities on different open systems (known as JTM *agencies*) in JTM *documents*. The function of the *JTM protocol* is to control the transfer of the various documents between JTM sites (entities). As in FTAM, documents have *types* which can (in the future) be registered {9834}. The document may also include *proformas*, which contain sufficient information to allow the recipient to generate another work specification for forwarding to a third site. Proformas may be nested, so that this process may result in several stages of processing at different open systems. See figure 20.1. When a recipient converts a proforma into a new work specification, this is referred to as (sub)*job spawning*. If the proforma has a nested proforma inside it, this becomes the 'outer' proforma in the new job specification. Spawning is only permitted in the full class specification.

20.2.3   Agencies

JTM is a co-operative application between (at least in the full class specification) any number of open systems, i.e. JTM agencies. To clarify the significance of the different types of agencies, consider the job sequence depicted in figure 20.1. Although this scenario is discussed in more detail later in the section, the following outline may assist in understanding the agency concept. In the figure, W submits a job. This is to be processed in two stages, first at X, then at Y. Finally, Y will dispose the output to Z, where it may be printed or stored. Note that although Z is identified as a host distinct from W, there is no reason why W and Z cannot be the same host, as the originating user will generally want the output returned to him. It is differentiated in the figure because it performs a different *function* from W, and it is the function of the site which determines which agency class(es) it falls into.

The JTM standard identifies four types of agency, as follows. Remember that JTM makes no attempt to specify what processing occurs <u>within</u> a particular agency, only its general function. Nor does JTM make any assumptions regarding the <u>physical location</u> of agencies; they are all logical entities.

- **Initiation agency**. This is the initial job submitter, open system W in the example. Since the document passed from W to X contains all of the nested proformas needed for subsequent JTM document creation (X to Y and Y to Z in this case), the initiation agency is therefore responsible for determining how (in general terms) and where the job will be processed; all of this appears in the work specification passed from W to X. The initiation agency can be regarded as the root entity in the CCR commitment tree (see chapter eighteen).

• **Source agency.** It may be that host W submits a job to run on host Y, but the actual source file to compile (or whatever) resides on host X. The job will thus need to 'collect' the necessary file(s) from host X en route to Y, which is thus a source agency. (The information added by X need not necessarily be in a file. For example it could be output from some program running at X. This type of agency is only permitted in the full class service.)

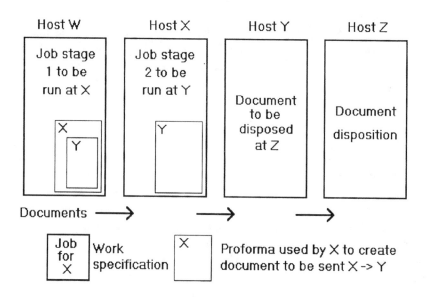

Figure 20.1 - Spawning of JTM work specifications

• **Sink agency.** In the figure, host Z is identified as performing 'document disposition'. This is in fact a term used in the UK JTMP protocol rather than ISO JTM, but perhaps conveys the meaning more clearly than a sink. The document received by Z will contain data (e.g. output results) to be 'stored' at Z. This would typically be to a file or a lineprinter. As indicated above, Z could be host W, in which case W would perform tasks as two logically distinct agencies.

• **Execution agency**. It is clear that a job must be 'run' somewhere. The host running the job is referred to in JTM terms as the execution agency. There may of course be more than one, if the job is processed in stages. The document forwarded by the execution agency typically contains the output to be disposed by the sink agency, although it may contain intermediate results for further processing at another execution agency (full class service only).

All of this can easily be related to the figure. The work performed by an agency is referred to as an *activity*. It is initiated (in an abstract sense) by the service user issuing a service primitive. (Service primitives are discussed in §20.4.2.) The following would be a typical sequence of activities, but is by no means the only possible one.

• W is the initiation agency, where the (human) user wishing to run the job is located. X is the source agency, where the program resides. Therefore the document passes from W to X in order to collect the source code.

• A second document is now forwarded from X to Y. This is created from the proforma contained within the document which X received from W. The document sent to Y instructs Y to run the job. Therefore Y is the execution agency in this case.

• The proforma X received from W also contained a nested proforma, which contained information to be used by Y. X converted this into an un-nested proforma in the document sent to Y. Y is instructed to send the results to X. Therefore the third and final document passes from Y (the execution agency) to Z (the sink agency).

20.2.4   Monitoring the progress of a job

One problem with traditional batch processing was that once the job (typically a card deck) was submitted, it effectively disappeared into a 'black hole' from which it might re-appear as output hours or days later, or not at all if the system crashed. Finding out precisely what had happened to the job was either difficult or impossible. On most systems, once the job had been submitted, as it was completely inaccessible to the user, it could not be deleted or altered in any way. It is not uncommon for a user to submit a job, then realise that he has associated the wrong data file with it, and thus would now like to cancel or suspend it. This is seldom possible on old-style batch processing systems. Not surprisingly, as users' expectations matured, restrictions such as these proved increasingly frustrating, not to mention expensive if the job had to be transferred via a network such as PSS. It became essential at the very least to provide some means of finding out what had happened to the job. When job submission became distributed over two or more geographical locations, provision of job monitoring and control facilities became vital.

Facilities are provided in JTM to *interrogate* a job to determine its current status, to *suspend* or *terminate* it, in some cases to *alter* the contents of a work specification, and for the *disposition of output* from a job. The basic class protocol provides support for monitor and display devices, filestores, printers, jobmills and some specified programming language. The facilities are discussed in more detail in later sections, and include the following:

> • *Reporting*. This involves sending small work specifications at 'significant times' during the job to a nominated destination which keeps a record of the job's progress on behalf of the (human) user. (The user specifies at the start if this is required, after which it is an automatic process.)

> • *Status checking and manipulation*. Here the user actively solicits reports (via work manipulation work specifications).

> • *User identification and authorisation*. This relates to such information as usercodes and/or passwords required at various sites, as well as other authorisations such as file update rights.

20.3   JTM concepts in more detail

20.3.1   Work specifications

The concept of a *work specification* is central to JTM. This is a 'message' passed between co-operating open systems, containing instructions for the receiver including what processing it should do, what further work specifications should be spawned, and so on. The entire JTM set of transactions is triggered by an *initial work specification* created as a result of an initiation service primitive (see §20.4.2). There are of course many other types of work specification, such as ones moving documents between open systems, specifying something to be executed (aspects of the job itself), requesting a report, providing a report, requesting a status change, and so on. We will encounter various types of work specification in this section.

Work specifications contain *fields* in which many different types of information can be stored. Precisely what is stored in a given work specification depends on its type, and there is a conceptual data structure within the service provider by means of which the work to be done can be specified. Fields are contained for the following types of information:

- Identification of the work to be done by the receiving open system. A unique name is assigned to the work specification for reference by subsequent reporting and manipulation work specifications; this is allocated when it is created, either following submission by the initiating agency, or following spawning as a result of earlier processing. The initiator's identity and time of submission are also provided.

- Authorisation of the work and accounting information. In particular note that distinct authorisations may be required for executing a job at Y and printing the results at Z.

- Information specifying where reports on the work are to be sent. *Job monitors* can be specified, to which selected status reports can be sent.

- In principle (at least in the full class) more than one job monitor can be specified, in which JTM needs to know which types of report to send to which job monitor.

- Information identifying the type of work specification.

- Details of the open systems which are to perform the work. The *target* open system is the one which carries out the final processing of the initial work. This is not necessarily the receiver of the initial work specification, as further ones may be spawned.

- The urgency of the work contained in the specification.

- Instructions for the recipient to hold parts of the work until specified events occur (such as the receipt of another work specification containing a related document).

- The *main body* of the work specification specifies the actions to be performed by the peer JTM service user to carry out the initial work defined in the specification. In other words it contains such things as program code and JCL instructions, which is user data as far as JTM is concerned. What happens to the local data is of no concern to JTM, except in the sense that there will be an outcome which will affect how JTM reports on the actions, and their success or failure may determine the future progress of the job.

- In addition there may be *proformas* specifying further work to be carried out when the initial work is completed. By implication this will be at another open system, otherwise it would be included in the main body.

20.3.2   Proformas and spawning

As suggested above, *proformas* are those parts of the work specification specifying further work, and they are used to form new work specifications as part of the processing of earlier work. In the full class service, these can be nested to any depth, and there can be several 'top level' proformas in a work specification.

The process of taking data from a proforma and using it to generate a new work specification is known as *spawning*. This is initiated in execution agencies. The top level proformas are 'promoted' to work specifications for forwarding, and the current open system fills in the missing fields based on the actions it has just taken on the received work specification. In the case of a nested proforma, it moves up one level of nesting. (In a sense this is like popping proformas off a stack.) The new (spawned) work specifications can contain data from the proforma and other fields of the parent work specification. It can also contain documents which have become available at this agency. (It is possible that the job was held until the document arrived from somewhere else; this is how general the full class JTM service is.)

20.3.3   OSI jobs

An *OSI job* is the term used to refer to the *total work on all open systems* arising either directly or indirectly from the initial work specification. An OSI subjob (or just *subjob*) is the total work arising from a single work specification, including the process of spawning another work specification but not the results of any such new work specifications. In other words the subjob is essentially complete when local processing of the received work specification is complete. (This implies that the act of getting the work specification between sites is not part of the subjob.) OSI *job submission* is the use of the JTM initiation service to create an initial work specification. Conceptually this is 'executed' at the initiating site, although that may merely be an abstraction of the mechanism of generating more than one work specification to start the job off.

20.3.4   Processing of work specifications

This further implies that the initial work specification may result in one or more source agencies being accessed, at the submitter's and/or other open systems. It is the job of the *JTM protocol* (which we will not be discussing) to 'replace a work specification with another at another open system', which is internationalese for saying that it is physically transferred to another open system. Documents within work specification may be passed to one or more sink agencies.

There are in fact three circumstances where new work specifications may be spawned using top level proformas

- on acceptance of a document by an agency;
- on demand from an activity in an agency;
- following completion of a sink or execution agency activity (the most typical case).

The spawned work specification may contain documents made available here, or references to other agencies where documents may be picked up. Once all activity resulting from the above processing is completed, the work specification will be destroyed. (This corresponds, in the CCR sense, to committing the atomic action comprising this work specification).

20.3.5　Reporting

Central to JTM is the ability to inform the (human) user what is happening to his job. This is essential when the job is being processed remotely, and more than one remote site may be involved. A further important feature is for the user to be able to modify (manipulate) his job during its currency. Therefore these topics will be discussed in some detail. Reporting is dealt with in this section, and manipulations are discussed in §20.3.6.

Background to JTM reporting

A *report* is simply encoded information recording the process or failure of an OSI job. The report is generated by the JTM service provider, possibly after interaction with a JTM agency. Reports are sent to open systems known as *OSI job monitors*, and are contained in *report work specifications*.

In order to understand the philosophy behind the reporting process, it is necessary to relate to human nature. In general people do not like boring, repetitive tasks. Therefore if a job is expected to take several hours to complete, they will not want to come back every 30 minutes to see if it has completed yet; they will want to be informed of significant events in the job's history, notably when it has completed. Similarly they do not want to sit at a VDU doing nothing except waiting for the wonderful news either. Therefore JTM must provide facilities for keeping an online log (in effect an audit trail) of each OSI, if the user requests it in the initial work specification. However the user may well become impatient if the job takes longer than expected, so it must be possible for him to ascertain the current position now. Therefore JTM also provides interrogation facilities.

To save having to write he/she every time, from now on 'he' should be taken to mean he/she.

He may thus decouple from the job after initiating it, and may nominate a *job monitor* which is to receive, on his behalf, either reports on significant events in the job's life, or specific reports at the user's request. Furthermore the user may require the monitor to forward all reports to a sink agency of his choice. If so, it is the sink agency's responsibility to present these reports in human readable form.

The location of the *primary monitor* will be fixed (determined by the service provider), and the user is not able to specify an alternative. However (in the full class specification) he can nominate one or more *secondary monitors* of his choice. The user can also decide which (if any) types of report will be sent to which monitor, and can alter this selection during the job's currency.

Report work specification content restrictions

Reports are carried in *report work specifications*, and various restrictions are imposed on the contents of these compared with other types of work specification:

- No user documents may be contained therein.

- They cannot be created by spawning. In other words they are the result of receiving a separate report request, not because the incoming subjob asked for one.

- They have the same identifier as the work specification being reported on.

- To avoid a familiar problem encountered with reports on failure, they cannot result in further reports, for example saying that the report is invalid. Invalid reports are simply discarded.

- A report work specification contains all of the permissions present in the work specification it is reporting on. This removes the possibility that the report will be rejected as unauthorised. (See §20.3.7.)

- Reports have top priority for transfer. (In fact they are joint equal with manipulations; see §20.3.6).

Various *types of event* can be reported on. The following list is comprehensive.

- The creation of a job.

- The transfer of (responsibility for) a work specification from one open system to another (done by the JTM protocol).

- The spawning of a new work specification.

- Acceptance of a document by a sink or execution agency.

- Normal termination of a work specification (i.e. the subjob has been completed and the job specification has been destroyed).

- Premature ending of a subjob due to the receipt of a STOP manipulation request. (See §20.3.6.)

- The killing (deletion) of a work specification and termination of the associated subjob due to the receipt of a KILL manipulation request. (See §20.3.6.)

- The modification of a subjob as a result of a manipulation request.

- Where errors have been detected in a work specification resulting in error diagnostics being embedded in it.

- If a work specification is being held pending the correction of errors in it.

- If abnormal termination of a work specification occurs due to errors.

- When accounting information related to subjob is generated (by the local systems environment). For example the cost of a compile/execute could be made known on completion.

- The generation of user messages by activity in execution agency. (These will be passed to the user.)

- The abnormal termination of a work specification due to a request for facilities which are not allowed in this class of service. Currently there are only two classes, basic and full. Basic class restrictions are discussed in §20.5.

- Modification of a work specification was attempted without the necessary authorisation.

Reports contain various *parameters*, as follows:

- The name of the open system generating the report.
- The identity and initiator of the subjob referred to.
- The type of event (from those listed above).
- The date and time the report was generated (if required).
- A text message whose contents are not constrained by JTM.

20.3.6   Manipulations

The other important user facility is *manipulations*, whereby the user can alter some aspect of his job. Users can manipulate reports, work specifications and transfers. Each is discussed in turn.

Work manipulation

These are the most important types of manipulation, as they allow the user to alter work specifications, i.e. his job as it progresses. Various primitive operations are permitted on the job, allowing one or more work specifications to be displayed, killed, stopped or modified. The instructions are conveyed in *work manipulation work specifications*. This is a two phase operation. The activity is first selected, then the operation is performed. The standard proposes powerful facilities, although what can be achieved with the basic class of service is restricted. The following paragraphs are intended to give a feeling for what can be achieved with the full class service.

- The *selector* determines the number of work specifications which will be involved.

- In the case of an *update*, the enclosed data is used to modify selected *fields* in work specifications or proformas.

- A *kill* operation deletes a work specification, which thereupon vanishes. This is destructive of the proformas as well, so no spawning will take place. (In the CCR sense, this is destructive of all changes which occurred as a result of the activity of this subjob, i.e. there is a rollback. Precisely what this means in a real job processor can be hard to define.)

- On the other hand a *stop* operation terminates the activity at the (execution) agency concerned, but the remainder of the subjob may proceed. In particular new subjobs may still be spawned, so that subsequent activities are not affected (except in the sense that they may behave differently as a result). A typical example would be a long batch job which the user decides to curtail because it is using up too much of his budget. The user still wants the results so far, which would vanish if the job was killed rather than stopped.

• A *display* operation is similar to the report display mentioned in a moment, but is of part(s) of work specifications in general. (The report display acts only on a report.) In effect this provides a snapshot of the current state of the job.

Transfer manipulation

The second category of manipulations is included mainly for completeness. Here, a transfer manipulation work specification is used which allows various transfer control records in another work specification to be altered. This is mainly intended for administrative use.

Report manipulation

This is the final category of manipulations, and while the standard document makes heavy weather of explaining what is happening, basically the aim is to allow the user to examine reports generated for his job, and delete them (with optional hardcopy) when he has finished with them. Notionally these are conveyed in report manipulation work specifications, although again this is an abstract notion if the user and the monitor are physically on the same system, which will often be the case. There are two types of manipulation work specification:

• **Delete**. Reports relating to a single subjob or a tree of subjobs (up to the entire OSI job) can be deleted.

• **Display**: In theory at least, this generates document(s) containing reports (constrained as for deletes). The standard further allows the user to nominate a sink agency (e.g. where the reports can be printed), and allows (again in theory) multiple manipulation work specifications to collect reports from various sites (by spawning). We say in theory because much of this is not permitted in the basic class, it is not clear in practice why a user might want reports printing at a remote site, and in any case the user, monitor and sink agency will typically all reside at the same physical location anyway.

444

20.3.7 Authorisation and accounting

Any OSI application is open to abuse, in this case illegal access to other people's programs and data, running of unauthorised jobs, and so on. Therefore protection has to be built in. Authorisation data is provided in fields of work specifications, including user/job authentication and validation information. Account data must also be provided which identifies the user. Typically this will include 'proof' of the right to use the job resource, or to access relevant files, and this could be by means of a password, or more secure techniques. Budget details could also be supplied.

20.4 Full class JTM service

20.4.1 Overview

The full class service is ambitious. It allows, for example, any number of proformas, nested to any depth, and assumes (somehow) that CCR will be able to co-ordinate all of the many interrelated subjobs which may result from all of this activity. In practice it proved easier to write ambitious prose than to turn this into reality, particular difficulties being encountered with the underlying CCR mechanism.

For this reason a basic class was also defined, which imposes severe restrictions as we shall see in §20.5. However it is not the intention here to go into great details about the service definition, and the overview which follows applies both to the full and basic class services, although the standard document defines the full class service, and then specifies the basic class restrictions separately.

20.4.2 JTM service primitives

As usual we will define the service in terms of *J-service primitives*. However this is a very complex service, and in fact each primitive name represents a group of related primitives. The purpose of each class of primitive will be discussed in the context of creating OSI jobs, transferring them between open systems, submitting them for processing, and so on. No primitive parameters will be shown. It should be noted also that some primitives map on to underlying CCR functions. The discussion will include some comments on this aspect.

It should also be noted that, unlike most service definitions, these primitives are <u>not relayed to peer service users</u>. In some cases a request will result in some other service primitive being issued to a peer user, but mostly they are provided for local consumption only, the underlying JTM protocol doing most of the work. It follows from this that although there will be ACSE associations between the various JTM entities, these associations are not visible at the service interface, so that we cannot say that a given primitive maps on to association establishment, for example. In that sense the JTM service is the 'highest' application service we have encountered so far; indeed in a sense it is so high that even ACSE is not visible.

OSI job initiation

This service must be invoked by the user to inform the initiation agency that an OSI job is to be created. The primitive (class) used maps on to CCR, to initiate an atomic action for the entire OSI job:

J-BEGIN request

This causes an OSI job to be initiated, and establishes an association between the user and the job for its lifetime. Note that this is <u>not</u> an application association of the type controlled by ACSE. There will be one (and only one) J-BEGIN at the start of each job. There is no response variant because the SDU is not directed to a peer service user. It is not confirmed either.

It should be noted that this primitive is used simply to make the details of the job (atomic action) known to the OSI environment (JTM/CCR). It is <u>not</u> used to create the initial work specification (subjob). This is the function of the next service primitive to be discussed. It should be further noted that the primitives to be described implement various services across notional service boundaries in different open systems. How the JTM service provider acts on receipt of request and response primitives is of no concern to the user. However JTM has a lot of work to do behind the scenes, particularly in the full class specification, to co-ordinate the various subjobs, transfer work specifications between open systems, inform the user what is happening, possibly make changes to subjobs in progress, make use of underlying CCR facilities, and so on. This is in the aegis of the JTM protocol specification, which we will not be discussing. Suffice it to say that the full class protocol specification has so far proved to be too difficult for even the experts to finalise. Possibly the formal definition techniques now available (see chapter twenty four) will make things easier for them in the future.

Work specification creation

In order for the job to start, the initiation agency must create work specifications to be sent to the relevant open systems for processing. The initiation agency operates on behalf of the user, determining what the user wishes to do and where. From this it can generate sufficient information to form one or more work specifications. These are passed to the JTM service provider by means of:

J-INITIATE-WORK request, confirm

The parameter is a work specification, and for obvious reasons we will not attempt to provide details here. This primitive submits job, status etc. work specifications which are acted on in their own right. There are distinct primitives for issuing work specifications which are supposed to 'chase' other work specifications and alter them in some way.

J-INITIATE-<TYPE>-MAN request, confirm

There are three variants of this primitive, which are used to submit (create) the three different types of manipulation work specification discussed in §20.3.6, viz. work (<TYPE> = WORK), report (<TYPE> = REPORT), or transfer control record (<TYPE> = TCR) manipulation work specifications.

Document movement

The following primitives are issued by the service provider in relation to documents which are to be passed to or from a sink or execution agency.

J-DISPOSE indication, response

This is used by JTM (the service provider) to pass a document to a sink or execution agency, creating a new task at the receiving agency. The response either confirms its acceptance by the agency, or specifies why it has been refused. (For example this agency may not currently be processing jobs).

J-GIVE indication, response

This is used by JTM to request from a source or execution agency a document which is required by another agency. The response is either the document or the reason why the document cannot be made available at this time. (For example the referenced document may not exist.)

J-ENQUIRE indication, response

JTM uses this primitive to obtain a list of document names from a source or execution agency for satisfaction of references. For example JTM may need to know which documents are currently held by this agency.

Agency actions

These primitives are used by execution agencies (and in one case sink agencies) to notify the service provider of significant events. Only the request variant is used, as the intention is to advise JTM of some event, not (directly) to pass something to another agency.

J–MESSAGE request

This is issued by an execution agency to pass (more accurately, ask the service provider to create) a USER-MESSAGE report work specification for delivery to another agency (a monitor, to which it will be DISPOSEd).

J–SPAWN request

According to the standard, this allows an execution agency to specify that demand spawning from a specified proforma is to occur. In plain English, a new subjob has just been created from a proforma in a previous work specification, and the service provider is being asked to relay this to the next agency involved in the job processing.

J–END–SIGNAL request

Either an execution agency or a sink agency may issue this primitive to notify JTM (in effect the initiation agency) that the current task (subjob) has been completed. (In CCR terms, this will be following earlier acceptance commitment; see §20.6.2.)

Agency control

The following primitives are used by the service provider to obtain or alter the status of a task currently being processed in an agency. They may be issued as the result of some action by the user (e.g. a status enquiry), or because of some problem at another agency (e.g. a referenced document does not exist).

J–STATUS indication, response

This allows the service provider to obtain (in the response) information on the progress of the referenced activity. The task itself is unaffected.

J–HOLD indication

This requests the temporary suspension of progress of an activity. It is not destructive of the task, which can (possibly) be resumed later. In fact the only defined effect of this primitive is to prevent the agency from issuing agency actions primitives, i.e. from generating new work specifications. This implies that it can continue with the current task to completion, although no new subjobs can be created.

J–RELEASE indication

This cancels a previous J-HOLD.

J–KILL indication

On receipt of this primitive, the agency is required to delete (destroy) this work specification. This is typically the result of a kill work manipulation; see §20.3.6. This may result in a J-ROLLBACK request (see below).

J–STOP indication

This instructs the agency to abort further processing of the specified task. For example if a user job is running, it will be terminated forthwith. Any spawning specified at the end of the subjob will take place, allowing subsequent stages of the OSI job to be performed. For example if an execution was terminated, the output so far can still be disposed. This is typically the result of a stop work manipulation; see §20.3.6.

CCR-related primitives

Agencies are required to notify the service provider of status changes which impact on the commitment or otherwise of atomic actions (subjobs). The following primitive parameters map on to user data fields of the corresponding CCR primitives described in chapter eighteen.

J–BEGIN unconfirmed	commitment level, diagnostic code indicator
J–READY unconfirmed	commitment level, optional warnings, optional accounting information
J–ROLLBACK unconfirmed	diagnostic, optional accounting information
J–RECOVER request, indication	(not used)

J–RECOVER response, confirm   diagnostic,   optional   accounting
                                information

Two other points are worth making here.

  • In theory there is also a J–PREPARE. However this is not
required in the basic mode service.

  • There was originally a J-REFUSE primitive. However this
had to be deleted, as the corresponding CCR primitive was removed
from that standard in the 1989 revision.

20.5   Basic class service restrictions

Basic class restrictions remove much of the functionality from JTM.
This is a mixed blessing:

  • It severely restricts what can be achieved, as will be seen.

  • On the other hand it makes its implementation more
feasible, and has wider support than the full class service among
practitioners. As mentioned earlier, even specifying the full class
protocol specification has proved extremely difficult, let alone
implementing it.

In the basic class service, a work specification to a single contained
document, and work specifications may only contain a single proforma.
Nesting of proformas is not permitted, nor is the collection of documents
from source agencies (en route). Expressed more formally, the restrictions
are as follows:

  • Only the following primitives are available (J- is implicit):
INITIATE-WORK, INITIATE-WORK-MAN, DISPOSE, GIVE,
TASKEND, STATUS, KILL, STOP.

  • Only one top level proforma is allowed, which may not
contain any nested proformas. Thus a maximum of two stages is
possible, typically to send a document for remote processing, and to
get the resulting output back. This restricts the service to simple
jobs such as X submitting a job to be run at Y, the proforma
specifying that the output should be returned to X (or possibly Z).

  • Only abnormal termination and manipulation termination
events can be reported on.

  • Only the primary monitor is allowed.

  • Only manipulations to stop, kill or display an OSI job are
permitted.

• Completion (level 3) commitment is not allowed (see §20.6.2). Indeed CCR now knows nothing about levels of commitment; see chapter eighteen.

• Various other restrictions are placed on what types of work can be performed. In particular it is not possible to pick up documents en route.

As has already been mentioned, only the basic class has stable protocol support at the moment, and progress on a full class JTM protocol specification is slow, and has relatively little support.

Apart from the anomaly of a service definition with no protocol, it leaves JTM looking very much like a subset of JTMP. The difficulties in full class protocol support are connected with the complexity of applying CCR mechanisms to an unconstrained tree of task specifications. CCR itself has had difficulties related to RDA, which is briefly discussed in chapter twenty three. The academic community had no such problems; they merely implemented JTMP over NIFTP, with no equivalent of CCR. Unfortunately developing an OSI conformant equivalent is not that simple.

20.6   Use of underlying services

We have hinted that both ACSE and CCR are used. In this section we briefly examine how the underlying services are used, although this is a complex area, and of necessity the discussion will be kept at a simple level. This section summarises how some of the underlying services are used.

The basic class job transfer is subject to CCR mechanisms to ensure reliability and the return of diagnostics. Associations between open systems among which tasks are to be processed are handled by ACSE. ROSE and RTSE are not used by JTM.

20.6.1   Use of ACSE

We stated above that service primitives do not map directly on to ACSE. ACSE is used to set up an association between peer JTM entities, the main purpose of which is to transfer work specifications between JTM open systems. The sole user of ACSE however is CCR, which is responsible for ensuring that the subjobs (branches of the atomic action which represents the entire OSI job) either all get executed, or not at all. But this is clearly an oversimplification, as the user can 'interfere' with a job as it is being processed, which makes it hard to define precisely what CCR is supposed to do.

20.6.2   Use of CCR

A work specification is transferred as a *transfer element* between JTM entities, and this is regarded as an atomic action, and is subject to the CCR procedures discussed in chapter eighteen. JTM uses CCR to guard against loss and duplication of subjobs, to ensure that every part of the job is performed exactly once.

The full class JTM service definition referred to three levels of commitment, which were supposed to map on to CCR. Working from the lowest to the highest, they were as follows:

> • Level 1 is *provider acceptance commitment*. This means that the JTM service provider has agreed to create a work specification, i.e. has returned a J-INITIATE-WORK confirm. To quote the standard, the OSI environment is now aware that this job exists.

> • Level 2 is *agency acceptance commitment*. With regard to the initial subjob, this is taken to mean that all source agencies have been accessed (to obtain the necessary documents, if this is allowed), all interactions with sink and execution agencies have resulted in the associated documents being secured by these agencies, and the job can be completed.

> • Level 3 is *completion commitment*. All aspects of the job have been completed. This level of commitment is not available to the basic class service.

We said 'were' rather than 'are' just now because changes to CCR required for TP (see chapter eighteen) abolished the notion of CCR levels of commitment. So if JTM wants levels of commitment, it has to provide mechanisms itself. This, among other changes to CCR, caused problems for JTM mapping to CCR, resulting in a JTM defect report. In fact the functions performed by JTM itself could equally well be performed using TP, and some experts feel that JTM has no long term future. Indeed the UK academic community appears to be one of the few supporters of JTM, and this largely because it is a descendant of JTMP (chapter nine) which they developed.

20.6.3   Use of the presentation layer

The JTM data types used conform to ASN.1, discussed in chapter seventeen, and constitute an abstract syntax which is a particular instance of a defined presentation context. Other contexts are used to specify the fields of work specifications and so on.

20.6.4   Use of the session layer

The basic class job transfer (of a work specification between open systems) of a connectionless, simplex nature, and the entire transfer is encoded as a single P-DATA (i.e. S-DATA) primitive. Session activities are not used.

21   Virtual Terminal (VT) Standards

21.1   Introduction

Terminal handling has always been a headache for systems designers. There is no such thing as a standard terminal. Some have hard copy, while others have a screen. In the case of screen devices, there may be differences in the page size, with 25 rows by 80 columns common but by no means universal. Further difficulties include the action of special keys and escape sequences. In chapter eight we examined the CCITT triple X (XXX) recommendations which provided the first standardised means of using terminals over X.25 networks. Basically what these recommendations offer is as follows:

• A terminal connects via a PSTN line to a PAD, which forms the characters from the terminal into X.25 packets for transmission to the remote host.

• The PAD defines the terminal in terms of a set of X.3 PAD parameters, which are made available to the remote host as well as the terminal.

• Recommendation X.28 defines how the terminal user accesses the PAD, to set parameters, set up virtual calls, communicate with the remote host, and so on.

• Recommendation X.29 defines what is in effect an application protocol between the PAD and the remote host, the principal aim of which is to provide the remote host with access to (and in some cases the capability to alter) PAD terminal parameters.

When this scenario is compared with OSI/RM, several fundamental weaknesses and incompatibilities immediately become clear.

• The PAD is merely an ad hoc interface between character terminals and X.25 networks. As such it is tied into X.25, and for terminals to access hosts via other networks, separate procedures would be required. Therefore XXX is network dependent. In effect, at the PAD end, there is no host worthy of the name at all.

• X.29 is in effect an application protocol grafted directly on top of X.25, a realisation of the network layer. There is no provision for the transport, session or presentation layers, not is it possible to form any application association between the terminal user and the host. In particular, in the event of a failure of the X.25 network, the terminal connection will be irretrievably lost.

- Perhaps most serious of all, there is no way in which the host can determine precisely what effect characters it sends are having on the terminal. It may be that the host 'knows' that the terminal is a Zenith Z29 (or whatever), and thus can deduce that sending some combination of escape sequences and text will format the screen in a particular way (e.g. for the UNIX EMACS editor), but there is no way in which this can be policed. In effect the host is playing a guessing game. Worse still, the fact that the host knows that the terminal is a Z29 implies that it is transmitting terminal-specific sequences. To support a different terminal type, a different set of escape sequences would in general be needed. This is precisely the sort of duplication which OSI seeks to eliminate.

While private and host PADs relieve the problems of XXX to some extent, by providing host support at the terminal end, typically the provision of a user interface which is superior to X.28, there is no way in which this removes the fundamental problems outlined above. What is needed is an entirely new approach, and this is what the VT standards set out to achieve.

21.2   Fundamental VT concepts

In this chapter we examine the salient features of the VT service {9040}. This is a very complex standard, and it is not the intention in this chapter to go into fine detail about the service definition or protocol specification, but rather to discuss the general VT philosophy, in order to give a feeling for what the standards are trying to achieve. At several points in the discussion, an attempt is made to clarify certain features in relation to typical terminal applications, and also in relation to the XXX recommendations (in particular X.3 and X.29) discussed in chapter eight.

21.2.1   The Conceptual Communications Area

One problem with the old XXX approach is that there is no consistent view of what is happening on the terminal, which is shared by both the remote host and the local terminal. The essence of VT is that both open systems (the one supporting the terminal, and the one supporting the application) should have a consistent view of what is actually happening to the terminal. On the other hand, this must be abstracted away from any specific type of terminal.

VT achieves this by providing an abstract representation of the terminal known as the *Conceptual Communications Area* (*CCA*). This is in theory a single, consistent representation of the abstract terminal, which operations at either end will update in a consistent way. In practice this is not possible due to the geographical separation of the two open systems. VT therefore provides mechanisms whereby a copy of the CCA is maintained at each open system, and mechanisms for ensuring that both open systems maintain a consistent view of the CCA.

The CCA contains three distinct types of information:

    • The *Conceptual Data Store* (*CDS*) in effect holds arrays of characters representing the screen's contents. It it is normally a two dimensional representation, at any given time, of the contents of the screen (say) of the terminal, including the characters displayed at each character position, and their attributes (e.g. bold, underline, font, colour as appropriate). It is also possible, in the case of buffered terminals which can 'remember' earlier screen contents, to regard the CDS as three-dimensional, with a memory of a number of earlier pages. (This also implies that this type of terminal operates in page mode.)

The source of updates to the CDS is ultimately either keyboard input or host application output. The updating of the CDS is a standardised procedure, which can be mapped on to ASN.1 as a defined presentation context, whereas the physical host-terminal dialogue is not. The CDS can be viewed as one or more *Display Objects* (*DOs*). These define part (or all) of the CDS in terms of the information contained, and where on the 'virtual screen' it appears. Thus altering the contents of the screen of the real terminal can be regarded as changing the (or a) DO. Whether the CCS contains one or more DOs depends on the mode of operation, as will be discussed in due course.

    • The *Control, Signalling and Status Store* (*CSS*) contains additional information relating to terminal functions not directly concerned with normal screen display. The CSS is viewed as a set of objects referred to as control objects (COs), reference information objects (RIOs) and device objects (no acronym).

        • *Control objects* (COs) are used to control such things as the terminal beep, status lights, status line contents and so on.

        • *Reference information objects* (RIOs) provide a means of defining what are, in effect, 'macros' which provide a shorthand means of changing the contents of the CDS (i.e. a DO). Referencing a given RIO causes a specific set of actions to be applied to the CDS. RIOs are used, for example, to set up screen proformas, as discussed in §21.6.2.

- *Device objects* are used with certain types of terminal which, for example, have an attached printer. Many VDUs have a 'print screen' key, which copies the screen to an attached printer. In effect, both the screen and the printer copy relate to the CDS. In VT, a relationship between the CDS and a specific device could be established by means of a device object.

Some VDUs used on multidrop lines (e.g. the Australian Standard VDU specified in the 1970s) have separate addresses (in the BSC or HDLC NRM context) for 'screen' and 'printer'. In the VT context these could also be mapped on to distinct device objects. Also be warned that DO refers to display object not device object. The choice of terminology in the VT standards is unfortunate.

We will provide specific examples of COs and RIOs later.

- The **Data Structure Definition** (**DSD**) is rather like a set of X.3 parameters, in that it defines various characteristics of the terminal which in some way constrain the manner in which the CCA can be accessed (which in turn represents the way the real terminal can be used).

21.2.2   The VT service model

It follows of course that VT requires full OSI host support for the terminal end, as well as for the application which the terminal user is accessing. This is one of the major differences between VT and XXX. There is no place in the VT standards for a terminal dialling up an X.25 network port; far more support than that is required.

Figure 21.1 shows how the VT service is modelled in terms of functions. It should be noted that the CCA is depicted as being shared by the two VT service providers. In fact this is not strictly true, as two copies of the CCA need to be maintained, one at X and one at Y. The point is that the VT protocol attempts to ensure that both X and Y have a consistent view of what the terminal is currently displaying (i.e. the CCA contents) at all times. This not only removes the element of guess-work from application software driving terminals, but also means that the application need no longer be tied to specific types of terminals, such as those from the same manufacturer as the host.

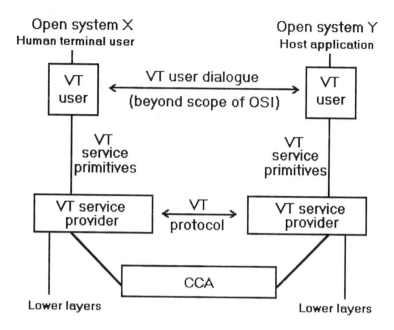

Figure 21.1 - Model of the VT service

21.3   Terminal types and classes

We have implicitly assumed in the above discussion that the terminal will be a 'glass Teletype' VDU, possibly with the addition of some value-added features such as support for various escape sequences for clearing the screen, positioning the cursor, and so on. One problem faced by the standard committees was the extent to which such value added features should be recognised in the standard. As argued above, it makes no sense to transmit the specific escape sequence to clear the screen on some particular type of VDU, but it makes every sense to provide an abstract operation which can be mapped to a screen clear on _any_ VDU, the precise means by which the actual VDU screen is cleared being of no concern to the VT procedures.

At this point it could be argued that ANSI escape sequences (ESC [something) exist, and, for example, on 'ANSI compatible' VDUs the screen can always be cleared by transmitting ESC [2 J. This is indeed true, but it is also true that most VDUs which support ANSI escape sequences in addition have their own peculiar (and incompatible) escape sequences as well. Unfortunately the ANSI standard is far from universally used. A perhaps more fundamental objection is that the above sequence implies the use of specific encoding, whereas what should be sought is a presentation context, and ASN.1 definitions. The VDU may use whatever physical sequence it wishes; this is of no interest whatsoever to VT. All that matters in the VT context is that when an instruction to clear the screen is given, somehow this will happen.

Thus what is proposed is various *primitive operations* which can be performed on the CCA (CDS, CSS or DSD), and it is for the local host or terminal controller (outside the scope of OSI) to determine precisely how these are to be applied to a specific terminal. Thus although something which is easy on a Zenith Z29 (such as a simple escape sequence to clear screen lines 5 to 13 inclusive say) might involve much more work if a simple glass Teletype were involved, this is of no concern to VT, which can specify the operation in a VDU-independent manner.

This leaves one obvious problem. Which types of VDU operation are worth including in the standard, and which should be omitted? Obviously something as basic as clearing the screen has to be included, but what about obscure facilities not found on every VDU, such as (perhaps) clearing screen lines 5 to 13 inclusive? The choice is far from easy in some cases. The most sensible approach is to adopt the procedure used in ASN.1, and provide some basic building blocks from which more complex operations can be generated.

Terminal standards posed a particular problem for ISO. One of the initial decisions which had to be taken was what *types* of terminals should be supported. We have mentioned glass Teletypes, and obviously these must be supported at all costs. But what other terminal types can be identified? Data entry terminals such as the Honeywell VIP, Burroughs (Unisys) TD800 series, IBM 3270, and so on, provide what is commonly known as *forms mode*, which involves splitting the screen area into fields which are unprotected (i.e. can be typed into by the user), coupled with protected screen zones which display field identifications (which cannot be altered by the user), thus providing the means to display a *screen proforma* into which the user can type data from batches of (paper) forms. Entries from the forms (name, address, date of birth, and so on) are typed into successive fields on the screen. When the form has been entirely entered, the user presses the 'send' key. Historically such terminals have generally been used on multidrop lines using BSC-like poll-select protocols (or more recently HDLC NRM). Once the send key has been pressed, next time the VDU is polled the fields (only) will get transmitted to 'central'. There is a clear case for VT support for this type of terminal as well. We discuss forms mode support in §21.6.2.

Other types of terminal have also been identified. The current VT concensus is that there will (ultimately) be five *terminal classes*, each of which groups together terminals with similar characteristics, as follows:

- **Basic class**. This covers simple dumb terminals such as glass Teletypes which can be represented, in the case of a VDU, as a two dimensional array of character cells (atomic objects). This is the 'classic' terminal type, the one which is covered by the CCITT XXX recommendations. This proved to be the easiest class to handle, and has received most attention to date.

- **Forms class**. This includes 'forms mode' data entry terminals of the type just discussed. These typically provide protected and unprotected fields, possibly simple validation of user entered fields, and possibly a tree structured hierarchy of relationships between fields, typified by the ASCII field separator characters US, RS, GS, FS. Protocol definition here will be more complex than for the basic class, as a wide variety of options is available on different terminals. Although much needed, this proved harder than the basic class, so for the time being a compromise position has been reached, as will be discussed in a moment.

- **Graphics class**. This includes graphics terminals which can typically draw pictures based on points, lines and curves, such as those in this book. The intention in this case is to define generic graphics operations rather than specific representations.

- **Image class**. This includes facsimile and raster scan graphics terminals where the screen (or whatever) can be represented using pixel (e.g. dot matrix) definitions. This might also be appropriate for certain graphics modes on PCs. In this case the representation has to be specified, as in general this cannot be abstracted to something generic such as a line.

- **Text class**. This class has been identified for use with terminals operating on data structures defined by the emerging Office Document Architecture (ODA) standards {8613}; these are briefly discussed in chapter twenty three.

As can be seen, these initial plans were ambitious. Indeed it was soon realised that they excessively so, and while it remains ISO's long-term intention to provide support for all of these classes, activity to date has concentrated on the *basic class*, together with some functions of the forms class (sometimes referred to as *page mode*). The current VT standards have somehow succeeded in combining complexity and restrictiveness. In a very real sense this reflects the extremely difficult task of achieving a worthwhile VT standard at all, given the divergence of terminal types and operating system conventions, and the range of views of different experts on what is required. What is provided so far is seen as only the beginning, although judging by progress so far, it could be many years yet before substantial progress is made beyond support for glass Teletypes and forms mode terminals.

Original proposals included a 'mixed class', combining features of two or more of the first four classes mentioned above (not the text class, which was dreamed up later), but this idea has now been superseded by a more formalised approach. It is now ISO's intention to develop standards for *terminal management*. This would be needed, for example, to provide a common framework for the individual classes. It might then be possible to support 'terminals' (PCs or workstations) operating in a windows environment, with (say) text in one window and graphics in another, without the need explicitly to define a mixed class. At the time of writing however, this idea has not progressed very far.

21.4   Operations on the CCA

As explained in §21.2.1, the CCA contains one or more Display Objects (DOs), containing a representation of (part of) the display's surface. For a typical VDU, a DO representing the entire display surface is in effect (in Pascal terms) an array [1..25,1..80] of [character,attribute]. DOs can be updated in several ways, as follows:

• **Text operations** alter the characters displayed on the screen, e.g. by writing new ('printable') characters to specific points on the conceptual screen. This affects only the character to be displayed, not its attributes (colour, highlighting and so on).

• **Attribute operations** on the other hand alter how the character is to be displayed rather than the character itself; attributes which can be specified may include the character's colour (foreground and background), emphasis, repertoire, and character font. Thus the following would all classify as the same character with different attributes: aa*aaa*ₐₐ. (This depends on whether the terminal attributes support these operations; changing the colour on a green screen monitor would be a waste of time.)

As an example, the aside you are reading at the moment is Times Roman 10 point normal font. The surrounding text is Times Roman 12 point normal font, while the section heading above is bold Helvetica 15 point font. All of this can be specified if appropriate for the VDU being used. Refer also to the discussion of ODA and SGML in chapter twenty three.

At this point it is worth reiterating that the term 'VDU' might well include PCs such as the one which produced this book, which are capable of a rich repertoire of character attributes. These would represent a new generation of 'terminal emulators' which did not pretend to be, say, a Zenith Z29 by emulating all of that terminal's escape sequences, but rather supported VT over the full OSI protocol stack. Clearly this could push even powerful 386-based

PCs and 68000 series workstations to the limit; older style 8086-based PCs can even have difficulty running a dedicated program emulating a single VDU type without having difficulty in acting fast enough on received characters at high data rates. (9600 bps counts as fast in this context.)

- **Erase operations** blank out part of the DO, i.e. clear all or a specified part of the screen (fill it with spaces).

- **Pointer updates** move the conceptual screen cursor. It is a general characteristic that when characters are written to a VDU, they are applied at the current cursor position.

- Proposed extensions to the standard (see §21.8) will support the moving of blocks of characters from one part of the screen to another. The original standard required the entire text to be retransmitted, which could be inefficient.

As well as a representation of the screen in the CDS, the CCA may also contain *Control Objects* (*COs*) within the CSS, which specify the types of actions which can be performed on the DO, rather than its actual contents. COs can also be updated since they contain attributes which can be negotiated. Typical of these is the *echo control object* which determines whether characters typed on the VDU should be echoed locally. This is an example of a Boolean control object. (Echo is true or false.) Control objects may also be character strings, symbolic (having a limited number of named values), integers or bit strings. Other possible control objects could include the VDU 'bell', and various lights on the VDU or a status line, indicating the VDU's current status. When we discuss forms mode in §21.6.2 we will encounter several more COs.

It is worth noting that the echo CO may be manipulated by either VT user, but once its attributes have been agreed, VT internal procedures ensure that terminal echoing is applied in a consistent way. No longer is there the possibility that both the terminal and the remote host will echo characters, as can happen with XXX. Furthermore, it is not the function of VT to implement the echoing; the echo CO merely indicates which open system is responsible, and if it is to be the application process, this must physically echo the characters.

Until the necessary registration procedures have been standardised {9834-3}, the definition of control objects other than those contained in the standard is an issue for implementors, but some work has been done in Europe by EWOS (see chapter five), which has defined COs for sequenced application, unsequenced application, sequenced terminal and unsequenced terminal dialogue types. Further details are beyond the scope of this discussion.

21.5   VT environment and operational modes

21.5.1   The VT environment and VTE-parameters

We first encountered the idea of terminal profiles in chapter eight, where we discussed PAD parameters, and identified terminal-host combinations with specific attributes. A similar concept is used in VT.

The *VT environment* (*VTE*) is a set of *VTE-parameters* which define the characteristics of a terminal in terms of its interaction with a remote application. In a sense it is rather like the set of X.3 PAD parameters, but is more powerful. Setting up a VT association involves negotiating parameters, in order to set up either a *partial VTE* (not all parameters are used) or a *full VTE* (all parameters have defined values). Some VTE parameters can also be negotiated during association establishment. The VTE parameters are contained in a (logically) separate area known as the data structure definition (DSD). One such parameter is the mode of operation (TWA/TWS - although this particular one cannot be negotiated).

21.5.2   VT operational modes

In chapter eight we identified two major classes of terminal-host interaction. To summarise, these were as follows:

   • **Line at a time mode**. Here the interaction with the host is a line at a time. Only complete lines will be accepted by the host, and the line input can be edited (at the host) before pressing the end of line key (usually CR). This is typical of 'traditional' operating systems based on the notion of card images, and is a hangover from the old days when input was via punched cards rather than VDUs.

   • **Native mode**. This is the type of interaction used with 'modern' operating systems such as UNIX, which are not constrained by the card image concept. Here, whatever is typed gets acted on as soon as practicable.

These two types of interaction are reflected in VT by providing two *operational modes,* which offer features broadly compatible with the above types of interaction. These are known as synchronous and asynchronous modes, as described below; a default profile is offered for each, broadly comparable with the X.3 profiles for line at a time and native modes. It is a conformance requirement that every VT implementation should support at least one of these profiles.

• In *Synchronous mode* (*S-mode*), there is a two way alternate dialogue, which can be interpreted as a command (e.g. a line, page or group of pages) from the terminal, followed by a similar response from the host. This models *line at a time mode*, but is more generalised than this, since there is no constraint that the command or response need correspond just to a line of terminal input or host output.

The term 'synchronous' implies that the terminal-host dialogue is synchronised, a meaning which is general in the application layer. It does not have anything at all to do with synchronous and asynchronous transmission as relevant in the physical layer. However an analogy exists, as long as it is not pursued too far. In the physical layer, groups of characters are synchronised in synchronous transmission. In the application layer, it is end-end open systems dialogues which are synchronised.

The VT service provider polices this dialogue by means of a *token*, which is negotiated between the two VT entities, and broadly maps on to the session service data token in half duplex (two way alternate, TWA) mode. The (service provider) owner of the token may alter its local DO, and notifies its peer of the changes it has made. Thus in effect there is only one DO, although there are two copies of it of course; changes to the DO are applied consistently to both copies. It should be noted that this is a *symmetrical* procedure, just as in the session layer. This is in marked contrast to XXX, where the procedures at the terminal and host ends are fundamentally different.

In S-mode, it is assumed that the local terminal (or VT service provider) will perform the necessary echoing of typed characters. This is controlled by the echo control object. It should be clear that in TWA mode the echoing cannot sensibly be performed by the host, as not only could there be a long delay before anything was echoed (since the host would not currently own the data token), but the act of echoing could also interfere with the TWA nature of the dialogue. Historically, hosts operating in this mode have not echoed in any case.

Access to the CCA is policed in S-mode, so that only the owner of the token is permitted to alter the screen's contents (change a DO); if this were not the case, it would leave the two VT-users with different views of the current state of the screen, which is precisely what the usage of the CCA is supposed to prevent. In addition a quarantining service is available, whereby the receiving VT-user is not notified of any changes to the DO until it has received all of them (i.e. it is time to pass the data token to the other VT entity).

It is worth mentioning that quarantining was originally considered to be a session layer function. In the event the session layer as currently specified offers no such service, leaving applications to offer this service if they wish.

Two organisations, NIST and EWOS (see chapter five) are co-operating in the definition of further S-mode *profiles*. A forms profile has been developed for administrative form-filling applications, and a paged profile is currently being defined for use by block mode terminals.

- In *Asynchronous mode* (*A-mode*), no such constraints are imposed on the dialogue. This maps on to the duplex (two way simultaneous) session service functional unit, with no token control of the data transfer. It is for the terminal user and host software (outside the scope of OSI) to determine who sends what and when, and as this depends on the particular conventions of the host application the terminal user is accessing, it is of no interest to VT.

In A-mode, echoing may be done locally or by the remote host. Again this is controlled by the echo control object.

21.5.3   VT profiles

It will come as no surprise to learn that various combinations of parameters are commonly encountered, and for this reason the VT standard defines various *VT-profiles*. These count as 'objects' of the type which will ultimately be registered according to registration procedures currently being developed {9834-4}. A VT-profile is negotiated during association establishment, and facilities exist for negotiating a switch to a different profile during the association. Profiles are provided within the standard to support the two operational modes discussed in the previous section.

Standard profiles

Two profiles are built into the base standard. These provide *default support* for the two operational modes, S-mode and A-mode discussed in §21.5.2. Conforming implementations must support at least one of these.

- **S-mode default profile**. This operational mode requires the session data token and half duplex functional unit. This is consistent with a DO whose contents are unambiguously known at the time the data token is exchanged (although there are always two copies of the CCA).

The default profile provides a scrolled display of 80 character lines. Paging is not supported. The pointer (cursor) may only be moved forwards (i.e. left to right or down), No support is provided for colour, font or emphasis, and the character set is in effect restricted to ASCII {646}. Typed characters are immediately forwarded, although XON/XOFF control by the user is supported.

This amounts to support a simple glass Teletype. One thing it lacks is the ability to buffer characters to optimise the usage of the underlying network. This in fact highlights one dilemma faced by VT standards. VT is not supposed to know anything about the underlying network. On the other hand the VT user needs to know that VT is using (e.g.) X.25 data packets in a (for him) cost effective manner. Simply hiding behind the QOS concept merely begs the question. In reality the VT service provider must apply some rules governing when to present data VTPDUs to the underlying service, but the default profile leaves this entirely to the service provider.

• **A-mode default profile**. Essentially this is similar to the S-mode default profile, in that it supports the same sort of glass Teletype. However Support <u>is</u> provided (abstractly) for data forwarding after 80 characters, or when any of the ASCII characters CR, LF, FF or VT (vertical tab) are typed, i.e. received by VT (the virtual terminal service).

It would have perhaps been better if a single standard default profile could have been agreed, but this proved impossible. It is an unfortunate characteristic of OSI that opposing schools of thought often have to be accommodated. In this case there are entrenched host operating systems supporting both native and line at a time mode, so that compromise was inevitable. It also seems that the acronym situation is getting rather out of hand!

EWOS and NIST profiles

Additional profiles which have either been specified or are being considered by EWOS/NIST include the following:

• *Line scroll*. This is intended to provide better support for glass Teletypes, which lack any screen management capabilities, than the default profiles.

• *Telnet*. This is mainly of interest in the USA, where there is a large DARPA community using the Telnet protocol over the TCP/IP protocol[1]. It is intended as a migration tool, to facilitate conversion to OSI. TCP/IP has been adopted by other organisations as well, including many in the UK. (We have excluded any discussion of such proprietary architectures from this book.)

• The need for a *paged* profile in S-mode has been identified, but it has so far not received any detailed attention. The default profiles have no understanding that the VDU screen is bounded in the vertical direction as well as the horizontal one.

• A *transparent* profile is intended for those users who wish to use VT in 'pass through' mode. In effect VT imposes no constraints on what can be done to the CCA, and it is left to users to ensure that consistent results are obtained from such accesses.

• Finally, as might be expected, a profile is being developed to provide a migration route to OSI from XXX. It is known as the *X.3 PAD interworking* profile.

21.6   VT functional units

As usual, the VT service is specified in terms of various functional units (FUs) which can be negotiated during association establishment. The following is a description of the main FUs provided at present. They fall into two categories, general VT facilities and forms mode additions.

21.6.1   General basic class support

• **Kernel**. This provides the minimum facilities to set up a VT association (using ACSE), and to transfer DOs using default profiles. Once a profile has been agreed it cannot be changed. Normally one of the base standard profiles will be used, although there is no reason why another one should not be agreed, either by private agreement or, in due course, a registered profile.

• **Switch profile negotiation**. This allows the current VT profile to be altered during a VT association. This requires a negotiation phase to be entered, as discussed in §21.7.2. The reason for wishing to do so is of no interest to VT, but could include the terminal user finishing with one host application and wishing to use another on the same host, where the applications require different conventions. For instance having read his electronic mail on the host (which is essentially a synchronous activity), the user may now wish to edit a file (which is essentially asynchronous in nature). It may be that the host VT service provider might request a profile switch in this case. Of course this is only one possible example.

It should be noted that if a profile change is negotiated during the association, the contents of the CCA after the switch are left undefiled. This problem is currently being addressed; see §21.8.

• **Multiple interaction negotiation**. The kernel FU allows a profile to be specified, but provides no means of 'fine tuning' individual VTE-parameters within that profile. This FU provides the ability to alter individual attributes. This may only be done at specific points in the dialogue, in what is referred to as the *negotiation active phase* (see §21.7.2).

What is provided is conceptually similar to, but much more powerful than, the X.29 procedure described in chapter eight. Unlike X.29, it is also a symmetrical procedure.

Negotiation takes the form of an 'offer' of an initial value (or set of values) for a named profile, to which a 'success' or 'failure' reply is returned. In the success case, a specific parameter value may be returned if a choice was offered.

• **Negotiated release**. This has the usual function of requiring the agreement of both users before the VT association may be released. This maps on to session service negotiated release. If its use is not agreed during association establishment, either the terminal user or the host may unilaterally terminate the association.

X.29 provided an 'invitation to clear' command, but this was not really negotiated release, as the terminal user was then expected to be logged out, and the host would in due course disconnect him if the PAD did not comply within a certain time. The VT procedure is symmetrical, and failure of negotiated release leaves the VT association intact. It is of no concern to VT why or if a release attempt may fail.

• **Urgent data**. At the time of writing this is the only clearly established use for *expedited* data in any OSI application. There have long been cases where a terminal user would wish to take drastic action because something had gone badly wrong, and VT provides two mechanisms for this. The following is a typical scenario.

A (human) user has run a program, and due to a bug, it is looping endlessly sending the same line of output again and again. Clearly if the terminal was connected directly to a UNIX system the user could type ^C to terminate the program. This would be processed by the UNIX system, and UNIX would abort the program (possibly after a delay caused by process scheduling constraints). On a direct connection, this is not a great problem.

Now consider the case where the terminal and UNIX are separated by several intervening networks. The ^C is merely another data character, and gets no preferential treatment. Therefore it takes the usual length of time (possibly several seconds) to reach the UNIX host. Meanwhile possibly hundreds of lines of further useless junk arrive, and the terminal user will have to pay for this (e.g. in PSS data volume charges). When the ^C arrives at the UNIX host, it may or may not get preferential treatment, and UNIX may or may not choose to flush its output buffers before terminating the program.

Clearly this scenario is quite unacceptable. VT offers two types of support for this type of problem.

- The *urgent data FU* provides a *soft break* facility, which is described next.

- Additionally there is a *break FU*, which will be discussed in a moment, which provides a *hard* (destructive) *break* facility.

In the case of a soft break, a VT protocol command (containing user data, possibly the ^C character) is relayed to the peer open system (e.g. the UNIX host) as quickly as possible. The VT protocol uses the underlying expedited data channel, if it is available, to transport this as a VT PDU. On receipt of this PDU, the soft break is relayed as an indication primitive to the peer VT user. What happens then is of no concern to VT itself, which (in the usual OSI manner) merely provides a mechanism which service users may avail themselves of. Therefore this does not really solve our problem, although the UNIX system may shut up as a result.

Thus the soft break mechanism has its limitations. For example it this will not be destructive of useless data currently in transit in the reverse direction, as it counts as 'user data' as far as lower layers are concerned. But it may receive priority treatment before and during transmission, and will (one hopes) receive priority treatment by the remote host's VT user.

In fact the urgent data FU allows two *priorities*, 'urgent' and 'high'. What has been discussed above is an example of the use of urgent priority, where the amount of information which can be transmitted is strictly limited. Large amounts of information can be transported using high priority, but although it will get preferential treatment (over 'regular' priority information) within the VT station, it will not necessarily do so in the underlying networks, as high priority information does not use the expedited data channel. (Indeed if no expedited channel is available in underlying networks, urgent messages will be downgraded to high priority.) In fact a soft break is considered to be more useful for relaying such things as system messages to be displayed on the status line of a VDU than for relaying a ^C.

One final point worth noting is that high and urgent priority updates (to the CCA) are not subject to token control. We have seen that urgent PDUs may be sent as expedited data. This implies that they are presented to the session layer (see §21.9) in S-EXPEDITED-DATA requests. If this is not possible, and in any case for high priority data, in S-mode they must be presented as S-TYPED-DATA requests. In this case it would not be possible to use session normal data, as only typed data may be transmitted against the data token direction of flow, and the data token is required for S-mode.

Further thought will reveal a potential problem here. We suggested in chapter sixteen that TYPED data may be given lower priority than normal data within the session layer entity, 'in the interests of efficiency of implementation'. This appears to be at odds with the requirement that typed data (high priority) should get preferential treatment over normal data (standard priority). It becomes clear that while the functionality of the session layer is completely independent of layers above it, in a real open system the implementation can be severely constrained by the applications will use it. By now you will appreciate that implementation is a complex area.

• **Break**. This is used to signal a *hard break*, i.e. can be used to represent the terminal user pressing the BREAK key. This key does not generate a character, but (at the physical level) sends a special 'out of band' signal. (On an asynchronous line, this is usually a 'start bit' lasting too long). This unit allows a 'hard break' VT-PDU to be forwarded to the peer VT entity, rather like the X.29 indication of break.

Unlike a soft break, this is destructive of any data in transit in the reverse direction. As a result the CDS is left in an undefined state, as the two copies cannot now be guaranteed to have the same contents. However it does seem to cater for our ^C problem.

• **Blocks**. The purpose of this unit, which was not part of the original draft standard, is to allow the terminal screen (as represented in the CCA) to be divided into rectangular zones, which can then, for example, be cleared independently of the contents of the rest of the screen. This facility could be used for the 'clear lines 5 to 13' example earlier. It could also be used to support forms mode terminals, since data entry fields can be defined in these terms. So far, however, it has found little support from implementors. This is largely because for forms mode applications, the fields FU provided in the forms mode extensions (see below) provides more flexibility, including rectangles as a valid subset. Few other applications have been identified which would find it a useful feature.

21.6.2   Forms mode additions

Originally forms mode data entry was envisaged as a distinct class from basic mode. The problem was the usual one. It would have taken too long to develop an agreed full forms mode class standard, and support for this type of terminal was seen as required in a shorter timescale. Therefore while it is still the long-term intention to specify a full forms class, some forms mode support has been built in as an extension to the basic class.

Additional functional units

The following additional FUs are currently provided to support forms mode.

- **Enhanced access rules**. Although access rules for control objects have not been discussed, they are rather primitive in the original standard, making certain types of update operation on the CCA rather messy to perform. In particular, any changes to the DO must be explicitly specified, and it is implied that the remainder of the DO will remain unaltered. It was generally felt that this was restrictive for data entry applications, and this FU provides more sophisticated access controls suited to this type of application.

- **Structured control objects**. Again, the notion that the CCA represents merely a two (or three) dimensional array of [character,attribute] pairs ignores the fact that forms mode data entry VDUs can display a tree-structured hierarchy of fields, together with protected areas which the user cannot access. This requires more complex control objects, which are provided by this FU. These are discussed briefly in a moment.

- **Fields**. On a data entry VDU, a screen proforma may contain various fields. For example, if the proforma represented an employee record, there might be fields to represent the employee name, address, payroll number, sex, date of birth, grade, and so on. Each field has special characteristics, and there is no way in which these can be adequately controlled without additional support. This FU defines a suitable structure for representing data entry fields in the CCA.

A field may be composed of any part or parts of the screen, which need not be either contiguous or rectangular. Field definition control objects have been defined, which are discussed in the following section.

- **Reference information objects (RIOs)**. The above employee record example specifies a particular type of *proforma* or *screen template*, into which employee details can be entered. This has to be displayed before data can be entered, and it has always been a problem where this should be stored.

Consider a tree network of the type discussed in chapter two. In general this will contain concentrators as well as multiplexers. The proforma could be stored at the central site, or at any concentrator. Storing it at the concentrator to which the terminals are connected will save on the transmission cost (and time) of having to download it every time it is needed, but there is the risk that when the central database is updated, the locally held proforma will no longer match the database structure (e.g. may lack some new fields, or have fields of incorrect length). The idea of defining *reference information objects* (in the CSS; see §21.2.1) is to specify commonly used proformas in a consistent way. Those commonly used (such as an employee record) can be registered, and any changes will automatically be applied to every terminal VT user as well, thus avoiding the problem of out-of-date local copies.

Additional control objects

The standard identifies a number of *additional COs* which are concerned with various aspects of data entry, as follows:

- **Field definition control object (FDCO)**. A field is any number of rectangular areas of the DO, which need not be contiguous, although the data applied to a field, or extracted from it is regarded as contiguous. (This is a far more powerful definition than either the block concept in the basic service, or indeed that used on most standard multidrop VDUs.) The FDCO defines the structure, ordering and some other attributes of each field. The data contained within each field is regarded as a single entity, regardless of how it may actually be fragmented around the screen (in various rectangles); the FDCO provides the necessary association. During the negotiation phase (see §21.7.2), attributes of fields can also be altered.

- **Context control object (CCO)**. This allows an initial field to be specified for data entry. It is also used to indicate which was the last field the user updated. This can be interpreted in terms of a user entering fields from a document into a proforma. If there are 8 fields, it may be that only fields 3-6 need to be entered. In traditional forms mode applications (using BSC-like poll/select procedures), although only the user-alterable fields would get transmitted, this could include fields which the user had not actually changed. Provision of the CCO allows more selectivity in what changes are transmitted (i.e. what DO changes are notified to the peer VT entity). The aim is to reduce the overhead of transmitting parts of the screen whose contents have not changed.

- **Field entry instruction control object (FEICO)**. In general, fields corresponding to entries on a form have restrictions placed on their contents. Obvious examples include restricting an 'age of employee' field to a bounded integer. The FEICO is a set of *field entry instruction records (FEIRs)*, each of which applies restrictions such as that in the example above.

- **Field entry pilot control object (FEPCO)**. Since field contents can be restricted, it follows that invalid data can be entered by the VDU typist. The FEPCO consists of a set of *field entry pilot records (FEPRs)*, each indicating what action VT should take if the entry for a given field is either incomplete or in error. (It may be quite valid for a field to be incompletely filled, for example for an address. However if a product code must always be 8 digits long, the field must be completely filled, as well as having to be an integer.)

- **Transmission policy control object (TPCO)**. This defines the relationship between the data entered into the fields and the data transmitted between peers. Again a loose analogy can be drawn with traditional forms mode techniques, where a number of possible conventions could be applied. The fields could all be completely sent, which is wasteful for a long field with only a few characters in it (e.g. 'Doe' in a surname field 20 characters long). Alternatively character compression techniques could be used so that multiple trailing spaces are not sent, or the ASCII 'separator' characters US, RS, GS and FS could be used to delimit fields, additionally providing hierarchical relationships between fields. What the TPCO does is to define a relationship between the transmitted and received data and the fields.

21.6.3   Functional unit combinations

Functional units are agreed (negotiated) at association establishment (see §21.7). As usual the initiator proposes FUs, and the responder either agrees or proposes a different set, subject to certain restrictions as follows.

- Multiple interaction negotiation cannot be selected without switch profile negotiation.

- Neither fields not reference information objects may be selected without structured control objects. The use of fields may require enhanced access rules as well.

In fact the negotiation process is slightly more complex than this. The result of the negotiation can be success, failure or success-with-warning, as will be seen in §21.7.

21.7   Outline of the VT service

The VT service definition is far more complex than the FTAM and JTM services discussed in the previous chapters. Details of individual services and primitives will therefore not be provided, although some primitives will be listed without comment.

The VT association occurs in a number of *phases*. Not all phases necessarily apply; this depends on the FUs selected. The relationship of the various aspects of the VT service with underlying services will be discussed in §21.9. One of the phases, the *idle phase*, is not really a phase at all. It simply means that no VT association with a peer open system has been established.

21.7.1   Data handling phase

This is entered by establishing an application association with another VT entity. At this point the use of an appropriate VT-profile, and A-mode or S-mode, are negotiated, together with the FUs which will apply to this VC association. Entry to the data transfer phase implies that the negotiation succeeded. If it failed, the association will also fail (except as discussed under the negotiation quiescent phase below).

The VT association is established by means of:

VT-ASSOCIATE confirmed   ACSE, negotiation etc. parameters

Data handling is the normal phase, available in every case, where data are transferred between VT entities and cause the receiving (i.e. objects in the copy of the receiving) CDS and/or CSS (see §21.2.1 for acronym explanations) to be updated. In fact there may be restrictions as to which CCA can be updated at the present time: (The token referred to is the session data token.)

- No restrictions (full duplex);

- only one of the users (simplex, no flow control);
- either user, subject to token ownership (half duplex);
- only one user, subject to token ownership (simplex, flow controlled).

Subject to these constraints, data (updates to the CDS) can be relayed by means of the following primitive:

VT–DATA unconfirmed   VT user data

A tutorial description of how the data handling phase operates in detail can be found elsewhere[2].

Delivery control

VT provides a *quarantine* service of the type originally envisaged for the session layer. If its use has been agreed, the sender may mark the end of a sequence of data with a *data mark*. The receiver will buffer all received data until it receives a data mark. In other words the data marks delimit sections of data which will only be delivered to the VT user when complete. The receipt of a data mark maps on to:

VT–DELIVER indication   (receive quarantined data)

This use of data marks and quarantining is known as *delivery control*.

In chapter nine we discussed what seems to be a similar facility in YBTS (the PUSH and DATA+PUSH primitives). Unfortunately YBTS was trying to do two quite distinct things with it. The fact that it was issued by NIFTP for relay (via X.25) to the peer NIFTP entity implies an application use for the PUSH. However it was also used by YBTS to force the sending station to transmit an X.25 packet, which is something no application has the right to do. We can now add this to the list of NIFTP incompatibilities at the end of chapter nineteen.

21.7.2   Negotiation phases

Negotiation active phase

Unless use of the multiple interaction and/or switch profile negotiation FU has been agreed during association establishment, the profile selected applies for the duration of the association. Otherwise the profile can be altered by entering the negotiation phase and agreeing on a new profile. The negotiation active phase is entered by means of a confirmed primitive, the response indicating whether the peer agreed to enter this phase:

VT–START–NEG confirmed   maybe enter negotiation active phase

Negotiation of parameters is achieved by means of the following service primitives:

VT–NEG–INVITE unconfirmed   proposed parameter changes

VT–NEG–ACCEPT unconfirmed   changes accepted

VT–NEG–REJECT unconfirmed   changes rejected

VT–END–NEG confirmed   leave negotiation phase

There are some restrictions on which VT entity may initiate negotiation, which are related to the operational mode, the current owner of the token, and which entity initiated the negotiation phase.

If the multiple interaction negotiation FU is being used, the association may be aborted from this phase. In other words either user can issue:

VT–ABORT request   user data

This maps on to the ACSE user abort service discussed in chapter eighteen, and is relayed as an indication.

Negotiation quiescent phase

However if a negotiation FU was proposed at association establishment time, the responder may accept the FU but refuse the profile. This is referred to as a *success-with-warning* negotiation outcome. This is an 'in limbo' phase where only two things are possible, entering the negotiation phase to agree a (different) profile, or giving up and releasing the association. Only when a profile has been agreed can data transfer proceed.

21.8   Planned extensions to VT

A number of extensions to VT are under consideration at the time of writing. These are as follows:

> • **Exception reporting**. At present all exception conditions are fatal, in the sense that the application association will be lost. The intention is to add a 'recoverable' category, where the association is not aborted, and the VT user determines how recovery will be effected.

- **Context retention**. Certain actions, including a profile switch during the association, are currently destructive of the CCA's contents. The intention here is to allow the contents of display and control objects to be preserved in these cases if required.

- **Ripple editing**. Some aspects of the current standard are inefficient. For example, in order to insert a character in the middle of the screen (CCA), at least some of the remainder of the screen has to be retransmitted, as the current standard lacks a 'block move' and, as discussed above, all changes to the DO must be explicitly indicated. This is particularly unfortunate since many screen editors traditionally send short escape sequences requesting block moves which effectively scroll down part of the screen so that a new line of text can be inserted in the middle. It is clearly a step backwards from this scenario to a VT model where the entire group of lines would have to be retransmitted in its new position. Ripple editing is designed to remove this problem by defining procedures for inserting and deleting characters, lines and pages, and for specifying that a block of text is to be copied from one part of the CCA to another, rather than physically having to transmit the entire block.

21.9   VT use of underlying services

We have already discussed the *use of ACSE* in the previous section. VT is the sole user of ACSE. Note that a *negotiated release* FU is available, so that the ACSE release may be conditional.

21.9.1   Use of the presentation layer

It goes without saying that there need to be different *presentation* contexts for terminal data, VT primitive parameters, and so on. It is also worth mentioning that the BCVT protocol abstract syntax has been registered as an ASN.1 object identifier. In what follows we will ignore this aspect and concentrate on the mappings on to session service.

21.9.2   Use of the session layer

Session primitives

The following session service primitive mappings are used by VT:

- **S-DATA** is used for all normal data transfer, and also for all updates to COs having normal priority.

- **S-TYPED-DATA** is used for changes to DOs of high priority, and also any transfers of urgent priority where session expedited data transfer is available. It is also used for delivery control functions (see §21.7.1).

- **S-EXPEDITED-DATA** is used for urgent functions, where S-EXPEDITED-DATA is available. This includes the soft break facility. (The availability of S-EXPEDITED-DATA is in itself no guarantee that N-EXPEDITED-DATA can be used.)

- **S-SYNC-MAJOR** is used for profile negotiation, and at the start and finish of parameter negotiation.

- **S-RESYNCHRONIZE** is used to convey the hard break facility. (The fact that it is a hard break as opposed to some other function is conveyed as session user data).

- **S-TOKEN-PLEASE** and **S-TOKEN-GIVE** are used to convey the session data token between VT entities.

Session requirements

The following session FUs are used: kernel, negotiated release, duplex (A-mode) or half duplex (S-mode), expedited data, typed data, resynchronise, and major synchronise.

21.10   References

1   A good discussion of Telnet, TCP-IP and related DARPA protocols may be found in the book by W. Stallings, 'Data and Computer Communications', published by MacMillan (1988).

2   C. J. Makemson, 'Guide to ISO Virtual Terminal Standards', UK Department of Trade and Industry, Information Systems Technology Unit, Technical Guide TG 109/1 (March, 1988).

22   Message Handling Systems (MHS)

22.1   Introduction

Message Handling Systems or *MHS* is a generic term used by CCITT to describe a generalised service by means of which hosts (users) may send messages to nominated destinations, with optional confirmation (or otherwise) of delivery. In this regard, *electronic mail* is one obvious (but by no means the only) application of MHS. MHS was first devised in the 1981-1984 CCITT study period, leading to a series of X.400 recommendations in 1984. At that time, the OSI presentation and application layers were not stable, and a number of interim decisions had to be made, which later necessitated substantial changes to the internal operation of MHS when it was reissued in 1988, reflecting the now stable presentation and 'application support' layers. In the process, some aspects of X.400(1984) were incorporated into generalised OSI services, notably ASN.1 (see chapter seventeen) and ROSE and RTSE (see chapter eighteen).

As well as now being fully compatible with OSI, X.400(1988) incorporates a number of additions and extensions to MHS itself. These include additional fields in messages and, nore significantly, the definition of a message store together with service definitions. Unfortunately there are a sufficient number of differences between X.400(1984) and X.400(1988) for there to be serious compatibility and interworking problems, and therefore it has been necessary in X.400(1988) to define a minimal mode of operation which is more or less compatible with X.400(1984). Again we have the usual problem of interim versions not being compatible with later, OSI conformant ones. This is a familiar story; the same thing happened with X.25 before it. Unfortunately such problems are inevitable during a period of rapid change. CCITT had an urgent requirement to provide MHS over X.25 networks before OSI was completely stable. Although the results were predictable, they were also inevitable. Although we will occasionally be forced to talk about the differences between the two versions, we will keep this to a minimum, and concentrate on X.400(1988).

Starting from X.400(1988), ISO have progressed standards which are collectively known as *Message Oriented Text Interchange Systems* (*MOTIS*) {10021}, and are (as far as possible) technically identical to MHS. To all intents and purposes therefore, MOTIS and MHS mean the same thing, although there are still a number of minor differences, as the standards are not yet identical, and there are no ISO equivalents (yet) for some CCITT recommendations. In this book we will refer to MHS, as this is the commonly used name.

MHS provides a store-and-forward message switching system which, superficially, resembles the BSC message switching systems discussed in part one of the book. There are a number of parallels. In a BSC-based message switching mesh, a message is forwarded to the next network node, where it is 'safe stored'. The receiving network node accepts responsibility for the message, and in turn forwards it to the next node, and so on until the destination host is reached. The same principle applies in MHS, with one crucial difference. In MHS, the store-and-forward nodes are not network nodes as they were with BSC; they are open system hosts. BSC had problems in deciding what a message was supposed to be. MHS has no such problems, as messages are switched between applications, which have a clear idea of what a message is, and have no need to be concerned with the details of what is happening 'underneath'. Recall the original definition of a message as a unit of information 'meaningful to a host'. Indeed a single hop in MHS could span several underlying networks and gateways. Thus MHS is a genuine message switching application, as opposed to a message switching network protocol. In a sense, it could be said that message switching has come of age.

At this point it is worth dispelling one myth surrounding MHS. While it defines a framework (services and protocols) for store-and-forward message switching, MHS is not in itself an electronic mail system. In order to provide such services, it was necessary to define a MHS-user application known as the *Interpersonal Messaging Service* (*IPMS*), which relates MHS to the particular case of email. While MHS defines interfaces to other telematic services (such as Telex, Teletex and facsimile, and also the postal service), IPMS is at present the only MHS application which has been standardised. We will examine IPMS at the end of the chapter. MHS could equally well be applied to such things as digitised voice, facsimile, telex and teletex messages, invoices and payments, and all manner of other things. The beauty of the MHS concept is its flexibility, although it also has to be said that this results in a certain abstraction in the MHS definition itself, and supporting standards (few of which exist yet) are needed to provide a working system in most of these cases.

As far as MHS itself is concerned, an electronic *message* is an abstract concept, with three basic components, which have clear parallels in the postal system:

> • An *envelope*, which identifies where the message is to be delivered, and the recipient of the message. The envelope logically 'encloses' the rest of the message.

- A *header*, which identifies what the message is about, and contains instructions for the recipient (rather like a 'complements slip' enclosed with a postal document).

- The *subject matter*, which is the main body of the message. It is possible to encode the subject matter in a variety of ways; such encoding is for other (e.g. telematics) standards to define. The message body may contain text, graphics (pictures), and various other information types, depending on the encoding specified.

22.2   Components of MHS

As is usual in CCITT recommendations, a MHS is defined as a collection of interconnected logical units with rather formal sounding names. Figure 22.1 shows a typical MHS, with units in various combinations. Note that the Message Store (MS) was not formally specified until 1988, although there has clearly always been a need for such a device.

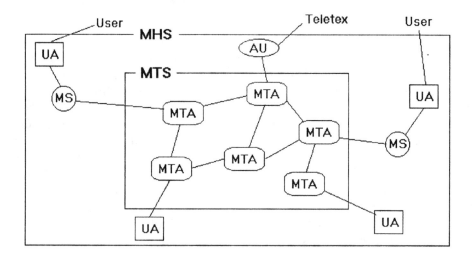

NOTEs:

UA	User Agent
MTA	Message Transfer Agent
AU	Access Unit (to/from other telematic services)
MS	Message Store
MHS	Message Handling System
MTS	Message Transfer System

Figure 22.1 - components of MHS

In the figure, a number of devices and acronyms are shown. A brief explanation of each is now provided, for reference in later sections. It is worth noting that all of these devices are pure abstractions. It is quite possible for a particular host to combine the functions of several different devices (e.g. UA, MS and MTA). The purpose of specifying all of these abstract devices is so that their functionality (such as the services provided and used) can be defined.

Message Handling System (MHS)

This term MHS is used to refer not only to the X.400 series of recommendations themselves, but also to the sum total of all of the devices and logical interconnections which, together, are specified by MHS recommendations (MOTIS standards). The users of MHS (human, other telematic services, or the postal service) are considered to be outside the scope of MHS itself.

User agent (UA)

This is a conceptual device which provides facilities (manual or automated) which allow the user to compose the various parts of the message. It then arranges for the message to be delivered via the mesh of MTAs to the (each) recipient specified in the envelope. It also provides a means for a user to retrieve messages from the message store.

Message Transfer Agent (MTA)

This is a store-and-forward message switch, which applies some routing algorithm to get messages to the destination, typically via other MTAs. In the fullness of time, the OSI Directory (chapter twenty three) will provide full global support for *originator/recipient* (*O/R*) names and locations. In the meantime, various PTTs have their own private conventions and directory lookup strategies. MTAs are also required to advise the sending UA if a message cannot be delivered for some reason, and may optionally be required to confirm delivery if successful. The received message is placed in a message store (MS) associated with the destination UA; this is discussed in a moment. The recipient can then retrieve the message from his (its) local MS. In cases where the destination open system (host) is reached, but there is no record of the recipient referred to, there is normally a 'dead letter' or *postmaster* recipient which the message will be sent to as a default. The protocols required for message delivery and end-end acknowledgement will be discussed later in the chapter.

MTA functions

In a sense, the Message Transfer Agents (MTAs) form the heart of MHS; every message gets routed through the network of MTAs. MTAs have the following broad functions:

- They provide *routing* to the MTA connected to the destination UA or MS. MTAs are thus responsible for applying routing algorithms to determine whether the required originator(s) or recipient(s) reside locally, and/or whether the messages need to be forwarded to other MTAs. In general this will require a given MTA to establish simultaneous MHS associations with several other MTAs. It is expected that MHS addresses will be in conformance with the requirements of the Directory (chapter twenty three).

- In practice, the mesh network of MTAs is expected ultimately to span the entire world, and therefore there will be various *naming domains*. Some MTAs will be required to act as 'domain boundaries', which will require additional functions such as address filtering and location of other domain MTAs.

- One aspect of MHS which must be mentioned at this point is that implementations of MHS(1984) exist, and future MHS(1988) implementations will be forced to interwork with the older systems for some years yet. Therefore one unfortunate MTA facility which must be provided is the ability to downgrade messages originating in a MHS(1988) environment so that they can be handled in a MHS(1984) setup. This will entail the removal of some fields in the message, where these relate to facilities not supported by MHS(1984). We will not be discussing this aspect of MHS in any detail.

Message Transfer System (MTS)

This is the name given to the set of MTAs co-operating to provide the message store-and-forward infrastructure. Superficially it has the characteristics of a mesh network of MTAs. Unlike mesh WANs, however, there is no requirement for duplicate paths between adjacent MTAs, and in any case the path taken is through one or more intervening networks and is the concern of lower OSI layers, not MHS which resides in the application layer.

Message Store (MS)

This conceptial device was added in 1988. It accepts incoming messages from MTAs, parses them, and stores them as appropriate. In the context of an electronic mail service, this corresponds to a mailbox, which the user can then peruse at his leisure. Again in this context, a sending user may wish to copy a message being sent to a remote recipient to his local mailbox as well, and notifications of (non-)delivery will be placed there as well. MHS allows MSs to have autonomous functions (independent of the user) such as automatic forwarding of messages (e.g. if the user has recently moved). It also provides submission and delivery services to the local UA. In fact, as we shall see in §22.4, the MS is at the core of the services defined in MHS(1988).

Access Unit (AU)

These are conceptual devices which allow interfaces to be set up to non-MHS telematic services. An access unit for Teletex was specified in 1984. In 1988, additional access to the postal system was also specified (physical delivery). Details of the interfaces to Teletex and the postal system will not be provided here. In any case the Teletex access unit specification has been removed from the X.400 series of recommendations. Access to Telex, facsimile and videotex is also possible via AUs.

22.3   MHS concepts

The above description of the functions of the MTA relates to internal issues. In the remainder of this chapter we will concentrate on the services provided by MHS, rather than the details of how the messages get routed through the MTS.

22.3.1   General MHS issues

The facilities provided by MHS support generic message switching as opposed to electronic mail, which is catered for separately as a MHS user application. Therefore these descriptions should be interpreted in the widest possible context. MHS has concern for neither the content of the messages it handles nor the encodings therein, although additional recommendations exist which define various usages (e.g. X.420 for IPMS) or encodings (e.g. T.61 for Teletex), and it is possible for facilities to be built in to support coding conversions where access is available from incompatible systems (e.g. conversion from the Telex 5-bit code to ASCII or Teletex code, or vice versa).

22.3.2   Store and forward message delivery

Each message is transferred between MTAs using a now familiar 'safe storage' technique. Each hop between MTAs is under the control of RTSE, which either reports successful delivery or transfer failure (possibly within a certain time). Since each MTA will retain the message until RTSE reports successful delivery, the risk of the message being lost in transit is minimised. However there still is a risk that the failure of an intermediate MTA could result in the message being lost. Therefore the end-end MTA transfer can be further controlled by ROSE. If the user requests this, ROSE will require (and police) delivery confirmation. In this case recovery will still be possible if the message is lost in transit, as the sender will still have a copy. This is referred to as *delivery notification* (or non-delivery notification), which is optional.

As an option prior to sending a message to a user whose existence is not certain, or to determine if the destination user's host can be reached at present (e.g. whether it is currently connected to the network), a *probe* facility is provided, which sends a short 'is this user reachable' message at minimal cost (overhead). This is clearly preferable to sending the entire message and getting it 'bounced' at or near the destination, although if there is a reasonable certainty that the destination host is running, there may be little point in probing first. After all one can always pick up the 'phone and find out!

Each message has an associated required QOS, which is used (in part) to determine the priority which should be attached to the message. MHS allows 3 priorities, low, medium (normal) and high (urgent). These map on to the priority mechanisms built into ROSE, as discussed later in the chapter. MHS uses ROSE to co-ordinate the request (message) and reply (delivery notification) paradigm. ROSE optionally uses RTSE to guarantee delivery of the request and the reply. The usage of ROSE and RTSE, together with the protocols which MHS uses to support message transfer, will be discussed later in the chapter.

At this point it would be useful to re-read the first few chapters of the whole book. Examine the weaknesses of the BSC message switching technique outlined there, and then consider to what extent the MHS/ROSE/RTSE scenario removes these problems.

Assuming that BSC can be used as an ISO data link protocol (which in theory it can), would the procedures described in this chapter be viable over such a network?

22.3.3   Addressing issues

A message may be submitted to *multiple destinations* (addressees). MHS will deliver a copy of the message to each addressee, although this could involve a high cost in terms of network traffic, depending on which open systems the addressees reside on. MHS internal procedures will attempt to minimise the path duplication of the various copies; in particular two copies will not follow the same route between adjacent MTAs. This is resolved by destination address analysis within the MTS.

An additional facility allows an *alternative recipient* (alternate [sic] recipient), which is normally a 'dead letter' address where the open system can be reached, but the precise user is not known to this system. A related facility is *message redirection*, where the intended recipient exists but is currently unavailable (e.g. for a human user, he may be on leave).

Addressees require to be *registered*. Registration details include an identifying name and any local restrictions (e.g. if only ASCII can be accepted, or there are restrictions on the maximum possible message length). A variety of naming and addressing techniques may be employed inside a message; a user mailbox is only one possibility. In part this depends on the *message type*, of which only one (email message - IPMS) has so far been standardised.

The 1988 re-issue introduced the idea of *distribution lists*. These can be sited at various points within MHS, and allow a nominated set of recipients to be specified using a shorthand name. The author is on the academic community 'PC-COMMS' distribution list on the JANET network (under NRS control), and receives regular mailshots on subjects in this area of interest.

An alternative to depositing the message in an (electronic) message store is to provide a means for *physical delivery*. The idea is that they will be routed to a nominated 'postal address' which is 'near' the recipient, who is not connected to an open system. The message will then be printed, and the envelope part of the message will be used in the obvious way. The message will complete its travels using the postal service.

22.3.4   Security issues

Distributed systems spanning many open systems are prone to unauthorised interference, particularly if the messages contain sensitive information. In theory all manner of interference is possible, from passively duplicating (examining) messages, through modifying their contents, to removing them altogether (having perused their contents). In addition, masquerading is possible, i.e. altering the message so that it appears that it came from a different address. Similar problems exist for the OSI Directory, discussed in chapter twenty three. To combat these potential threats, various security measures were introduced in the 1988 revision. These require encryption techniques, the details of which are beyond the scope of this book. Facilities available include the following, although not all implementations will necessarily make use of all (or even any) of the facilities for every message:

- *Integrity checking.* Checks can be made to determine if the contents survived intact. Unfortunately this does not protect against passive monitoring. Indeed this is not really possible within the application layer. The idea is to make the encryption technique sufficiently secure that passive monitoring will merely yield undecipherable information. Unfortunately the control fields of lower layer protocols may still yield valuable information (such as the originator's host), and MHS has no control over these.

- *Authentification.* This guards against fraudulent users masquerading as genuine ones, thereby gaining unauthorised access. This implies that the sender includes some information (suitably encrypted) which is meaningful only to the recipient, and without which the message will be rejected as invalid.

- *Proof and non-repudiation.* Proof is to a third party that a message was delivered to the intended recipient. One threat here of course is that the original message will be removed, but the confirmation to the third party will remain (or be fraudulently inserted). Non-repudiation prevents a user from denying that he (it) previously sent or received a message.

22.4   MHS services

X.400(1988) defines four basic types of service as follows.

- **MS-bind/unbind service elements**. The service model specifies two types of service, provided by an association between the MS and UA (notionally offered by the MS), and by an association between the MS and MTS (notionally offered by the MTS). In addition, associations need to be established between MTAs to deliver a message through the MTS. The MS-bind/unbind service elements are used to establish/terminate these associations. In the case of the UA-MS association, the bind may be used to authenticate the UA, i.e. to determine that this UA (acting on behalf of some user application or person) is entitled to use MHS, and the types of operation which the user may perform. This maps on to the ROSE bind and unbind services, which in turn map on to ACSE to establish and terminate the association. MHS only allows one association at a time to be set up between a given pair of open systems, although of course there is no restriction on how many different open systems can be associated with at any time.

```
MSBind ::= SET {
    TO {IndirectSubmission [5], retrieval [5], administration [5] -- identifies port --}
    BIND
            ARGUMENT    MSBindArgument          -- association request --
            RESULT      MSBindResult            -- success --
            ERROR       MSBindError             -- failure (not shown below) --
}

MSBindArgument ::= SET {
        initiator-name              ORAddressAndOrDirectoryName,
        initiator-credentials       [2] InitiatorCredentials,
        security-context            [3] IMPLICIT SecurityContext OPTIONAL,
        fetch-restrictions          [4] Restrictions OPTIONAL -- default none --,
        ms-configuration-request    [5] BOOLEAN DEFAULT FALSE }

MSBindResult ::= SET {
        responder-credentials       [2] ResponderCredentials,
        available-auto-actions      [3] SET SIZE (1..max) of AutoActionType
                                                            OPTIONAL,
        available-attribute-types   [4] SET SIZE (1..max) of AttributeType
                                                            OPTIONAL,
        alert-indication            [5] BOOLEAN DEFAULT FALSE,
        content-types-supported     [6] SET SIZE (1..max) OF OBJECT
                                                    IDENTIFIER OPTIONAL }

                            (etc)
        NOTEs:
                --      enclose comments
                [5]     tag
```

Figure 22.2 - ASN.1 definition of MTS bind operation

A full discussion of bind and unbind operations is beyond the scope of this chapter. However part of the ASN.1 definition of the bind operation is reproduced in figure 22.2, mainly for interest, as it will not be discussed here.

• **Message submission service element (MSSE).** This is available to the MHS service user (via the UA), either *directly* to the MTS, or *indirectly* via the MS. These are discussed in §22.4.1.

• **Message delivery service element (MDSE)** and **message retrieval service element (MRSE)**. These are concerned with placing messages in the (remote) MS and retrieving them from the (local) MS respectively, on behalf of the user. These are discussed in §22.4.2 and §22.4.3 respectively.

• **Message administration service element (MASE)**. This provides registration and credential alteration services. We will not be discussing these.

Figure 22.3 shows how these service elements can be viewed as a hierarchy. The MHS services outlined above and discussed in more detail in the following subsections, are provided by what MHS refers to as *ports*. This is merely an abstraction for the convenience of specifying the services rather than a set of real ports. Figure 22.4 shows the logical relationship between the various ports in relation to the UA, MS and MTS. Three types of port are defined in the context of UA-MS and MS-MTS interactions, the *retrieval port*, the *submission port* and the *administration port*.

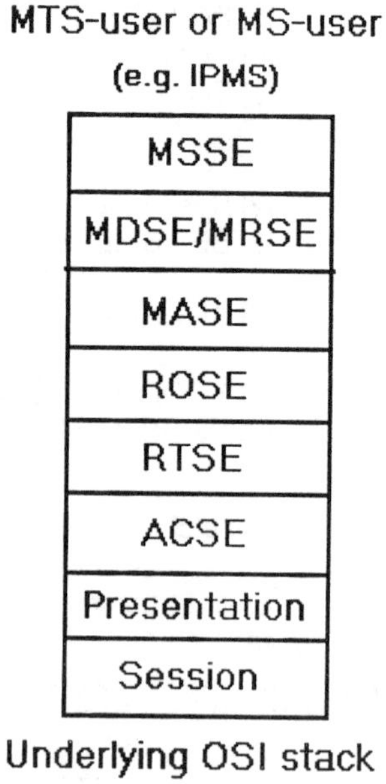

MTS-user or MS-user

(e.g. IPMS)

MSSE
MDSE/MRSE
MASE
ROSE
RTSE
ACSE
Presentation
Session

Underlying OSI stack

Figure 22.3 - The MHS services stack

We will in due course discuss these services in more detail. However it should be emphasised at this point that the detailed specifications are very complex, including parameter lists extending over an entire page in some cases. Therefore no attempt will be made to provide details of abstract service primitives as we have done for most other OSI service elements. Instead, a brief summary of parameter classes will be provided.

It should also be noted that the hierarchy implied in figure 22.3 is merely conceptual. In particular although ROSE, RTSE and ACSE are shown in the figure as a simple hierarchy, ROSE and RTSE make context-specific use of underlying layers, as discussed in more detail in subsequent sections.

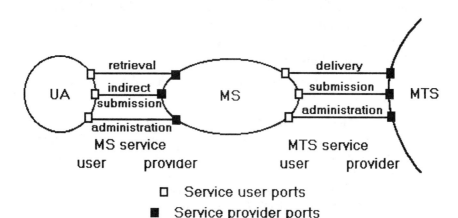

Figure 22.4 - message store abstract services

22.4.1   Message submission service element

The *Message Submission Service Element* (*MSSE*) define services provided to the MS by the *MTS submission port*. Conceptually this is a service provided by the MTS (i.e. the MTA local to the MS) to a MS, but of course message submission is something initially requested by the user. There are in fact two cases to consider.

• *Direct submission* is from the MS to the MTS, and it is assumed that the MS already holds the message which is to be transferred. Four services are provided, message submission, probe submission, cancel deferred delivery and submission control. Each is discussed in turn.

• *Indirect submission* is not part of this service, but is a service provided by the MS to the UA, whereby the MS can receive a message which it will then submit using the service elements discussed in this section. Indirect submission is mentioned for completeness in §22.4.4. Specifically, the indirect submission port is provided by the MS to the UA, and handles message and probe submission by the user, cancel deferred delivery and submission control (MTS usage constraints).

Message submission service

This allows a user to submit a message for transfer and delivery to one or more recipients. Each message is assigned a unique identifier so that, for example, it can be identified by a subsequent cancel deferred delivery; see later. Various parameters (referred to in X.411(1988) as *arguments*) are also associated with the submission. These are grouped in the recommendation as follows.

- The *originator* is the user issuing the message. This is obvious.

- The *recipient* identifies who (in the abstract sense) will receive a copy of the message. It comprises several arguments including the recipient name, whether an alternative recipient is allowed (and if so who), and whether the identities of other recipients of the message should be made known to each recipient. (In the context of IPMS (§22.6), this last facility relates to 'blind copy recipient'.)

- The *priority* may be normal, non-urgent or urgent, with normal as a default.

- *Conversion* arguments indicate whether conversion to another format is allowed, given that some types of conversion may degrade the information content of a message. (As an example, conversion from ASCII to the IA2 Telex code would lose all lowercase letters; this may not be acceptable.)

- *Delivery time* arguments specify that the message must not be delivered before and/or after some specified time.

- The *delivery method* can optionally be used to indicate the nature of the receiving device, including interfaces to other telematic services. The methods permitted include an ASCII terminal, a telephone, teletex, videotex, facsimile, physical (mail) or normal MHS delivery (to a MS).

- In the case of *physical delivery*, additional arguments are provided to clarify the action which should be taken, such as whether registered mail is to be used.

- Arguments are also provided which control *report requests* (delivery notification) to the originator. These can be always required, required only if the message cannot be delivered, or never required.

- Various *security* arguments may be specified, such as whether authentication or content integrity checks are required.

- Last but not least, the *content* of the message identifies its generic type to the service user. This may be specified as IPMS (1984 or 1988 versions), external (for interworking with MHS(1984) systems), and some others including 'inner envelope', where the message in effect contains JTM-like proformas which the recipient can use to formulate further messages for onward delivery. Another argument is of course the actual contents themselves. These are normally transparent to MHS (in effect MHS user data), except that conversion to another format may be required, and they can optionally be encrypted.

Probe submission service

This is in many ways similar to the message submission service, except that instead of sending a message, the aim is to determine whether a message can be delivered. Therefore arguments which need to be provided are (broadly speaking) some of the originator, recipient, conversion, delivery method, physical delivery, report request, security and content arguments above.

It should be noted that there are no delivery time arguments. The result indicates whether the message could be delivered now. It the actual message is required not to be delivered for some time, it may be that it will fail even though the probe succeeded. Clearly the probe service must be used with care.

Cancel deferred delivery service

This allows a user to cancel the delivery of an earlier message where delivery was not to occur until some specified time after submission. Clearly if delivery of the message was not required to be delayed, it cannot be cancelled, as this could well result in a cancel request chasing the message around several MTAs in an attempt to catch it up. This would be both expensive and wasteful of resources. The only argument required is the message identifier, which is unique for a given user.

Submission control service

The MTS at any time can provide various services to the user. The submission control service allows the user temporarily to alter (restrict) the service provided (to the MS) by the MTS. This applies only to message and probe submission. Any actions which were outstanding but are now forbidden will be held in abeyance (not abandoned) until such time as they can be completed.

The restrictions are specified as various controls, which can be updated selectively or removed entirely. Controls (restrictions) can be applied to priority, maximum content length, permissible security contents, and so on. The reply to a control request will state whether any messages or probes are now being held by MTS pending permission to submit them (i.e. pending removal of the control).

22.4.2 Message delivery service element

The *Message Delivery Service Element* (*MDSE*) defines services provided to the MS by the *MTS delivery port*. Specifically, these handle message delivery (to the user), report delivery (the outcome of an earlier submission) and delivery control (MTS usage constraints). Again, each will be discussed in turn.

Message delivery service

This allows the MTS to deliver messages to the recipient(s) associated with a given MS. Arguments which are provided include the MTS-identifier (which is the same as the submission identifier), together with *delivery arguments* such as the delivery and submission times, a delivery identifier, the recipient's name (both actual and intended must be specified if these are different), together with submission arguments as detailed in §22.4.1. (Report requests are excluded.)

Report delivery service

This service allows a (remote) MS to generate delivery reports to be returned to the sender, if required by the sender. (If the message failed to reach the MS, the negative reply will come from elsewhere.)

Delivery control service

This allows the MTS user to restrict the operations possible on this port. It is similar to submission control, except that it acts on message delivery and report delivery.

22.4.3   Message retrieval service element

The *Message Retrieval Service Element* (*MRSE*) defines services provided to the UA by the *MS retrieval port*. Messages received via the MTS are stored in the MS, which is a logical device the details of which are implementation dependent. At some later time, the user (via the UA) may access messages which have arrived. Drawing a loose analogy with electronic mail, the MRSE can be thought of as representing those aspects of the access mechanisms which are concerned with 'reading ones mail'.

Operations which are defined in this context include the following.

• **Summarise**. This allows a user to obtain selected details (such as headers) of all or some messages. Various constraints can be applied to the selection as discussed in a moment.

• **List**. As its name suggests, this provides a list of available messages.

• **Fetch**. This allows the user to obtain a copy of a message. Fetching a messages does not remove the message from the MS.

• **Delete**. This deletes the copy of the message.

• **Alert**. This provides for a notification that a message (possibly of some specified type) has arrived.

Unix users may wish to compare this with the 'biff y' command, which turns on mail notifications. Note however that this relates to one of many possible uses of MHS. In fact it relates to IPMS rather than MHS itself.

MRSE provides several mechanisms for *restricting the search* for applicable messages, in particular the following:

```
Range ::= CHOICE
    {        sequence_number_range        [0] NumberRange,
             creation_time_range          [1] TimeRange            }
```

Figure 22.5 - ASN.1 definition of range on MRSE

• **Range**. This restricts the search by specifying an upper and/or lower bound to the message sequence number or delivery time. The default is all messages. As is usual in MHS, all operations are defined using ASN.1. To illustrate the use of ASN.1, the range is specified as in figure 22.5.

- **Filter**. This allows various tests to be applied, including the following.

  - Tests such as =, >= and <= (e.g. on the creation date).
  - Restricting matches to those messages containing some specified substring (e.g. the name of a particular originator).
  - Matching only messages in which some particular attribute is present.
  - Approximate matching, the details of the algorithm being left to the implementor.
  - Matching only messages with some specified attribute value present (for example true, false, attribute undefined).

- **Selector**. This restricts matches to a contiguous range (e.g. of number); selections within this range can then be further restricted either by a filter or by specifying a maximum permissible number of matches.

- **Entry information selection**. This specifies which parts of the message contents will be returned as entry information.

22.4.4   Indirect submission service element

The *Indirect Submission Service Element* defines services provided to the UA by the *MS submission port*. It is used by the UA to submit a message to the MS which in turn will submit it for onward transfer via the MTS. Whether this is a genuine relay service by the MS depends on the implementation. No real message store may be involved unless a local copy is to be kept, although of course a copy needs to be kept somewhere in the host until its delivery is confirmed (by ROSE using RTSE), in case it needs to be sent again. As this maps directly on to the MTS submission service described in §22.4.1, we will not discuss it further here.

22.4.5   Use of ROSE priorities

As explained in chapter eighteen, ROSE offers eight priorities. These are all used by MHS. The following are some examples of usage.

- The highest priority (0) is reserved for association release (ROSE UNBIND). The next (1) is for rejections and errors.

- Delivery confirmations (ROSE RESULT) are given a priority of 2, higher than that offered to any other message or service type.

- Submission and delivery control is given the next highest priority (3).

- Messages can be sent at three prioritites, 7 (the lowest) for non-urgent messages, 6 for normal messages and 4 for urgent messages.

- Probes are sent at priority 5, i.e. they are treated like 'fairly urgent' messages.

22.5   MHS protocols and use of underlying services

MHS(1988) uses ROSE and RTSE (chapter eighteen) as underlying mechanisms; these in turn map on to ACSE, the presentation layer and the session layer (using activities). Various protocols are defined in MHS which utilise these underlying facilities, and these will be discussed in this section. In addition, MHS recognises further additional protocols for providing access, e.g. from Teletex.

Three principal protocols are defined in MHS(1988). Each protocol is assigned a number, and will be discussed in turn. In each case we will also discuss how the protocol relates to the support ASEs, ROSE, RTSE and ACSE.

- **MTS access protocol (p3)**. This operates between the MS and MTS, to provide the services discussed in §22.4.1 and §22.4.2.

- **MTS transfer protocol (p1)**. This operates internally within the mesh of MTAs, to forward messages (and return confirmations) to their intended destinations.

- **MS access protocol (p7)**. This operates between the UA and MS, to provide the services discussed in §22.4.3 and §22.4.4.

These protocols are designed to operate over the underlying session service (half duplex with activity management), and using transport protocol class TP0. In addition, provision is made for various *message content protocols* controlling the format of messages. The **IPMS protocol (p22**, formerly p2) is currently the only one defined within the MHS recommendations; it is mentioned in §22.6. Others, such as a Teletex access protocol, also exist but are defined elsewhere.

The protocol numbering scheme may seem rather strange. It is in fact a hangover from the MHS(1984) recommendations, where the principal protocols were numbered p1, p2 and p3. Protocol p7 did not exist in MHS(1984), as it relates to the MS which did not exist at that time. (P3, the MTS access protocol, operated directly between the UA and the MTS.) The protocol originally designated p2 in X.420(1984) operated between endpoint UAs in MHS(1984), i.e. above p1 and p3, but has now has become p22 (IPMS protocol) in X.420(1988), recognising the fact that this is not a mainstream MHS protocol, but a MHS user protocol. A further protocol defined in MHS(1984), the teletex access protocol, no longer forms part of the MHS recommendations.

22.5.1   MTS access protocol (p3)

This protocol operates between a MS and a MTS. See figure 22.1. It therefore provides the mechanism for implementing the delivery, submission and administration services offered by the MTS, as explained in §22.4 and depicted in figure 22.4.

The description which follows is in many minor ways inaccurate. It has been necessary to introduce a number of simplifications in the interests of explaining a complex area in a few short paragraphs. The recommendations themselves of course contain the precise details, but these are far too advanced for an introductory text such as this one. Indeed books have been written just on MHS[1], although at the time of writing, most if not all deal with the now obsolescent 1984 version of the recommendations.

In characteristic MHS manner, each service is optionally confirmed, which makes it a candidate for the ROSE mechanism. Unlike the standards for lower OSI layers (or FTAM and JTM for that matter), the recommendations make no reference to service primitives or parameters, so that it is not strictly correct to refer to requests, indications, responses and confirms in the normal way, even though this is in effect what the delivery and submission services provide, although they are provided by ports rather than service interfaces. The reason that CCITT do not use the service interface/primitive approach is that the communicating partners on the two open systems are not peer instances of the same service, as they are for example in the case of the session service; they are to be viewed as superior and subordinate entities, and are different ASEs. The superior ASE is considered to be the MS entity, since it uses the services of the MTS, the service provider, which can therefore be viewed as the subordinate entity. It may however be more helpful to consider the protocol as relaying service data units (primitives), although it must again be stressed that this is not how the services and protocols are defined in the recommendations. Having issued suitable warnings about how the following discussion is to be interpreted, we will now disregard the CCITT terminology in the following, simplified, explanation.

- In MHS terms, the *request* (in the request/reply paradigm) is passed from the MS to the MTS. This can be viewed as (but to reiterate is <u>not</u>) a service primitive request relayed to the peer as an indication primitive. The corresponding p3 PDU maps directly on to the ROSE INVOKE service described in chapter eighteen. The request in the case of the delivery service will typically be a message (or probe) sent by the MS, and routed to a remote MS through the MTS (mesh of MTAs). In the case of the delivery, the request is a message received by the MS.

One difficulty with the notion of a service provider and a service user is immediately apparent. We stated above that the MTS is the service provider and the MS is the service user; indeed this is what X.413 says. However in one case the MS issues the request; in the other case it is the MTS. So clearly this notion of a service user and service provider is not intended to be taken too literally; the service user does not necessarily initiate the request/reply dialogue (i.e. issue the ROSE INVOKE). To understand the significance of this, it is necessary to understand that the ROSE BIND maps on to the ACSE ASSOCIATE primitive (see chapter eighteen). The association class specified at this time determines which ROSE entity is permitted to initiate the dialogue (issue the request, i.e. the ROSE INVOKE). Clearly the MS must allow the MTS to issue the request if it is to receive a message from the MTS. So when we referred above to superior and subordinate ASEs, this relates to establishing the application association, not to issuing the request. It further follows that while we showed a services stack in figure 22.3, this must not be taken too literally, as the interactions between the different ASEs defy such neat classification. (This stack is defined in X.419.)

The above discussion should give some feeling for just how complex the application layer is, and why it took the experts so many years to agree on how the application layer should be structured. A full discussion of application association establishment, and the hierarchical relationship between applications, would complicate the discussion far more than is the intention in this description.

• The *reply*, which is optional, maps similarly to the ROSE RESULT service, again discussed in chapter eighteen. The optional nature of this service reflects the fact that, for example, a user may not require confirmation of successful delivery of a message, only notification if a problem arises.

ROSE in turn may use RTSE to guarantee delivery of the request, and similarly the reply, in which case the turn is transferred to the other ROSE entity (and a new session activity is started). This is optional, depending on the parameters of the BIND. (The ASEs to be used have to be determined (passed to ACSE) at the BIND stage; this determines whether RTSE is to be used.)

22.5.2   MTS transfer protocol (p1)

This is an internal MHS protocol which operates between MTAs in the mesh. It is responsible for delivering individual messages and confirmations across the 'mesh' of MTAs. At this level of protocol there can be no association between a particular message and its delivery confirmation, so that p1 simply uses RTSE to ensure delivery of the message to the next MTA.

P1 operates logically below p3, and each invocation of p3 generates one or two p1 exchanges, typically for the user message and (possibly) the delivery confirmation message. P1 maps in a similar way to p3 on to ACSE in order to implement the ROSE BIND and UNBIND operations.

Some clarification is appropriate here. An application association exists between a pair of open systems. It determines the protocol stack to be used (typically ROSE, RTSE, ACSE, over presentation). One association is required between every pair of open systems which communicate. As many UAs, MSs and MTAs can be involved in the transfer of a single message and its delivery confirmation, several different associations need to be set up. These include an association between the UA and the MS, between the MS and the nearest MTA, between adjacent MTAs, and so on. The association between the UA and the nearest MTA may need to exist until the confirmation returns, whereas associations between adjacent MTAs can be discarded once the message or confirmation has reached the next MTA. Between adjacent MTAs, the ROSE request and reply are (for example) a message, and confirmation that it has reached the next MTA.

22.5.3   MS access protocol (p7)

This protocol operates between a UA and a MS, in cases where these are physically separate. (In many implementations they may well both be part of the same host, in which case this protocol is not required, and indeed the retrieval and indirect submission service elements may well be pure abstractions in many cases.) As this is yet again a request/reply paradigm, once more ROSE is used to co-ordinate the request and reply in a manner which by now should be very familiar.

P7 is in many respects similar to p3, except that it operates between the UA and the MS, rather than between the MS and MTS. In this case the

UA is viewed as the service user, and the MS as the service provider. The main difference is that the service user (the UA) issues the request in all cases, whereas in the case of p3, the service provider issues the request to send a message to the UA.

22.6   The Interpersonal Messaging System (IPMS)

This is a value added service provided, in effect, as a shell around MHS. It performs three basic functions:

- It relates the abstract MHS services to the specific case of electronic mail between human users. It renames the various MHS services provided by MSSE, MDSE, MRSE and MASE so that they relate to the specific email application. This provides three *ports*, known as the *origination, reception* and *management* ports. In addition the mail messages themselves are referred to as *interpersonal messages* (*IPMs*). Figure 22.6 shows the IPMS system as it is seen by the service user. It also relates the IPMS ports to the generic MHS submission, delivery and administration ports shown in figure 22.4. It should be noted that aspects of the underlying MHS services such as BIND and UNBIND (use of ACSE and ROSE) are not visible at this level. It is not the intention of IPMS to define the user interface in anything other than abstract terms. This also means that the underlying MHS system has no knowledge that it is transferring IPMs.

- It provides a standardised message format. This consists of a *heading* and *body*. See figure 22.7.

    - The heading may be divided into *fields*, which represent such things as the originator (From:), the primary recipients (To:), copy recipients (Cc:), a replied-to field (Re:), blind copy recipients (who are not made aware who the other recipients were), subject, and such things as the expiry time (obsolete unless delivered by this time), the reply time (by which a reply is expected), the importance (low, medium and high, the significance of which is for the users to determine), and sensitivity (corresponding to classifications such as unclassified, restricted, secret and so on).

    - The body of the message is similarly divided into *body parts*, each of which may be in a variety of specified formats, including ASCII, digitised voice, facsimile, teletex, videotex, encrypted and so on. Options are also provided for

500

bilaterally defined, nationally defined and externally defined formats.

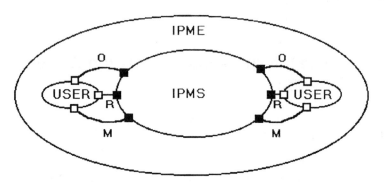

IPMS PORTS: O = Origination   R = Reception   M = Management

MHS
EQUIVALENTS: Submission   Delivery   Administration

NOTE:
   IPME   IPMS environment

Figure 22.6 - the IPMS environment

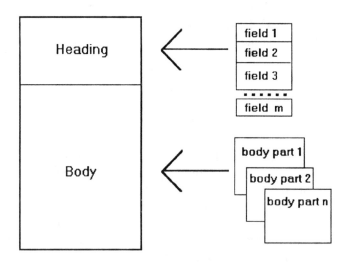

Figure 22.7 - structure of interpersonal message

There is an ASN.1 BodyPart CHOICE type which specifies exactly what can be contained within a body part. In turn the body is represented in ASN.1 terminology as a SEQUENCE OF BodyPart.

- X.220 also includes a specification of the *IPM protocol* (*p22*). This in effect, operates between peer UAs over the entire underlying MHS. Details may be found in the recommendation.

The IPM originator and recipient identities are expressed in directory terminology as O/R identifiers. The directory is discussed in chapter twenty three.

22.7 Reference

1 See for example the book by P. Vervest, 'Electronic Mail and Message Handling', Pinter (1985). This gives a good coverage of MHS(1984). The author is not aware of any books devoted to MHS(88) at the time of writing.

23 Miscellaneous OSI standards

23.1 Introduction

In this chapter we first examine the progress which has been made in some areas of OSI management, and later briefly review some applications which were in the course of development at the time of writing. For obvious reasons early work concentrated on the detailed specification of the various lower layers, followed by the most urgent applications such as FTAM, JTM, VT and MHS. But it is clear that however wonderful the OSI framework is, it is of limited usefulness unless means are provided which allow open systems to identify and locate their peers, and mechanisms are provided for registering various 'objects' such as application names, commonly used abstract syntaxes and the like.

While work on some aspects of this is at an advanced stage, progress is only now being made in some other areas. Because most of this work is mainly of interest to implementors and protocol definers, we will not go into very much fine detail, concentrating instead on the overall concepts involved.

23.2 Management issues

Once an OSI framework and applications were developed and becoming stable, ISO (and CCITT) could devote their efforts towards making the OSI environment usable. Later in this chapter we discuss the CCITT Directory project in some detail, and in a moment we mention registration procedures which are being developed.

Hand in hand with this is the need for overall management of the OSI environment, and ISO are actively involved in the specification of several standards relating to OSI management, including the *Common Management Information Service* (*CMIS*) {9595}, a supporting *Common Management Information Protocol* (*CMIP*) {9596}, system management functions {10040, 10164} and standards defining the structure of management information {10165}. However these are mentioned for completeness only, as this area is beyond the scope of this book. It could be several years before this area reaches stability.

23.3   Registration

At various points in earlier chapters, we have referred to 'objects' of various types which need to be referenced by different hosts. These include document types, ASN-1 object identifiers, VTE-profiles, VT control objects, AP and AE titles, abstract syntaxes, transfer syntaxes, application contexts and so on. The idea of the registration service is to set up *registration authorities* which will keep the names of various standard objects which are referenced by OSI applications. By co-ordinating the naming in this way, further standardisation can be imposed on naming conventions.

Registration is of course tied in with the OSI Directory. In a sense it may be viewed as a user of the directory service, as object identifiers are one of the many types of information which can be held in a directory. At present there is considerable activity in this area, but it was mostly at an early stage at the time of writing. As the aim of this book is to introduce basic OSI concepts rather than delve into detailed management issues, registration will not be discussed further.

23.4   Profiles

The idea of *OSI profiles* is to be able to define combinations of features of various layers which must be supported by conforming open systems. We will examine four profiles, two governmental, and two sponsored by private organisations. *Government OSI profiles* are known as *GOSIP*s. The advent of GOSIPs has greatly strengthened the hand of OSI as opposed to proprietary architectures such as SNA, since all future government IT purchases must be 'OSI compliant', which effectively precludes such products as SNA, unless these are modified to become OSI-compatible.

23.4.1   UK GOSIP

The precise details of UK GOSIP are Crown Copyright. What follows is abstracted from the DTI OSI products guide (referenced in the preface). Basically the current version specifies support for the following:

- Use of X.25 in WANs, or CSMA/CD bus or Token Ring with LANs. (Note that neither slotted ring nor token bus is currently supported.) Connection oriented services are viewed as the 'strategic direction', although connectionless services are permitted over LANs.

- Use of transport TP0 over X.25 (all applications), and TP4 over LANs. TP4 is required for conversion between the COTS and the connectionless variants of LLC.

- Use of FTAM, X.400(1984), X.400(1988) and VT. (Support for X.400(1988) is currently under consideration.) Note that all of these are expected to operate over TP0 unless a LAN intervenes.

- Definition of various information interchange formats and character repertoires.

UK GOSIP has also been adopted with little change by such countries as Australia and Israel.

23.4.2   US GOSIP

The basic aims of US GOSIP are similar to those of UK GOSIP, to provide a framework for defining which OSI products will comply with Federal purchasing requirements. There are however some notable differences between the two; indeed there are potential sources of incompatibility.

- The main difference is the specification of TP4 over CLNS (as opposed to TP0 over CONS) as the 'strategic direction' for all network/application combinations. This implies the use of TP4 over X.25 for all applications except MHS, which uses TP0. (It has to; MHS is specified that way.) The profile supports any IEEE-supported LAN (i.e. CSMA/CD bus, token bus and token ring).

The use of TP4 above X.25 seems to be overkill, as TP4 provides too much functionality (just as TP0 provides too little). One reason for this decision is that the USA have always favoured datagrams. TP4 is required to support LLC connectionless modes, and it can of course then be used over X.25 at no extra implementation cost. You may recall that it was ANSI which was primarily responsible for the inclusion of a datagram facility in X.25(1980), although this was subsequently removed.

- The original version supports both FTAM and MHS(1984), and this provision has been mandatory for US Federal procurement since August 1990. The current version includes a forms mode VT class which is compatible with UK GOSIP. Support for MHS(1988) will be provided in due course.

23.4.3   Manufacturing Automation Protocol - MAP

MAP, which is strictly a profile not a protocol, was an initiative of General Motors Corporation in the USA. It is specifically intended for use in shop floor environments such as (motor) production lines, and is therefore both very specific in its aims, and rather restrictive in other contexts. It provides support for FTAM, VT, the OSI Directory and particularly MMS {9506} over *token bus* LANs. (MMS and the Directory are both discussed later in this chapter.) Only token bus LANs are considered to have the predictable transfer characteristics required; this was discussed in chapters twelve and thirteen. There is of course no place for WANs in this scenario.

Support for VT and FTAM is not mandatory. In fact the MMS specification provides rudimentary support for some VT and FTAM functions, and suggests that full VT or FTAM should be used if the rudimentary terminal and file handling facilities provided in MMS are considered to be inadequate.

MAP and TOP are referred to as protocols rather than profiles for historical reasons. Originally they were more concerned with the choice of a suitable LAN access method (token bus for MAP, CSMA/CD for TOP) than with specifying a complete OSI stack. The term profile is of more recent origin, and the term 'protocol' has stuck.

23.4.4   Technical and Office Protocol - TOP

TOP, which again is really a profile, was an initiative of Boeing Aircraft Corporation in the USA, and was originally specified for use in their design offices, although it now has wider appeal. It therefore has an entirely different role from MAP. The following OSI components are specified:

> • Various VT profiles, MHS(1984), a MAP-compatible FTAM profile, and various ODA-based information interchange formats. (ODA is briefly discussed in §23.7.3.)

> • Support for any IEEE LAN standard. (Originally only the CSMA/CD bus was supported.) Again the use of WANs is not appropriate.

23.4.5   Other profiles

Although they will not be discussed here, a number of other OSI profiles have been defined. These include European (EC) profiles and various NIST (National Institute of Standards and Technology) profiles in the USA. There are incompatibilities between some profiles which claim to serve the same area. For example it appears that there may be some incompatibility between US GOSIP and UK GOSIP, particularly in the use of the transport protocol, and in the relative weights given to connection oriented and connectionless services. Perhaps this merely reflects the fact that Europe and the USA do not always agree on the general direction which networking should take. At least there are clear signs of convergence.

23.5   Correctness of implementations

At the time of writing, all of the OSI services and protocols are specified mainly in terms of a 'plain English' description, backed up by various tables and diagrams, and in the case of application standards by ASN.1 data structure definitions. The problem with this type of natural language specification is that it may contain ambiguities, or be capable of more than one interpretation. This can potentially lead to incompatible implementations, all of which, it is argued, obey the rules as set down in the standard. If this happens it is the standard which is at fault, not the implementor, but such situations are very hard to eliminate using natural language alone. One reason for placing such emphasis on protocol testing is that differences in implementation resulting from an incompletely specified standard are by no means rare.

The following example related to HDLC illustrates how differences in interpretation can potentially lead to widely differing implementations. The HDLC standard states that SREJ may be used to request the retransmission of a single outstanding I-frame. Does this merely state the obvious, that a given SREJ frame can only contain a single N(R) which must refer to the missing I-frame, or is there some further implied meaning, which prompted ISO to add this remark as 'clarifying information'? This author has encountered descriptions of SREJ in books which claim that once one an SREJ has been issued, no further ones can be generated until it has either been satisfied or abandoned. This is one possible interpretation of the phrase 'single outstanding I-frame', but it appears to be an incorrect interpretation, as elsewhere HDLC requires the 'oldest unsatisfied SREJ N(R)' to be repeated with the F bit if the P bit is received, which implies that more than one unsatisfied SREJ is possible. The problem in this case is that the standard includes redundant information which can lead to incorrect interpretations. In the context of RLP (chapter six), it makes a tremendous difference whether more than one SREJ is permitted at a time. But equally the standard may omit to state something because the writer thought that it would be obvious, whereas in the event this proves not to be the case at all.

It is for this reason that much effort has been devoted to formal specification techniques. Most notable among these is perhaps the Vienna Definition Method (VDM)[1], which uses complex mathematical logic in an attempt to prove the correctness of program specifications. While this is a powerful tool, it requires considerable mathematical expertise, and great care must be exercised in its use.

23.5.1 Formal description languages

ISO have long recognised the need for a more formal approach to protocol specification than natural language descriptions and pages of state transition diagrams, which have for many years been included in service definitions and protocol specifications. State transition diagrams and similar techniques may suffice for simple service definitions and protocol specifications, but they rapidly become unmanageable as the complexity increases, thereby largely defeating the object of having them in the first place. We have seen the potential problems introduced by natural language descriptions. For these and other reasons ISO have been working on more formalised approaches, and 1989 finally saw the publication of standards for two formal description techniques, LOTOS {8807} and ESTELLE {9074}. We will briefly examine each technique in turn.

LOTOS

This is short for *Language of Temporal Ordering Specification,* and is a technique based on the 'temporal ordering of observational behaviour', from which it can be inferred that it is related to time sequence diagrams such as those used in standards and recommendations to depict the flow of service primitives. Many books (such as Halsall on pp. 124-139) also use this technique to illustrate various acknowledgement techniques, by showing, for example, the flow of HDLC frames in the two directions on a link. LOTOS is an attempt to introduce a more rigorous approach, by specifying a system in terms of how the system appears to behave (change) when viewed externally. It is clearly applicable to service definitions and protocol specifications, which are based on time sequences of primitives and underlying PDUs, as a service is entirely defined by what the service users submit and receive, i.e. the external interface.

LOTOS is a mathematical technique using the Calculus of Communicating Systems (CCS)[2] developed at the University of Edinburgh. It also uses the abstract data type language ACT ONE[3] to represent data structures and value expressions.

LOTOS descriptions are available for the session service and protocol, and are being developed for the transport service and protocol.

ESTELLE

ESTELLE on the other hand is a development of the state transition diagram technique, providing much needed formalism.

ESTELLE is based on the Pascal programming language. In other words it is quite different from LOTOS. The standard states that ESTELLE can be used formally to describe service definitions and protocol specifications. This however merely begs the question of why both LOTOS and ESTELLE are needed. The answer is that LOTOS seeks to specify a service or protocol in terms of what the service user sees (its external behaviour). There are however some protocols where the external behaviour gives little clue to what is happening internally, and the connectionless network protocol {8473} is a typical case in point. Indeed the whole idea in this case is that the user does not know what is happening internally! An ESTELLE formal description of this connectionless internet protocol is currently in the early stages of development.

23.5.2   Protocol conformance issues

Having specified a protocol, it now has to be implemented. Many protocols are exceedingly complex, presenting implementors with a number of familiar problems.

• How can implementors be certain that every feature of the protocol has been catered for, and is correctly implemented? It is not unheard of for implementations to crash weeks or even months after installation when some obscure facility finally gets used and is either not supported or does not work properly.

• Which aspects of the protocol must be supported, and which are considered to be optional? One of the many problems with natural language descriptions is that it is not always clear whether some facility is or is not optional.

• In the early days of OSI, incompatible implementations which all claimed to conform to the relevant standard were not unheard of either. It is virtually impossible to remove ambiguities completely from natural language descriptions, which is one major reason for devising formal description techniques such as LOTOS and ESTELLE in the first place. However these techniques are still too recent to have had a significant impact yet.

Should protocol implementations be tested for conformance to the standard before they are used? Clearly the answer has to be 'yes'. The problem is how this can be achieved. There are two major problems.

• Who should do the testing? British Telecom have traditionally required X.25 DTE implementations to undergo testing before hosts were permitted to use the PSS network. In the early days this caused considerable delays before some hosts could get 'permission to connect'. However commercial products soon became available which were tried and tested, so that in practice it was normally sufficient to use a proven product which had already been tested. But while this is adequate for a single protocol, there are so many different OSI protocols and potential users that BT alone cannot possibly test all OSI products at all levels of the hierarchy.

The solution to this problem was to set up dedicated *protocol testing centres*, of which the best known in the UK is perhaps the National Computing Centre (NCC) in Manchester. (BT and NPL are others.) These centres identify which aspects of the software should be tested, and devise test suites. While this can never guarantee absolute conformance, it does help to iron out the great majority of problems with implementations, and common misinterpretations of established protocol specifications are of course well known by the experts, and can easily be trapped.

• Unfortunately this 'solution' is too superficial. One crucial question has not yet been asked, and since this discussion is all about standardisation, it is obvious that the question is how the testing can be standardised so that the results of testing at different test centres are directly comparable. If NCC were to pass a protocol implementation which BT would have failed, or vice versa, this would obviously make a mockery of the whole testing concept.

The solution is to provide rules for testing centres. These are known as **Protocol Implementation Conformance Statements (PICS)**. PICS *proformas* are being developed for most protocols at the session layer and above, as well as for X.25 packet mode procedures {8878}, HDLC LAPB {7776} and LAN LLC {8802-2}. In the case of the more complex protocols such as FTAM, additional standards specifying *conformance test suites* are being developed as well. There is currently much activity in this area within ISO. While it is important for implementors, it will not have an impact on the standards themselves (unless defects are found in them, which occasionally happens).

23.6   The OSI Directory

23.6.1   Introduction

Suppose that you wish to make a telephone call. You are unsure of the number, but know the name of the person you wish to call. We all take telephone directories and directory enquiries for granted. In the days of computerised directory enquiries, it is not even necesssary to the exact details of the called party. Provided that sufficient information (such as a keyword or address) can be provided, his number can usually be retrieved from an online database in a matter of seconds.

But what happens when one looks at the corresponding situation in networks? There have been attempts at providing directories almost since networking began. For example there was a *Name Server* on the original Cambridge Ring. Any host could broadcast to the name server, and would be given the current address of the required facility (e.g. printer server, time server). But this only applied to a finite set of resources on a single LAN. More recent LAN developments include such things as Sun's *Yellow Pages*, which provide a directory service across a set of interconnected LANs. In the UK academic community, the *Name Registration Service* was set up so that any computer at any University could be given a unique name, which would be understood by all other University computers. It is thanks to NRS that the author can quote a unique email address, allowing an entire community of users to address electronic mail to him if they wish. But they must know both his name and his email address in the first place, which highlights the fundamental problem which needs to be solved for OSI to take off.

The big difference between the telephone service and networking is that the need for a telephone directory service was seen at an early date. In networks however, the situation was quite different. Networking had progressed some way before any consideration at all was given to interworking outside proprietary networks or closed user groups. Thus although there were many ad hoc and proprietary systems, each serving a defined community of hosts, nothing existed which had the potential to be applied on a global scale. After all closed user groups can produced limited printed directories for human users, and host computers can have all necessary addresses built into lookup tables, as the number of such addresses will not normally be large.

There is no such possibility in an OSI environment, as the number of addresses which can be accessed is in theory limitless. What is needed now is a standard mechanism whereby an OSI host can obtain the address of another OSI host anywhere in the world, by providing some user-friendly name. For example it should be sufficient for a user in the USA to be able to say something like 'United Kingdom, University of Manchester, Department of Computer Science, BMarsden' to find out how to access me, leaving the rest to the directory system.

In the early days of OSI there was no such mechanism, which increasingly restricted attempts at interconnection, except within specific groups which could set up private, ad hoc, directory systems. All of this changed in 1989 when CCITT published their X.500(1988) Directory Recommendations.

The X.500 series of recommendations are intended to be technically identical to the ISO standards {9594-1 to 9594-8}, although two DPs are also being produced {9594-9 and 9594-10} which had no CCITT counterparts at the time of writing.

For the first time, the problem of providing a global directory which contains details of hosts, persons and devices, and which could be interrogated online, has been tackled. In this section we will examine some of the more salient features of the Directory recommendations. Unfortunately as with many OSI application areas, a detailed treatise would require a book of its own, so the material here should be regarded only as an introduction to an area which is receiving a great amount of attention at present.

The Directory was originally developed by CCITT to support MHS, in particular IPMS, and we will reflect this bias by using examples relating to electronic mail. However just as MHS can be used for other things than simply IPMS (electronic mail), so the Directory also has far wider scope.

23.6.2   Elements of the Directory system

The X.500 series of recommendations specify an electronic directory for use in OSI. The logical structure of the directory, access methods and management issues are all covered. It is the intention that the directory will contain information on a variety of things, including 'communication-related objects', users and network resources. The directory is distributed in nature, which implies that a collection of open systems will in effect implement a distributed database containing details of various objects involved in communications. Clearly it will be impracticable for a single site to contain directory information for more than its local community. What is provided is a means for this site to communicate with its peers to obtain the information it does not hold itself.

Having read the chapter on MHS, and knowing that these are CCITT-originated recommendations, there will be a familiar ring to the names given to the various components of the directory system.

> • The *Directory User Agent* (*DUA*) acts on behalf of an enquirer. The enquirer could be a human user wishing to obtain the IPMS address of a colleague, or an application requiring the address of a peer which it wishes to associate with. Procedures are defined which define the interaction between the user and a DUA.

• The DUA in turn accesses an interconnected set of *Directory System Agents* (*DSAs*). Protocols are specified both between a DUA and its local DSA, and internally between DSAs to retrieve the desired information. See figure 23.1.

• The *Directory Information Base* (*DIB*) is the name given to the sum total of directory information. This information is distributed among the DSAs, so that (for example) information on hosts and persons in Manchester would be held at a DSA host there rather than in one sited in London. In some cases certain information may appear in more than one DSA, i.e. be replicated.

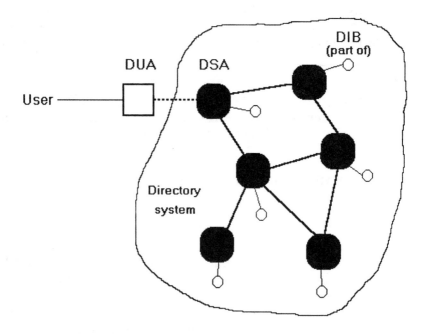

Figure 23.1 - elements of the Directory system

• The *Directory Information Tree* (*DIT*) is a naming framework determining the structure of the DIB. The DIT is concerned with the way in which entries are identified and arranged in relationship to each other. Basically this is a tree structure. A hypothetical example is given in figure 23.2.

23.6.3 Directory services provided

The Directory system supports a variety of types of action on the DIT, ranging from simple enquiries to complex searches and updates.

Information may be held about people (including name, title, function, telephone, telex, fax, email and postal addresses). The search facilities provided including facilities corresponding to 'white pages' and 'yellow pages'. The directory itself is a hierarchical structure of *directory objects*, each of which has various attributes which define its contents. The following types of access are catered for:

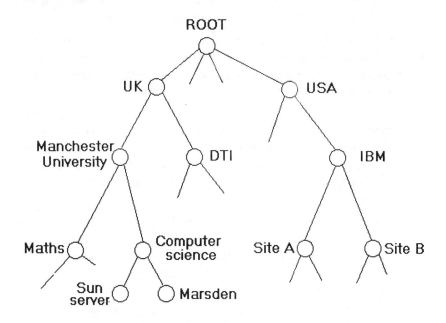

Figure 23.2 - example directory information tree

• **Read**. A specific object is accessed, returning some or all attributes.

• **Compare**. The directory checks for a match with some specified attribute(s). This includes password checking, although the actual password is inaccessible to the user.

• **List**. For a given node in the DIT, all immediate subordinates can be listed.

• **Search**. Some filter can be applied, and all matching entries in some specified part of the DIT will be returned. The concept of a filter is similar to that encountered in MHS.

• **Abandon**. This causes the directory to terminate processing, and any results so far may also be discarded. One possible reason for this might be to terminate a search which is either taking too long, or costing too much money. In the latter case the protocol designers have to be very careful, as there is a general problem in abandoning searches of this type. That is that unless care is taken in the design, the abandon command could well end up chasing the original enquiry round all of the DSAs involved, thereby generating additional network traffic (and usage charges), which is quite the reverse of what was intended. Constraints can also be specified so that, for example, the system might abandon the enquiry if it took too long; these are discussed later.

In addition, various types of update are possible. These include adding, removing and modifying entries, and modifying what the recommendations refer to as the 'relative distinguished name' of an entry. Using this set of primitive operations, various types of access are provided.

- In the simplest type of enquiry, a *lookup*, a person (or program) supplies the name of a 'directory object' and an attribute type. The contents of that entry are returned, i.e. the value(s) corresponding to that attribute type. This would be a way to obtain PSAP addresses, MHS addresses, or telephone or telex numbers, for example.

- A more 'user-friendly' approach is to assign names to commonly accessed objects, of the type which a human user can relate to. This is a shorthand way of specifying the object name and type, similar in concept to that used in specifying FTAM document types.

- For users who cannot specify either of the above types of details, but can provide some keyword(s), e.g. 'Manchester University Computer Science', a *browse* option is available. This is more powerful than a simple enquiry, and allow the enquirer to 'wander' through the DIB. (In general this will be an expensive way to access the DIB.)

- *Searching* a portion of the DIT for all entries having specified attribute types and values, and returning selected attributes from those entries. For example a list of professors could be returned for the above example.

- Comparing a supplied attribute value with that of an entry specified by its directory name. This is a type of *Yellow Pages* service. Recommendation X.520 specifies various attribute categories such as system, labelling (e.g. names of people), geographical (country, locality, state/county, street address), organisational, business, postal addresses, telecommunications addresses (telephone, telex, facsimile) and OSI application.

• Various *update* functions are provided, although it is anticipated that a relatively small percentage of directory accesses will involve updating anything. The options include adding, removing or modifying a directory entry, and altering its name (identifier). Clearly there is a security aspect to this (authentication) which is crucial to the correct operation of the directory. Both 'simple authentication' (e.g. password) and 'strong authentication' (using cryptographic techniques) are provided; the latter is discussed in recommendation X.509.

23.6.4   Operation of the Directory system

As can be seen from figure 23.1, there are a number of parallels with MHS as discussed in the previous chapter, although to see the similarities, one has to compare the Directory with a version of MHS ignoring the message store (in effect with MHS(1984)). For example the DUA relates logically to the UA in MHS, and the DSA similarly relates to the MHS MTA. Furthermore there is a 'mesh' of DSAs, just as there was a mesh of MTAs. However what is involved in the actual directory lookup is potentially far more complex than in MHS. Basically the Directory system works as follows.

• A user accesses his local DUA, using some defined access technique. This is expressed as a service definition (although details will not be provided), and X.500 specifies what information is exchanged over this interface, leaving details of the implementation to individual organisations.

• The DUA then formulates a *query* on behalf of the user, and passes this to its local DSA using the **directory access protocol** (**DAP**), which uses ROSE (see chapter eighteen) as an underlying mechanism. This broadly corresponds to the MTS access protocol (p3) of MHS.

• It may be that the local DSA can answer the query itself, in which case no other DSA will be involved, and there will be a simple enquiry-response transaction between the DUA and DSA.

• If however the DSA does not itself possess the required information, it uses its **DIT knowledge** (see below) to identify which other DSA (or DSAs) will be able to supply the required information. There are then two possibilities:

• The local DSA has the required information. In this case there is a simple enquiry-response dialogue between the DUA and its DSA. In most cases this is to be preferred, as it minimises traffic on underlying networks. (This implicitly assumes that either no network, or only a LAN, separates the DUA from its nearest DSA. This is an implementation issue.)

• There will inevitably be cases where the local DSA has either none or only part of the information required. Various options are provided to cater for this eventuality:

• The DSA may obtain the information from other DSAs automatically, using the *directory system protocol* (*DSP*), which also uses ROSE; this corresponds to the MHS MTS transfer protocol (p1). This technique is known as *chaining* where a single other DSA is involved, and *multicasting* where several remote DSAs are interrogated, and the reply to the DUA is amalgamated from more than one remote DSA reply. The DSP can (at the risk of oversimplification) be generalised as one or more enquiry-response communications between the source DSA and remote DSA(s). Each transaction is controlled by ROSE.

Note that both DAP and DSP uses ACSE for binding and unbinding to the directory, and ROSE for managing directory transactions (request-reply). These in turn use presentation (i.e. session) activity management over transport TP0. This is all in keeping with the general CCITT philosophy, which is not surprising since this is a CCITT-originated standard. It is the same layering which is used in MHS(1988), and is consistent with the currently defined application layer structure.

• The DSA may instead elect to return a *referral* to the DUA. Instead of returning the information sought, the DSA informs the DUA which (remote) DSA is believed to possess the required information. The DUA can then obtain the information from the DSA itself.

Security and control issues

One major problem which is currently exercising the minds of designers is *security*. A distributed directory of this type is particularly prone to unauthorised tampering, which if successful would not only cause severe damage to the directory itself, but would also prejudice applications relying on the integrity of the directory information received. Therefore special precautions are vital. The DSA attempts to 'prove' that the information it provides is secure by including a cryptographic *signature* in its replies. This is in addition to any encryption provided at the presentation layer or elsewhere. Secure *access control* such as user authentication is also vital in the case of updates, as only authorised users can be allowed to alter anything. *Masquerading* (i.e. one user 'stealing' and then using another user's identification, thereby pretending to be that user in order to make accesses which are not allowed in his case) is one area of particular concern to system designers.

Another problem is that a directory enquiry is potentially boundless, and without *control*, a careless enquiry by a user could result in masses of information being returned from a large number of DSAs, possibly at great expense to the user. Therefore various controls may be applied to enquiries. These include imposing a limit on the volume (e.g. number of lines) of returned information, imposing a time limit on the enquiry, placing restrictions on the types of information which may be accessed, applying scope limits on search and list operations, and providing mechanisms such as 'and' and 'not' which can be used to match attribute values.

23.6.5   The Directory Information Base

Directory Schema and object classes

This is a set of rules governing the allowed content of the DIB. Each directory entry is of a defined *object class*, such as a person, a laser printer, an organisation, and so on. The directory schema ensures that each entry has the appropriate attributes for its class (e.g. a machine cannot have a date of birth), and valid values of the attributes.

The standard identifies various features of object classes:

- *Standard* object class. The standard includes what are in effect a set of building blocks from which more complex classes can be constructed. This is similar to the approach used in ASN.1 for building complex data types from simple ones. The standard object classes are defined in recommendation X.521, and include top (everything), country, locality, organisation, organisational unit, person, organisational person, organisational role, residential person and application class. Each has an ASN.1 definition; the generic object identifier *objectClass* is used to specify object identifiers for specific object classes such as country.

- Provision is made for the specification of *user-defined* object classes. This is important given the diverse nature of possible use of the directory.

- A *structural* object class relates to a real object, such as a person. An *auxiliary* object class modifies a structural one by adding or altering attributes. An auxiliary object class does not have to correspond to a real world object.

- The attributes of object classes may be *inherited*, allowing a hierarchy of classes to be defined. Child object classes inherit the attributes of their parents. Therefore child classes are more specific than their parents. Thus 'lecturers' and 'secretaries' are more specific than 'employees of Manchester University Computer Science', which in turn is more specific than mere 'employees of Manchester University'.

- Object classes may in fact inherit the attributes of more than one object class; this is known as *multiple inheritance*.

DIT knowledge

The DIT defines the layout of the DIB among the various DSAs. In order for the Directory system to work in a predictable and orderly manner, the 'network' of DSAs must be organised according to strictly defined rules. These must provide a means by which a DSA may determine which other DSA holds what information, and how it can be located. This is controlled by what is known as the *DIT knowledge* of a DSA. DSAs are organised into a logical tree structure. Each DSA knows the identity of at least its *superior* and all of its immediately *subordinate* DSAs. This knowledge alone allows only rather inefficient tree scanning in order to locate information. Normally a DSA would have additional knowledge in specific areas, so that it can directly access the required DSA for commonly required information not held locally. To assist in this, DSAs may 'import' knowledge information from other DSAs, in terms of the naming contexts which the other DSAs contain. The *naming context* refers to that part of the directory held by a given DSA, and refers to the root of the subtree of information in this DSA. For example in figure 23.2, a DSA for Manchester University might contain information for Mathematics, Computer Science and so on, together with information on the location of naming contexts for other UK Universities. References to directory entries for Computer Science could be passed down the tree to the subordinate DSA located in the Computer Science Department. (All of this is pure theory at the time of writing.)

Attributes

A directory entry is composed of one or more attributes, which consist of a *type* and one or more *values*. A typical example might be 'telephone number' as an attribute of a telecommunications address, and

'071-246 8091' as a valid value. It is for the directory schema to see to it that only sensible values get placed in attributes of each type, although precisely how the directory schema is to be managed is still under consideration.

Each attribute type is given an unique ASN.1 object identifier value, and the associated ASN.1 syntax specifies all valid forms of associated values. An example for the search guide attribute is shown in figure 23.3.

One complication is that the Directory envisages that **domains** will be set up, each comprising DUAs and DSAs. A domain could comprise a country, and organisation, the academic community, or almost anything similar. It is clear that all attribute types and object classes used in a domain must be understood unambiguously by all DSAs and DUAs in that domain. Much of this is of concern mainly to implementors, and therefore not of particular interest here. It is also a complex area which is still undergoing development at the time of writing.

```
searchGuide ATTRIBUTE
    WITH ATTRIBUTE SYNTAX
            Guide
    ::=         {attributeType 14}

Guide ::=   SET {
    objectClass         [0]     OBJECT-CLASS OPTIONAL,
    criteria            [1]     Criteria}

Criteria ::=   CHOICE {
    Type                [0]     CriteriaItem,
    and                 [1]     SET OF Criteria,
    or                  [2]     SET OF Criteria,
    not                 [3]     Criteria}

        (etc)
```

Figure 23.3 - ASN.1 specification of a search attribute type

23.7   Miscellaneous applications and standards

In the remainder of the chapter, we will briefly examine some standards, many of which are currently under development. Most are still at the DP stage, many specify encodings rather than procedures, and none will be discussed in any detail.

23.7.1   Telematics standards

In this section we briefly examine CCITT-originated standards covering what are known generically as *Telematic services*. *Teletex*, *facsimile* and *videotex* will each be discussed briefly. The term telematics is rather loosely used by CCITT to cover user-orientated data transmission services, of which the Telex system, available for many years and still universally available, was the prototype. As well as the abovementioned services, MHS is often stated to be a telematic service. However there is one crucial difference. Teletex and the like merely specify means of encoding information for specific applications. On the other hand the MHS concept has matured into a full-blown application service with full OSI support. MHS can have a service user such as IPMS.

In fact IPMS allows mail messages to be encoded in various ways, including teletex, facsimile and videotex format, as well as ASCII.

Teletex

This is sometimes referred to as 'super Telex'. CCITT's motivation in producing Teletex recommendations as early as 1980 (in what at the time were the S-series, but in 1984 became the T-series) was to provide a replacement for the antiquated Telex system which many of us have come to hate. Telex is based on a 5-bit transmission code known as Baudot (or, in CCITT terminology, International Alphabet number Two or IA2). This is a 5-bit code, and uses a transmission speed of about five characters per second. No parity bit is used, nor is error protection provided on Telex messages. Apart from being appallingly slow and error-prone, it has built-in character set restrictions such as the inability to use lowercase letters, and a very restricted repertoire of special characters. The use of 'figure shift' and 'letter shift' so that the same code means different things according to context can make entire sections of messages unreadable if transmission errors occur. In short, it is not surprising that a replacement was sought as a matter of urgency.

Teletex removes many of these restrictions, by utilising a sensible transmission speed, providing a character set rich in special symbols (many of which a typical word processor cannot reproduce), and by using (initially) the reliability and error protection afforded by an underlying X.25 network. However its acceptance has been rather slow because, despite its glaring drawbacks, the Telex system can be used on a world-wide basis, which is still something for the future as far as Teletex is concerned.

In the OSI context, Teletex has a lot to answer for. Work on the specification of Teletex began almost as soon as that of X.25, which meant that it was largely specified before even OSI/RM itself had been finalised. It was therefore necessary for CCITT to make various assumptions about how OSI would develop, which in due course they also incorporated in MHS recommendations after OSI/RM had become an international standard, but before the OSI transport layer and above had become stable. The most notable outcomes were the use, in effect, of a null transport layer over X.25 networks, the use of rather odd procedures relating to activities, and effectively no use of the presentation layer. This approach was reflected in the X.400(1984) MHS series of recommendations.

The 'null transport layer' subsequently matured (if that is the right word) into the TP0 protocol class discussed in chapter fifteen, and the other features resulted in the inclusion of activity management in the session layer, and the need for MHS(1984) to use a special 'pass through' presentation mode effectively bypassing the OSI presentation layer. The most fundamental problem however was that TP0 was not originally designed to work over networks such as X.25, since it cannot handle the signalled RESETs and DISCONNECTs which X.25 has every right to generate. This had a number of impacts on both MHS and OSI, which were variously discussed in chapters eighteen and twenty two.

Facsimile

This is similar to Teletex in that it is an encoding technique. In this case it is intended for use between 'Group 4 Facsimile' stations. Facsimile is a commonly used means of transferring document images by means of a raster scan technique. For many years it has been used by the Meteorological Office to transmit weather maps to outstation sites. The problem with using the traditional technique of using modulation over the PSTN is that not only is it slow, but transmission errors introduced by line noise can rather make a mess of the received image, which in bad cases can be unusable. The CCITT Facsimile recommendations aim to provide a solution to these problems by specifying digital encoding techniques using the OSI stack..

Videotex

This is a system which caters for online interactive services such as the display (on a VDU screen in a suitable format) of stock market prices. Services of this type are offered by various common carriers, including British Telecom.

23.7.2   Manufacturing Message Specification (MMS)

This standard {9506} is being progressed, with the support of General Motors, to provide a message passing service {9506-1} for hosts interworking in a manufacturing environment. A typical example is for messages passed between computers and robots on a production line. The standard is based on a client-server (request-reply) model, and the protocols used {9506-2} are asymmetric. The basic idea is that the client issues a request message to a server. The server then performs the actions specified in the request message (if it can), and returns a response message indicating the outcome. A typical example might be an instruction for a robot to weld a car door; the robot would respond either when the weld was complete so that the production line could be advanced to the next stage, or if some problem had made it impossible to comply with the instruction. The idea is that the implementation of the action (e.g. by a robot) will be by its executing some program or subroutine, and therefore the service also provides mechanisms for manipulating these programs or subroutines.

The MMS service

The MMS service definition {9506-1} uses the concept of a *Virtual Manufacturing Device* (*VMD*), which models the external behaviour of the device as seen by the server. It is for a particular implementation to map this VMD on to an actual device such as a robot, numeric controller, process control device, or whatever.

Various MMS services are defined, and these are summarised below. An attempt has been made to related then to a typical application such as the control of a (General Motors) car assembly line, although the standard is intended for any suitable application. The services are deliberately intended to provide as wide as possible range of support; there may well be no practical way in which some services can be implemented as yet. The VT and FTAM services included are merely to support MMS, and are not suitable for other purposes; it is assumed that distinct VT and FTAM implementation will be used as necessary.

- *VMD support.* This provides mechanisms for identifying a device, to read and alter VMD component names, and to obtain the status of a device. This could be used, for example, to determine the current status of an assembly line, or to reassign tasks.

- *Domain management services.* These allow for the management of such things as device subroutines and data within (e.g.) robots, which are referred to as domains.

- *Program invocation management* services. These allow for the execution, control, monitoring and termination of a program on the server system.

- *Variable access* services. These allow generalised read/write access to the remote server's store (including management of any variable names and types which may be defined there). In a sense this may be viewed as a remote 'tuning' facility.

- *Semaphore management,* i.e. the control and co-ordination of shared resources. A car assembly line is complex, and it is essential that things get done in the correct order; it may be that several actions are interrelated and need careful co-ordination.

In a sense the systems to which this standard can be applied have many of the characteristics of a distributed operating system using message passing as an IPC mechanism.

- *Operator communication* services. It is assumed that an operator console is available which can be used for system messages or operator commands. To facilitate this, MMS includes a very cut-down VT specification, which is tailored to this specific service.

- *Event and journal management* services are provided to allow events and actions to be defined, monitored and logged (including the possibility of an 'audit trail').

- *File services.* A very cut-down subset of FTAM is included, which allows the transfer and management of sequential, unstructured files of octets (which are intended to contain program segments and data).

The current standard is general in nature, and could be applied in principle in a range of environments. More specific standards (e.g. perhaps one for car assembly lines) could become available in the future.

23.7.3   ODA and SGML

SGML is short for ***Standard Generalised Markup Language***. As can be inferred from its name, it has to do with the 'marking up' of documents for typesetting. This is in effect the conversion of a document in some abstract representation into a printed image. This book was marked up by printing the pages on a laser printer. In fact SGML itself does not provide any such facility. It is a meta-language which can be used to define new languages which do, of which the *Office Document Language* (*ODL*), used in the ***Office Document Architecture*** (***ODA***) standards is the main existing example at present. It can be inferred from this that we are discussing standards concerned with the description of documents for transfer between open systems. Neither SGML nor ODA is concerned with such presentation aspects as character fonts, pitch, italicisation and so on, which is known as Specific Markup, but with the information content. Thus although it may be specified that some text is to be emphasised, whether this means that it will be in bold, italic or whatever is for the recipient to decide, one presumes in some consistent 'house style'.

ODA {8613-1..8} is intended for use in distributed office systems. A typical application is the transfer of word processed documents which share various layout characteristics (paragraph and page boundaries, headers, footers, and so on) but which use different representations of these attributes. ODA has also been adopted by CCITT as part of its Telematics standards (T.41x series).

ODA knows about such things as *logical structure* (e.g. chapters, paragraphs, headings) and *layout structure* (e.g. pagination). Formatted processable documents can be revised with the physical layout preserved. Content is separated from logical and layout structure, allowing various ODA-independent ways of defining the *contents* (e.g. text, graphics). An ODA document also contains a *document profile* (e.g. author's name; nothing to do with OSI profiles of course).

ODIF is the *Office Document Interchange Format*, which uses ASN.1, and is therefore machine readable. The ODA standard also defines an *Office Document Language* (*ODL*), providing a 'human readable markup' for ODA documents. ODL may be combined with SDIF (see below).

Various *Document Application Profiles* (*DAPs*) identify a number of specific document classes. These vary from simple sequences of paragraphs with no formatting information, to complex documents with hierarchical chapter/section/subsection structures with automatic numbering, headers, footers, multiple columns, and so on.

SGML on the other hand is more concerned with publishing issues. The standard {8879} was published in 1986. A supporting standard {9069} defines a *SGML Document Interchange Format* (*SDIF*) which is already used for magnetic tape and disk transfer, as well as being intended for use over OSI connections. Hence it is concerned with paragraphs, headings, contents lists and so on. *Tags* are placed in the document to locate and define each of the different attributes.

Current ISO work (in SC18) is concentrated in two areas, *Document Style Semantics and Specification Language* (*DSSSL*) and *Standard Page Description Language* (*SPDL*).

23.7.4 Transaction Processing (TP)

This is a major emerging application standard. Some would argue that TP is a support application, and hence should have been discussed in chapter eighteen. However it is far more than merely a supporting service. Unfortunately the standard is both exceedingly complex and still under development, so that it is impossible to do it justice in a book such as this. Therefore what follows is a brief summary of the salient features, and the information in this section is also subject to change.

TP is designed to provide a framework for distributed transaction processing. This may in principle involve several geographically separate application entities. TP manages transactions between these entities by defining a hierarchical relationship between them (i.e. a tree structure), and nominating the *initiator* of the transaction as the root. TP now views a related set of transactions in a CCR-like manner, except that it extends the CCR philosophy in a hierarchical manner. On completion of the transactions, the root invites its sons to offer commitment, and this passes recursively down the tree. At a given level in the tree, once all sons have committed, that entity can in turn offer commitment to its parent, and so on until commitment has been offered to the root, when the atomic action comprising all of the transactions in the tree is then deemed to have been completed. TP makes use of CCR to provide the necessary underlying commitment and related mechanisms outlined above. In effect TP can be viewed as a 'value added' addition to CCR. TP provides a tree-like association between individual transactions, each of which is subject to CCR procedures.

It is worth mentioning that in order to be able to support TP satisfactorily, CCR had to undergo major 'surgery', so that the 1989 version of CCR differs in a number of important respects from the original version. It is this more recent version which was discussed in chapter eighteen.

TP appears to be suitable for JTM-type applications (chapter twenty), where the full specification allows job specifications to spawn further specifications at the receiver, thus generating a tree structure rooted on the submitter of the job, very much as described above. However JTM currently uses CCR, and in any case, as will be seen, only the full mode JTM is capable of generating a real tree of transactions, and at present this has no stable protocol support. In fact the changes made to CCR caused problems for JTM, and a JTM defect report had to be issued.

TP also appears to be suitable for the emerging RDA standard discussed briefly in chapter twenty three. However these are likely to use ROSE and/or CCR directly (depending on complexity). Given that CCR itself has been the cause of considerable difficulty, notably in relation to conflicting requirements of JTM and the emerging RDA standard, it may be several years before all of the odd inconsistencies and duplication in this area are sorted out. In this sense it seems like the session layer all over again.

However many experts see TP as the application of the future, possibly obsoleting JTM, which has relatively little support.

Although TP is a recent standard, which (at the time of writing) was still at the DIS stage, it has strong support in the UK. The National Westminster Bank is well advanced with one of the first UK implementations. This bank has a very large ISDN network, and ITSU are watching developments there with considerable interest. Both ULCC and Salford University are also involved in the specification and implementation of TP.

23.7.5   Remote Database Access (RDA)

Work on *Remote Data Access* (*RDA*) is at an early stage, the main standard being at DP stage {9579}. It is intended to cover applications such as a client (user) accessing a server (database) to determine the contents of some record in the database, in other words a simple enquiry-response database access. Two scenarios are in fact envisaged in the standard:

- Simple *point-point mode*. Where a single client and server are involved, a simple exchange of messages is all that is required. In this case it is intended that RDA should make use of the *ROSE* application support service (see chapter eighteen); this is precisely the type of application which ROSE was designed for in the first place. This is expected to be the main use of RDA, at least initially.

- In a more complex scenario, RDA could be used with *distributed databases*. Here the scenario is more complex, with several OSI hosts involved. In this case it is expected that RDA will instead make use of *TP* (see above) and *CCR* (again see chapter eighteen), although a basic *transaction management* service is incorporated in RDA in lieu of this.

   This usage of TP and CCR has caused delays in the standardisation of CCR, and problems for JTM. The entire area is extremely complex.

Central to RDA is the concept of a *dialogue*. This can roughly be equated to an enquiry and its response, and RDA includes *dialogue management services*, which allow a dialogue to be started, ended, suspended and resumed. This sounds rather like session layer activities, but there is a major difference. A RDA dialogue can span many application associations, or an application association may contain many RDA dialogues, so that it is impossible to relate a dialogue directly to an activity on a particular session connection. Other services provided include the following:

• **Control**, for cancelling or determining the status of an RDA operation. This is comparable to the similar function in JTM.

• **Resource handling**. This is (vaguely) intended to cover which databases may be accessed from this RDA host, and sounds rather like the NEST defined for use in JTMP (see chapter nine).

• **Language services**. One problem with databases is that it is often necessary to access groups of records using selection criteria. An example is 'all employees who live in Manchester'. For this purpose various database access languages exist, so that a user can produce a customised interrogation of a selected group of records, being provided with details of those which match. By now you will have got the drift. What is needed in the OSI context is a *virtual database access language*. RDA defines, in a rather abstract way, how language operations can be defined and invoked.

Unfortunately RDA depends on a number of standards which have not yet emerged, and is therefore some way from being a viable standard in its own right.

23.7.6 Electronic Data Interchange (EDI)

This standard {9735} has a rather convoluted name, *Electronic Data Interchange for Finance, Administration, Commerce and Transport*. Not surprisingly it is usually known either by its acronym, *EDIFACT*, or just as *EDI*. It is yet another way of exchanging documents, referred to as messages, this time ones of a 'commercial' nature. It will come as no surprise to learn that the ISO standard resulted from a compromise between incompatible ANSI and United Nations standards.

EDIFACT *messages* contain *data elements*, which may be grouped into *segments*. It has been decided to create a directory of common data elements {7372} in order to impose standardisation in this area.

Initial EDIFACT drafts did not address the issue of how the messages are to be transferred over an application association. Both FTAM and MHS are seen as suitable, and CCITT are currently considering possible MHS support for EDIFACT, by providing another MHS user protocol (rather like IPMS; the protocol number has yet to be determined).

23.8 Concluding remarks

In this book we have introduced the background to, and concepts of, OSI. We started by examining the deficiencies of earlier protocols such as

BSC, and traced the somewhat tortuous transition to OSI. The current situation is that all layers, including the application layer, are now reasonably stable. The 'basic modes' of the principal applications, VT, FTAM, JTM and MHS are also stable, although many extensions to these standards are under active consideration. Most work however is now devoted to the provision of a global management framework (notably the Directory and registration procedures) which will allow adequate support for OSI, something which is urgently needed, and without which the kind of interworking taken for granted in the telephone system will still not be possible. In addition, work is underway on many new applications, some of which are still at the working draft stage. (Appendix B lists the main OSI standards, including their current status at the time of writing, although of course the information on status will become out of date. A regular series of reports appears[4] listing the current status of OSI standards.)

So the OSI framework is there, and there is at least adequate (if not ideal in some cases) support for the main applications. Once the Directory and related standards are finalised, it will start to become possible to access the OSI equivalent of 'directory enquiries' to locate peer applications, and identify such things as presentation contexts by reference to 'object registration servers', but at the time of writing this goal is still some way off. The UK academic community's Name Registration Service (NRS; see chapter nine) was one of the first concerted attempts to provide such a community-wide service; extending this type of concept on a world-wide basis is a daunting task indeed.

There is still much work to be done, and the acceptance of OSI itself as the way forward is by no means universal. Indeed there may always be a role for proprietary (non-OSI) systems in some specialised areas. Clearly this is not the end of the story, and no doubt it will eventually be necessary to write a fourth edition of this book, though not for several years (one hopes). The main problem here is that the volume and complexity of OSI standards increases all the time, and it was never the intention of this book to provide a full coverage of the type necessary for implementors. This third edition is already nearly twice as long as the second edition, and there are many application areas which have not been covered in any sort of detail. This book is primarily intended as a student text, and more specialised books, or the standards themselves, must be consulted for detailed information of this nature. Therefore most of the new developments will probably be beyond the scope of a book such as this, and it is likely that only the chapter you are reading now will have to change radically in any new edition.

For those of you who will be working in the OSI field, it is hoped that this book has provided a good insight into the 'hows and whys' of the subject. For the rest, it will hopefully have served the purpose of making OSI concepts more widely known and understood. It was always a 'design goal' to concentrate on the reasons for adopting a given approach, rather than merely quoting verbatim from standard documents, most of which are written by and for experts in any case. It is for you the reader to judge whether the goal has been achieved.

23.9 References

1   See for example D. Bjorner and C. B. Jones, 'Formal Specification and Software Development', Prentice Hall (1982).

2   R. Milner, 'A Calculus of Communicating Systems', Springer-Verlag (1980).

3   H. Ehrig et al., 'ACT ONE: an Algebraic Specification Language with Two Levels of Semantics', Bericht-Nr. 80-03, Technical University of Berlin (1983).

4   The ACM Special Interest Group (SIG) publication Computer Communication Review regularaly contains OSI status reports by A. Lyman Chapin which consist of lists of OSI standards (both ISO and CCITT), with the current status and most recent publication date. The latest available at the time of writing appeared in July, 1990, and was used as the basis of appendix B.

A   Acronyms

This is a comprehensive list of OSI and other acronyms. It includes some which are not referenced in this book. Where relevant the name of the related standard, protocol etc. is provided as well as what the acronym stands for. In some cases the same acronym can mean two, three or even more different things according to context.

A	Asynchronous (as in A-mode; VT)
ABM	Asynchronous balanced mode (HDLC)
ABME	Asynchronous balanced extended mode (HDLC)
ACK	Positive acknowledgement (ASCII)
ACK0,ACK1	Numbered acknowledgements (BSC)
ACM	Association for Computing Machinery (USA)
ACSE	Association control service elements (application services)
ADD	Addendum (ISO/IEC; now amendment (AM))
AE	Application entity
AFIPS	American Federation of Information Processing Systems (USA)
AK	Data acknowledge (TPDU)
AM	Amendment (ISO/IEC)
AP	Application process
APDU	Application PDU
ARP	Abnormal release - user (PPDU)
ARPA	advance research projects agency (USA)
ARQ	Automatic repeat (retransmission) request (acknowledgements)
ARU	Abnormal release - user (PPDU)
ASCII	American standard code for information interchange
ASE	Application service element
ASN	Abstract syntax notation
AU	Access unit (e.g. for teletex) (MHS)
BAS	Basic activity subset (session service; obsolete)
BBP	Basic block protocol (Cambridge ring)
BCC	Block check character (error check, BSC)
BCD	Binary coded decimal (as used in X.25 addresses)
BCS	Basic combined subset (session service; obsolete)
BCVT	basic class VT
BDLC	Burroughs data link control (Unisys)
BDT	Bulk data transfer (FTAM)
BNA	Burroughs (Unisys) network architecture (proprietary)
BNF	Backus Naur (normal) format
BSC, BISYNC	Binary synchronous communication (protocol)
BSI	British Standards Institute (Institution)
BSP	Byte stream protocol (Cambridge ring)
BSS	Basic synchronisation subset (session service; obsolete)
BTRL	British Telecom Research Laboratories
CA	(With) collision avoidance (CSMA)
CASE	Common application service elements (application support; obsolete, now replaced by ACSE, CCR, ROSE, RTSE); also computer aided software engineering
CC	Connection confirm (TPDU)

CCA	Conceptual communications area (VT)
CCITT	International Telegraph and Telephone Consultative Committee
CCO	Context control object (VT)
CCR	Commitment, concurrency and recovery (application support)
CCRSE	CCR service elements (alternative name)
CD	Context delete (PPDU); (with) collision detection (CSMA); committee draft (ISO/IEC; replaces DP)
CDA	Context delete ack (PPDU)
CDAM	Committee draft amendment (ISO/IEC; replaces PDAD)
CDS	Conceptual data store (VT)
CDTR	Committee draft technical report (ISO/IEC; replaces PDTR)
CEN	European standards centre
CENELEC	Electronics equivalent of CEN
CEPT	Conference of European PTTs
CGM	Computer graphics metafile (application)
CHILL	CCITT high level language
CL	Connectionless
CLDLS	CL data link service
CLNP	CL network protocol
CLNS	CL network service
CLPP	CL presentation protocol
CLPS	CL presentation service
CLSP	CL session protocol
CLSS	CL session service
CLTP	CL transport protocol
CLTS	CL transport service
CMDR	Command reject (HDLC, obsolete)
CMI	Common management information systems (application)
CMIP	Common management information protocol (application)
CMIS	Common management information service (application)
CMS	Batch service operated by MCC
CO	Connection oriented; control object (VT)
CODLS	CO data link service
CONS	CO network service
COPP	CO presentation protocol
COPS	CO presentation service
COSP	CO session protocol
COSS	CO session service
COTP	CO transport protocol
COTS	CO transport service
CP	Connect presentation (PPDU)
CPA	Connect presentation accept (PPDU)
CPR	Connect presentation refuse (PPDU)
CR	Cambridge ring (LAN); carriage return (ASCII); connection request (TPDU)
CRC	Cyclic redundancy check (error check)
CSMA	Carrier sense multiple access (LAN)
CSMA/CA	.... with collision avoidance
CSMA/CD	.... with collision detection (Ethernet)
CSS	Control, signalling and status store (VT)
DAD	Draft addendum (ISO/IEC; now draft amendment (DAM))

DAM	Draft amendment (ISO/IEC; replaces DAD)
DAP	Directory access protocol (directory); document application profiles (ODA)
DARPA	Defense advance research projects agency (USA)
DC	Disconnect confirm (TPDU); define context (PPDU)
DCA	Define context ack (PPDU); Defense Communications Agency (USA)
DCE	Data circuit terminating equipment (CCITT)
DCPU	Data communication protocols unit (UK academic)
DCS	Defined context set (presentation)
DECNET	See DNA
DIB	Directory information base (directory)
DIS	Draft international standard (ISO/IEC)
DISC	Disconnect (HDLC)
DIT	Directory information tree (directory)
DIX	DEC, Intel and Xerox (Ethernet)
DLC	Data link connection
DLE	Data link escape (ASCII)
DLPDU	Data link protocol data unit
DLSDU	Data link service data unit
DM	Disconnected mode (HDLC)
DNA	Distributed network architecture (DEC, proprietary)
DO	Display object (VT)
DOA	Distributed office applications
DP	Draft proposal (ISO/IEC; now committee draft (CD))
DQDB	Distributed queue dual bus (MAN)
DR	Disconnect request (TPDU)
DSA	Directory system agent (directory)
DSD	Data structure definition (VT)
DSP	Directory system protocol (directory)
DSSSL	Document style semantics and specification language (SGML)
DT	Data (TPDU)
DTAM	Document transfer, access and management (application)
DTE	Data terminal equipment (CCITT)
DTI	Department of Trade and Industry (UK)
DTR	Draft technical report (ISO/IEC); data terminal ready (V.24)
DU	Data unit (FTAM)
DUA	Directory user agent (directory)
DXE	Data exchange equipment (X.75)
EA	Expedited acknowledge (TPDU)
EBCDIC	Extended BCD interchange code
EC	European Commission (or Community)
ECMA	European Computer Manufacturers' Association
ED	End delimiter (LAN); expedited data (TPDU)
EDI	Electronic data interchange (application)
EDIFACT	EDI for finance, administration, commerce and transport
EDTPDU	Expedited TPDU
EIA	Electrical industries association (USA)
EMACS	An editor used on UNIX systems
ENQ	Enquiry (ASCII)
EOT	End of transmission (ASCII)

EPSS	Experimental packet switching system (UK)
ER	Error (TPDU)
ESC	Escape (ASCII)
ESTELLE	Formal description technique based on an extended state transition model
ETB	End of transmission block (ASCII)
ETS	European telecommunication standard
ETSI	European Telecommunication Standards Institute
ETX	End of transmission (ASCII)
EWOS	European Workshop for Open Systems
FADU	File access data unit (FTAM)
FCS	Frame check sequence (error check)
FDCO	Field definition control object (VT)
FDDI	Fibre distributed data interface (LAN)
FDT	Formal description technique
FDX	Full duplex
FE	Format effector (ASCII)
FEICO	Field entry instruction control object (VT)
FEIR	Field entry instruction record (VT)
FEP	Front end processor
FEPCO	Field entry pilot control object (VT)
FEPR	Field entry pilot record (VT)
FF	Formfeed (ASCII)
FJCC	Fall (autumn) joint computer conference (AFIPS)
FRMR	Frame reject (HDLC)
FS	File separator (ASCII); frame status octet (token ring)
FTAM	File transfer, access and management (Application)
FTP	File transfer protocol (generic and ARPA)
FTSC	Federal Telecommunications Standards Committee (USA)
FU	Functional unit
GFI	General format identifier (X.25)
GKS	Graphical kernel system (application)
GOS	Grade of service (subset of QOS)
GOSIP	Government OSI profile
GS	Group separator (ASCII)
GSM	Groupe Special Mobile (part of CEPT)
HDLC	High level data link control
HDX	Half duplex
HT	Horizontal tab (ASCII)
IA	International alphabet (CCITT)
IA2	CCITT version of Telex (Baudot) code
IA5	CCITT version of ASCII code
IDLC	International data link control (ICL)
IEC	International Electrotechnical Commission (United Nations)
IEE	Institute of Electrical Engineers (UK)
IEEE	Institute of Electrical and Electronic Engineers (USA)
IMP	Interface message processor (ARPA)
IP	Internet protocol (DARPA, proprietary)
IPC	Inter-process communication
IPM	Interpersonal message (IPMS)
IPME	IPMS environment (IPMS)

IPMS	Interpersonal messaging system (MHS)
IPSS	International packet switching service
IS	International standard (ISO/IEC)
ISDN	Integrated services digital network
ISO	International Organization for Standardization, alias International Standards Organisation (United Nations)
ITB	End of intermediate transmission block (EBCDIC)
ITSU	Information technology standards unit (DTI)
ITU	International Telecommunications Union (United Nations)
JANET	Joint academic network (UK)
JCL	Job control language (generic)
JNT	Joint network team (UK academic)
JOVE	" Jonathan's own version of EMACS " (UNIX editor)
JTC	Joint technical committee (of ISO and IEC)
JTM	Job transfer and manipulation (application)
JTMP	Job transfer and manipulation protocol (UK academic)
LAN	Local area network
LAP	Link access procedures (HDLC/X.25)
LAPB	Balanced link access procedures (HDLC/X.25)
LAPD	Digital link access procedures (ISDN)
LC	Logical channel (e.g. X.25)
LF	Linefeed (ASCII)
LLC	Logical link control (LAN)
LOTOS	Language of temporal ordering specification (formal description technique)
MAC	Medium access control (LAN)
MAN	Metropolitan area network (IEEE)
MASE	Message administration service elements (MHS)
MCA	Micro channel architecture (IBM proprietary PC bus)
MCC	Manchester Computing Centre (formerly UMRCC)
MDSE	Message delivery service elements (MHS)
MHS	Message handling systems (application, CCITT name for MOTIS)
MIN	Multiple interaction negotiation (VT)
MLP	Multilink procedures (X.25 LAPB)
MMS	Manufacturing message service (application)
MOTIS	Message oriented text interchange system (application, ISO name for MHS)
MRSE	Message retrieval service elements (MHS)
MSSE	Message submission service elements (MHS)
MTA	Message transfer agent (MHS)
MTS	Message transfer system (MHS)
MUX	Multiplexer
NAK	Negative acknowledgement (ASCII)
NC	Network connection
NCC	National Computing Centre (Manchester, UK)
NCMS	Network connection management subprotocol
NEST	Network status table (JTMP)
NET	European telecommunication 'norm' (standard) (French acronym)
NFS	Network file system (Sun, proprietary)
NIFTP	Network independent file transfer protocol (UK academic)
NIST	National institute of science and technology (USA)

NITS	Network independent transport service (old name for YBTS)
NNNN	Telex 'control sequence'
NPL	National Physical Laboratory (UK)
NRM	Normal response mode (HDLC)
NRME	Normal response extended mode (HDLC)
NRS	Name registration service (UK academic)
NS	Network service
NSAP	Network SAP
NUL	Time fill (ASCII)
NVT	Network virtual terminal
ODA	Office document architecture (application)
ODIF	Office document interchange format
ODL	Office document language
O/R, OR	Originator/recipient (directory, MHS)
OSF	Open Software Foundation (promoting a version of UNIX)
OSI	Open systems interconnection (really!)
OWS	One way simultaneous (simplex)
PAD	Packet assembly/disassembly unit (XXX)
PC	Presentation connection (or personal computer!)
PDAD	proposed draft addendum (ISO/IEC; now proposed draft amendment (PDAM))
PDAM	proposed draft amendment (ISO/IEC; replaces PDAD)
PDN	Public data network
PDTR	Proposed draft technical report (ISO/IEC)
PDU	Protocol data unit
PhC	Physical connection
PhPDU	Physical protocol data unit
PhSDU	Physical service data unit
PHIGS	Programmer's hierarchical interactive graphics interface (application)
PICS	Protocol implementation conformance statement
PLP	Packet layer protocol (X.25)
PLS	Physical (layer) signalling (unit) (LAN)
PPDU	Presentation PDU
PSAP	Presentation SAP
PSDN	Public switched digital network
PSDU	Presentation SDU
PSE	Packet switching exchange (PSS)
PSN	Packet sequence number
PSS	Packet switchstream (BT network)
PSTN	Public switched telephone network
PSU	Power supply unit (CR)
PTT	Post, telegraph and telephone authority (national common carrier)
PVC	Permanent VC (X.25)
QOS	Quality of service (all OSI layers)
RA	Resynchronise [abandon] (PPDU)
RAA	Resynchronise [abandon] ack (PPDU)
RBT	Remote batch terminal
REJ	Reject (HDLC)
RDA	Remote database access (application)
RFC	Request for comments (ARPANET standard)

RIM	Request initialisation mode (HDLC)
RIO	Reference information object (VT)
RJ	Reject (TPDU)
RLP	Radio link protocol (GSM)
RM	Reference model (OSI)
RNEG	Negative reply (NIFTP)
RNR	Receive not ready (HDLC)
RO,ROS	Remote operations (application support, notably MHS(84))
ROSE	Remote operations service elements (application support)
RPC	Remote procedure call
RPOA	Registered private operating agency (CCITT, X.25)
RPOS	Positive reply (NIFTP)
RR	Receive ready (HDLC)
RS	Record separator (ASCII)
RSET	Reset (HDLC)
RT,RTS	Reliable transfer (application support, notably MHS(84))
RTS	Request to send (V.24 modem signalling condition - physical layer)
RTSE	Reliable transfer service elements (application support)
RVI	Reverse interrupt (BSC)
S	Synchronous (as in S-mode; VT)
SABM	Set ABM(HDLC)
SABME	Set ABME (HDLC)
SARM	Set ARM (HDLC)
SARME	Set ARME (HDLC)
SAP	Service access point
SC	Session connection; sub-committee (ISO/IEC)
SD	Start delimiter (LAN)
SDIF	SGML document interchange format
SDLC	Synchronous data link control (IBM)
SDU	Service data unit
SFD	Start frame delimiter (LAN)
SFT	Start file transfer (NIFTP)
SG	Study group (CCITT)
SGML	Standard generalised markup language (application)
SIG	Special interest group (ACM)
SIM	Set initialisation mode (HDLC)
SITA	International air transport agency [French acronym] (network)
SJCC	Spring joint computer conference (AFIPS)
SLP	Single link procedure (X.25 LAPB)
SNA	Systems network architecture (IBM, proprietary)
SNRM	Set NRM (HDLC)
SNRME	Set NRME (HDLC)
SSP	Single shot protocol (Cambridge ring)
SPDL	Standard page description language (ODA)
SPDU	Session PDU
SP	Synchronisation point (session)
SPSN	Synchronisation point sequence number (session)
SQL	Standardised query language (RDA)
SREJ	Selective reject (HDLC)
SSDU	Session service data unit
STX	Start of transmission (ASCII)

SYN	Synchronous idle (ASCII)
TC	Transport connection; transmission control (ASCII characters); technical committee (ISO/IEC); transport capability data (PPDU)
TCC	Transport capability data ack (PPDU)
TCP	Transmission control protocol (DARPA, proprietary)
TCR	Transfer control record (JTM)
TD	Transfer presentation data (PPDU)
TE	Transfer expedited data (PPDU)
TG	Technical guide (e.g. BT, ITSU)
TIP	Terminal interface message processor (ARPA)
TM	Transfer and manipulation (FTAM)
TPn	Class n transport protocol
TPCO	Transmission policy control object ('VT)
TPDU	Transport PDU
TR	Technical report (ISO/IEC)
TS	Transport service (OSI or generic)
TSDU	TS data unit
TTD	Temporary text delay (BSC); transfer presentation typed data (PPDU)
TUG	Technical user guide (e.g. BT for PSS)
TWA	Two way alternate
TWS	Two way simultaneous
UA	Un-numbered acknowledge (HDLC); user agent (MHS)
UDLC	Universal data link control (Unisys)
UDP	User datagram protocol (DARPA, proprietary)
UI	Un-numbered information (HDLC)
ULCC	University of London Computer Centre
UMRCC	University of Manchester Regional Computer Centre, now known as the Manchester Computing Centre (MCC)
UNIX	An operating system originally developed by Berkeley University, widely used for OSI standardisation work
US	Unit separator (ASCII)
VC	Virtual circuit (generic); virtual call (X.25)
VDM	Vienna definition method (formal specification technique)
VFS	Virtual filestore (FTAM)
VMD	Virtual manufacturing device (MMS)
VT	Virtual terminal; vertical tab (ASCII)
VTE	Virtual terminal environment (VT)
VTP	Virtual terminal protocol (generic)
VTPDU	VT protocol data unit
VTPM	VT protocol machine (VT)
WACK	Wait before acknowledge (BSC)
WAN	Wide area network
WG	Working group
XID	Exchange identification (HDLC)
XOFF	Stop sending flow control (ASCII)
XON	Resume sending flow control (ASCII)
XXX	Triple X (X.3/X.28/X.29)
YBTS	Yellow book transport service (UK academic)
YP	Yellow pages (Sun, proprietary)
ZCZC	Telex 'control sequence'

B   Selected ISO Standards

This appendix lists the principal OSI-related standards, and is based on a standards list in Computer Communication Review (ACM SigComm), July 1990, pp. 83 ff, to which the author makes due acknowledgement. This list includes all standards referenced e.g. {7498} within the main part of the book. It also includes, for completeness, many others which have not been discussed. In some cases there are equivalent CCITT recommendations; such recommendations are listed in appendix C. As this book has not covered the physical layer in detail, only the physical layer service definition is provided.

Standards are listed in ascending numerical order, classified according to the OSI layer to which they relate. A few superseded standards are mentioned as well. Application standards are further subdivided for easier reference. Particularly **important application standards are highlighted**. (This is not done with lower layer standards, as almost everything would end up being highlighted.)

Some standards have several parts. For example {7498} covers the Reference Model itself. In fact the standard is in several parts, {7498-1}, {7498-2} and so on. Although there is actually no such standard as {7498}, we use the standard number to identify the purpose of the set of standards in such cases.

ABBREVIATION	MEANING
AM	Amendment with IS status (ADD)
DAM	Draft amendment (DAD)
PDAM	Proposed draft amendment (PDAD)
DIS	Draft International Standard
DP	Draft Proposal
ADD	Addendum with IS status
DAD	Draft Addendum (DIS status)
PDAD	Proposed DAD (DP status)
TR	Technical Report
DTR	Draft Technical Report
CDTR	Committee DTR (PDTR)
PDTR	Proposed DTR
COR	Technical Corrigendum
DTC	Draft Technical Corrigendum
CD	Committee draft (DP)
PICS	Protocol Implementation Conformance Statement

Figure B.1 - Use of Abbreviations in ISO Standard List

Table B.1 shows the principal abbreviations used with standards. Note that the old names (DP, ADD etc.) are used rather than the new ones (CD, AM etc.) in the following list. Most abbreviations refer to document status. Where no status appears in brackets, it may be assumed that the standard had reached full International Standard (IS), ADD (AM) or TR status at the time of writing, although the situation is of course subject to continuous change. A working draft may be taken to mean an embryo standard which has yet to be formally balloted for DP status. (Where the ballot is in progress, it is referred to as a DP.) These are generally referred to as DPs (or whatever).

Number	Status	Title (Sometimes abbreviated)

Reference Model

7498		**OSI/RM**
7498-1		Basic Reference Model
7498-1	ADD1	Connectionless data transmission
7498-1	PDAD2	Multipeer Data Transmission
7498-1	COR1	Technical Corrigendum
7498-2		Security Architecture
7498-3		Naming and Addressing
7498-4		Management Framework
8509	TR	Service Conventions

Layer independent and multi-layer standards

8807		LOTOS (Formal Description Technique)
8807	PDAD1	Graphical Representation (G-LOTOS)
8824		**ASN.1 Specification**
8824	DAD1	ASN.1 Extensions
8825		**ASN.1 Basic Encoding Rules**
8825	DAD1	Encoding Rules for ASN.1 Extensions
9074		ESTELLE (Formal Description Technique)
9074	PDAD1	ESTELLE Tutorial (working draft)
9496		CHILL (CCITT High level Language)
9646		Conformance Testing Methodology and Framework
9646-1	DIS	General Concepts
9646-2	DIS	Abstract Test Suite Specification
9646-3	DIS	Tree and Tabular Combined Notation
9646-4	DIS	Test Realisation
9646-5	DIS	Requirements of Test Laboratories and Clients for Conformance Testing Assessment.[1]

[1] The National Computing Centre in Manchester was the first Protocol Testing site in the UK. Others have now been established as well, notably by British Telecom.

9646-6	DP	Test Laboratory Operations (working draft)
9834		Procedures for Registration Authorities
9834-1	DIS	General Procedures (for registration of...)
9834-2	DIS	Document Types
9834-3	DIS	Object Identifiers
9834-4	DIS	VTE Profiles
9834-5	DIS	VT Control Objects
9834-6	DP	Application Process and Entity titles
9834-as[2]	DP	Abstract Syntaxes (working draft)
9834-ts	DP	Transfer Syntaxes (working draft)
9834-ac	DP	Application Contexts (working draft)
9834-st	DP	System Titles (working draft)
10000		International Standardised OSI Profiles
10000-1	TR	Taxonomy Framework
10000-2	TR	Taxonomy of Profiles
10167	DTR	Application Guide-lines for ESTELLE, LOTOS and SDL.
10181		OSI Security Model
10181-1	DP	Security Framework
10181-2	DP	Authentication Framework

General application layer and support applications

8649		**ACSE Service Definition**
8649	DAD1	Peer-Entity Authentification during Association Establishment
8649	DAD2	Connectionless ACSE Service
8649	PDAD3	A-CONTEXT Management Service (working draft)
8649-3		(CCR - superseded - see 9804)
8650		**ACSE Protocol Specification**
8650	DAD1	Peer Entity Authentification
8650	PDAD2	PICS Proforma
8650	PDAD3	A-CONTEXT Management
8650	PDAD4	Application Entity Titles
8650-3		(CCR - superseded - see 9805)
9066		**Reliable Transfer (RTSE)**
9066-1		Model and Service Definition
9066-2		Protocol Specification
9072		**Remote Operations (ROSE)**
9072-1		Model, notation and Service Definition
9072-2		Protocol Specification
9545		**Application Layer Structure**
9545	PDAD1	Connectionless Operation (working draft)
9804		**Commitment, Concurrency and Recovery (CCR) Service Definition**

---

[2] It is common practice for ISO and CCITT to use provisional letters rather than numbers for initial attempts at emerging standards. CCITT once had a draft recommendation X.pi which defined how protocol identification was encoded into call request packets. Such standards and recommendations are eventually assigned numbers (or abandoned).

Management and the Directory

---

[3] At the time of writing, the PDADs, DP 9594-9 and DP 9594-10 have no CCITT numbered equivalent.

10164-6	DP	Log Control
10164-7	DP	Security Alarm Reporting
10164-sm	DP	Software Management (working draft)
10165		Structure of Management Information
10165-1	DP	Management Information Model (working draft)
10165-2	DP	Definition of Management Information
10165-3		(Withdrawn)
10165-4	DP	Guide-lines for Definition of Managed Objects

Applications discussed in detail

8505		(MOTIS - superseded - see 10021)
8571		**File Transfer, Access and Management (FTAM)**
8571-1		General Introduction
8571-1	PDAD1	Filestore Management
8571-1	PDAD2	Overlapped Access (working draft)
8571-2		Virtual Filestore Definition
8571-2	PDAD1	Filestore Management
8571-2	PDAD2	Overlapped Access (working draft)
8571-3		File Service Definition
8571-3	PDAD1	Filestore Management
8571-3	PDAD2	Overlapped Access (working draft)
8571-4		File Protocol Specification
8571-4	PDAD1	Filestore Management
8571-4	PDAD2	Overlapped Access
8571-5	DP	PICS Proforma (working draft)
8831		**Job Transfer and Manipulation (JTM) Concepts and Services**
8832		JTM Basic Class Protocol
8832	PDAD1	Full Class Protocol (under review)
8883		(MOTIS - superseded - see 10021)
9040		**Virtual Terminal (VT) Service Definition - Basic Class**
9040	ADD1	Extended Facility Set
9040	DAD2	Additional Functional Units 9041 Virtual Terminal (VT) Protocol Specification - Basic Class
9041	ADD1	Extended Facility Set
9041	DAD2	Additional Functional Units
9041	PDAD3	PICS Proforma
9065		(IPMS - superseded - see 10021)
10021		**Message Oriented Text Information Systems (MOTIS).** (See also X.400(88), appendix C[4].)
10021-1	DIS	System and Service Overview
10021-2	DIS	Overall Architecture
10021-3	DIS	Abstract Service Definition Conventions
10021-4	DIS	Message Transfer System (MTS) - Abstract Service Definition and Procedures

---

[4] MOTIS is technically equivalent to MHS(88). However there is as yet no ISO equivalent of X.403 or X.408.

10021-5	DIS	Message Store (MS) - Abstract Service Definition
10021-6	DIS	Protocol Specifications
10021-7	DIS	Interpersonal Messaging System (IPMS)
10170		FTAM Conformance Test Suite
10170-1	DP	Structure and Test Purposes

Graphics Application Standards

7942		Graphical Kernel System (GKS) Functional Description
7942	DAD1	Audit Trail Metafile
8632		Computer Graphics Metafile (CGM) (aka Picture Description Information Storage and Transfer Metafile)
8632-1		Functional Specification
8632-1	DAD1	Audit Trail Metafile
8632-1	PDAD2	3D Static Picture Capture Metafile
8632-2		Character Encoding
8632-3		Binary Encoding
8632-4		Clear Text Encoding
8671		GKS Language Bindings
8671-1		FORTRAN
8671-2		Pascal
8671-3		Ada
8671-4	DP	C (working draft)
8805		GKS for Three Dimensions (GKS-3D) Functional Description
9592		Programmer's Hierarchical Interactive Graphics Interface (PHIGS)
9592-1		Functional Description
9592-1	AM1	PHIGS Plus Support
9592-2		Archive File Format
9592-2	AM1	PHIGS Plus Support
9592-3		Clear-text Encoding for Archive File
9592-3	AM1	PHIGS Plus Support
9592-4	DIS	PHIGS Plus
9593		PHIGS Language Bindings
9593-1		FORTRAN
9593-2	DIS	Pascal
9593-3		Ada
9593-4	DIS	C
9636		Interfacing Techniques for Dialogues with Graphical Devices: Functional Specification
9636-1	DIS	Overview, Profiles and Conformance
9636-2	DIS	Control
9636-3	DIS	Output
9636-4	DIS	Segments
9636-5	DIS	Input and Echoing
9636-6	DIS	Raster
9973	TR	Registration of Graphical Items

ODA, SGML and Related Standards

8613		Text and Office Systems - Office Document Architecture (**ODA**) and Interchange Format (ODIF). (See also T.400, appendix C.)
8613-1		Introduction and General Principles
8613-1	DAD1	Document Application Profile Proforma and Notation
8613-2		Document Structures
8613-2	DAD1	Formal Specification of ODA Document Structures
8613-4		Document Profiles
8613-4	PDAD1	Additive Extensions for Filing and Retrieval Attributes
8613-4	PDAD2	Document Application Profile Proforma and Notation
8613-4	PDAD3	Formal Specification
8613-5		Document Interchange Format
8613-6		Character Content Architectures
8613-7		Raster Graphics Content Architectures
8613-8		Geometric Graphics Content Architectures
8613-9		Tiled Raster Graphics Content Architectures
8879		Standard Generalised Markup Language (**SGML**)
8879	AM1	Amendment 1
9069		SGML Document Interchange Format (SDIF)
9070		Registration Procedures for Public Text Owner Identifiers
9541		Font and Character Information Interchange
9541-1	DIS	Architecture
9541-2	DIS	Interchange Format
9541-3	DIS	Character Identification Method
9541-4	DIS	Character Collections
9541-5	DIS	Font Attributes and Character Model
9541-6	DIS	Font and Character Attribute Subsets and Applications
9541-7	DP	Font Interchange
9573	TR	Techniques for using SGML
10033	DP	Office Document Interchange - Flexible Disks
10037	TR	Guide-lines for SGML Syntax-Directed Editing Systems
10179	DP	Document Style Semantics and Specification Language (DSSSL)
10180	DP	Standard Page Description Language

Other Application Layer Standards

9506		Manufacturing Message Specification
9506-1	DIS	Service Definition
9506-2	DIS	Protocol Specification
9579		Remote Database Access (**RDA**)
9579-1	DP	General Model, Services and Protocol (working draft)
9579-2	DP	SQL Specialisation (working draft)
9735		Electronic Data Interchange (EDIFACT)
9955	DP	Banking Information Interchange (guide-lines to developers)
10031		Distributed Office Applications
10031-1	DIS	General Model
10031-2	DIS	Referenced Data Transfer

10160	DP	Documentation: Interlibrary Loans Service Definition
10161	DP	Documentation: Interlibrary Loans Protocol Specification
10162	DP	Bibliographic Search, Retrieval and Update Service
10163	DP	Bibliographic Search, Retrieval and Update Protocol
10166		Document Filing and Retrieval
10166-1	DIS	Abstract Service Definition and procedures
10166-2	DIS	Protocol Specification

Presentation Layer

8822		CO Service Definition
8822	ADD1	CLPS
8822	PDAD2	Support of Session Symmetric Synchronisation
8822	PDAD3	Unlimited User Data
8823		CO Protocol Specification
8823	DAD1	Protocol PICS
8823	PDAD2	Support of Session Symmetric Synchronisation
8823	PDAD3	Unlimited User Data

Session Layer

8326		CO Service Definition
8326	ADD1	Symmetric Synchronisation
8326	ADD2	Unlimited User Data
8326	DAD3	CL Service Definition
8326	AM1	Amendment 1
8327		CO Protocol Specification
8327	ADD1	Symmetric Synchronisation
8327	ADD2	Unlimited User Data
8327	DAD3	PICS Proforma
9548	DIS	Connectionless Session Protocol
9571	TR	LOTOS Description of Session Service
9572	TR	LOTOS Description of Session Protocol
10168		Session Protocol Conformance Test Suite
10168-1	DIS	Structure and Test Purposes
10168-4	DIS	Test Management Protocol Specification

Transport Layer

8072		Service Definition
8072	ADD1	Connectionless Mode
8073		CO Protocol Specification
8073	ADD1	Network Connection Management Subprotocol
8073	ADD2	TP4 Operation over CO Network Service
8073	DAD3	PICS Proforma
8073	PDAD4	Transport Protocol Enhancements
8073	COR1/2	Technical Corrigenda
8602		CL Protocol Specification
10023	PDTR	LOTOS Description of Transport Service
10024	PDTR	LOTOS Description of Transport Protocol (working draft)

10025		Transport Protocol Conformance Testing
10025-1	DIS	General Principles
10025-2	DP	Test Suite Structures and Test Purposes

Network Layer

8208		X.25 PLP (Packet Layer Protocol) for DTE
8208	ADD1	Alternative LCN Allocation
8208	ADD3	Static Conformance Requirements
8348		Service Definition
8348	ADD1	Connectionless Mode
8348	ADD2	Network Layer Addressing
8348	ADD3	Additional Features
8473		CL Network Protocol (Internetwork protocol)
8473	ADD3	Assumptions Regarding Underlying Data Link Service
8473	PDTR?	ESTELLE Description (Working draft)
8648		Internal Organization of the Network Layer
8648	DTC1	Technical Corrigendum
8878		Use of X.25 to Provide CONS
8878	ADD1	Protroction and Priority
8878	ADD2	Use of X.25 PVC to Provide CONS
8878	DAD3	Conformance
8878	PDAD4	PICS Proforma
8878	COR1	Technical Corrigendum
8880		Protocol Combinations to Support Network Service
8880-1		General Principles
8880-2		Provision and Support for CONS
8880-2	PDAD1	Addition of ISDN Environment
8880-3		Provision and Support for CLNS
8881		Use of X.25 PLP in LANs
8882		X.25 DTE Conformance Testing
8882-1	DIS	General Principles
8882-2	DP	Data Link Test Suite (strictly a Data Link Layer standard)
8882-3	DIS	Packet Level Conformance Suite
9542		End-Intermediate Routing Information Interchange Protocol (for CLNS)
9574		Provision of CONS bt DTE connected to ISDN
9574	PDAD1	Where DTE Connects Directly to Remote DTE
9575	TR	OSI Routing Framework
9577	TR	Protocol Identification in Network Layer
10028	DP	Network Layer Intermediate System Relaying Functions
10029	TR	Operation of X.25 Interworking Unit
10030	DIS	End-Intermediate Routing Information Interchange Protocol (for 8878 X.25 CONS)
10172	DTR	Network/Transport Protocol Interworking Specification
10177	DP	Intermediate System Support of CONS using 8208 in Accordance with 10028
10588	DP	Use of X.25 PLP with X.21/X.21 bis to Provide CONS
10589	DP	Intermediate-Intermediate Routing Information Interchange Protocol (for 8473 CLNS Internet Protocol)

Data Link and Physical Layers

8886	DIS	Data Link Service Definition
10022	DP	Physical Service Definition
1155		Basic Mode (BSC) - Use of Longitudinal Parity (BCC)
1745		Basic Mode Control procedures (1975)
2111		Basic Mode Control Procedures - Code Independent Information Transfer (1985)
2628		Basic Mode Control Procedures - Complements
2629		Basic Mode Control Procedures - Conversational Information Message Transfer
3309		HDLC - Frame Structure (1984)
3309	ADD1	Start/Stop Transmission
3309	DAD2	Start/Stop Extended Transparency Options
4335		HDLC - Consolidation of Elements of Procedure (1987)
4335	ADD1	UI and SREJ Extensions
4335	ADD2	Enhancement of XID Function Utility
4335	ADD3	Start/Stop Transmission
4335	DAD4	Multi-Selective Reject
7478		Multi-link Procedures
7478	COR1	Technical Corrigendum
7776		HDLC - X.25 LAPB-compatible Version (1986)
7776	COR1/2	Technical Corrigenda
7776	PDAD1	PICS Proforma
7809		HDLC - Consolidation of Classes of Procedures (1984)
7809	ADD1	UI Extensions
7809	ADD2	Description of Optional Functions
7809	ADD3	Start/Stop Transmission
7809	PDAD4	List of Standard DL Protocols Using HDLC Classes of Procedures
7809	PDAD5	Connectionless Class of Procedures
7809	DAD6	Extended Transparency Options for Start/Stop Transmission
7809	DAD7	Multi-Selective Reject
8471		HDLC - Balanced Classes of Procedures - Address Resolution /Negotiation in Switched Environments
8802		Local Area Networks - Mostly equivalent to IEEE 802
8802-1		Introduction
8802-2		Logical Link Control
8802-2	DAD1	Flow Control Techniques for Bridged LANs
8802-2	DAD2	Acknowledged Connectionless Mode (LLC type 3)
8802-2	PDAD3	PICS Proforma
8802-2	DAD4	Editorial Changes and Technical Corrigenda
8802-3		CSMA-CD - Access Method and Physical Layer Specification
8802-3	DAD1	Medium Attachment Unit and Medium Specification for 10BASE2
8802-3	DAD2	Repeater Details for 10BASE2 and 10BASE5
8802-3	DAD3	Medium Attachment Unit and Medium Specification for 10BROAD36
8802-3	PDAD4	Medium Attachment Unit and Medium Specification for 1BASE5 (StarLAN)

8802-3	DAD5	Medium Attachment Unit and Medium Specification for Vendor Independent Optical Fibre Inter-repeater Link
8802-3	PDAD6	Summary of IEEE802.3 First Maintenance Ballot
8802-4		Token Bus - Access Method and Physical Layer Specification
8802-5	DIS	Token Ring - Access Method and Physical Layer Specification
8802-5	PDAD1	4 and 16 Mbps Specification
8802-5	PDAD2	MAC Sublayer Enhancement
8802-5	PDAD3	Management Entity Specification
8802-5	PDAD4	Source Routing MAC Bridge
8802-5	PDAD5	PICS Proforma
8802-7		Slotted Ring - Access Method and Physical Layer Specification
8885		HDLC - General Purpose XID Frame Information Field Content and Format
8885	ADD1	re. Parameter Negotiation Subfields
8885	ADD2	Start/Stop Transmission
8885	DAD3	Private Parameter Negotiation Subfield
8885	DAD4	Extended Transparency Options for Start/Stop Transmission
8885	DAD5	Multi-Selective Reject
8885	PDAD7	FCS NegotiationUsing Parameter Negotiation Subfield
9234	DIS	Industrial Synchronous Data Link for TWS or TWA Mode
9314		Fibre Digital Data Interface (FDDI)
9314-1		Physical Layer Protocol
9314-2		Medium Access Control
9314-3	DIS	Physical Layer Medium Dependent (PMD)
9314-4	DP	Single Mode Fibre/PMD
9314-5	DP	Hybrid Ring Control (FDDI-II)
10038	DP	MAC Bridges
10039	DP	MAC Service Definition
10174	PDTR	Logical Link Control (type 2) Test Purposes
10178	PDTR	LAN Link SAP Structure and Coding

C   Selected CCITT Recommendations

This list includes the main CCITT OSI-related recommendations in the X-, T- and F-series. The list is not intended to be complete. With the exception of the PDN access (X-series) recommendations, it may be assumed that unless the recommendation is marked § there is an equivalent ISO standard which is technically either identical or very similar.

CCITT recommendations are grouped into sets of 'Facsicles', colour coded according to year of publication. The 1988 series are blue; the 1984 series are orange. (Earlier series are no longer relevant.) The recommendations listed here are generally those in the blue book series. For completeness however, both the orange and blue MHS recommendations are listed. Note that some recommendations appeared too late to be included in the blue book facsicles, and have (or will be) published separately by CCITT.

Number   Title (Sometimes abbreviated)

OSI reference model, services and protocols

X.200	OSI/RM
X.207	Application layer structure
X.208	ASN.1
X.209	ASN.1 basic encoding rules
X.210	OSI service conventions
X.211	Physical service definition
X.212	Data link service definition
X.213	Network service definition
X.214	Transport service definition
X.215	Session service definition
X.216	Presentation service definition
X.217	ACSE service definition
X.218	RSTE service definition
X.219	ROSE service definition
X.223	Use of X.25 to provide the CONS (equivalent to ISO 8878)
X.224	Transport protocol specification
X.225	Session protocol specification
X.226	Presentation protocol specification
X.227	ACSE protocol specification
X.228	RTSE protocol specification
X.229	ROSE protocol specification
X.237	CCR service definition
X.247	CCR protocol specification

ss (selected recommendations)

PAD specification
Hardware interface between DTE and DCE (PDNs)
Alternative to X.21 based on familiar V.24 (RS-232C) 25-pin modem connector and circuits

X.25	DTE-DCE interface for packet mode terminals (hosts) to packet switched PDNs. Incorporates HDLC LAPB {7776} and X.21/X.21 bis.
X.28	Procedures between terminal and PAD
X.29	Procedures between PAD and remote host
X.32	Dial-up procedures to PDNs
X.75	International networking procedures between X.25 PDNs

Message handling systems (MHS) - 1988 series

X.400	System and service overview
X.402	Overall architecture
X.403§	Conformance testing
X.407	Abstract service definition conventions
X.408§	Encoded information type conversion rules
X.411	Message Transfer System - abstract service definition and procedures
X.413	Message store - abstract service definition
X.419	Protocol specifications
X.420	Interpersonal Messaging System (IPMS)

Message handling systems (MHS) - 1984 series

X.400	System model and service elements
X.401	Basic service elements and optional facilities
X.408	Encoded information type conversion rules
X.409	Presentation transfer syntax and notation (superseded by X.208)
X.410	Remote operations (ROS) and reliable transfer (RTS) (superseded by X.218, X.219, X.228 and X.229)
X.411	Message transfer layer
X.420	Interpersonal messaging user agent layer
X.430	Access protocol for Teletex terminals

The OSI Directory

X.500	Overview of concepts, models and services
X.501	Information framework
X.509	Authentification framework
X.511	Access and system services definition
X.518	Procedures for distributed operation
X.519	Access and system protocols specification
X.520	SELECTED attribute types
X.521	Selected object classes

Telematics services (selected recommendations)

F.200	Teletex service definition
T.60	Terminal equipment and network dependent communication procedures
T.61	Representation of data (teletex)
T.62	Session and document control procedures
T.70	Network independent transport service definition
T.100	Videotex services
T.400	Document transfer and manipulation (DTAM) - General introduction
T.411	Office document architecture (ODA) and office document interchange format (ODIF) - introduction and general principles
T.412	ODA and ODIF - Document structures
T.414	ODA and ODIF - Document profiles
T.415	ODA and ODIF - Document interchange format
T.416	ODA and ODIF - Character content architectures
T.417	ODA and ODIF - Raster graphics content architectures
T.418	ODA and ODIF - Geometric graphics content architectures
T.419§	DTAM - composite graphic content architectures
T.431§	DTAM - Introduction and general principles
T.432§	DTAM - Service definition
T.433§	DTAM - Protocol specification
T.441§	DTAM - Operational structure

Index

554

GENERAL COMPUTING BOOKS

Compiler Physiology for Beginners, M Farmer, 279pp, ISBN 0-86238-064-2
Dictionary of Computer and Information Technology, D Lynch, 225 pages, ISBN 0-86238-128-2
File Structure and Design, M Cunningham, 211pp, ISBN 0-86238-065-0
Information Technology Dictionary of Acronyms and Abbreviations, D Lynch, 270pp, ISBN 0-86238-153-3
The IBM Personal Computer with BASIC and PC-DOS, B Kynning, 320pp, ISBN 0-86238-080-4
Project Skills Handbook, S Rogerson, 143pp, ISBN 0-86238-146-0

PROGRAMMING LANGUAGES

An Intro to LISP, P Smith, 130pp, ISBN 0-86238-187-8
An Intro to OCCAM 2 Programming: 2nd Ed, Bowler, et al, 109pp, iSBN 0-86238-227-0
C Simply, M Parr, 168pp, ISBN 0-86238-262-9
Cobol for Mainframe and Micro: 2nd Ed, D Watson, 177pp, ISBN 0-86238-211-4
Comparative Languages: 2nd Ed, J R Malone, 125pp, ISBN 0-86238-123-1
Fortran 77 for Non-Scientists, P Adman, 109pp, ISBN 0-86238-074-X
Fortran 77 Solutions to Non-Scientific Problems, P Adman, 150pp, ISBN 0-86238-087-1
Fortran Lectures at Oxford, F Pettit, 135pp, ISBN 0-86238-122-3
LISP: From Foundations to Applications, G Doukidis et al, 228pp, ISBN 0-86238-191-6
Programming for Change in Pascal, D Robson, 272pp, ISBN 0-86238-250-5
Prolog versus You, A Johansson, et al, 308pp, ISBN 0-86238-174-6
Simula Begin, G M Birtwistle, et al, 391pp, ISBN 0-86238-009-X
Structured Programming with COBOL & JSP: Vol 1, J B Thompson, 372pp, ISBN 0-86238-154-1, Vol 2, 354pp, ISBN 0-86238-245-9
The Intensive C Course: 2nd Edition, M Farmer, 186pp, ISBN 0-86238-190-8
The Intensive Pascal Course: 2nd Edition, M Farmer, 125pp, ISBN 0-86238-219-X

ASSEMBLY LANGUAGE PROGRAMMING

Coding the 68000, N Hellawell, 214pp, ISBN 0-86238-180-0
Computer Organisation and Assembly Language Programming, L Ohlsson & P Stenstrom, 128pp, ISBN 0-86238-129-0
What is machine code and what can you do with it? N Hellawell, 104pp, ISBN 0-86238-132-0

PROGRAMMING TECHNIQUES

Discrete-events simulations models in PASCAL/MT+ on a microcomputer, L P Jennergren, 135pp, ISBN 0-86238-053-7
Information and Coding, J A Llewellyn, 152pp, ISBN 0-86238-099-5
JSP - A Practical Method of Program Design, L Ingevaldsson, 204pp, ISBN 0-86238-107-X
Modular Software Design, M Stannett, 136pp, ISBN 0-86238-266-1

Linear Programming: A Computational Approach: 2nd Ed, K K Lau, 150pp,
ISBN 0-86238-182-7
Programming for Beginners: the structured way, D Bell & P Scott, 178pp,
ISBN 0-86238-130-4
Software Engineering for Students, M Coleman & S Pratt, 195pp,
ISBN 0-86238-115-0
Software Taming with Dimensional Design, M Coleman & S Pratt, 164pp,
ISBN 0-86238-142-8
Systems Programming with JSP, B Sanden, 186pp, ISBN 0-86238-054-5

MATHEMATICS AND COMPUTING

Fourier Transforms in Action, F Pettit, 133pp, ISBN 0-86238-088-X
Generalised Coordinates, L G Chambers, 90pp, ISBN 0-86238-079-0
Statistics and Operations Research, I P Schagen, 300pp, ISBN 0-86238-077-4
Teaching of Modern Engineering Mathematics, L Rade (ed), 225pp,
ISBN 0-86238-173-8
Teaching of Statistics in the Computer Age, L Rade (ed), 248pp, ISBN 0-86238-090-1
The Essentials of Numerical Computation, M Bartholomew-Biggs, 241pp,
ISBN 0-86238-029-4

DATABASES AND MODELLING

Computer Systems Modelling & Development, D Cornwell, 291pp,
ISBN 0-86238-220-3
An Introduction to Data Structures, B Boffey, D Yates, 250pp, ISBN 0-86238-076-6
Database Analysis and Design: 2nd Ed, H Robinson, 378pp, ISBN 0-86238-018-9
Databases and Database Systems: 2nd Ed, E Oxborrow, 256pp, ISBN 0-86238-091-X
Data Bases and Data Models, B Sundgren, 134pp, ISBN 0-86238-031-6
Text Retrieval and Document Databases, J Ashford & P Willett, 125pp,
ISBN 0-86238-204-1
Information Modelling, J Bubenko (ed), 687pp, ISBN 0-86238-006-5

UNIX

An Intro to the Unix Operating System, C Duffy, 152pp, ISBN 0-86238-143-6
Operating Systems through Unix, G Emery, 96pp, ISBN 0-86238-086-3

SYSTEMS ANALYSIS & SYSTEMS DESIGN

Systems Analysis and Development: 3rd Ed, P Layzell & P Loucopoulos, 284pp,
ISBN 0-86238-215-7
SSADM Techniques, Lejk, et al, 350pp, ISBN 0-86238-224-6
Computer Systems: Where Hardware meets Software, C Machin, 200pp,
ISBN 0-86238-075-8
Microcomputer Systems: hardware and software, J Tierney, 168pp,
ISBN 0-86238-218-1
Distributed Applications and Online Dialogues: a design method for application
systems, A Rasmussen, 271pp, ISBN 0-86238-105-3

HARDWARE

Computers from First Principles, M Brown, 128pp, ISBN 0-86238-027-8
Fundamentals of Microprocessor Systems, P Witting, 525pp, ISBN 0-86238-030-8

ELECTRICAL & ELECTRONIC ENGINEERING

Analogue & Digital Signal Processing & Coding, P Grant, 450pp,
ISBN 0-86238-206-8
Handbook of Electronics, J de Sousa Pires, approx 750pp, ISBN 0-86238-061-8
Electricity, T Johansson, 960pp, ISBN 0-86238-208-4
Interference-free Electronics, S Benda, ISBN 0-86238-255-6

NETWORKS

Computer Networks: Fundamentals and Practice, M D Bacon *et al,* 109pp,
ISBN 0-86238-028-6
Data Networks 1, Ericsson & Televerket, 250pp, ISBN 0-86238-193-2
Data Networks 2, Ericsson & Televerket, 159pp, ISBN 0-86238-221-1
Telecommunications: Telephone Networks 1, Ericsson & Televerket, 147pp,
ISBN 0-86238-093-6
Telecommunications: Telephone Networks 2, Ericsson & Televerket, 176pp,
ISBN 0-86238-113-4

GRAPHICS

An Introductory Course in Computer Graphics, R Kingslake, 146pp,
ISBN 0-86238-073-1
Techniques of Interactive Computer Graphics, A Boyd, 242pp, ISBN 0-86238-024-3
Two-dimensional Computer Graphics, S Laflin, 85pp, ISBN 0-86238-127-4

APPLICATIONS

Computers in Health and Fitness, J Abas, 106pp, ISBN 0-86238-155-X
Developing Expert Systems, G Doukidis, E Whitley, ISBN 0-86238-196-7
Expert Systems Introduced, D Daly, 180pp, ISBN 0-86238-185-1
Handbook of Finite Element Software, J Mackerle & B Fredriksson, approx
1000pp, ISBN 0-86238-135-5
Inside **Data Processing: computers and their effective use in business: 2nd Ed,**
A deWatteville, 150pp, ISBN 0-86238-252-1
Modelling with Spreadsheets, A Rothery, 200pp, ISBN 0-86238-258-0
Proceedings of the Third Scandinavian Conference on Image Analysis, P
Johansen & P Becker (eds) 426pp, ISBN 0-86238-039-1
Programmable Control Systems, G Johannesson, 136pp, ISBN 0-86238-046-4
Risk and Reliability Appraisal on Microcomputers, G Singh, with G Kiangi,
142pp, ISBN 0-86238-159-2
Statistics with Lotus 1-2-3: 2nd Ed, M Lee & J Soper, 207pp, ISBN 0-86238-244-0

HCI

Human/Computer Interaction: from voltage to knowledge, J Kirakowski, 250pp, ISBN 0-86238-179-7

Information Ergonomics, T Ivegard, 228pp, ISBN 0-86238-032-4

Computer Display Designer's Handbook, E Wagner, approx 300pp, ISBN 0-86238-171-1

INFORMATION AND SOCIETY

Access to Government Records: International Perspectives and Trends, T Riley, 112pp, ISBN 0-86238-119-3

CAL/CBT - the great debate, D Marshall, 300pp, ISBN 0-86238-144-4

Economic and Trade-Related Aspects of Transborder Dataflow, R Wellington-Brown, 93pp, ISBN 0-86238-110-X

Information Technology and a New International Order, J Becker, 141pp, ISBN 0-86238-043-X

People or Computers: Three Ways of Looking at Information Systems, M Nurminen, 1218pp, ISBN 0-86238-184-3

Transnational Data Flows in the Information Age, C Hamelink, 115pp, ISBN 0-86238-042-1

SCIENCE HANDBOOKS

Alpha Maths Handbook, L Rade, 199pp, ISBN 0-86238-036-7

Beta Maths Handbook, L Rade, 425pp, ISBN 0-86238-140-1

Nuclear Analytical Chemistry, D Brune *et al*, 557pp, ISBN 0-86238-047-2

Physics Handbook, C Nordling & J Osterman, 430pp, ISBN 0-86238-037-5

The V-Belt Handbook, H Palmgren, 287pp, ISBN 0-86238-111-8

Chartwell-Bratt specialise in excellent books at affordable prices.

For further details contact your local bookshop, or ring Chartwell-Bratt direct on **081-467 1956** (Access/Visa welcome.)

Ring or write for our *free* catalogue.

Chartwell-Bratt (Publishing & Training) Ltd, Old Orchard, Bickley Road, Bromley, Kent, BR1 2NE, United Kingdom.
Tel 081-467 1956, Fax 081-467 1754

Data Networks 1: by Ericsson, Televerket

Beginning with an explanation of the basics of data communication, the book progressively builds the reader's knowledge to cover the design, construction, protocols, and signalling of the most common networks in use. Hardware, security and standards are covered, as are protocols V.24, X.21 and X.25. The OSI model is explained and set in the context of its background and actual use today. Explanation of network structures and functions is supported by a practical example of coordinated traffic. Discussion then progresses to signalling, routing and control in telecommunication networks and signalling in circuit and packet switched networks. After a chapter on terminal equipment, the final section details a wide range of existing data networks, including leased lines, Public Circuit Switched Data Networks (including telex, switched data traffic in the telephone network) packet switched networks (ARPA, Eripax) Private Networks (IBM's SNA structure; DCA from Sperry/Univac; DNA from DEC; DSA from Honeywell Bull; ORION) and Local Area Networks (Ethernet; Net/One; IBM's Token Ring; PABX).

This book, and volume 2 detailed below, are used in basic telecommunications education by Ericsson and the Swedish national telephone company Televerket.

1990, ISBN 0-86238-193-2

Data Networks 2: by Ericsson, Televerket

Contents: DATA TRANSMISSION - INTRODUCTION: Complex signals and their appearance; Factors affecting data link quality; Line classes; Correction of data links; Modems; High speed lines in the telenetwork; FUNDAMENTAL PLANS: Numbering plan; Charging plan; Other fundamental plans; PLANNING OF DATA NETWORKS: Collection of basic data; Forecasting; Planning for expansion and following up; OPERATION AND MAINTENANCE BASICS: Operational reliability in data networks; Organisation of operation and maintenance; Examples from Sweden of operation and maintenance; Equipment for operation and maintenance; ISDN: Motivation for ISDN; Services in ISDN; Subscriber connection to ISDN; Network design; Coordinated traffic; Types of traffic - examples; Terminal equipment; Network components; Transmission; signalling; Planning; CCITT RECOMMENDATIONS: INDEX.

1990, ISBN 0-86238-221-1

Telecommunications: Telephone Networks 1

by Ericsson, Televerket

These books have been written by Ericsson Telecom and the Swedish Telecommunication Administration and are widely used in their basic training, in Sweden and throughout Europe. **Contents:** Networks for telecommunication; Basic requirements of the telephone network; Demands on the telephone network; PCM-technology; Transmission media; SPC-technology in digital and analogue environments; CCITT; Fundamental plans; Numbering plan; Changing plan; Other fundamental plans; Network design; National digital networks; Network functions - introduction; The telephone and the subscriber line network; Functions of the local exchange; Functions of other types of exchange; Signalling; Subscriber signalling; Channel associated signalling; Line and register signalling; The R2 (MFC) register signalling system; Common channel signalling; The signalling network; The synchronisation network; Mobile telephony.

1986, 147 pages, ISBN 0-86238-093-6

Telecommunications: Telephone Networks 2

Contents: Transmission; Transmission parameters; Transmission techniques; Transmission media; Transmission systems - example; Subscriber equipment; Equipment in the subscriber line net; Digital coupling; Digital coupling systems; Equipment for signalling; Control; Subscriber switches; Traffic theory; Prognosis; Optimising; Operation and maintenance - introduction; Operation; Maintenance; Example from operating and maintenance of a digital net; Organisation of operation and maintenance; ISDN; Subscriber equipment for ISDN; Applications in ISDN; Techniques and functions in ISDN.

1987, 176 pages, ISBN 0-86238-113-4